Lincoln S. [illegible]

CHEMICAL THERMODYNAMICS

CHEMICAL THERMODYNAMICS

I. PRIGOGINE
PROFESSOR IN THE UNIVERSITÉ LIBRE DE BRUXELLES
(FACULTY OF SCIENCE)

AND

R. DEFAY
PROFESSOR IN THE UNIVERSITÉ LIBRE DE BRUXELLES
(FACULTY OF APPLIED SCIENCES)

TRANSLATED BY

D. H. EVERETT
LEVERHULME PROFESSOR OF INORGANIC AND PHYSICAL CHEMISTRY, UNIVERSITY OF BRISTOL; FORMERLY PROFESSOR OF CHEMISTRY AT UNIVERSITY COLLEGE, DUNDEE IN THE UNIVERSITY OF ST. ANDREWS

JOHN WILEY & SONS INC
NEW YORK, N. Y.

Published throughout the world except
the United States by Longmans Green & Co Ltd

First published 1954
Second impression by photolithography 1962

PRINTED IN GREAT BRITAIN
BY JARROLD AND SONS LTD, NORWICH

CONTENTS

CHAPTER I

Thermodynamic Variables

CHAPTER II

Principle of Conservation of Energy

CHAPTER III

Principle of the Creation of Entropy

CHAPTER IV

Affinity

CHAPTER V

Average Values of the Affinity

CHAPTER VI

Chemical Potential

CHAPTER VII

Ideal Systems and Reference Systems

CHAPTER VIII

Standard Affinities

CHAPTER IX

The Nernst Heat Theorem

CHAPTER X

Perfect Gases

CHAPTER XIV

Phase Changes

CHAPTER XV

Thermodynamic Stability

CHAPTER XVI

Stability and Critical Phenomena

CHAPTER XVII

Theorems of Moderation

CHAPTER XVIII

Displacements along an Equilibrium Line

CHAPTER XIX

Equilibrium Processes, Relaxation Phenomena and Transformations of Second Order

CHAPTER XX

Solutions

CHAPTER XXI

Solution-Vapour Equilibrium

CHAPTER XXII

Solution-Crystal Equilibrium : Eutectics

CHAPTER XXIII

Solution-Crystal Equilibrium : Mixed Crystals and Addition Compounds

CHAPTER XXIV

The Thermodynamic Excess Functions

CHAPTER XXV

Regular Solutions and Athermal Solutions

CHAPTER XXVI

Associated Solutions

CHAPTER XXVII

Electrolyte Solutions

CHAPTER XXVIII

Azeotropy

CHAPTER XXIX

INDIFFERENT STATES

INTRODUCTION

I

THE science of thermodynamics is concerned with macroscopic variables, such as volume, pressure, temperature and concentration, and with the relationships between them. It therefore employs a method of description of material systems which differs fundamentally from that used in mechanics where the parameters employed refer to the position and momentum of the individual particles in the system. This difference is necessary in order to define the state of thermodynamic equilibrium.

J. Willard Gibbs, in his celebrated memoir *On the equilibrium of heterogeneous substances*, stated the conditions of thermodynamic equilibrium in a form which has not been surpassed either in its elegant simplicity or in its generality. There is no problem concerning thermodynamic equilibrium which cannot, in principle at least, be dealt with by Gibbs' methods.

The work of Gibbs was essentially theoretical and its full importance in physical chemistry was appreciated only after its wide applicability had been demonstrated by extensive experimental researches. Among these may be mentioned, for example, the work of Bakhuis Rooseboom which focused attention on the phase rule. At the same time Planck, van Laar, Duhem and van der Waals demonstrated clearly the importance of the concept of chemical potential and completed several aspects of Gibbs' work.

Since then further progress has extended the field of applicability of Gibbs' chemical thermodynamics. Thus the introduction of the ideas of fugacity and activity by G. N. Lewis enabled the thermodynamic description of imperfect gases and of real solutions to be expressed with the same formal simplicity as that of perfect gases and ideal solutions. These results were completed when N. Bjerrum and E. A. Guggenheim introduced osmotic coefficients.

However, the method of Gibbs makes no specific study of physico-chemical transformations such as chemical reactions : the quantities employed are functions of state which relate either to the system as a whole (such as the internal energy) or to a given component (such as the chemical potential). An alternative approach based on the early work of Helmholtz, van't Hoff and Nernst employs quantities which are associated with the chemical reaction itself, such as the heat of reaction or the maximum work. These are, however, inconvenient since they are not functions of the instantaneous state of the system, but depend for example upon whether the processes considered are carried out at constant pressure or at constant volume. This leads to obscurities and complications to which P. Van Rysselberghe* in particular has drawn attention.

The van't Hoff-Nernst approach thus lacks a function of state associated with the chemical reaction. A second objection is that although stress is placed on the chemical reaction, consideration is in effect limited to a study of equilibrium states and of reversible changes despite the fact that quantities like the heat of reaction only have a precise and simple meaning in practice if the system considered actually undergoes a chemical reaction in a finite time. In other words a thermodynamics of chemical reactions must necessarily be a thermodynamics of irreversible phenomena.

Théophile De Donder showed that this paradox could be resolved elegantly by the explicit calculation of the *uncompensated heat*, or better of the *entropy production*, resulting from a chemical reaction. To do this it is necessary to introduce a new function of state, the *affinity*, characteristic of the reaction and closely related to its irreversibility. In a series of papers since 1920, De Donder has developed a new formulation of chemical thermodynamics by combining the fundamental features of both the Gibbs method and those of the van't Hoff-Nernst school.

II

The idea of the production of entropy plays a central role in the present work. The entropy of a system, which is an extensive quantity relating to the system as a whole, can vary for two reasons and for two reasons only: either by a *transport of entropy* to or from the outside world across the boundary of the system, or by the *production of entropy* by irreversible phenomena taking place within the system. If d_eS denotes the amount of entropy received from the surroundings in a given time interval, and d_iS is the internal entropy production during the same time, then

$$dS = d_eS + d_iS. \tag{1}$$

The second principle of thermodynamics postulates that

$$d_iS \geqslant 0. \tag{2}$$

Irreversible phenomena can create entropy but cannot destroy it,

* P. Van Rysselberghe, *Chem. Rev.*, 16, 29, 37 (1935).

while if a system is in thermodynamic equilibrium the rate of entropy production is zero.

The essential advantage of this formulation of the second principle is that the inequality (2) is valid whatever may be the exact conditions under which the system changes. The fundamental problem of the thermodynamics of irreversible phenomena is the explicit evaluation of the entropy production.

In the present volume, which deals with Chemical Thermodynamics, this problem will not be examined in its most general aspects, but attention will be restricted to systems in a state of *partial equilibrium*. It will be assumed that thermal and mechanical equilibrium has been established with the surroundings and between the various parts of the system; on the other hand equilibrium may or may not have been established with respect either to the possible chemical reactions or to the distribution of matter between the various phases of the system.

To describe these transformations, De Donder has made systematic use of the concept of the *degree of advancement* or *extent of reaction*, denoted by ξ. The state of systems studied here can be defined in general by two physical variables such as the volume and temperature and one parameter ξ for each physicochemical change that can occur in the system. The concept of extent of reaction or extent of change can be applied not only to chemical reactions and phase changes which can be represented by stoichiometric equations, but also to changes such as the order-disorder transformation in alloys for which no chemical equation can be written.

For the systems considered in the present volume the evaluation of the entropy production is straightforward and introduces immediately the concept of *affinity*. This nomenclature is justified by the fact that the affinity always possesses the same sign as the velocity of reaction, and can be regarded as the driving force of the reaction.

The method developed here is in many ways analogous to that employed by Schottky, Ulich and Wagner.* Both methods emphasize the criterion for establishing the irreversibility of a chemical reaction and for deciding whether the reaction will proceed spontaneously in a particular direction. In De Donder's method this criterion appears immediately: the production of entropy must be positive. On the other hand Schottky, Ulich and Wagner employ as the criterion of irreversibility the "loss of useful work" associated with the real process when compared with a hypothetical reversible process. As is shown in chap. III, these criteria are equivalent for isothermal changes. For non-isothermal changes, however, the concept of loss of useful work

* W. Schottky, H. Ulich and C. Wagner, *Thermodynamik* (Berlin, 1929).

2

has no clear physical interpretation. The method employed here in which the entropy production is evaluated, has the great advantage that it can be applied to the study of irreversible phenomena of all kinds.

III

The successful development of the thermodynamics of irreversible phenomena depends on the possibility of an explicit evaluation of the production of entropy, and for this it is necessary to assume that the thermodynamic definition of entropy can be applied equally to systems which are not in equilibrium, that is to states whose " mean lifetime " is limited. We are thus confronted immediately with the problem of the domain of validity of the thermodynamic treatment of irreversible phenomena, which can be determined only by a comparison of the results of the thermodynamic treatment with those obtained by the use of statistical mechanics. This problem will be dealt with in more detail in the third volume of this work ; meanwhile the main conclusions can be summarized as follows.

It can be shown that for systems in partial equilibrium such as those studied in the present volume the thermodynamic definition of entropy is applicable provided that the transformations they undergo (chemical reactions and phase changes) are sufficiently slow that the equilibrium distribution of energy among the component molecules is not disturbed appreciably. This restriction may eliminate from consideration certain chain reactions, explosive reactions and related phenomena, but the thermodynamic definition may be regarded as a good approximation for the majority of physicochemical changes.*

IV

This book is the first volume of a *Treatise on Thermodynamics* based on the methods of Gibbs and De Donder. It deals with the following topics : fundamental theorems, homogeneous systems, heterogeneous systems, stability and moderation, equilibrium displacements and equilibrium transformations, solutions, azeotropy, and indifferent states. The second volume deals with surface tension and adsorption while the third and last will be concerned with irreversible phenomena.

The present volume is a new edition of volumes I and II of *Thermodynamique chimique conformément aux méthodes de Gibbs et De Donder*.† By combining the two previous volumes into one it has been possible

* Cf. I. Prigogine, *Physica*, 15, 272 (1949) ; I. Prigogine and E. Xhrouet, *ibid.*, 15, 913 (1949) ; I. Prigogine and M. Mathieu, *ibid.*, 16, 51 (1950).

† I. Prigogine and R. Defay, *Thermodynamique chimique conformément aux méthodes de Gibbs et De Donder*, tome I (Paris and Liège, 1944) tome II (Paris and Liège, 1946).

to avoid repetition, and at the same time to include a fuller discussion of the production of entropy, of critical mixing, critical phenomena, transformations of second order, and the relationship between the thermodynamic properties and molecular structure of solutions.

Throughout, care has been taken to deal not only with the more elementary applications, which are in fact the only ones which are treated in most recent textbooks of thermodynamics, but also those requiring a much more elaborate development. It is for this reason that an unusually large amount of space has been devoted for example to the study of thermodynamic stability.

The above list of the topics dealt with in this volume emphasizes the necessarily large part played by equilibrium states in thermodynamics. Nevertheless the advantages of the present method are apparent in many places, for example in the discussion of the thermodynamic coupling of chemical reactions, of relaxation phenomena and of moderation and stability. These problems deal in essence with the properties of systems slightly removed from thermodynamic equilibrium. The criterion of irreversibility based on the entropy production indicates immediately how the state of the perturbed system will change through time. It is clear that the concept of entropy production has its most important application in dealing with irreversible processes such as thermal diffusion and electrical diffusion potentials. It has therefore seemed appropriate to deal with these problems separately in the third volume.

Finally it should be stressed that the viewpoint adopted is essentially phenomenological. The remarkable development of statistical methods has not reduced in any way the importance of classical thermodynamics. This method enables us on the one hand to inter-relate phenomena which at first sight appear to be quite distinct, such, for example, as osmotic pressure and the lowering of freezing point of solutions. On the other hand it enables a distinction to be made between those macroscopic properties of a system which depend on a particular molecular model, and those which can be deduced on more general grounds and which are common to a class of substances. Thus phenomenological thermodynamics and statistical thermodynamics are complementary to one another. No attempt is made here to develop the statistical approach in detail, although from time to time statistical mechanical results are employed where they help in the understanding of thermodynamic behaviour. Thus only a very brief discussion is given of Nernst's theorem the justification of which is purely in the realm of statistical mechanics : the reader who wishes to pursue such topics in greater detail is referred to the excellent accounts of statistical mechanics which are now available. In contrast, much more emphasis is placed on the general thermodynamic theorems, such as the phase rule and the theorems of Duhem, Gibbs-Konovalow, Saurel and Jouguet, which are applicable to complex systems containing any number of phases and components.

The authors express their deep gratitude to their teacher, Th. De Donder who initiated them in his methods. It is to him alone that their ability to undertake this work is due.

We wish also to emphasize the benefit we have derived from the close relationship which has been established between our group of workers and that of the Physical Chemistry Laboratory of the University of Brussels directed by Professor Timmermans, and which has enabled us to maintain close contact with experimental work in the field of the thermodynamics of solutions.

We also thank Messrs. A. Desmyter, J. Marechal and V. Mathot for the assistance they have given in the preparation of the text, and finally to the *Centre National Belge de Chimie Physique* for grants which have enabled this new edition to be prepared.

TRANSLATOR'S PREFACE

This book is a translation of the 1950 edition of *Thermodynamique Chimique* by Prigogine and Defay, revised to include work up to the end of 1951, together with an appendix dealing briefly with further published work up to the end of 1953.

It is the first full and comprehensive account in English of the principles and applications of the thermodynamic methods developed by De Donder and his school in Brussels. This work has hitherto been little known outside the continent of Europe, and this translation has been prepared in the hope that it will play a useful part in the development of modern thermodynamics.

I was encouraged to undertake this translation by the late Professor M. G. Evans, F.R.S., and it will stand, I trust, as another example of the wide influence which, through his quiet enthusiasm, he exerted over British physical chemistry.

Throughout the preparation of this book I have received the fullest co-operation from the original authors, not only in providing new material for the revision, but also in their readiness to allow me to make a number of changes in the presentation. To facilitate the assimilation of De Donder's thermodynamics into the more familiar techniques of the Gibbs method, the notation employed in the French edition has been extensively modified to conform more closely with established conventions. The changes made are discussed separately below.

I wish to acknowledge the value of numerous discussions concerning the translation which I have had with many friends and colleagues, and in particular to thank Mr. J. L. Copp, Dr. R. Parsons and Mr. D. A. Landsman. I am also greatly indebted to Mr. F. L. Swinton and Mr. A. J. B. Cruickshank for invaluable help in the checking and final revision of the proofs, and to Miss M. Roxburgh for her secretarial assistance. It has been a great pleasure to co-operate with the staff of the publisher, and the reader himself is left to judge the excellence of Messrs. MacLehose's printing of a difficult manuscript.

Dundee, *January* 1954 D. H. EVERETT

NOTATION

In the absence of a universally accepted system of notation for thermodynamic quantities, authors of textbooks of thermodynamics are faced with the responsibility of making a choice whenever the existing systems are in conflict. In the present instance the symbolism used by Prigogine and Defay in their French Edition, although following in many ways what is becoming, it seems, the " European system ", differs in several substantial respects from any of the more widely adopted systems. The responsibility of adapting their notation to bring it into closer agreement with international usage without destroying the " atmosphere " of the original has therefore fallen to the translator. In many instances it has been necessary to adopt compromise solutions to the problems which have arisen, and the following notes indicate the reasons for the various decisions and outline the general structure of the system of notation adopted. I am very grateful to the original authors who gave me a free hand in this adaptation. I have also been greatly assisted by discussion with various colleagues and by correspondence, in particular, with Professor E. A. Guggenheim, F.R.S., and Mr. R. P. Bell, F.R.S. I have not always accepted their suggestions, but have appreciated their comments which have helped me reach what I hope to be rational decisions.

The Symbols Committee of the Royal Society of London has recently compiled a list of recommended symbols, signs and abbreviations which supersedes an earlier report compiled jointly by the Chemical Society, the Faraday Society and the Physical Society in 1937. General agreement appears also to have been reached among the American Scientific Societies but there are still certain discrepancies between the two systems which are likely to remain, despite the efforts of both the International Unions of Chemistry and Physics to obtain complete agreement.

In the main the present work follows the recommendations of the Royal Society in so far as the general usage of letters of both Latin and Greek alphabets is concerned. The original French text has, however, been followed in the employment of lower case letters for molar quantities ; thus U is the internal energy of a system, u is the mean molar internal energy while u_i is the partial molar internal energy of component i. Lower case letters are, of course, not infrequently employed by physicists to denote *specific* quantities, i.e. per gram. The number of occasions when ambiguity can exist between molar and specific quantities is rare, but in this volume it has been considered expedient to avoid all possibility of confusion by underlining specific quantities. Thus $\underline{u}$ is the internal energy per gram, and $\underline{\mu}$ the chemical potential defined in terms of mass. In most actual applications of the equations given here this distinction is in fact unnecessary.

The use of lower case letters has certain advantages, especially from a didactic standpoint. In the first place it avoids confusion between quantities relating to the whole system and mean molar quantities. To the experienced reader it is nearly always clear from the context which is meant, but where the usage changes (especially when this happens without comment) less experienced readers can easily become confused. Secondly this usage means that nearly all intensive quantities are denoted by lower case symbols, and extensive quantities by capitals. The main exceptions are T, for absolute temperature, m, for mass, and M, for molecular weight. In these cases the practice is so well established that it would be unwise to suggest a change.

The symbol for the *affinity* of a reaction has been modified. In the French edition it is denoted by A, but to avoid the possibility of confusion with the American usage of A for Helmholtz free energy, we have adopted the sanserif A. This is not inconsistent with the use of sanserif type for vectors, for the affinity may be regarded formally as the driving force of a chemical reaction ; correspondingly the *velocity of reaction*, v, is also printed in sanserif.

The use of modifying signs has also been examined carefully and certain departures from the French edition have seemed expedient. The main signs adopted are summarized below.

i, as a subscript, is the generalized *component* of a system and includes components 1 ... c. Solutes are sometimes denoted by subscript s to distinguish them from the solvent which is taken as component 1.

α, as a superscript, is the general symbol for a *phase*, and includes phases 1 ... ϕ. When just two phases are considered these are often denoted by the prime ($'$) and the double prime ($''$).

ρ, as a subscript, is the general symbol for a *reaction* and includes reactions 1 ... r.

ξ, modified when necessary by ρ, denotes the *extent of reaction* defined on p. 10.

The three bulk *states of matter* are denoted by the superscripts s, solid ; l, liquid and g, gaseous ; condensed phases are sometimes denoted by c.

The properties of a *pure substance* are denoted by a superscript ^{0}.

The use of this symbol to denote " standard " thermodynamic quantities is then permissible only when these refer to the pure substance as standard state. Some other convention is needed to denote the more general " *standard quantities* " defined in equation (7.51), where the standard state may for example refer to an infinitely dilute solution. After much consideration the symbol $^{\ominus}$ has been introduced. This symbol is based on the circle, and is thus closely related to the more common (but occasionally confusing) notation for standard quantities. It seems useful, however, to associate it with the *plimsoll mark* which, appropriately enough, refers to a reference state of loading of a ship ; this use of an ideogram has, we believe, some value in keeping the essential nature of " standard states " in prominence.

Quantities denoted by the plimsoll symbol are still, in general, functions of temperature and pressure ; the idea of " standardization " of temperature and pressure is not stressed. When necessary we denote quantities at the *standard pressure* (which for convenience is nearly always chosen as the unit of pressure) by the superscript †, quantities at a *standard volume* (which for convenience is always chosen as the unit of volume) are denoted by ‡. Quantities referring to a (usually hypothetical) *ideal system* are denoted by ^{id}.

We employ γ to denote the *activity coefficient* defined relative to the pure substance and γ^* the activity coefficient defined relative to an infinitely dilute solution. The only other use of a superscript asterisk (except in the statistical mechanical discussion of intermolecular forces and liquids) is to distinguish the *pressure* p from the *fugacity*, p^*.

Other subscripts and superscripts are employed in the usual manner and require no special comment (see List of Symbols below).

The *change* of a thermodynamic quantity (X say) on passing from a state α to β is denoted by $\Delta_{\alpha}^{\beta}X$, in particular for the change from phase $'$ to phase $''$ we have $\Delta_{'}^{''}X$. For the processes of *sublimation*, *evaporation* and *fusion* $\Delta_s X$, $\Delta_e X$, and $\Delta_f X$ are used.

The symbols most characteristic of the De Donder school are $r_{T,p}$, $r_{T,V}$ and $\Delta_{T,p}$ denoting respectively the *heats of reaction* at constant pressure and constant volume (with the old thermochemical convention that heat evolved is positive), and the *volume change of reaction* at constant T and p. These symbols have been discarded and we employ

$$h_{T,p} \quad \text{for} \quad -r_{T,p} = (\partial H/\partial\xi)_{T,p},$$
$$u_{T,V} \quad \text{for} \quad -r_{T,V} = (\partial U/\partial\xi)_{T,V},$$
$$v_{T,p} \quad \text{for} \quad \Delta_{T,p} = (\partial V/\partial\xi)_{T,p},$$

and have introduced also

$$s_{T,p} = (\partial S/\partial\xi)_{T,p}.$$

Because of the more usual thermodynamic convention regarding the sign of changes in H and U, $h_{T,p}$ and $u_{T,V}$ are of opposite sign to $r_{T,p}$ and $r_{T,V}$.

As far as possible we have preferred to write these derivatives with respect to ξ in full; quite frequently, however, to avoid cumbersome equations, the abbreviated symbols are employed. These correspond in effect to denoting partial derivatives with respect to ξ by the lower case symbol, to which are attached as subscripts the variables which are held constant in the differentiation. Since the De Donder approach places special emphasis on the variable ξ, it seems reasonable to employ, when expedient, a special notation for differentiation with respect to this variable.

Following this convention we have also replaced the symbols $\mathscr{G}_{T,p}$ and $\mathscr{F}_{T,V}$ by $-a_{T,p}$ and $-a_{T,V}$ respectively:

$$-\mathscr{G}_{T,p} = -\left(\frac{\partial^2 G}{\partial \xi^2}\right)_{T,p} = \left(\frac{\partial \mathbf{A}}{\partial \xi}\right)_{T,p} = a_{T,p};$$

$$-\mathscr{F}_{T,V} = -\left(\frac{\partial^2 F}{\partial \xi^2}\right)_{T,V} = \left(\frac{\partial \mathbf{A}}{\partial \xi}\right)_{T,V} = a_{T,V}.$$

LIST OF SYMBOLS

THE name of the symbol is followed by the number of the formula and the page where this quantity is defined or introduced. Where the notation of this translation differs from that of the French edition, the original notation is given in brackets.

Latin alphabet

$\mathbf{A}$	affinity, (3.21), p. 38.	(A)
$\mathbf{A}^{\ominus}$	standard affinity, table 7.1, p. 86.	(A')
$\mathbf{A}_i^{\ominus}$	standard affinity of formation of substance i, p. 93.	(A_γ^0)
$\mathbf{A}_\rho$	affinity of reaction ρ, (3.31), p. 41.	(A_ρ)
$\bar{\mathbf{A}}_{T,V}$, $\bar{\mathbf{A}}_{T,p}$	mean values of the affinity, (5.16), (5.17), p. 63.	$(\bar{A}_{T,V})$, $(\bar{A}_{T,p})$
$\mathbf{A}^{\text{id}}$	affinity in an ideal system, (7.26), p. 82.	(A^*)
$\mathbf{A}^m$	standard affinity in very dilute solution when concentration is expressed in molalities, (20.77), p. 325.	$(A^{\bullet\bullet})$
a_i	activity of component i, (7.60), p. 88.	(a_γ)
$a_{T,p}$	partial derivative of affinity with respect to ξ at constant T and p, (4.59), p. 59.	$(-\mathscr{G}_{T,p})$

$a_{T,V}$	partial derivative of affinity with respect to ξ at constant T and V, (4.63), p. 59.	$(-\mathscr{F}_{T,V})$
a	cohesion, (11.33), p. 145.	
B	second virial coefficient, (11.13), p. 139.	
b	covolume, (11.33), p. 145.	
$C_{V,\xi}$	heat capacity of system at constant volume and composition, (2.8), p. 21.	
$C_{p,\xi}$	heat capacity of system at constant pressure and composition, (2.14), p. 24.	
$c_{V,i}$	partial molar heat capacity of i at constant volume, (2.9′), p. 22.	
$c_{p,i}$	partial molar heat capacity of component i at constant pressure, (2.18), p. 25.	$(c_{p\gamma})$
c_p^E	excess heat capacity per mole, (24.7), p. 382.	(c_{pe})
c_p^{config}	configurational heat capacity, (19.17), p. 295.	(C_{pc})
$c_p(0)$	temperature independent term in the equation for heat capacity of a perfect gas at constant pressure, (10.15), p. 120.	(c_p^0)
$c'(T)$	temperature dependent term in equation for heat capacity of a perfect gas, (10.14), (10.15), p. 120.	
c	number of components, p. 2.	
c_i	molar concentration of component i, (1.6), p. 2.	(c_γ)
$D(T/\Theta)$	Debye function, (12.41), p. 166.	
d	symbol for differentiation.	
D	diameter of a molecule, (12.52), p. 170.	
d	distance separating two molecules, (12.52), p. 170.	
e	base of natural logarithms.	
F	Helmholtz free energy, (3.15), p. 36.	
f	Helmholtz free energy per mole.	
$f^\ddagger$	part of molar Helmholtz free energy of gas independent of volume, (10.12′), p. 118.	$(\Phi(T))$
G	Gibbs free energy, (3.16), p. 36.	
g	Gibbs free energy per mole, (6.46), p. 72.	
g^M	Gibbs free energy of mixing per mole, (24.1), p. 381.	(g_m)
g^E	excess Gibbs free energy, (24.2), p. 381.	(g_e)
$g^{M,\text{id}}$	Gibbs free energy of mixing in ideal solution, (24.2), p. 381.	(g_m^*)

H	enthalpy or heat content function, (2.14′), p. 24.	
$\boldsymbol{h}$	Planck's constant, (10.13), p. 119.	
h	enthalpy per mole.	
h_i	partial molar enthalpy of component i, (2.34), p. 29.	(h_γ)
$h_i^\ominus$	standard partial molar enthalpy, table 7.1, p. 86.	(h'_γ)
h_i^M	partial molar enthalpy of mixing of i, table 7.2, p. 91.	(h''_γ)
h^E	excess enthalpy, or heat of mixing, (24.4), p. 381.	(h_e)
$h_{T,p}$	heat of reaction at constant temperature and pressure, $[\equiv(\partial H/\partial\xi)_{T,p}]$, (2.13) and (2.17), p. 24.	$(-r_{T,p})$
$h_{T,\xi}$	latent heat of pressure change at constant temperature and composition, $[\equiv(\partial H/\partial p)_{T,\xi}-V]$, (2.14), p. 24.	
I	ionic strength, (27.38), p. 443.	
I	moment of inertia, (10.22), p. 123.	
i	as subscript, refers to generalized component.	(γ)
id	as superscript, refers to value of a quantity in an ideal system, p. 79.	(*)
i	vapour pressure constant, (14.12), p. 195.	
j	as subscript, refers to a second generalized component.	(i)
j	number of conditions of insolubility, (29.5′), p. 469.	(i)
j	chemical constant, (10.18), p. 121.	
$K(T,p)$, $K_x(T,p)$	equilibrium constant in terms of mole fractions, (7.27), p. 82; (7.34), p. 83; (7.75), p. 90; (10.38), p. 127; (10.45), p. 128.	
$K_p(T)$	equilibrium constant in terms of partial pressures, (10.38), p. 127; (10.44), p. 128.	$(K(T))$
$K_c(T)$	equilibrium constant in terms of molar concentrations (10.38), p.127; (10.46), p. 128.	$(K^\bullet(T))$
$K_c(T,p)$	equilibrium constant in very dilute solutions in terms of molar concentrations (20.69), (20.70), p. 324.	$(K^\bullet(T,p))$
$K_m(T,p)$	equilibrium constant in very dilute solutions in terms of molality, (20.69′), (20.70′), p. 324.	$(K^{\bullet\bullet}(T,p))$
$\boldsymbol{k}$	Boltzmann's constant, (3.45), p. 45.	

ln	natural logarithm.	
$\log_{10}$	logarithm to base 10.	
$l_{T,\xi}$	latent heat of volume change at constant temperature and composition, $[\equiv(\partial U/\partial V)_{T,\xi}+p]$, (2.8), p. 21.	
M_i	molecular weight of substance i, (1.2), p. 2.	(M_γ)
m	total mass of system, (1.1), p. 2.	
m_i	mass of component i, (1.1), p. 2.	(m_γ)
m_i	molality of i, (20.50), p. 322.	
m^α	mass of phase α, p. 2.	
m_i^α	mass of component i in phase α, p. 2.	(m_γ^α)
$\boldsymbol{N}$	Avogadro's number, pp. 45, 119.	$(\mathcal{N})$
N	number of molecules in a system, p. 45 ; number of sites on a lattice, (19.46), p. 301.	$(\mathcal{N})$
N_i	number of molecules of component i, p. 319.	$(\mathcal{N}_\gamma)$
n	total number of moles, (1.2), p. 2.	
n_i	number of moles of component i, (1.2), p. 2.	(n_γ)
n^α	number of moles in phase α, (1.5), p. 2.	
n_i^α	number of moles of i in phase α, p. 2.	(n_γ^α)
$P(T/\Theta)$	Planck-Einstein function, p. 120.	
p	pressure, p. 1.	
p_i	partial pressure of component i, (10.24), p. 124.	(p_γ)
p_i^*	fugacity of component i, (11.53), p. 150.	(φ_γ)
$p_{T,V}$	pressure change accompanying reaction at constant temperature and volume, $[\equiv(\partial p/\partial\xi)_{T,V}]$, (4.63), p. 59.	$(\varDelta_{T,V})$
p_i^0	pressure at which two phases of pure i are in equilibrium at a temperature T^0, p. 276.	
Q	heat received by a system, (2.1), p. 20.	
Q'	uncompensated heat, (3.4), p. 34.	
$\mathbf{R}$	universal gas constant, (10.3), p. 116 ; p. 117.	
r	total number of independent reactions including transfers from one phase to another, p. 14 ; (29.5), p. 469.	
r'	number of independent chemical reactions, p. 16 ; (29.1), p. 468.	
r''	number of independent transfers from one phase to another (transport reactions), (29.6), p. 469.	
r	distance between two molecules, p. 140 ; (12.56), p. 171 ; (25.11), p. 397.	
r^*	see (12.57), p. 171 ; (25.11), p. 397.	

S	entropy, (3.1), p. 34.	
s	entropy per mole.	
s_i	partial molar entropy of component i, (4.47), p. 56.	(s_γ)
$s_i^\ominus$	standard partial molar entropy of i, table 7.1, p. 86.	(s'_γ)
$s^\dagger$	molar entropy of gas at unit pressure, (10.10), p. 118.	(σ^*)
$s^\ddagger$	molar entropy of gas at unit volume, (10.9), p. 118.	(σ)
$\underline{s}^\alpha$	entropy of phase α per unit mass (specific entropy), (29.44), p. 480	(s^α)
s^M	entropy of mixing per mole, (20.17), p. 315.	(s_m)
s^E	excess entropy per mole, (24.3), p. 381.	(s_e)
$s_{T,p}$	entropy change of reaction at constant temperature and pressure, $[\equiv(\partial S/\partial\xi)_{T,p}]$, (6.35), p. 71.	
T	absolute temperature, p. 1.	
T_c	critical temperature, p. 230.	
T_λ	Curie temperature, p. 300.	
T_i^0	temperature at which two phases of pure component i are in equilibrium at a pressure p^0, p. 274.	
t	time, p. 13.	
U	internal energy, (2.1), p. 20.	(E)
u	internal energy per mole.	(e)
u_i	partial molar internal energy of component i, (6.29), p. 70.	(e_γ)
u^M	energy of mixing per mole, (20.16), p. 315.	(e_m)
u^E	excess energy per mole, (24.6), p. 382.	(e_e)
$u_{T,V}$	heat of reaction at constant temperature and volume, $[\equiv(\partial U/\partial\xi)_{T,V}]$, (2.8), p. 21.	$(-r_{T,V})$
V	volume, p. 2.	
$V_{i,j}$	interaction energy between molecules i and j, (24.17), p. 385.	
v	molar volume, (1.19), p. 4.	
v_i	partial molar volume of component i, (1.17), p. 4.	(v_γ)
$v_i^\ominus$	standard partial molar volume of i, table 7.1, p. 86.	
$\underline{v}^\alpha$	volume of phase α per unit mass (specific volume), (29.44), p. 480.	(v^α)

v^M	volume of mixing per mole, (20.14), p. 314.	(v_m)
v_i^M	partial molar volume of mixing of i, table 7.2, p. 19.	(v_γ'')
v^E	excess volume per mole, (24.5), p. 382.	(v_e)
v_f	free volume of a liquid, p. 168.	
$v_{T,p}$	volume change of reaction at constant temperature and pressure, $[\equiv(\partial V/\partial\xi)_{T,p}]$, (6.34), p. 71.	$(\Delta_{T,p})$
$\mathbf{v}$	rate of reaction, (1.43), p. 13.	
W	work, (2.1), p. 20.	$(\mathscr{T})$
W	configurational energy, (24.21), p. 387.	
$W_{A,B}$	see (24.24), p. 387.	
w	variance, (13.5), p. 175 ; (29.8), p. 470.	
w_i	weight fraction of component i, (13.12), p. 187	(κ_γ)
$X_{i,j}$	see p. 386.	
x_i	mole fraction of component i, (1.3), p. 2.	(N_γ)
z	number of nearest neighbours of a molecule, p. 386.	
z_i	charge on an ion of kind i, p. 437.	

Greek alphabet

α	as superscript, general symbol for a phase, p. 2.	
α	coefficient of thermal expansion, (12.1), p. 156	
α^{config}	configurational thermal expansion, (19.27), p. 297.	
α	constant characterizing a regular solution, (16.48), p. 246 ; (25.6), p. 394.	
β	pressure coefficient, (12.2), p. 156.	
β_A	fraction of A in monomeric form, (26.14), p. 413.	
γ_i	activity coefficient in symmetrical system of reference, (7.62), p. 88.	(f_γ)
γ_i^*	activity coefficient in asymmetrical system of reference (21.23), p. 336.	(f_γ')
$\gamma_\pm$	mean ionic activity coefficient, (27.23), p. 440.	$(f_\pm)$
δ	symbol for an increment.	
∂	symbol for partial differentiation.	
δ	see (25.22), p. 399.	
δ_i	solubility parameter of i, (25.10), p. 395.	
Δ_a	change of a thermodynamic function during azeotropic process.	
Δ_f	change of a thermodynamic function on fusion.	

Δ_s	change of a thermodynamic function on sublimation.	
Δ_v	change of a thermodynamic function on vaporization.	
$\Delta_{\prime}^{\prime\prime}$	change of a thermodynamic function on going from phase ′ to ″.	
ϵ	dielectric constant, (27.76), p. 447.	(D)
ϵ	degree of reaction, degree of change, $(0<\epsilon<1)$, p. 13.	
$\epsilon_{i,j}$	interaction energy between i and j molecules, p. 140 ; (12.56), p. 171 ; (25.11), p. 397.	
ϵ^*	see (12.58), p. 171 ; (25.11), p. 397.	
Θ	characteristic temperature, (10.13), p. 119 ; (12.41), p. 166.	
θ	elevation of boiling point, (21.60), p. 349 ; depression of freezing point, (22.7), p. 359.	
θ_c	cryoscopic constant, (22.12), p. 359.	
θ_e	ebullioscopic constant, (21.62), p. 349.	
ϑ	see (25.22), p. 399.	
κ	compressibility, (12.1), p. 156.	(χ)
κ^{config}	configurational compressibility, (19.26), p. 297.	
Λ	energy of vaporization per molecule, (24.23), p. 387.	
Λ^*	see (12.62), p. 172 ; (25.14), (25.15), p. 398.	
λ	see (18.31), (18.32), p. 277.	
λ	as subscript, refers to Curie point, p. 300.	
λ	as superscript, general index in polynomial, (21.40), p. 339.	
μ_i	chemical potential of i, (6.15), p. 68.	(μ_γ)
μ_i^{id}	ideal chemical potential of i, (7.64), p. 88.	(μ_γ^*)
$\mu_i^{\ominus}$	standard chemical potential of i, (7.1), p. 78.	$(\zeta_\gamma, \mu_\gamma')$
μ_i^0	chemical potential of i in pure state, (7.1′), p. 78.	
$\mu_i^{\dagger}$	chemical potential of i at unit pressure, (10.11), p. 118.	(η_γ)
$\mu_{\pm}$	mean ionic chemical potential, (27.19), p. 440.	
$\underline{\mu}_i$	chemical potential of i per unit mass (specific chemical potential), (29.39), p. 480	$(\boldsymbol{\mu}_\gamma)$
μ_i^c	part of chemical potential of i in very dilute solution, in terms of molar concentration, (20.49), p. 322.	$(\zeta_\gamma^{\bullet})$

μ_i^m part of chemical potential of i in very dilute solution, in terms of molality, (20.53), p. 322. ($\xi_\gamma^{\bullet\bullet}$)

$\mu_{i,j}$ partial derivative of μ_i with respect to n_j with temperature, pressure and all other n_i constant, (6.53), p. 74.

ν_i stoichiometric coefficient of i, (1.37), p. 10.

$\nu_{i,\rho}$ stoichiometric coefficient of i in reaction ρ, (1.49), p. 14.

ν algebraic sum of stoichiometric coefficients, (2.25), p. 26.

ν number of ions produced by dissociation of an electrolyte, (27.48), p. 444.

ν fundamental vibration frequency, (10.13), p. 119.

ξ extent of reaction; extent of change, (1.37), p. 10.

ξ_ρ extent of reaction ρ, (1.49), p. 14.

π osmotic pressure, (20.84), p. 327.

Σ symbol for summation.

ρ as subscript, general symbol for reaction, p. 14.

τ time of relaxation, (19.6), p. 292.

ϕ number of phases, p. 174.

ϕ osmotic coefficient, (20.8), p. 313.

φ volume fraction, (25.42), p. 406.

$\chi_{A,B}$ average degree of association, (26.17), p. 413.

χ_A average degree of association of molecules A, (26.18), p. 413.

ψ see p. 490.

ψ_s see (29.98), p. 495.

Ω number of distinct quantum states, (3.45), p. 45.

CHAPTER I

THERMODYNAMIC VARIABLES

1. Introductory Definitions.

All quantities corresponding to a macroscopic property of the system under consideration are called *thermodynamic variables*. These may be for example, its volume V, the pressure p, the absolute temperature T, the mass m of the system, or its refractive index.

It is a matter of experience that when we have specified a certain number of macroscopic properties of a system, then all the other properties are fixed. For a given system under certain circumstances there will be a definite number of properties or variables to be fixed before the *state* of the system is completely defined. For hydrogen gas, for example, it is normally only necessary to specify two properties, say the temperature and pressure, but for certain problems we must also specify the percentage of each of the *ortho* and *para* forms of the hydrogen molecule.

We have a free choice of which particular variables to select, but *once they are chosen* all other variables are fixed. For a gas we may choose either the temperature and pressure, the temperature and density, pressure and refractive index, or any other pair of physical properties which are convenient for the purpose in hand.

We can also describe the changes which a system undergoes by specifying the way in which the chosen variables change with time; the way in which all other properties of the system change will then be determined.

Those variables which are chosen to represent a system are called the *independent variables*, and all other variables which are, in principle, calculable in terms of them are *dependent variables*. It is important to remember that initially we have a free choice of the independent variables, but once made we cannot change our choice arbitrarily in the course of a problem. All changes of variable must be made in accordance with the correct mathematical procedure.

Let us consider first the variables which fix the composition of a given system which may consist of one or more phases. *By definition a phase is homogeneous or uniform throughout its extent.*

In this volume we shall not discuss the effect of external force fields (*e.g.* gravitational, electrostatic or magnetic) upon the thermodynamic properties of a system. This definition of a phase is therefore sufficient. In more general terms we may include within the definition regions of space in which the properties vary continuously. Thus a solution of a substance of high molecular weight is to be regarded as one phase, despite the fact that when in equilibrium in an ultracentrifuge the concentration of the solution is no longer uniform, but increases as we move away from the centre of rotation.

If $m_1, m_2 \ldots m_c$ are the masses of the c *components* of the system its total mass is

$$m = m_1 + m_2 + \ldots m_c = \sum_i m_i, \quad (i = 1, 2 \ldots c). \tag{1.1}$$

We now denote the gram molecular weight of component i by M_i, and, by convention, take it to be the same in all phases. By convention also, the gram molecular weight of oxygen is assigned the value 32·000 grams. The number of moles of i is then given by

$$n_i = \frac{m_i}{M_i}, \quad (i = 1, 2 \ldots c), \tag{1.2}$$

and the total number of moles is $n = \sum_i n_i$.

If the system consists of one phase only, the *mole fraction* x_i of the component i is defined by

$$x_i = \frac{n_i}{\sum_i n_i} = \frac{n_i}{n}, \tag{1.3}$$

whence

$$\sum_i x_i = 1. \tag{1.4}$$

If the system contains several phases we must make use of *two* indices i and α to represent respectively the component, and the phase considered ; thus m_i^α indicates the mass of the component i in the phase α. The mole fraction x_i^α of i in the phase α is then defined by

$$x_i^\alpha = \frac{n_i^\alpha}{\sum_i n_i^\alpha} = \frac{n_i^\alpha}{n^\alpha}. \tag{1.5}$$

Furthermore the *molar concentration* of i in the phase α may be written

$$c_i^\alpha = \frac{n_i^\alpha}{V^\alpha}. \tag{1.6}$$

c_i^α is the number of moles of i contained in unit volume of the phase α.

2. Extensive and Intensive Variables.

Quantities such as the volume V, the mass m, and the number of moles n in a system are called *extensive* variables since their values depend on the total quantity of matter present in the system.

On the contrary, variables such as the temperature T, the pressure p, and the mole fraction x_i of the component i are *intensive* variables since they have definite values at each point in the system. The value of an intensive variable may either be the same throughout the system or change from one point to another.

Systems of One Phase.

To illustrate the distinction between extensive and intensive variables let us consider the volume V, of a single phase system containing n_i moles of the component i. Since a phase is by definition homogeneous one third of the total volume V contains one third of the n_i moles of the component i and, in general, a volume kV (where k is an arbitrarily chosen positive constant) contains kn_i moles of this component. If we write

$$V = V(T, p\,;\; n_1, \dots n_c)^* \tag{1.7}$$

as the equation of state of the system giving the dependent variable V in terms of the independent variables T, p, $n_1 \dots n_c$, we have then

$$kV = V(T, p\,;\; kn_1, \dots kn_c), \tag{1.8}$$

which expresses the fact that the system at a temperature T, pressure p, and containing kn_1 moles of component 1, kn_2 moles of component 2, ... kn_c moles of component c, occupies a volume kV. We may rewrite equation (1.8) more explicitly

$$V(T, p\,;\; kn_1, \dots kn_c) = kV(T, p\,;\; n_1, \dots n_c). \tag{1.9}$$

This relation is identically satisfied whatever may be the values of T, p, $n_1 \dots n_c$ and k. We note that *the factor k multiplies the extensive variables $n_1 \dots n_c$ and V.*

Homogeneous functions : Euler's Theorem. The function $f(x, y, z \dots)$ is called homogeneous of the mth degree in the variables $x, y, z \dots$ if we have identically

$$f(kx, ky, kz, \dots) \equiv k^m f(x, y, z, \dots). \tag{1.10}$$

If we differentiate with respect to k we obtain a second identity :

$$\frac{\partial f(kx, ky, kz, \dots)}{\partial kx} \cdot x + \frac{\partial f(kx, ky, kz, \dots)}{\partial ky} \cdot y + \dots$$
$$\equiv mk^{m-1} f(x, y, z, \dots). \tag{1.11}$$

In particular, if $k = 1$, this may be written

$$\frac{\partial f}{\partial x} x + \frac{\partial f}{\partial y} y + \frac{\partial f}{\partial z} z + \dots \equiv mf(x, y, z, \dots). \tag{1.12}$$

* To express the fact that a dependent variable z is a function of the two independent variables x and y we make use of the notation $z = z(x, y)$.

This is *Euler's theorem.* Furthermore it follows from the theory of partial differential equations* that conversely any function $f(x, y, z \ldots)$ which satisfies (1.12) is homogeneous of the mth degree in $x, y, z \ldots$.

In thermodynamics we are concerned mainly with the two simplest cases :

1. *Homogeneous functions of the first degree*, $(m=1)$. Here we have

$$f(kx, ky, kz, \ldots, kr, \ldots) \equiv kf(x, y, z, \ldots, r, \ldots),$$

and corresponding to (1.12) :

$$\sum_r \frac{\partial f}{\partial r} r \equiv f(x, y, z, \ldots, r, \ldots). \tag{1.13}$$

2. *Homogeneous functions of the zeroth degree*, $(m=0)$. In this case

$$f(kx, ky, kz, \ldots, kr, \ldots) \equiv f(x, y, z, \ldots, r, \ldots),$$

and

$$\sum_r \frac{\partial f}{\partial r} r = 0. \tag{1.14}$$

Comparing (1.9) and (1.10) we see that V is a homogeneous function of the first degree in the independent variables $n_1 \ldots n_c$. Hence from (1.13)

$$\sum_i \frac{\partial V(T, p;\ n_1, \ldots n_c)}{\partial n_i} n_i \equiv V(T, p;\ n_1, \ldots n_c). \tag{1.15}$$

Differentiating this identity with respect to n_j at constant T, p, where j is one of the numbers 1, 2 ... c we have for each j :

$$\sum_i \frac{\partial^2 V}{\partial n_i \partial n_j} n_i + \frac{\partial V}{\partial n_j} \equiv \frac{\partial V}{\partial n_j},$$

whence

$$\sum_i \frac{\partial^2 V}{\partial n_i \partial n_j} n_i = 0. \tag{1.16}$$

Partial Molar Quantities : Equation (1.16) may be simplified by introducing the quantity v_i called the *partial molar volume* of the component i defined by :

$$v_i = \left(\frac{\partial V}{\partial n_i}\right)_{T, p}. \tag{1.17}$$

Equation (1.15) can now be written

$$V = \sum_i n_i v_i, \tag{1.18}$$

which gives the relation between the total volume and the partial molar volumes of the components. For a single component (1.18) reduces to the obvious relation

$$V = nv. \tag{1.19}$$

* *Cf.* for example : T. Chaundy, *The Differential Calculus* (Oxford 1935), p. 157.

Equation (1.16) may now be written in terms of partial molar volumes :

$$\sum_i n_i \left(\frac{\partial v_i}{\partial n_j}\right)_{Tp} = 0 \tag{1.20}$$

or

$$\sum_i n_i \left(\frac{\partial v_j}{\partial n_i}\right)_{T,p} = 0, \tag{1.21}$$

thus showing that the values of the partial molar volumes of the different components are not independent. For a binary system (1.20) becomes

$$n_1 \left(\frac{\partial v_1}{\partial n_1}\right)_{T,p} + n_2 \left(\frac{\partial v_2}{\partial n_1}\right)_{T,p} = 0. \tag{1.22}$$

If v_1 is known as a function of T, p ; n_1, n_2, the partial derivative of v_2 with respect to n_1 can be calculated from (1.22).

We see from (1.21) that the partial molar volumes satisfy the identity (1.14) ; this characterizes them as homogeneous functions of the zeroth degree. Hence

$$v_i(T, p\,;\; kn_1, \ldots kn_c) = v_i(T, p\,;\; n_1, \ldots n_c) \text{ for all } i. \tag{1.23}$$

If the system is increased in size k times, the values of these variables are unaltered ; the partial molar volumes are thus *intensive variables*, and may be expressed as functions of the other intensive variables such as T, p and the mole fractions.

As an example, let us consider a system consisting of a mixture of perfect gases ; the total volume of the system is an extensive variable given by (*cf.* chap. X) :

$$V = \frac{nRT}{p} = (n_1 + n_2 + \ldots n_c)\frac{RT}{p}\,.$$

We see that V is a function of T and p and is homogeneous of the first degree (*i.e.* linear) in n_1, n_2 ... n_c. On the other hand the partial molar volumes

$$v_i = \left(\frac{\partial V}{\partial n_i}\right)_{T,p} = \frac{RT}{p} \quad (i = 1, 2 \ldots c)$$

are functions of the intensive variables T, p and are themselves intensive variables.

Later on we shall consider other extensive variables Y which will correspond to intensive variables y_i defined by

$$y_i = \left(\frac{\partial Y}{\partial n_i}\right)_{T,p}. \tag{1.24}$$

The results obtained above will apply equally to these new variables Y and y_i, and we have in general, in place of (1.18), (1.20) and (1.21), the formulae

$$Y = \sum_i n_i y_i \tag{1.25}$$

and

$$\sum_i n_i \left(\frac{\partial y_i}{\partial n_j}\right)_{T,p} = 0 \tag{1.26}$$

or

$$\sum_i n_i \left(\frac{\partial y_j}{\partial n_i}\right)_{T,p} = 0. \tag{1.27}$$

In the case of a single component we have also

$$Y = ny. \tag{1.28}$$

Systems of Several Phases.

We now pass on to systems formed of several phases. Each of these phases is, by definition, homogeneous so that we may apply the above equations to each phase in turn. If we denote the volume of the phase α by V^α, we may rewrite (1.18)

$$V^\alpha = V^\alpha(T, p; \; n_1^\alpha, n_2^\alpha, \ldots n_c^\alpha). \tag{1.29}$$

In place of (1.17) we now have

$$v_i^\alpha = \left(\frac{\partial V^\alpha}{\partial n_i^\alpha}\right)_{T,p}, \tag{1.30}$$

where v_i^α is called the partial molar volume of i in the phase α. Furthermore

$$\sum_i n_i^\alpha v_i^\alpha = V^\alpha \tag{1.31}$$

and the total volume of the system is

$$V = \sum_\alpha V^\alpha. \tag{1.32}$$

All these relations apply equally to other extensive variables.

3. Properties of the Partial Molar Volume.

Significance of the derivative $(\partial V/\partial n_i)_{T,p}$.

The derivative

$$v_i = \left(\frac{\partial V}{\partial n_i}\right)_{T,p}$$

is the limit, for $dn_i \to 0$, of the ratio of the increase in volume dV to the number of moles dn_i which, when added to the system at constant T and p, produce this increase in volume. It is clearly also equal to the increase in volume produced by the addition of 1 mole of i to a solution, the initial volume of which is very large compared with the molar volume of i.

Thus, suppose we know the volume of an equimolar mixture of water and alcohol. We now add 18 cm³ of water. If the initial volume is sufficiently large, the increase in volume is not 18 cm³, but only 16·5 cm³; this is the partial molar volume of water in the given solution.

It sometimes happens that v_i is negative. Thus, for example, if a little magnesium sulphate is added to an aqueous solution of this salt, the volume decreases; whence $v_{MgSO_4} < 0$.

Calculation of Partial Molar Volumes by the Bakhuis-Rooseboom Method.

For a two component system the partial molar volumes may be evaluated graphically by plotting the *mean molar volume* of the mixture,

$$v = \frac{V}{n_1 + n_2},$$

against the mole fraction of the second component (fig. 1.1). If at some point (v, x_2) on the curve a tangent is drawn it cuts the v-axis $(x_2 = 0)$ at the point B and the ordinate at $x_2 = 1$ at C such that $OB = v_1$ and $DC = v_2$ where v_1 and v_2 are the partial molar volumes of 1 and 2 in a mixture containing a mole fraction x_2 of the second component.

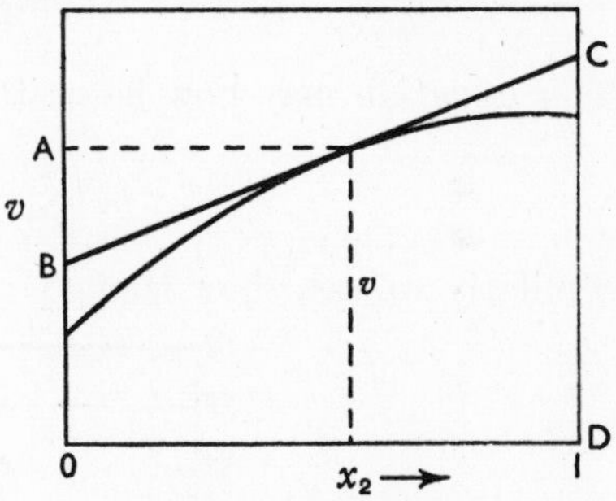

FIG. 1.1. Graphical determination of partial molar volumes.

To prove this we consider equation (1.22) for two components:

$$n_1 \left(\frac{\partial v_1}{\partial n_2}\right)_{T,p} + n_2 \left(\frac{\partial v_2}{\partial n_2}\right)_{T,p} = 0,$$

which on division by n gives

$$x_1 \left(\frac{\partial v_1}{\partial n_2}\right)_{T,p} + x_2 \left(\frac{\partial v_2}{\partial n_2}\right)_{T,p} = 0. \qquad (1.33)$$

We know, however, that by employing mole fractions we can express partial molar volumes in terms of intensive variables, so that if we choose x_2 as the independent variable we may write

$$v_1 = v_1(T, p, x_2) = v_1\left(T, p, \frac{n_2}{n_1 + n_2}\right).$$

It is thus easily shown that equation (1.33) can be written

$$x_1 \left(\frac{\partial v_1}{\partial x_2}\right)_{T,p} + x_2 \left(\frac{\partial v_2}{\partial x_2}\right)_{T,p} = 0. \qquad (1.34)$$

However, $V = n_1 v_1 + n_2 v_2$, and dividing this by $(n_1 + n_2)$ we have

$$v = x_1 v_1 + x_2 v_2 = (1 - x_2) v_1 + x_2 v_2. \tag{1.35}$$

Differentiating (1.35) with respect to x_2

$$\left(\frac{\partial v}{\partial x_2}\right)_{T,p} = -v_1 + v_2 + (1 - x_2)\left(\frac{\partial v_1}{\partial x_2}\right)_{T,p} + x_2\left(\frac{\partial v_2}{\partial x_2}\right)_{T,p}$$

We see, from (1.34), that the last two terms cancel, leaving

$$\left(\frac{\partial v}{\partial x_2}\right)_{T,p} = v_2 - v_1. \tag{1.36}$$

Multiplying throughout by x_2 we obtain

$$x_2\left(\frac{\partial v}{\partial x_2}\right)_{T,p} = x_2 v_2 - x_2 v_1 = (x_2 v_2 + x_1 v_1) - (x_1 v_1 + x_2 v_1) = v - v_1.$$

This equation may now be written :

$$v_1 = v - x_2\left(\frac{\partial v}{\partial x_2}\right)_{T,p} = OA - BA = OB.$$

Similarly we can show that $v_2 = DC$.

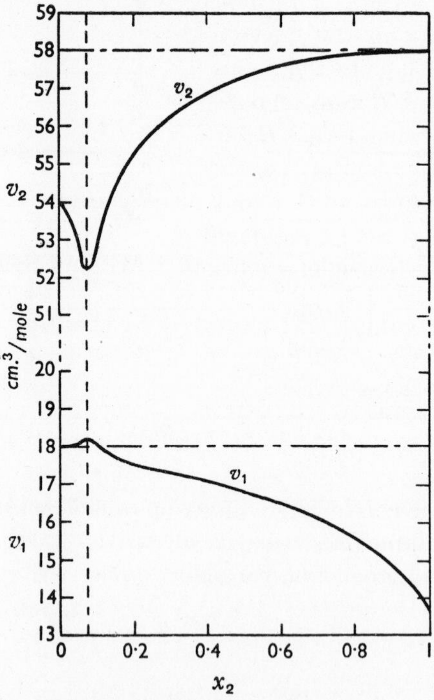

FIG. 1.2. Partial molar volumes in the system water + ethyl alochol at 20 °C. and atmospheric pressure.
v_1 = partial molar volume of water.
v_2 = partial molar volume of alcohol.

Returning to the example of alcohol + water mixtures for which the partial molar volumes, v_1 for water and v_2 for alcohol, are shown in fig. 1.2 as functions of x_2, we notice that both curves exhibit extreme values at the same value of x_2; this is in agreement with equation (1.34) according to which, if the slope of one curve becomes zero, the other must also be zero.

Partial Molar Volumes at Extreme Dilutions.

The behaviour of partial molar quantities at high dilutions may be examined using equation (1.34). Suppose for example that x_2 tends to zero. Two cases may arise : $(\partial v_1/\partial x_2)_{T,p}$ may either tend to zero, or it may remain finite. In the latter case $(\partial v_2/\partial x_2)_{T,p}$ must become infinite since its product with x_2/x_1 (which tends to zero), remains finite. The two possibilities are illustrated schematically in figs. 1.3 and 1.4.

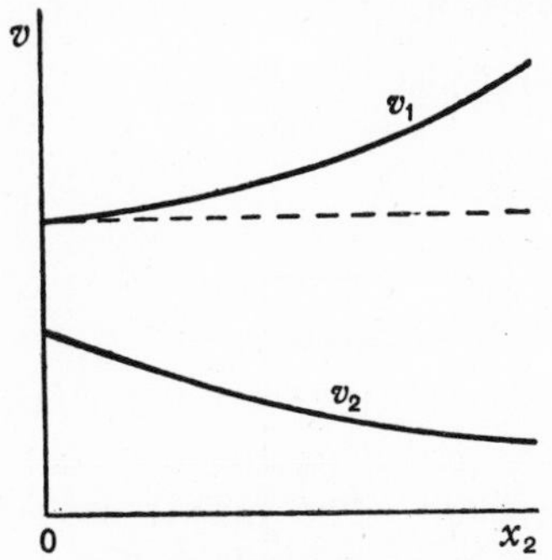

FIG. 1.3. Partial molar volumes at high dilution.

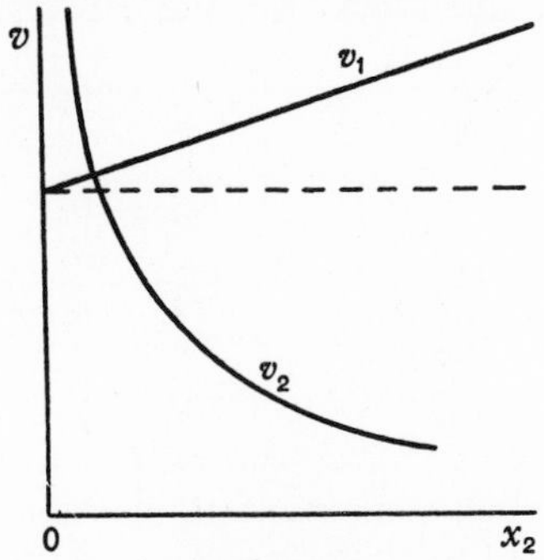

FIG. 1.4. Partial molar volumes at high dilution.

Experimentally we find that real systems exhibit the behaviour corresponding to fig. 1.3. As $x_2 \to 0$, $(\partial v_1/\partial x_2)_{T,p}$ also tends to zero, and the partial molar volume of component 1 approaches a value independent of the mole fraction of 2, *i.e.* its molar volume in the pure state.

4. Chemical Reactions in a System of c-Components.

Now that we have studied the general properties of extensive and intensive variables, we may pass on to a more detailed examination of the variables which determine the composition of a system in which physico-chemical processes may occur.

First we must define the term *closed system*. A system is described as *closed* if during the process under consideration no transfer of matter either into or out of the system takes place. In other words, the masses of the various components in each phase of the system can vary only as a result of spontaneous physico-chemical reactions occurring within the system. These may be either changes of the physical state of a component, or chemical transformations among the molecules present.

Let us consider first a system consisting of one phase in which a single reaction can take place. Suppose we represent this reaction by:

$$\nu_1 R_1 + \nu_2 R_2 + \ldots \nu_j R_j \rightarrow \nu_{j+1} P_{j+1} + \ldots \nu_c P_c,$$

where $R_1, \ldots R_j$ are the reactants and $P_{j+1}, \ldots P_c$ the products. $\nu_1 \ldots \nu_c$ are then called the molar or stoichiometric coefficients of the components 1, 2 ... c. In the following discussion the stoichiometric coefficients of components which are formed as the reaction proceeds to the right are given a positive sign, while for the components which are consumed ν is taken as negative.

It follows from the *law of definite proportions* that the increase in mass of a component i which is being formed in the reaction is proportional to its molecular weight M_i and to its stoichiometric coefficient ν_i in this reaction. We can therefore write

$$\left.\begin{array}{l} m_1 - m_1^0 = \nu_1 M_1 \xi \\ \ldots\ldots\ldots\ldots\ldots\ldots \\ m_i - m_i^0 = \nu_i M_i \xi \\ \ldots\ldots\ldots\ldots\ldots\ldots \\ m_c - m_c^0 = \nu_c M_c \xi \end{array}\right\}, \tag{1.37}$$

where ξ is called the *extent of reaction** or simply the *reaction co-ordinate*. The symbols m_i^0 refer to the *initial masses* of the components at zero time at which the extent of reaction, ξ, is also zero. The initial state is thus defined by $\xi = 0$; and a state in which $\xi = 1$ corresponds to the conversion of $\nu_1 \ldots \nu_j$ gram molecules of $R_1 \ldots R_j$ to $\nu_{j+1} \ldots \nu_c$ gram molecules of $P_{j+1} \ldots P_c$. If a system passes from state $\xi = 0$ to $\xi = 1$, *one equivalent of reaction* is said to have occurred.

By adding together the equations (1.37) and remembering that, in accordance with the *principle of conservation of mass*, the total mass of the system remains constant in the course of time we obtain

$$0 = \sum_i \nu_i M_i. \tag{1.38}$$

This is the *stoichiometric equation* for the reaction concerned.

We see from equations (1.37) that for a closed system in which only one reaction occurs, we can replace the variables $m_1 \ldots m_c$ by the variables ξ and $m_1^0 \ldots m_c^0$. The thermodynamic state of a system for which $m_1^0 \ldots m_c^0$ are given, will thus be determined by two physical variables (*e.g.* T and p), and a single chemical variable ξ.

* This parameter was introduced by De Donder and used systematically by him in his later work, *cf.* [5], p. 117 eqn. (318).

N.B. Reference numbers in square brackets refer to the Bibliography at the end of the book.

Equations (1.37) may now be differentiated with respect to time, remembering that the initial masses are constant, to give

$$\left.\begin{array}{l}\dfrac{dm_1}{dt}=\nu_1 M_1\dfrac{d\xi}{dt}\\ \cdots\cdots\cdots\cdots\cdots \\ \cdots\cdots\cdots\cdots\cdots \\ \dfrac{dm_c}{dt}=\nu_c M_c\dfrac{d\xi}{dt}\end{array}\right\} \qquad (1.39)$$

or

$$\boxed{\frac{dm_1}{\nu_1 M_1}=\frac{dm_2}{\nu_2 M_2}=\ldots=\frac{dm_c}{\nu_c M_c}=d\xi}\ . \qquad (1.40)$$

Instead of defining the chemical state of the system in terms of $m_1 \ldots m_c$, we may employ the number of moles of the various components : $n_1, \ldots n_c$. Equations (1.37) now become

$$\left.\begin{array}{l}n_1-n_1^0=\nu_1\xi\\ \cdots\cdots\cdots\cdots \\ n_i-n_i^0=\nu_i\xi \\ \cdots\cdots\cdots\cdots \\ n_c-n_c^0=\nu_c\xi\end{array}\right\}, \qquad (1.41)$$

where $n_1^0, \ldots n_c^0$ are the number of moles of the components when $t=0$.

Similarly (1.40) may be written

$$\boxed{\frac{dn_1}{\nu_1}=\frac{dn_2}{\nu_2}=\ldots=\frac{dn_c}{\nu_c}=d\xi}\ . \qquad (1.40')$$

The mole fraction of component i is given by

$$x_i=\frac{n_i}{\sum\limits_i n_i}=\frac{n_i^0+\nu_i\xi}{\sum\limits_i n_i^0+\xi\sum\limits_i \nu_i}=\frac{n_i^0+\nu_i\xi}{n^0+\nu\xi}, \qquad (1.42)$$

where $\nu=\sum\limits_i \nu_i$.

It is convenient to pause at this point to consider the meaning and usefulness of the concept of " extent of reaction " which has not previously been employed extensively in English language texts. First we have modified the term from the literal translation " degree of advancement of a reaction " ; the longer form does not convey any more essential information and may be confused with a similar but distinct quantity " degree of reaction " defined by Zemansky.*

* M. W. Zemansky, *Heat and Thermodynamics*, 2nd Edn., (New York, 1943), p. 325.

Secondly we notice that, in its most general form, the extent of reaction is defined in terms of an arbitrary initial composition. As a particular case we may choose as the initial state that in which no products of reaction are present, that is $n_1 \ldots n_j$ have certain given values while $n_{j+1} \ldots n_c$ are all zero.

Then
$$\begin{aligned} n_1 &= n_1^0 + \nu_1 \xi \\ &\ldots\ldots\ldots\ldots \\ n_j &= n_j^0 + \nu_j \xi \\ n_{j+1} &= \nu_{j+1} \xi \\ &\ldots\ldots\ldots\ldots \\ n_c &= \nu_c \xi. \end{aligned}$$

For example, we may consider the reaction

$$2NH_3 \rightleftharpoons N_2 + 3H_2$$

for which
$$\nu_{NH_3} = -2\,; \quad \nu_{N_2} = 1\,; \quad \nu_{H_2} = 3$$

and
$$\frac{dn_{NH_3}}{-2} = \frac{dn_{N_2}}{1} = \frac{dn_{H_2}}{3} = d\xi.$$

If initially n_{N_2} and n_{H_2} are zero, then at any instant

$$\begin{aligned} n_{NH_3} &= n^0_{NH_3} - 2\xi = n^0_{NH_3}\left(1 - \frac{2\xi}{n^0_{NH_3}}\right), \\ n_{N_2} &= \quad \xi \quad = n^0_{NH_3}\left(\frac{\xi}{n^0_{NH_3}}\right), \\ n_{H_2} &= \quad 3\xi \quad = n^0_{NH_3}\left(\frac{3\xi}{n^0_{NH_3}}\right), \end{aligned}$$

we see therefore that $\xi/n^0_{NH_3}$ is the quantity which in an elementary treatment of chemical equilibria we call the *degree of dissociation.*

In the same way, for the ionization of a weak acid

$$HA \rightleftharpoons H^+ + A^-$$

$$\nu_{HA} = -1\,; \quad \nu_{H^+} = 1\,; \quad \nu_{A^-} = 1.$$

$$\begin{aligned} n_{HA} &= n^0_{HA} - \xi = n^0_{HA}\left(1 - \frac{\xi}{n^0_{HA}}\right), \\ n_{H^+} &= \quad \xi \quad = n^{0A}_{H}\left(\frac{\xi}{n^0_{HA}}\right), \\ n_{A^-} &= \quad \xi \quad = n^0_{HA}\left(\frac{\xi}{n^0_{HA}}\right). \end{aligned}$$

Here again ξ/n^0_{HA} is the same as the *degree of ionization* employed in simple treatments.

We notice that while the degree of dissociation, or degree of ionization may have any value from $0 \to 1$, the extent of reaction may have (in these two examples) values $0 \to n^0_{NH_3}$ and $0 \to n^0_{HA}$ respectively. It may be asked why we do not define, instead of ξ, a quantity such as ξ/n^0_1 which runs from $0 \to 1$ as the reaction proceeds from left to right. This course has been adopted by Zemansky who defines a variable ϵ which he calls the *degree of reaction*. The definition of ϵ is not however as simple as that of ξ, and moreover ξ can refer to any initial state. Another important reason for employing the extensive variable ξ is that, as we shall see later, it is directly related to the production of entropy in a spontaneous change.

5. Rate of Reaction.

The rate of reaction at time t may be defined as

$$\boxed{\mathbf{v} = \frac{d\xi(t)}{dt}} \quad . \tag{1.43}$$

It is the ratio of the change (positive, zero or negative) in the extent of reaction to the time interval dt (always taken as positive) during which this change takes place. This definition is due to De Donder.

The rate of reaction can also be expressed in terms of the rate of consumption or production of moles of the components; for by (1.40′)

$$\frac{dn_i}{dt} = \nu_i \mathbf{v} \tag{1.44}$$

or, using (1.40), in terms of the actual masses of the components,

$$\frac{dm_i}{dt} = \nu_i M_i \mathbf{v}. \tag{1.45}$$

In practice we frequently measure the rate of change of the molar concentration c_i of the components. Since by definition, *cf.* (1.6),

$$c_i = n_i/V, \tag{1.46}$$

we have from (1.44)

$$\frac{dc_i}{dt} = \frac{d}{dt}\left(\frac{n_i}{V}\right) = \frac{\nu_i}{V}\mathbf{v} - \frac{n_i}{V^2} \cdot \frac{dV}{dt} \cdot \tag{1.47}$$

If the reaction is not accompanied by a change of volume

$$\frac{dc_i}{dt} = \frac{\nu_i}{V}\mathbf{v}. \tag{1.48}$$

6. Simultaneous Reactions.

Suppose that the system under consideration undergoes r simultaneous *independent* reactions.* Then instead of the single stoichiometric equation (1.38) we shall now have a set of r equations

$$\left.\begin{array}{l} 0=\sum_i \nu_{i,1} M_i \\ \cdots\cdots\cdots\cdots \\ \cdots\cdots\cdots\cdots \\ 0=\sum_i \nu_{i,r} M_i \end{array}\right\}, \tag{1.49}$$

where $\nu_{i,1}$ and $\nu_{i,r}$ are respectively the stoichiometric coefficients of the component i in the 1st and rth reactions. This set of equations may be written in the more concise form

$$0=\sum_i \nu_{i,\rho} M_i \quad (\rho=1,\, 2 \ldots r), \tag{1.50}$$

and equations (1.40) and (1.40′) may be expressed more generally

$$\frac{d_\rho m_1}{\nu_{1,\rho} M_1}=\frac{d_\rho m_2}{\nu_{2,\rho} M_2}=\ldots=\frac{d_\rho m_c}{\nu_{c,\rho} M_c}=d\xi_\rho, \tag{1.51}$$

and

$$\frac{d_\rho n_1}{\nu_{1,\rho}}=\frac{d_\rho n_2}{\nu_{2,\rho}}=\ldots=\frac{d_\rho n_c}{\nu_{c,\rho}}=d\xi_\rho. \tag{1.52}$$

The symbol $d_\rho n_i$ represents the change in the number of moles n_i of component i in the time dt, arising from the ρth reaction. The rate of the ρth reaction is then given by

$$\mathbf{v}_\rho=\frac{d\xi_\rho}{dt}. \tag{1.53}$$

The total change in n_i as a result of all the r reactions will be given by

$$dn_i=d_1 n_i+d_2 n_i+\ldots+d_r n_i=\sum_\rho d_\rho n_i, \tag{1.54}$$

or using (1.52) and (1.53)

$$\frac{dn_i}{dt}=\sum_\rho \nu_{i,\rho} \mathbf{v}_\rho. \tag{1.55}$$

*The expression *independent* has essentially the same meaning as in mathematical terminology. A series of reactions is described as independent if no one of the stoichiometric equations can be derived from the others by linear combination. For example, in an aqueous solution of ammonia the following reactions can occur :

$$NH_3 + H_2O = NH_4^+ + OH'$$
$$NH_4^+ + H_2O = NH_3 + H_3O^+$$
$$2H_2O = H_3O^+ + OH'$$

but only two of these reactions are independent since any one of them can be derived by addition or subtraction of the other two. It is of course immaterial which two reactions we choose to represent the behaviour of the system. A rigorous mathematical definition is given in chap. XXIX.

Example: For the system carbon + oxygen + carbon monoxide + carbon dioxide we have two independent reactions

$$2C + O_2 = 2CO \quad (\rho = 1),$$
$$C + O_2 = CO_2 \quad (\rho = 2).$$

For the first reaction

$$\frac{d_1 n_C}{-2} = \frac{d_1 n_{O_2}}{-1} = \frac{d_1 n_{CO}}{2} = d\xi_1,$$

and for the second

$$\frac{d_2 n_C}{-1} = \frac{d_2 n_{O_2}}{-1} = \frac{d_2 n_{CO_2}}{1} = d\xi_2,$$

whence

$$dn_C = -2d\xi_1 - d\xi_2; \quad \frac{dn_C}{dt} = -2\mathbf{v}_1 - \mathbf{v}_2,$$

$$dn_{O_2} = -d\xi_1 - d\xi_2; \quad \frac{dn_{O_2}}{dt} = -\mathbf{v}_1 - \mathbf{v}_2,$$

$$dn_{CO} = 2d\xi_1; \quad \frac{dn_{CO}}{dt} = 2\mathbf{v}_1,$$

$$dn_{CO_2} = d\xi_2; \quad \frac{dn_{CO_2}}{dt} = \mathbf{v}_2.$$

7. Systems of Several Phases.

Later on we shall wish to study systems consisting of several phases in which a number of chemical reactions may occur. It will therefore be useful to show how the results of the previous paragraph can be extended to the more general case. Instead of (1.50) we now have

$$0 = \sum_i \sum_\alpha \nu_{i,\rho}^\alpha M_i, \tag{1.56}$$

where $\nu_{i,\rho}^\alpha$ is the stoichiometric coefficient of i in the phase α with respect to the ρth reaction.

Equations (1.51) and (1.52) are now written

$$\frac{d_\rho m_i^\alpha}{\nu_{i,\rho}^\alpha M_i} = d\xi_\rho, \tag{1.57}$$

$$\frac{d_\rho n_i^\alpha}{\nu_{i,\rho}^\alpha} = d\xi_\rho. \tag{1.58}$$

The increase in the mass of i in the phase α as a result of the r simultaneous reactions is therefore,

$$dm_i^\alpha = \sum_\rho d_\rho m_i^\alpha = \sum_\rho \nu_{i,\rho}^\alpha M_i d\xi_\rho, \tag{1.59}$$

while the increase in the mass of i in the whole system is obtained by summing (1.59) for all phases

$$dm_i = \sum_\alpha dm_i^\alpha = \sum_\alpha \sum_\rho \nu_{i,\rho}^\alpha M_i d\xi_\rho. \tag{1.60}$$

Analogous formulae are obtained for the corresponding changes in the number of moles of each component.

It is advantageous to introduce

$$\nu_{i,\rho}=\sum_{\alpha}\nu^{\alpha}_{i,\rho}, \tag{1.61}$$

which enables us to simplify (1.56) to

$$0=\sum_{i}\nu_{i,\rho}M_i\,; \tag{1.62}$$

while (1.60) becomes

$$dm_i=\sum_{\rho=1}^{\rho=r}\nu_{i,\rho}M_i d\xi_\rho. \tag{1.63}$$

We must notice that $\nu_{i,\rho}$ as defined by (1.61) is zero if the reaction consists simply of the passage of the component i from one phase to another (*cf.* the example below). It follows that the summation which figures in (1.63) is unaffected by such transfers, and indeed it is obvious that the passage of a component from one phase to another will not alter the total amount of the component in the whole system. We may therefore write more explicity

$$dm_i=\sum_{\rho=1}^{\rho=r'}\nu_{i,\rho}M_i d\xi_\rho, \tag{1.64}$$

where the summation is taken over the r' reactions which are not just transfers from one phase to another. In terms of number of moles, this equation becomes

$$dn_i=\sum_{\rho=1}^{\rho=r'}\nu_{i,\rho}d\xi_\rho. \tag{1.64'}$$

Equations (1.64) and (1.64′) will find frequent application in subsequent chapters.

It is usual to employ the symbols (g), (s), (l) attached to the normal chemical symbol to denote the gas, solid and liquid states respectively. For example

$$H_2(g)+\tfrac{1}{2}O_2(g)\rightarrow H_2O(s).$$

is the reaction for the formation of ice from the gaseous elements H_2 and O_2. While, for the formation of solid sodium sulphate, we have

$$2Na(s)+S(s)+2O_2(g)\rightarrow Na_2SO_4(s).$$

If a compound is formed in aqueous solution, its state is denoted by (aq); thus

$$N_2(g)+3H_2(g)\rightarrow 2NH_3(aq).$$

Examples :

(1) The freezing of water can be represented by

$$H_2O\,(l)\rightarrow H_2O\,(s).$$

We have one component and two phases. The stoichiometric coefficients for this reaction are

$$\nu^l_{H_2O} = -1 \; ; \; \nu^s_{H_2O} = +1.$$

Hence

$$n^l_{H_2O} = (n^l_{H_2O})^0 - \xi \; ; \; n^s_{H_2O} = (n^s_{H_2O})^0 + \xi,$$

and from (1.58)

$$\frac{d_1 n^l_{H_2O}}{-1} = \frac{d_1 n^s_{H_2O}}{+1} = d\xi_1.$$

The stoichiometric equation (1.56) reduces for this transfer reaction to

$$0 = -M_{H_2O} + M_{H_2O}.$$

Furthermore for this reaction

$$\nu_{H_2O} = \nu^l_{H_2O} + \nu^s_{H_2O} = 0.$$

(2) The thermal dissociation of calcium carbonate involves the reaction

$$CaCO_3\,(s) = CaO\,(s) + CO_2\,(g)$$

and the system contains three phases: solid $CaCO_3$ (phase 1), solid CaO (phase 2) and gas (phase 3).

Therefore

$$\nu^1_{CaCO_3} = -1 \; ; \; \nu^2_{CaO} = +1 \; ; \; \nu^3_{CO_2} = +1,$$

and because of (1.58)

$$\frac{d_1 n^1_{CaCO_3}}{-1} = \frac{d_1 n^2_{CaO}}{+1} = \frac{d_1 n^3_{CO_2}}{+1} = d\xi_1.$$

The stoichiometric equation (1.56) becomes

$$0 = -M_{CaCO_3} + M_{CaO} + M_{CO_2}.$$

As explained above this simply expresses the condition of conservation of mass in the reaction. The definition (1.61) gives in this case

$$\nu_{CaCO_3} = -1 \; ; \; \nu_{CaO} = +1 \; ; \; \nu_{CO_2} = +1,$$

which are the same as the values obtained above. This must always be so when each component only reacts in a single phase; the sum in (1.61) then reduces just to a single term.

8. Generalized Definition of Extent of Change.

So far we have defined the extent of reaction for physico-chemical transformations which obey the law of definite proportions and which are characterized by a stoichiometric equation such as (1.38). The idea of the extent of reaction can also have a definite meaning for more general transformations. Consider, for example, a copper and gold alloy at a temperature sufficiently low for the arrangement of the copper atoms to be completely ordered with respect to the gold atoms; then if we take ξ as the degree of order of the system* it can be used to

* For a definition of long-range and short-range order see Fowler and Guggenheim [20], chap. XIII.

characterize the reaction order→disorder which occurs as the temperature is raised, even though the change cannot be represented by a stoichiometric equation in the normal way. In these circumstances it is more appropriate to call ξ the *extent of change.*

9. Changes in a Closed System.

Let us consider a uniform closed system in which a single chemical reaction occurs, and assume that the state of the system is completely determined by the variables T, p ; $n_1 \dots n_c$. Because of the set of equations (1.41), all the states of this closed system can be described by the three variables T, p, ξ. During a change in the system these variables will be definite functions of one single variable, the time. We may remind ourselves of this by writing, for a given process

$$T = T(t)\ ;\quad p = p(t)\ ;\quad \xi = \xi(t). \tag{1.65}$$

We note, however, that the three functions will have quite different properties. Thus we can easily impose upon the system a variation of temperature and pressure in accordance with some given law : in other words, the functions $T(t)$ and $p(t)$ can be quite arbitrary. On the other hand, our control over the variable ξ is very much more limited, since $d\xi/dt = \mathbf{v}$, the reaction velocity (*cf.* 1.43). The rate of reaction is itself a function of the state of the system, and we may write

$$\frac{d\xi}{dt} = \mathbf{v}(T, p, \xi). \tag{1.66}$$

If we now replace T and p in this equation by the functions of time which we can assign quite arbitrarily we obtain the differential equation

$$\frac{d\xi}{dt} = \mathbf{v}(t, \xi). \tag{1.67}$$

This equation has only one solution, $\xi = \xi(t)$ since we are given the initial value of ξ (*i.e.* $\xi_0 = 0$) when $t = t_0$. Thus if we specify arbitrarily the function $T(t)$ and $p(t)$, the function $\xi(t)$ will be completely determined by (1.67).*

10. Open Systems.

In paragraphs 4-9 we have limited our discussion to closed systems which can exchange energy but not matter with their surroundings. In an open system the change dm_i in the mass of component i in a time interval dt, will be the sum of the changes arising as a result of internal chemical reactions, given by the formulae developed in the preceding paragraphs, and of transport across the boundaries of the system to or

* *Cf.* Th. De Donder, *Bull. Ac. Roy. Belg.* (*Cl. Sc.*), **23**, 936 (1937) ; **24**, 15 (1938).

from the surroundings. We shall denote this transport of mass by $d_e m_i$. For the case of a single chemical reaction

$$dm_i = \nu_i M_i d\xi + d_e m_i. \tag{1.68}$$

Open systems play an important part in many branches of science such as meteorology* and biology.† For example a cloud from which rain is falling is an open system ; and similarly living beings are open systems which are continually exchanging matter with the outside world both by their respiration and their metabolism.

If we sum (1.68) for all i, remembering the condition (1.38), we obtain

$$dm = \sum_i d_e m_i = d_e m. \tag{1.69}$$

This equation shows that the variation in the total mass of a system, during a time interval dt, is equal to the mass received by the system from the outside world ; it is an expression of the classical principle of *conservation of mass.*

* J. van Mieghem, *Thermodynamique atmospherique* (Paris, 1942).

† L. von Bertalanffy, *Naturwiss*, 28, 52 (1940) ; 32, 26 (1944).

CHAPTER II

PRINCIPLE OF CONSERVATION OF ENERGY

1. Statement of the Principle of Conservation of Energy.

The *first law of thermodynamics* introduces the concept of energy and expresses the fact that the change in the energy of a system is equal to the amount of energy received from the external world in the time interval considered. In particular the energy of an isolated system is constant, and it is from this fact that the alternative name *principle of conservation of energy* is derived. We shall consider only closed systems (*cf.* chap. I, § 4) which exchange energy with their surroundings either in the form of heat or by mechanical work at the boundaries of the system. The variation in the internal energy for an infinitesimal change taking place in the time interval t to $t+dt$ will be

$$dU = dQ + dW, \tag{2.1}$$

where dQ and dW represent the heat and the work received by the system during this process, and U is the *internal energy* of the system. Heat *received* by the system is taken as positive, while heat *given out* by the system is regarded as negative.

In using (2.1) we must of course measure the heat, the internal energy and the work in *the same units*. The following table gives the relations between the principal units used in physical chemistry. Note that throughout we employ the *small calorie*, which is denoted by cal.

TABLE 2.1*

$\longrightarrow$	*erg*	*kg.m.*	*litre atm.*	*cal.*	*abs. joule*
1 erg	1	$1{\cdot}0197 \times 10^{-8}$	$9{\cdot}869 \times 10^{-10}$	$2{\cdot}390 \times 10^{-8}$	10^{-7}
1 kg.m.	$9{\cdot}807 \times 10^{7}$	1	$9{\cdot}678 \times 10^{-2}$	2·343	9·807
1 litre atm.	$1{\cdot}0133 \times 10^{9}$	10·332	1	24·218	101·33
1 cal.	$4{\cdot}1840 \times 10^{7}$	0·42640	$4{\cdot}129 \times 10^{-2}$	1	4·1840
1 abs. joule	10^{7}	0·10197	$9{\cdot}869 \times 10^{-3}$	0·2390	1

This table is read horizontally in the way indicated by the arrow at the left. Thus 1 erg is equal to $1{\cdot}0197 \times 10^{-8}$ kg. m., or $9{\cdot}869 \times 10^{-10}$ litre atm., *etc.*

* For the values of the principal physical constants see R. T. Birge, *Phys. Soc. Rep. Prog. Phys.*, 8, 90 (1941). Note also that in conformity with the recommendation of the International Union of Physics (S. G. 48-6, 1948) the calorie is defined as 4·1840 abs. joules. The above table has been revised in accordance with the latest recommendations of the Bureau of Standards, *Tables of Selected Values of Chemical Thermodynamic Properties* (Washington, 1947).

If the surface Ω enclosing the system is subjected to a uniform external pressure p normal to Ω, we have

$$dW = -p\,dV \tag{2.2}$$

provided that no other external work is done by the system.

In the present book we shall employ the first law of thermodynamics in the simple form

$$\boxed{dU = dQ - p\,dV}\,. \tag{2.3}$$

We shall study later the role of capillarity, macroscopic kinetic energy and the influence of external fields of force.*

The internal energy is a function of the state of the system, and can therefore be expressed in terms of the independent variables which characterize the state. If, for example, at a time t, the state of the system is determined by the independent variables T, V, $n_1 \dots n_c$, the internal energy can be written

$$U = U(T,\, V,\, n_1 \dots n_c). \tag{2.4}$$

For a closed system, we have, by virtue of (1.41)

$$U = U(T,\, V,\, \xi,\, n_1^0 \dots n_c^0) = U(T,\, V,\, \xi), \tag{2.5}$$

since we can regard $n_1^0 \dots n_c^0$ as given once and for all.

The *total* differential of the internal energy (2.5) is

$$dU = \left(\frac{\partial U}{\partial T}\right)_{V,\xi} dT + \left(\frac{\partial U}{\partial V}\right)_{T,\xi} dV + \left(\frac{\partial U}{\partial \xi}\right)_{T,V} d\xi. \tag{2.6}$$

2. Heats of Reaction and Thermal Coefficients in the Variables T, V, ξ.

By comparing (2.3) and (2.6), we see that one may write

$$dQ = C_{V,\xi} dT + l_{T,\xi} dV + u_{T,V} d\xi, \tag{2.7}$$

where

$$\left.\begin{aligned} \left(\frac{\partial U}{\partial T}\right)_{V,\xi} &= C_{V,\xi}, \\ \left(\frac{\partial U}{\partial V}\right)_{T,\xi} &= l_{T,\xi} - p, \\ \left(\frac{\partial U}{\partial \xi}\right)_{T,V} &= u_{T,V}. \end{aligned}\right\} \tag{2.8}$$

$C_{V,\xi}$, $l_{T,\xi}$ and $u_{T,V}$ are called the thermal coefficients for the variables T, V and ξ.

* For a more detailed discussion of the fundamentals of the principle of conservation of energy *cf.* De Donder [5]; Planck [36]; Duhem [16]; M. Born, *Phys. Zeit.* **22**, 218, 249, 282 (1921); P. W. Bridgman, *The Nature of Thermodynamics* (Harvard, 1941).

We must now examine the physical interpretation of these coefficients.

(*a*) *At constant* V *and* ξ, *we have*

$$dQ = C_{V,\xi}\, dT,$$

so that $C_{V,\xi}$ is the *amount of heat required to raise the temperature of the system one degree while both the composition and volume of the system are unchanged.**

$C_{V,\xi}$ is called *the heat capacity at constant volume and composition.*

The heat capacity is an extensive property. For if we consider two homogeneous systems in the same physico-chemical state, one of which is twice the size of the other, then the former will require twice as much heat as the latter to raise its temperature by the same amount.

In particular, if the system consists of one mole of a single component in a single physical state, its heat capacity at constant volume is called the *molar heat capacity of the pure substance* at constant volume, and is denoted by c_V^0.

For a homogeneous system of n moles of a single component

$$C_V = nc_V^0$$

in which we omit the subscript ξ since no chemical reaction is involved.

In general we have, from Euler's theorem, (chap. I, p. 4)

$$C_{V,\xi} = \sum_i n_i c_{V,i}, \tag{2.9}$$

where $c_{V,i}$, is the intensive property defined by

$$c_{V,i} = \left(\frac{\partial C_{V,\xi}}{\partial n_i}\right)_{T,p}, \tag{2.9'}$$

and is called the partial molar heat capacity at constant volume of i in the mixture.

In the same way as the partial molar volume of a component i in a solution is not necessarily equal to the molar volume of the pure component, so the partial molar heat capacity of i in the mixture may differ from the molar heat of pure i. This difference is negligible in gaseous mixtures, but it may be important in the case of liquid and solid solutions. Indeed in some cases the partial molar heat capacity may be negative.

The partial molar heat capacities may be evaluated, for example, by the graphical method described in chap. I, § 3.

(*b*) *At constant* T and ξ, we have

$$dQ = l_{T,\xi}\, dV,$$

* Strictly, we should of course define $C_{V,\xi}$ as the limit to which the ratio of the amount of heat received to the temperature rise resulting tends, as the change in temperature tends to zero.

and $l_{T,\xi}$ is thus the heat which must be supplied to the system to maintain a constant temperature when the volume is increased by a unit amount in the absence of chemical reactions. It may be called the *latent heat of volume change* of the system.

Let us take as an example a mixture of O_2 and N_2 (*e.g.* air). No reaction occurs between these gases at ordinary temperatures so that ξ is constant. If we confine the gas mixture in a cylinder and allow the gas to do work against a piston, then the gas will tend to cool. If no heat is supplied to the gas, then from (2.3)

$$dU = -p\,dV$$

which shows that the internal energy decreases in the course of the expansion, which will therefore be accompanied by a fall in temperature. To counteract the fall in temperature, that is to carry out the expansion at constant T, heat must be supplied to the system. The heat required is $l_{T,\xi}$ per unit increase in volume.

Equation (2.8),

$$l_{T,\xi} = \left(\frac{\partial U}{\partial V}\right)_{T,\xi} + p,$$

shows that for a perfect gas for which, by definition, the energy is independent of the volume at constant T (*cf.* chap. X, § 1) we have

$$l_{T,\xi} = p \quad \text{(perfect gas).} \tag{2.10}$$

(c) *At constant T and V*

$$dQ = u_{T,V}\,d\xi.$$

Since dQ is the heat received by the system, $u_{T,V}$ is *the heat received by the system when the reaction proceeds an extent $d\xi$ at constant T and V.**

Thus if $u_{T,V}$ is *negative*, the reaction proceeds with the evolution of heat, (*exothermic reaction*); while if $u_{T,V}$ is positive, heat is absorbed when the reaction proceeds (*endothermic reaction*).

For a finite transformation at constant T and V in which ξ goes from ξ_0 to ξ_1, the heat given out by the reaction is

$$Q_{T,V} = \int_{\xi_0}^{\xi_1} u_{T,V}\,d\xi.$$

In particular, if $u_{T,V}$ is independent of ξ we have

$$Q_{T,V} = u_{T,V}(\xi_1 - \xi_0),$$

and for one equivalent of reaction, that is for $\xi_1 - \xi_0 = 1$, we have

$$Q_{T,V} = u_{T,V}.$$

* Although we have introduced the symbol $u_{T,V}$ as an abbreviation for $(\partial U/\partial \xi)_{T,V}$ we shall, for clarity, usually write this derivative out in full.

In this case, the heat absorbed when the reaction proceeds one equivalent at constant T and V, is a direct measure of $u_{T,V}$.

On the other hand, if $u_{T,V}$ varies with ξ, a measurement of the heat evolved for unit reaction gives a mean value for $u_{T,V}$.

3. Heat of Reaction and Thermal Coefficients in the Variables T, p, ξ.

We now have in place of (2.6)

$$dU = \left(\frac{\partial U}{\partial T}\right)_{p,\xi} dT + \left(\frac{\partial U}{\partial p}\right)_{T,\xi} dp + \left(\frac{\partial U}{\partial \xi}\right)_{T,p} d\xi \tag{2.11}$$

and also

$$dV = \left(\frac{\partial V}{\partial T}\right)_{p,\xi} dT + \left(\frac{\partial V}{\partial p}\right)_{T,\xi} dp + \left(\frac{\partial V}{\partial \xi}\right)_{T,p} d\xi. \tag{2.12}$$

This second relationship is now necessary since V is no longer an independent variable.

Substitution in (2.3) then leads to

$$\boxed{dQ = C_{p,\xi} dT + h_{T,\xi} dp + h_{T,p} d\xi}\,, \tag{2.13}$$

where we have written

$$\left.\begin{aligned} \left(\frac{\partial U}{\partial T}\right)_{p,\xi} + p\left(\frac{\partial V}{\partial T}\right)_{p,\xi} &= C_{p,\xi} \\ \left(\frac{\partial U}{\partial p}\right)_{T,\xi} + p\left(\frac{\partial V}{\partial p}\right)_{T,\xi} &= h_{T,\xi} \\ \left(\frac{\partial U}{\partial \xi}\right)_{T,p} + p\left(\frac{\partial V}{\partial \xi}\right)_{T,p} &= h_{T,p} \end{aligned}\right\}. \tag{2.14}$$

The quantities $C_{p,\xi}$, $h_{T,\xi}$ and $h_{T,p}$ are the thermal coefficients in the variables T, p and ξ. In these variables it is frequently advantageous to use the energy function called the *enthalpy* or *heat content* defined by

$$H = U + pV, \tag{2.14'}$$

and in terms of which the equations have a simpler form.

The first law can then be written :

$$dQ = dH - p\,dV - V dp + p\,dV = dH - V dp, \tag{2.15}$$

whence

$$dQ = \left(\frac{\partial H}{\partial T}\right)_{p,\xi} dT + \left[\left(\frac{\partial H}{\partial p}\right)_{T,\xi} - V\right] dp + \left(\frac{\partial H}{\partial \xi}\right)_{T,p} d\xi. \tag{2.16}$$

This equation can be identified with (2.13) by writing

$$C_{p,\xi} = \left(\frac{\partial H}{\partial T}\right)_{p,\xi}; \quad h_{T,\xi} = \left(\frac{\partial H}{\partial p}\right)_{T,\xi} - V; \quad h_{T,p} = \left(\frac{\partial H}{\partial \xi}\right)_{T,p}. \tag{2.17}$$

The significance of this second set of thermal coefficients can be seen immediately.

$C_{p,\xi}$ is the amount of heat which must be added to the system to raise the temperature by one degree at constant pressure and composition; it is called *the heat capacity of the system at constant pressure and composition.* It is an extensive quantity and we have from Euler's theorem that

$$C_{p,\xi} = \sum_i n_i c_{p,i}, \tag{2.18}$$

where

$$c_{p,i} = \left(\frac{\partial C_{p,\xi}}{\partial n_i}\right)_{T,p}$$

and is called the partial molar heat capacity at constant pressure for the component i in the mixture.

$h_{T,\xi}$ is usually negative and $(-h_{T,\xi})$ is the amount of heat which must be removed from the system for unit increase in pressure to maintain constant temperature when the system is compressed at constant composition. We may call this *the latent heat of pressure change at constant temperature and composition.* It must be related to the heat of expansion $l_{T,\xi}$; for to change the pressure at constant T and ξ, we must alter the volume. We shall derive the relation between these below (§ 4). For a mixture of perfect gases the internal energy is independent of pressure and (2.14) gives

$$h_{T,\xi} = p\left(\frac{\partial V}{\partial p}\right)_{T,\xi}$$

and using the equation of state $pV = n\mathbf{R}T$ we find

$$h_{T,\xi} = -\frac{n\mathbf{R}T}{p} = -V \quad \text{(perfect gas).} \tag{2.19}$$

$h_{T,p}$ is the *heat of reaction at constant T and p*; it is the amount of heat absorbed by the system for unit reaction at constant T and p. Once again it should be noted that usually we shall not employ the abbreviated symbol $h_{T,p}$, but will write out the derivative $(\partial H/\partial \xi)_{T,p}$ in full.

4. Relations between Thermal Coefficients.

To derive the relationship between the thermal coefficients $C_{V,\xi}$, $l_{T,\xi}$ and $u_{T,V}$ with T, V and ξ as variables, and $C_{p,\xi}$, $h_{T,\xi}$ and $h_{T,p}$ with T, p and ξ as variables, it is most convenient to consider first the total differential dU in the variables T, V, ξ:

$$dU = \left(\frac{\partial U}{\partial T}\right)_{V,\xi} dT + \left(\frac{\partial U}{\partial V}\right)_{T,\xi} dV + \left(\frac{\partial U}{\partial \xi}\right)_{T,V} d\xi,$$

and then to replace dV by the value given by (2.12) in terms of T, p, ξ. We obtain

$$dU=\left[\left(\frac{\partial U}{\partial T}\right)_{V,\xi}+\left(\frac{\partial U}{\partial V}\right)_{T,\xi}\left(\frac{\partial V}{\partial T}\right)_{p,\xi}\right]dT+\left(\frac{\partial U}{\partial V}\right)_{T,\xi}\left(\frac{\partial V}{\partial p}\right)_{T,\xi}dp$$
$$+\left[\left(\frac{\partial U}{\partial \xi}\right)_{T,V}+\left(\frac{\partial U}{\partial V}\right)_{T,\xi}\left(\frac{\partial V}{\partial \xi}\right)_{T,p}\right]d\xi. \tag{2.20}$$

Comparing this with (2.11) we have

$$\left.\begin{aligned}\left(\frac{\partial U}{\partial T}\right)_{p,\xi}&=\left(\frac{\partial U}{\partial T}\right)_{V,\xi}+\left(\frac{\partial U}{\partial V}\right)_{T,\xi}\left(\frac{\partial V}{\partial T}\right)_{p,\xi}\\ \left(\frac{\partial U}{\partial p}\right)_{T,\xi}&=\left(\frac{\partial U}{\partial V}\right)_{T,\xi}\left(\frac{\partial V}{\partial p}\right)_{T,\xi}\\ \left(\frac{\partial U}{\partial \xi}\right)_{T,p}&=\left(\frac{\partial U}{d\xi}\right)_{T,V}+\left(\frac{\partial U}{\partial V}\right)_{T,\xi}\left(\frac{\partial V}{\partial \xi}\right)_{T,p}\end{aligned}\right\}, \tag{2.21}$$

and employing equations (2.8) and (2.14) we can then write the above relations in the form

$$C_{p,\xi}=C_{V,\xi}+l_{T,\xi}\left(\frac{\partial V}{\partial T}\right)_{p,\xi}, \tag{2.22}$$

$$h_{T,\xi}=l_{T,\xi}\left(\frac{\partial V}{\partial p}\right)_{T,\xi}, \tag{2.23}$$

$$h_{T,p}=u_{T,V}+l_{T,\xi}\left(\frac{\partial V}{\partial \xi}\right)_{T,p}. \tag{2.24}$$

These are the required relations between the thermal coefficients in the two sets of variables T, V, ξ and T, p, ξ.

Example : Mixture of Perfect Gases.

We have already obtained expressions for $l_{T,\xi}$ and $h_{T,\xi}$ for a mixture of perfect gases (2.10 and 2.19). Furthermore

$$\left(\frac{\partial V}{\partial T}\right)_{p,\xi}=\frac{n\boldsymbol{R}}{p}\quad\text{and}\quad\left(\frac{\partial V}{\partial \xi}\right)_{T,p}=\frac{\boldsymbol{R}T}{p}\left(\frac{dn}{d\xi}\right)=\frac{\boldsymbol{R}T\nu}{p}, \tag{2.25}$$

where $\nu=\sum\limits_i \nu_i$ is the sum of the stoichiometric coefficients.

Equations (2.22) and (2.24) thus become

$$C_{p,\xi}-C_{V,\xi}=n\boldsymbol{R}, \tag{2.26}$$

$$h_{T,p}-u_{T,V}=\nu\boldsymbol{R}T, \tag{2.27}$$

or
$$(\partial H/\partial\xi)_{T,p}-(\partial U/\partial\xi)_{T,V}=\nu\boldsymbol{R}T.$$

(2.26) is the classical formula of Mayer giving the simple relation between the heat capacities of a perfect gas mixture at constant pressure and volume, while (2.27) shows that for a reaction involving perfect gases the difference between the heats of reaction at constant pressure and volume is determined by the sum of the stoichiometric coefficients ν. Thus for a reaction such as

$$H_2+I_2=2HI$$

for which $\nu=0$, we have $(\partial H/\partial\xi)_{T,p}=(\partial U/\partial\xi)_{T,V}$;

while for $$N_2 + 3H_2 = 2NH_3,$$
$$\nu = -2,$$
and $$(\partial H/\partial \xi)_{T,p} = (\partial U/\partial \xi)_{T,V} - 2RT.$$

5. The Clausius and Kirchhoff Equations.

In the last section we derived the relations between the thermal coefficients $C_{V,\xi}$, $l_{T,\xi}$, $u_{T,V}$ on the one hand and $C_{p,\xi}$, $h_{T,\xi}$, $h_{T,p}$ on the other. We shall now show that the coefficients in each group are simply related among themselves.

The internal energy U being a function of T, V, ξ, we have the identities

$$\frac{\partial^2 U}{\partial V \,.\, \partial T} \equiv \frac{\partial^2 U}{\partial T \,.\, \partial V}; \quad \frac{\partial^2 U}{\partial V \,.\, \partial \xi} \equiv \frac{\partial^2 U}{\partial \xi \,.\, \partial V}; \quad \frac{\partial^2 U}{\partial T \,.\, \partial \xi} \equiv \frac{\partial^2 U}{\partial \xi \,.\, \partial T}, \tag{2.28}$$

so that from equations (2.8) we have

$$\left.\begin{aligned} \left(\frac{\partial C_{V,\xi}}{\partial V}\right)_{T,\xi} &= \frac{\partial}{\partial T}\left(\frac{\partial U}{\partial V}\right)_{T,\xi} = \left[\frac{\partial (l_{T,\xi} - p)}{\partial T}\right]_{V,\xi} \\ \frac{\partial}{\partial T}\left(\frac{\partial U}{\partial \xi}\right)_{T,V} &= \frac{\partial}{\partial \xi}\left(\frac{\partial U}{\partial T}\right)_{V,\xi} = \left(\frac{\partial C_{V,\xi}}{\partial \xi}\right)_{T,V} \\ \frac{\partial}{\partial V}\left(\frac{\partial U}{\partial \xi}\right)_{T,V} &= \frac{\partial}{\partial \xi}\left(\frac{\partial U}{\partial V}\right)_{T,\xi} = \left[\frac{\partial (l_{T,\xi} - p)}{\partial \xi}\right]_{T,V} \end{aligned}\right\}. \tag{2.29}$$

These equations are called the *Clausius equations* although the second, which relates the heat capacity change to the temperature coefficient of the heat of reaction, is also called *Kirchhoff's equation*; and the last equation, giving the effect of volume on the heat of reaction, was first derived by De Donder.

We may proceed in an analogous manner in the variables T, p, ξ and so obtain from (2.17) a second group of Clausius equations:

$$\left.\begin{aligned} \left(\frac{\partial C_{p,\xi}}{\partial p}\right)_{T,\xi} &= \left[\frac{\partial (h_{T,\xi} + V)}{\partial T}\right]_{p,\xi} \\ \frac{\partial}{\partial T}\left(\frac{\partial H}{\partial \xi}\right)_{T,p} &= \left(\frac{\partial C_{p,\xi}}{\partial \xi}\right)_{T,p} \\ \frac{\partial}{\partial p}\left(\frac{\partial H}{\partial \xi}\right)_{T,p} &= \left[\frac{\partial (h_{T,\xi} + V)}{\partial \xi}\right]_{T,p} \end{aligned}\right\}. \tag{2.30}$$

The second of these equations is sometimes known as *Kirchhoff's second equation*.

Furthermore, since $C_{p,\xi}$ is a function of the state of the system we see that

$$\left(\frac{\partial C_{p,\xi}}{\partial \xi}\right)_{T,p} = \sum_i \left(\frac{\partial C_{p,\xi}}{\partial n_i}\right)_{T,p} \frac{dn_i}{d\xi} = \sum_i \nu_i c_{p,i}, \tag{2.31}$$

where $c_{p,i}$ is the partial molar heat capacity of i defined in (2.18).

Kirchhoff's second equation may therefore be rewritten in the form

$$\frac{\partial}{\partial T}\left(\frac{\partial H}{\partial \xi}\right)_{T,\,p} = \sum_i \nu_i c_{p,\,i}. \tag{2.32}$$

This equation is of importance since it enables us to calculate the heat of a reaction at any temperature provided that it is known at one temperature, and that we know the heat capacities of the components taking part in the reaction. We have usually to assume that the partial molar heat capacities are equal to the molar heat capacities in the pure state. This assumption is usually fully justified for gas reactions.

For this purpose it is convenient to express the heat capacities of gases in a power series of the form

$$c_p = a + bT + cT^2 \ldots$$

and this is usually satisfactory at moderately high temperatures (*cf.* chap. X, § 3). Table 2.2 gives the equations appropriate to a number of simple compounds in the temperature range 300-2000° K.

TABLE 2.2

Molar Heat Capacities of Gases between 300 *and* 2000 °K*

Gas	c_p *in cal/mole. deg.*	*max. deviation in %*
H_2	$6{\cdot}88 + 0{\cdot}066 \times 10^{-3}T + 0{\cdot}279 \times 10^{-6}T^2$	<1
N_2, HBr	$6{\cdot}30 + 1{\cdot}819 \times 10^{-3}T - 0{\cdot}345 \times 10^{-6}T^2$	<2, <3
O_2	$6{\cdot}26 + 2{\cdot}746 \times 10^{-3}T - 0{\cdot}770 \times 10^{-6}T^2$	1
CO, HI	$6{\cdot}25 + 2{\cdot}091 \times 10^{-3}T - 0{\cdot}459 \times 10^{-6}T^2$	<2
NO	$6{\cdot}21 + 2{\cdot}436 \times 10^{-3}T - 0{\cdot}612 \times 10^{-6}T^2$	<2
HCl	$6{\cdot}64 + 0{\cdot}959 \times 10^{-3}T - 0{\cdot}057 \times 10^{-6}T^2$	2
H_2S	$6{\cdot}48 + 5{\cdot}558 \times 10^{-3}T - 1{\cdot}204 \times 10^{-6}T^2$	<2
H_2O	$6{\cdot}89 + 3{\cdot}283 \times 10^{-3}T - 0{\cdot}343 \times 10^{-6}T^2$	2
SO_2	$8{\cdot}12 + 6{\cdot}825 \times 10^{-3}T - 2{\cdot}103 \times 10^{-6}T^2$	see below
HCN	$7{\cdot}01 + 6{\cdot}600 \times 10^{-3}T - 1{\cdot}642 \times 10^{-6}T^2$	<3
CO_2	$6{\cdot}85 + 8{\cdot}533 \times 10^{-3}T - 2{\cdot}475 \times 10^{-6}T^2$	<3
COS	$8{\cdot}32 + 7{\cdot}224 \times 10^{-3}T - 2{\cdot}146 \times 10^{-6}T^2$	see below
CS_2	$9{\cdot}76 + 6{\cdot}102 \times 10^{-3}T - 1{\cdot}894 \times 10^{-6}T^2$	see below
NH_3	$5{\cdot}92 + 8{\cdot}963 \times 10^{-3}T - 1{\cdot}764 \times 10^{-6}T^2$	<1
C_2H_2	$8{\cdot}28 + 10{\cdot}501 \times 10^{-3}T - 2{\cdot}644 \times 10^{-6}T^2$	see below
CH_4	$3{\cdot}38 + 17{\cdot}905 \times 10^{-3}T - 4.188 \times 10^{-6}T^2$	2

* *Cf.* W. M. D. Bryant, *Ind. Eng. Chem.*, **25**, 820 (1933); *cf.* also R. H. Ewell, *ibid.*, **32**, 147 (1940); C. M. Thacker, H. O. Folkins and E. L. Miller, *ibid.*, **33**, 584 (1941).

The maximum deviation for SO_2, COS, CS_2 and C_2H_2 are about 2% between 400 and 2000 °K, but rise to about 5% below 400 °K.

Example : Let us consider again the synthesis of ammonia

$$N_2+3H_2=2NH_3$$

for which the heat of reaction determined at 25 °C is found to be

$$(\partial H/\partial \xi)_{298,1\,\mathrm{atm.}} = -22{,}080 \text{ cal. (see table 8.1)}$$

We wish to know the heat of reaction at 932 °K.

If we assume that the partial molar heat capacities of the compounds in the mixture are equal to the corresponding molar heat capacities in the pure state, we have using the equations given in table 2.2,

$$\begin{aligned}\sum_i \nu_i c_{p,i} &= -3c_{p,\,H_2}-c_{p,\,N_2}+2c_{p,\,NH_3},\\ &= -15{\cdot}10+15{\cdot}909\times 10^{-3}T-4.020\times 10^{-6}T^2\\ &= \frac{\partial}{\partial T}\left(\frac{\partial H}{\partial \xi}\right)_{T,p}.\end{aligned}$$

Integrating from 0 to T we have

$$\begin{aligned}(\partial H/\partial \xi)_{T,1\,\mathrm{atm.}} &= h_{0,1}-15{\cdot}10T+15{\cdot}909\times 10^{-3}T^2/2-4{\cdot}020\times 10^{-6}T^3/3\\ &= h_{0,1}-15{\cdot}10T+7{\cdot}954\times 10^{-3}T^2-1{\cdot}34\times 10^{-6}T^3. \qquad (2.33)\end{aligned}$$

At $T=298$ °K, $(\partial H/\partial \xi)_{T,1\,\mathrm{atm.}} = -22{,}080$ cal. so that substituting these values in (2.33) we can evaluate the integration constant $h_{0,1}$ which is found to equal $-18{,}250$ cal. The heat of reaction at any other temperature is thus given by

$$(\partial H/\partial \xi)_{T,1\,\mathrm{atm.}} = -18{,}250-15{\cdot}10T+7{\cdot}954\times 10^{-3}T^2-1{\cdot}34\times 10^{-6}T^3 \qquad (2.33')$$

and in particular at $T=932$ °K, we find $(\partial H/\partial \xi)_{T,1} = -26{,}500$ cal. in agreement with Haber's* direct calorimetric determination which gave a value of $-26{,}320 \pm 200$ cal.

6. Heat of Reaction and Enthalpy.

The heat of reaction may be rewritten in terms of the partial molar enthalpies of the compounds defined by

$$h_i=\left(\frac{\partial H}{\partial n_i}\right)_{T,p}, \qquad (2.34)$$

when it becomes

$$\left(\frac{\partial H}{\partial \xi}\right)_{T,p}=\sum_i\left(\frac{\partial H}{\partial n_i}\right)_{T,p}\frac{dn_i}{d\xi}=\sum_i \nu_i h_i. \qquad (2.35)$$

The heat change of reaction is thus seen to equal the difference between the sum of the partial molar enthalpies of the products of reaction, each multiplied by the appropriate stoichiometric coefficient, and the

* F. Haber, *Z. Electrochem.* 20, 597 (1914) ; *cf.* S. Tamaru, *J. Soc. Chem. Ind.*, 35, 81 (1916).

corresponding sum for the reactants. This expression for the heat of reaction is of frequent use.

If r simultaneous reactions take place in the system we have for the heat of reaction of the ρth reaction

$$\left(\frac{\partial H}{\partial \xi_\rho}\right)_{T,p} = \sum_i \nu_{i,\rho} h_i \quad (\rho = 1 \ldots r). \tag{2.36}$$

We now show that if a given reaction may be considered as a linear combination of other reactions, its heat of reaction is equal to the corresponding linear combination of the heats of reaction.

To simplify the argument let us consider for example the reaction

$$2C\,(diamond) + O_2(g) \rightarrow 2CO\,(g), \qquad (1) \tag{2.37}$$

which may be considered as a linear combination of the reactions

$$\left.\begin{aligned} C(d) + O_2(g) &\rightarrow CO_2(g), && (1') \\ \text{and} \qquad 2CO\,(g) + O_2(g) &\rightarrow 2CO_2(g)\,; && (2') \end{aligned}\right\} \tag{2.38}$$

for by subtracting equation (2′) from twice equation (1′) we obtain equation (1). This may be written symbolically :

$$\text{reaction } (1) = 2 \times \text{reaction } (1') - \text{reaction } (2'), \tag{2.39}$$

which is equivalent to saying that the stoichiometric coefficients for reaction (1) are a linear combination of the stoichiometric coefficients for (1′) and (2′) according to the formula

$$\nu_{i,1} = 2\nu_{i,1'} - \nu_{i,2'}. \tag{2.40}$$

Thus

$$\left(\frac{\partial H}{\partial \xi_1}\right)_{T,p} = \sum_i \nu_{i,1} h_i = 2\sum_i \nu_{i,1'} h_i - \sum_i \nu_{i,2'} h_i, \tag{2.41}$$

or

$$\left(\frac{\partial H}{\partial \xi_1}\right)_{T,p} = 2\left(\frac{\partial H}{\partial \xi_{1'}}\right)_{T,p} - \left(\frac{\partial H}{\partial \xi_{2'}}\right)_{T,p}. \tag{2.42}$$

Thus we see that *heats of reaction may be added together in just the same way as the equations for chemical reactions.* This fact is of use when the heat of a particular reaction is difficult to measure experimentally, but the reaction can be split up into other reactions whose heats are more easily determined. This is the basis of *Hess's law of constant heat summation.*

Note : If a physico-chemical change occurs in a system either at constant volume or constant pressure, the heat received during this change depends only upon the initial and final states so that

(1) at constant volume, (2.3) gives,

$$Q = \int_A^B dQ = \int_A^B dU = U_B - U_A, \tag{2.43}$$

(2) at constant pressure, (2.15) gives,

$$Q = \int_{A'}^{B'} dQ = \int_{A'}^{B'} dH = H_{B'} - H_{A'}. \tag{2.44}$$

These equations are the basic equations of calorimetry.

CHAPTER III

PRINCIPLE OF THE CREATION OF ENTROPY

1. Reversible and Irreversible Phenomena.

Let us consider a system which undergoes the transformation ABC. This change is said to be *reversible* if there exists a change CBA such that: (a) the variables characterizing the state of the system return through the same values, but in the inverse order and (b) exchanges of heat, matter and work with the surroundings are of the reverse sign and take place in the reverse order. Thus, for example, if in the trajectory ABC (fig. 3.1), the system receives a quantity of heat Q, it must give up the same quantity in the inverse trajectory CBA. It is important to remember that this must remain true however close together A, B and C may be.

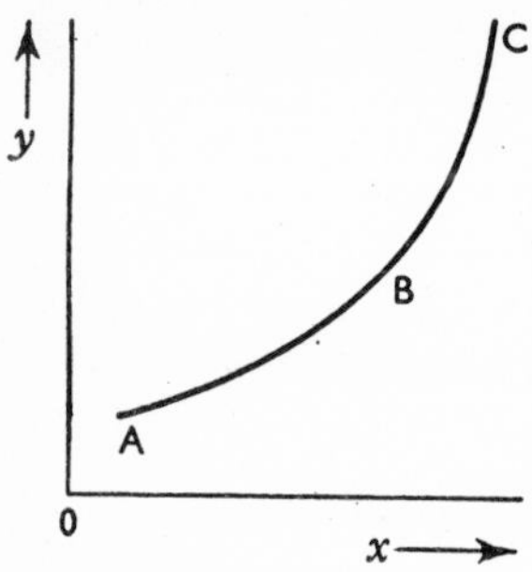

FIG. 3.1.

All changes which do not satisfy these two conditions are termed *irreversible*.

No change which takes place in nature is reversible. All are irreversible although real processes can be devised approaching as nearly as we wish to reversible processes. Thus reversible processes may be regarded as idealizations which are the limits to which real processes can approach under appropriate conditions.

Thus if we consider a wide U-tube containing water in which initially the water level is higher in one arm than in the other. The level in this arm falls, passes through the equilibrium position, and then rises in the other arm to nearly the same level; the reverse process then occurs. If we were able to reduce friction and viscosity to zero, we should obtain in the limit a reversible change.

As a second example we shall consider the *reversible* dissociation of a gas. Water vapour in a closed vessel at 1200 °C dissociates and the following equilibrium is established

$$H_2O \rightleftharpoons H_2 + \tfrac{1}{2}O_2.$$

At this temperature, and at a given pressure the mole fraction of water x_{H_2O}, present in the vapour is fixed; it is the equilibrium position A

(fig. 3.2). If the temperature is raised a little, corresponding to A', the system is no longer in equilibrium; more water molecules will dissociate and tend to bring the point representing the state of the system back on to the line AB. If, however, the temperature is increased steadily the system will follow the line $A'B'$, which by suitable adjustment of the rate of temperature rise can be made to lie very close to AB. At B' we cease raising the temperature and allow the system to reach the equilibrium state B. From this point we could return to A by lowering the temperature and allowing the system to pass through a series of states corresponding to $B''A''$. The path $B''A''$ does not pass through the same states as $A'B'$, so that the process $A'B'$ is not reversible. However, by suitable control of the temperature change we can always keep the temperature only infinitesimally above that corresponding to equilibrium without ever allowing it to equal the equilibrium value (for then the reaction would cease); in this way $A'B'$ can be made to approximate to AB as closely as we wish. Thus AB can be regarded as an idealization of an actual process, and we say that an equilibrium change is a reversible change to which real changes can approach as closely as we wish by carrying out the transformation sufficiently slowly. An equilibrium change is thus seen to be formed of a succession of equilibrium states of the system. In chemistry, equilibrium processes are the only reactions which can be treated as reversible phenomena.

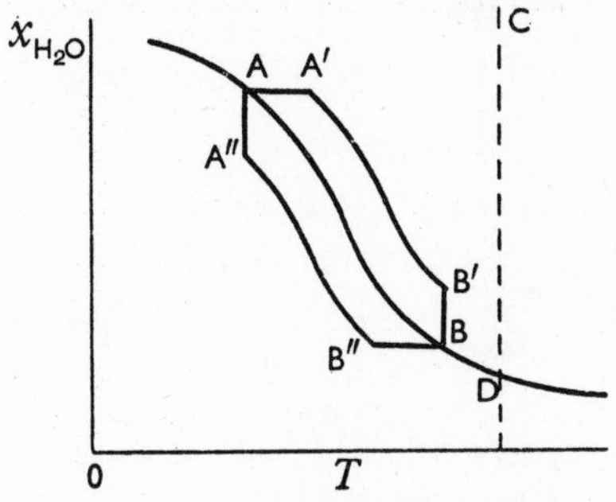

FIG. 3.2. Reversible dissociation of water.

As shown by these examples, real phenomena are all irreversible and it is only by considering hypothetical idealized processes that one can talk of reversible processes. But we must also recognize that there are many phenomena which cannot be idealized in this way, and an important recent development in thermodynamics is its extension to handle processes which are fundamentally irreversible.

We shall consider some examples of phenomena of this type. All real chemical reactions, and all changes which occur at a finite rate are irreversible. For example, if we consider a system in a state corresponding to C in fig. 3.2, and suppose the temperature is kept constant. The system will pass through the process CD; this cannot be reversed along DC since at each point along this line the rate of dissociation of water molecules is greater than their rate of formation. Furthermore we see that the change $C \rightarrow D$ cannot be related to any ideal reversible process.

Other examples of irreversible processes are the equalization of temperature in a system, mechanical friction, viscous flow in fluids, the Joule effect, and diffusion. The idealization of changes as reversible involves the suppression of all phenomena such as those just listed, and very often this is quite impracticable.

2. Statement of the Second Law of Thermodynamics: Entropy Changes and Entropy Creation.

The classical definition of the second law* is that, for all *reversible* changes in a closed system at a uniform temperature T,

$$dS = \frac{dQ}{T}, \quad \text{(reversible).} \tag{3.1}$$

This equation introduces the function of state S, called the *entropy of the system*, and simultaneously defines the absolute temperature T. For a closed system the state is defined by the variables T, V, ξ so that

$$S = S(T, V, \xi). \tag{3.2}$$

For all *irreversible* changes in a closed system

$$dS > \frac{dQ}{T}, \quad \text{(irreversible).} \tag{3.3}$$

Following Clausius we may now introduce a new quantity dQ', always positive, which represents the difference between $T\,dS$ and dQ in the course of an irreversible change. It is defined by

$$dS - \frac{dQ}{T} \equiv \frac{dQ'}{T} > 0, \quad \text{(irreversible).} \tag{3.4}$$

Equations (3.1) and (3.3) can now be combined to give

$$dS = \frac{dQ}{T} + \frac{dQ'}{T} \text{ with } \begin{array}{ll} dQ' = 0, & \text{reversible,} \\ dQ' > 0, & \text{irreversible.} \end{array} \tag{3.5}$$

Clausius called dQ' the *uncompensated heat*, which is always positive or zero; in classical thermodynamics it played a purely qualitative part. It was used to delimit reversible changes for which $dQ' = 0$, and when dealing with non-equilibrium states it was sufficient to write $dQ' > 0$ without attempting an explicit calculation of its value.

It may be stressed here, that although we adopt the term "uncom-

* For a more detailed discussion and enunciation of the second law see Duhem [15], [16]; H. Planck [36]; H. Poincaré, *Thermodynamique* (Paris, 1908); De Donder [5].

pensated heat " for historical reasons, it is not a particularly happy choice. The heat dQ is a certain quantity of energy *which the system exchanges with the outside world* and which passes through the surface separating the system from its surroundings. On the other hand the uncompensated heat dQ' arises from irreversible changes taking place in the *interior* of the system.

This distinction between heat which is exchanged with the outside world, and that which is produced within the system enables us to give a physical significance to equation (3.5). The entropy of a system can vary *for two reasons and for two reasons only* ; either by the transport of entropy to or from the surroundings through the boundary surface of the system, or by the *creation of entropy* inside the system.

If these two contributions are written d_eS and d_iS respectively :

$$dS = d_eS + d_iS. \tag{3.6}$$

For a closed system, as we have seen,

$$d_eS = \frac{dQ}{T}\ ;\quad d_iS = \frac{dQ'}{T}. \tag{3.7}$$

The entropy created in the system is thus equal to the Clausius uncompensated heat divided by the absolute temperature ; this gives the uncompensated heat a physical significance.

The inequality (3.4) states that the creation of entropy is always positive, that is to say irreversible processes can only create entropy, they cannot destroy it. We note that for an *isolated* system

$$dS = d_iS > 0. \tag{3.8}$$

This is the classical statement that the entropy of an isolated system increases with time. On the other hand in a non-isolated system the transport of entropy dQ/T may be positive or negative, and the entropy of the system may either increase or decrease. What is necessarily positive is not the change in entropy dS, but the production of entropy in the interior of the system.

The idea of the creation of entropy will play a fundamental role throughout this work. Instead of limiting ourselves to qualitative statements as to the sign of the entropy production however, the method we shall employ is based upon its quantitative evaluation. This enables us to discard the limitation imposed by the classical method to a discussion of reversible processes, and permits the development of the thermodynamics of irreversible phenomena, based on a study of real transformations.

3. Thermodynamic Potentials.

Before proceeding to the evaluation of the production of entropy, we must introduce the idea of thermodynamic potentials.

The two laws of thermodynamics may be combined, using (2.3) and (3.5), to give for any infinitesimal, irreversible change in a closed system

$$dU + p\,dV = T\,dS - dQ', \tag{3.9}$$

where $dQ' > 0$.

We now put formula (3.9) into various forms corresponding to various experimental conditions under which physico-chemical changes can take place. For this purpose we introduce certain new thermodynamic functions which are known as *thermodynamic potentials.*

Equation (3.9) may be written

$$dU = T\,dS - p\,dV - dQ'. \tag{3.10}$$

Thus for all irreversible reactions taking place *at constant S and V*

$$dQ' = -dU > 0. \tag{3.11}$$

Thus an irreversible change at constant entropy and volume is accompanied by a *decrease* in the internal energy. The internal energy thus plays the part of an indicator of irreversible processes for changes at constant S and V. If the energy remains constant, the system cannot undergo any irreversible changes, while if the energy decreases, irreversible processes must be taking place in the system. The internal energy is thus described as the thermodynamic potential associated with the physical variables S and V.

We may introduce other functions which play the same role for changes taking place under other conditions.

Thus using the definition of enthalpy given in chap. II (p. 24).

$$H = U + pV \tag{3.12}$$

(3.10) may be written

$$dH = T\,dS + V\,dp - dQ'. \tag{3.13}$$

For an irreversible reaction at constant S and p, we have therefore

$$dQ' = -dH > 0. \tag{3.14}$$

Thus, an irreversible change *at constant entropy and pressure* is accompanied by a *decrease in the enthalpy* ; we say that the enthalpy is the thermodynamic potential associated with the physical variables S and p.

We now define the Helmholtz free energy (F) and the Gibbs free energy (G) by the relations

$$F = U - TS, \tag{3.15}$$

$$G = U - TS + pV = H - TS, \tag{3.16}$$

and we see that substitution in (3.10) gives

$$dF = -S\,dT - p\,dV - dQ', \tag{3.17}$$

$$dG = -S\,dT + V\,dp - dQ'. \tag{3.18}$$

For an irreversible change at constant T and V we have therefore

$$dQ' = -dF > 0 \tag{3.19}$$

while at constant T and p,

$$dQ' = -dG > 0. \tag{3.20}$$

The functions F and G are the thermodynamic potentials associated with the variables T, V and T, p, respectively. They too indicate the presence of irreversible phenomena in changes in which the corresponding variables are maintained constant.

We must remember however that irreversible changes can occur under more general conditions than those just outlined; we have already seen (chap. I, § 9) that any change can be represented by giving the values of two physical variables as a function of time.

The choice of the thermodynamic potential to indicate the presence of irreversible changes, and the possibility of employing such a potential, depends upon the type of change considered. On the other hand the definition of irreversibility in terms of the creation of entropy—zero in the absence of irreversible processes, and positive in their presence—is completely general.

4. The Creation of Entropy in Physico-chemical Changes in Uniform Systems.

We now pass to the explicit calculation of entropy production. We shall consider here the very important special case in which mechanical and thermal equilibrium are already established. Mechanical equilibrium excludes the production of entropy by viscous flow, while uniformity of temperature, which is necessary for thermal equilibrium, excludes the internal production of entropy arising from the transport of heat between two regions at different temperatures. Similarly we assume that diffusion equilibrium has been attained within each phase of the system. The only production of entropy which can take place in a system of this kind is that associated with chemical reactions, with the transport of matter from one phase to another, or in general with any change which can be expressed in terms of a reaction co-ordinate ξ.

In the last volume of this work we shall free ourselves from these limitations and evaluate the production of entropy in the most general case.* The case considered here is sufficient for all applications to systems in which the production of entropy arises only from chemical

* *Cf.* [37].

reactions and phase changes, and for which the temperature, pressure (neglecting the effect of gravity) and composition within each phase is *uniform*.

The systems which we shall consider are therefore those which are in *partial equilibrium*. Equilibrium is already established with respect to certain variables such as temperature and pressure, and no irreversibility is associated with any change in these variables. On the other hand equilibrium is not attained with respect to redistribution of matter among constituents susceptible to chemical reaction, nor with respect to redistribution of matter among the different phases of the system, nor in general with respect to any changes which can be characterized by the parameter ξ (*cf.* chap. I, § 8).

A simple example of a system of this kind is a mixture of perfect gases capable of reacting chemically, in which there is a Maxwellian distribution of molecular speeds, but where the concentrations are not those corresponding to chemical equilibrium among the components.

Let us first consider a system in which only one change takes place, the extent of change at any instant being ξ. Suppose that in the time interval dt the value of ξ changes by an amount $d\xi$. Since this is the only irreversible process in the system the production of entropy must be determined solely by ξ and we may write

$$\boxed{dQ' = \mathbf{A}\, d\xi \geqslant 0}\,. \tag{3.21}$$

The inequality corresponds to spontaneous reaction while the equality corresponds to equilibrium. This fundamental equation, which is due to De Donder,* introduces the function of state $\mathbf{A}$ called the *affinity* of the reaction, for reasons which will soon be apparent.

Suppose T and p are chosen as physical variables, then since the uncompensated heat is uniquely related to the increase in the chemical variable $d\xi$, and is independent of the increments dp and dT which occur concurrently, dQ' will be the same whatever may be the values of dp and dT during the change under consideration. In other words we need not limit our consideration of affinity to conditions of constant temperature or of constant pressure. The function $\mathbf{A}$ defined by (3.21) does not depend upon the kind of transformation considered, but depends solely on the state of the system at a particular instant. In general we may express the state of the system in terms of physical variables x and y (*e.g.* T, p or T, V ...) and

$$\mathbf{A} = \mathbf{A}(x, y, \xi). \tag{3.22}$$

* Th. De Donder, *Bull. Ac. Roy. Belg.* (*Cl. Sc.*) (5) **7**, 197, 205 (1922).

We notice that the inequality (3.21) applies equally to open systems. For open systems only differ from closed systems in the exchanges of matter and energy, which take place with the surroundings. The transport of entropy d_eS for open systems includes the term dQ/T together with others related to the transport of matter. On the other hand the production of entropy by chemical reactions in the bulk of the system remains unaltered. We shall return to a more detailed study of open systems in the last volume of this work.

De Donder's inequality (3.21) may also be derived by different reasoning which we shall now consider.

5. Production of Entropy and Rate of Reaction.

Let us consider a system whose state is completely determined by the variables T, p, ξ. In a system of this kind the temperature and pressure must be uniform, for if not we should also have to include as variables defining the state of the system, not only the values of T and p at one point, but their gradients throughout the system.

We have already seen that the speed of reaction $\mathbf{v}$ may be regarded as a function of state (*cf.* 1.66), so that

$$\frac{d\xi}{dt} = \mathbf{v}(T, p, \xi). \tag{3.23}$$

We now proceed to show that in this system the uncompensated heat is necessarily of the form (3.21).* Equation (2.13) may be substituted in (3.5), and differentiated with respect to t to give

$$\frac{dQ'}{dt} = T\frac{dS}{dt} - \frac{dQ}{dt} = \left[T\left(\frac{\partial S}{\partial T}\right)_{p,\xi} - C_{p,\xi}\right]\frac{dT}{dt} + \left[T\left(\frac{\partial S}{\partial p}\right)_{T,\xi} - h_{T,\xi}\right]\frac{dp}{dt} + \left[T\left(\frac{\partial S}{\partial \xi}\right)_{T,p} - \left(\frac{\partial H}{\partial \xi}\right)_{T,p}\right]\frac{d\xi}{dt}, \tag{3.24}$$

where the three coefficients of dT/dt, dp/dt, and $d\xi/dt$ are functions of T, p, ξ. But dT/dt and dp/dt which are the changes of the temperature and pressure in unit time are quantities which we can vary at will and which may be given either positive or negative values (*cf.* chap. I, § 9). Thus (3.24) shows that, for a given state of the system, if the coefficients of dT/dt and dp/dt are not zero, then by assigning dT/dt and dp/dt suitable values we may give dQ'/dt any value we wish; in particular we can make dQ'/dt negative which is contrary to the second law. It is thus necessary for these coefficients to be zero, that is

$$T\left(\frac{\partial S}{\partial T}\right)_{p,\xi} - C_{p,\xi} = 0\,; \quad T\left(\frac{\partial S}{\partial p}\right)_{T,\xi} - h_{T,\xi} = 0. \tag{3.25}$$

* R. Defay, *Bull. Ac. Roy. Belg.* (*Cl. Sc.*), **24**, 347 (1938).

Equation (3.24) thus reduces to the same form as (3.21) with

$$-\mathbf{A} = \left(\frac{\partial H}{\partial \xi}\right)_{T,p} - T\left(\frac{\partial S}{\partial \xi}\right)_{T,p} . \tag{3.26}$$

This provides an alternative demonstration of De Donder's equation, and at the same time proves the important formulae (3.25) and (3.26).

If we consider the variables T, V, ξ the same arguments as above lead to

$$T\left(\frac{\partial S}{\partial T}\right)_{V,\xi} - C_{V,\xi} = 0\ ;\ T\left(\frac{\partial S}{\partial V}\right)_{T,\xi} - l_{T,\xi} = 0. \tag{3.27}$$

and

$$-\mathbf{A} = \left(\frac{\partial U}{\partial \xi}\right)_{T,V} - T\left(\frac{\partial S}{\partial \xi}\right)_{T,V} . \tag{3.28}$$

We shall return later to consider the physical significance of these formulae.

6. Significance of the Affinity.

De Donder's inequality (3.21) gives

$$\frac{dQ'}{dt} = \mathbf{A}\frac{d\xi}{dt} = \mathbf{A}\mathbf{v} \geqslant 0 , \tag{3.29}$$

whence for

$$\mathbf{A} > 0,\quad \mathbf{v} \geqslant 0\ ;$$
$$\mathbf{A} < 0,\quad \mathbf{v} \leqslant 0\ ;$$
$$\mathbf{A} = 0,\quad \mathbf{v} = 0\ ;$$

for if we had $\mathbf{v} \neq 0$ with $\mathbf{A} = 0$ we should have a chemical reaction proceeding at a finite rate in a reversible manner, which is impossible (*cf.* this chapter, § 1).

We see therefore that the *affinity is always of the same sign as the rate of reaction*, and that if the *affinity is zero the rate of reaction is zero, i.e. the system is in equilibrium.*

The converse of the last statement is, however, not true, for if we consider the possible values of $\mathbf{v}$ we have either

$$\mathbf{v} \neq 0, \text{ whence } dQ' > 0 \text{ and } \mathbf{A}\mathbf{v} > 0$$

which is satisfied by either $\mathbf{v} > 0,\quad \mathbf{A} > 0\ ;$

or $\mathbf{v} < 0,\quad \mathbf{A} < 0\ ;$

or $\mathbf{v}=0$, whence $dQ'=0$ and $\mathbf{A}\mathbf{v}=0$ which may be satisfied either by

$$\mathbf{v}=0 \text{ and } \mathbf{A}=0 \quad \textit{true equilibrium},$$

or

$$\mathbf{v}=0 \text{ and } \mathbf{A}\neq 0 \quad \textit{false equilibrium}.$$

We describe a system as being in a state of false equilibrium when no reaction proceeds even though the affinity of the reaction is not zero. For example a mixture of hydrogen and oxygen does not react at ordinary temperatures, even though its affinity is large as may be shown by introducing a catalyst or initiating the reaction by a spark.

Neglecting the case of false equilibrium, we see that

$$\mathbf{A}=0 \tag{3.30}$$

is *the necessary and sufficient condition for the equilibrium* in a chemical reaction.

In the axes T, p, ξ the equilibrium condition

$$\mathbf{A}(T, p, \xi)=0$$

determines, for each value of T and p the equilibrium value of ξ,

$$\xi=\xi_e(T, p).$$

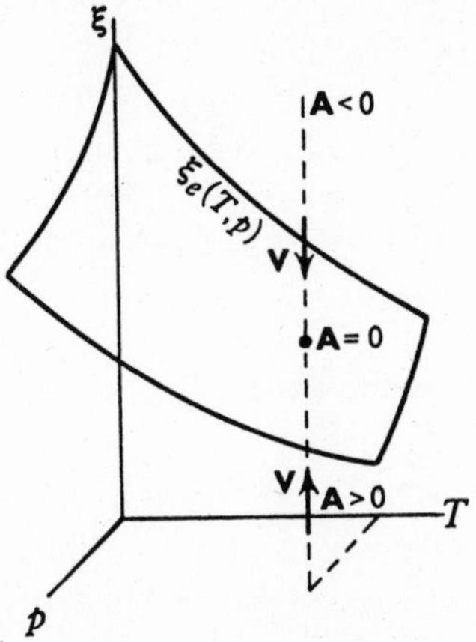

FIG. 3.3. The equilibrium surface in co-ordinates T, p, ξ.

The equilibrium surface $\mathbf{A}(T, p, \xi)=0$ or $\xi=\xi_e(T, p)$ divides space into two regions, in one $\mathbf{A}>0$ and in the other $\mathbf{A}<0$ (see fig. 3.3).

7. Simultaneous Reactions.

The results of the preceding paragraphs are readily extended to the case in which several simultaneous chemical reactions occur in the system. De Donder's inequality gives for the uncompensated heat

$$dQ'=\sum_{\rho} \mathbf{A}_\rho d\xi_\rho \geqslant 0 \tag{3.31}$$

where $\mathbf{A}_\rho$ is, by definition, the affinity of the ρth reaction and ξ_ρ is the corresponding extent of reaction. Each reaction is thus assigned an affinity. As before, if *all* the affinities $\mathbf{A}_1, \mathbf{A}_2 \dots \mathbf{A}_r$ are zero then so also are the rates of reaction $\mathbf{v}_1, \mathbf{v}_2 \dots \mathbf{v}_r$; that is, if the affinities are all zero, $dQ'=0$, and no irreversible changes can take place in the system. If we divide (3.31) by dt and put $\dfrac{d\xi_\rho}{dt}$ equal to the rate of the ρth reaction (*cf.* 1.53) we have

$$\frac{dQ'}{dt}=\sum_{\rho} \mathbf{A}_\rho \mathbf{v}_\rho \geqslant 0. \tag{3.32}$$

The production of entropy per unit time by the chemical reactions is thus given by the sum of the products of the rates of the chemical reactions, and the affinities which promote them. This property will also appear later when we consider the production of entropy by other irreversible processes. Thus in the case of the production of entropy in a system in which the temperature is non-uniform, the rate of production of entropy will be found equal to the product of the rate of flow of heat and the temperature gradient. The latter quantity plays the same part in heat conduction as the chemical affinity does in chemical reaction.

We also notice that the production of entropy (3.32) which must be positive appears as the sum of the entropy productions, positive or negative, of the various reactions which are occurring simultaneously. Thus it is possible, for a system in which two reactions take place, to have

$$\boldsymbol{A}_1\mathbf{v}_1 < 0 \quad \text{and} \quad \boldsymbol{A}_2\mathbf{v}_2 > 0 \tag{3.33}$$

provided that

$$\boldsymbol{A}_1\mathbf{v}_1 + \boldsymbol{A}_2\mathbf{v}_2 > 0. \tag{3.34}$$

The first reaction is then called the *coupled* and the second the *coupling* reaction. Thermodynamic coupling thus allows the coupled reaction to proceed in a direction opposite to that dictated by its affinity. This is, however, only possible when there exist other coupling reactions which proceed at a sufficient rate. We shall come across this coupling in another form in the last volume of this work in the study of thermal diffusion in which diffusion plays a role analogous to the coupled reaction, while the thermal conductivity corresponds to the coupling reaction.

Thermodynamic coupling is an essential feature of living systems. For example the synthesis of urea is coupled with the combustion of glucose and other substances in the liver.* This synthesis may be represented schematically by

$$2NH_3 + CO_2 \rightarrow (NH_2)_2CO + H_2O \quad \text{(coupled reaction)}$$
$$\tfrac{1}{6}C_6H_{12}O_6 + O_2 \rightarrow CO_2 + H_2O \quad \text{(coupling reaction).}$$

The affinities of these reactions under standard conditions are found to be

$$\boldsymbol{A}_1 = -11{,}000 \text{ cal.}$$
$$\boldsymbol{A}_2 = +115{,}000 \text{ cal.}$$

The rate of the coupled reaction cannot exceed a certain upper limit, obtained from (3.34) as

$$\mathbf{v}_1 \leqslant \frac{\boldsymbol{A}_2\mathbf{v}_2}{\boldsymbol{A}_1}. \tag{3.35}$$

* For a detailed discussion, see P. Van Rysselberghe, *Bull. Ac. Roy. Belg.* (*Cl. Sc.*), **22**, 1330 (1936); **23**, 416 (1937).

In all instances where experiments have been carried out, this inequality has been verified (*cf.* Van Rysselberghe, *loc. cit.*).

We may stress at this point that the conception of the role played by irreversible processes developed here is quite different from that in classical thermodynamics. In the latter, irreversible changes appear only as undesirable effects which reduce the efficiency of heat engines and which one must attempt to eliminate. On the other hand thermodynamic coupling, enables us to predict results such as separations and syntheses, which would be quite impossible to derive in the absence of a consideration of irreversible changes.

Thermodynamic coupling has, of course, no influence on equilibria, since for true equilibrium all the reaction velocities are zero and

$$\mathbf{A}_1 = \mathbf{A}_2 \ldots = \mathbf{A}_r = 0. \tag{3.36}$$

8. Comparison with the method of Schottky, Ulich and Wagner.

The thermodynamic method developed in this work is analogous in several ways to that of Schottky, Ulich and Wagner [42]. Both have the same aim : to develop a consistent thermodynamic treatment of chemical reactions. They both place the main emphasis upon the chemical reaction, whereas in Gibbs' work the stress is laid on the components of a system and their chemical potentials. Both begin from the same point : the recognition of the essential fact that, except for the *special limiting case* of equilibrium reactions, chemical reactions are all irreversible phenomena, and both discuss the way in which this irreversibility manifests itself.

We may take first Schottky and his collaborators' point of view.

Combination of the two laws of thermodynamics (2.1), (3.1) and (3.3) gives

$$dW \geqslant dU - T\,dS, \tag{3.37}$$

where the equality refers to reversible changes, and the inequality to irreversible changes. In particular, if the change is isothermal, we have (*cf.* 3.15)

$$dW \geqslant dF \quad \text{(isothermal change)}. \tag{3.38}$$

If we fix our attention on two states 1 and 2, infinitesimally near together, through which the system passes during some particular irreversible, isothermal change, the work received by the system during this change will be, by (3.38)

$$dW_{irr.} > dF. \tag{3.39}$$

Schottky and his collaborators assume that there always exists between the states 1 and 2 another route by which we can pass from 1 to 2 reversibly. For the change from 1 to 2 along this path

$$dW_{rev.} = dF \tag{3.40}$$

whence

$$dW_{irr.} > dW_{rev.} \tag{3.41}$$

Thus the irreversibility is characterized by the fact, that the work *received* by the system in the actual change, is greater than that which it would receive if we could go reversibly from state 1 to state 2.

We may also speak of the work *done* by the system being less than the work which the system could do by passing reversibly from 1 to 2. *This loss of work is a measure of the irreversibility of the process.*

Let us calculate this loss of work. The work received in the real (irreversible) process is (*cf.* 2.2)

$$dW_{irr.} = -p\,dV. \tag{3.42}$$

On the other hand the reversible work for an *isothermal* change is obtained by substituting (3.21) in (3.17) with $dT = 0$:

$$dW_{rev.} = dF = -p\,dV - \mathbf{A}d\xi. \tag{3.43}$$

The criterion of irreversibility (3.41) thus gives

$$dW_{irr.} - dW_{rev.} = \mathbf{A}d\xi > 0. \tag{3.44}$$

The loss of work is thus simply equal to the uncompensated heat, and we obtain De Donder's fundamental inequality. Schottky, Ulich and Wagner's method thus leads to the same results as ours, but requires the association of a hypothetical reversible process with each real irreversible change.

In the case of *non-isothermal* changes difficulties arise with Schottky's method. The reversible work done between two given states depends, by virtue of (3.37) on the path taken, and it cannot be defined unequivocably.*

On the other hand the method adopted in this work, based upon the creation of entropy, is independent of all hypotheses as to the type of irreversible process under consideration.

9. Statistical Interpretation of the Production of Entropy.

As mentioned in the introduction, the approach employed in this work is essentially phenomenological. We shall not therefore give a systematic exposition of the interpretation of thermodynamic functions in terms of statistical mechanics. Excellent accounts of statistical

* For a further discussion of this point *cf.* R. Defay and I. Prigogine, *Bull. Ac. Roy. Belg. (Cl. Sc.)*, (5), **33**, 222 (1947).

thermodynamics are available,* and here we need only recall the statistical definition of entropy which we shall employ frequently in succeeding chapters.

Consider a system formed of a single component having an energy U, volume V and containing N molecules. If, corresponding to specified values of these variables, there are altogether $\Omega(U, V, N)$ distinct quantum states of the system, then the entropy is defined as

$$S = \boldsymbol{k} \ln \Omega(U, V, N) \tag{3.45}$$

where $\boldsymbol{k}$ is the Boltzmann constant ($=\boldsymbol{R}/\boldsymbol{N}$, where $\boldsymbol{R}$ is the gas constant and $\boldsymbol{N}$ is Avogadro's number).

As an example of the application of this definition we may consider a system comprising two compartments A and B each of the same volume. The molecules contained in them are considered not to interact with one another, and to be distinguishable. We now proceed to calculate the contribution to the entropy arising from the different possible distributions between the two compartments. We suppose first that we have N^A molecules in one compartment and $N^B = N - N^A$ in the other. To this particular distribution between the two compartments will correspond

$$\frac{N!}{N^A!\,N^B!} \tag{3.46}$$

quantum states. The total number of states corresponding to all possible ways of dividing the molecules between the compartments is†

$$\Omega = \sum_{\substack{\text{all possible}\\ N^A}} \frac{N!}{N^A!\,N^B!} = 2^N. \tag{3.47}$$

The entropy will thus be given, in this case, by

$$S = \boldsymbol{k} N \ln 2. \tag{3.48}$$

We note that in the study of macroscopic systems we need, in effect, only consider the maximum term in the sum (3.47) which is easily seen to be

$$\frac{N!}{\left[\left(\frac{N}{2}\right)!\right]^2} = \left(\frac{N}{\mathrm{e}}\right)^N \Big/ \left(\frac{N}{2\mathrm{e}}\right)^N = 2^N, \tag{3.49}$$

* The standard work of reference is Fowler and Guggenheim [20]. An excellent introduction is given by G. S. Rushbrooke, *Introduction to Statistical Mechanics*, (Oxford, 1949).

† This follows from Newton's binomial formula :

$$(1+x)^N = \sum_{N^A} \frac{N!}{N^A!\,N^B!} x^{N^B},$$

when x is put equal to unity

in which we have employed Stirling's approximate formula for $N!$* *i.e.*

$$N! = \left(\frac{N}{\mathrm{e}}\right)^N.$$

The maximum term corresponds to the equilibrium distribution in which $N^A = N^B = \frac{1}{2}N$. We have thus calculated directly the entropy corresponding to the equilibrium distribution. To show how the entropy production accompanying the change from some initial distribution to the equilibrium state can be expressed in the form (3.21), we introduce the extent of change ξ to measure the number of molecules which have passed from one compartment to the other. If, initially, there are N_0^A and N_0^B molecules in the two compartments, then at any instant

$$N^A = N_0^A - \xi\,; \quad N^B = N_0^B + \xi. \tag{3.50}$$

The entropy corresponding to a given value of ξ will then be†

$$S(\xi) = \boldsymbol{k} \ln \Omega(U, V, N, \xi). \tag{3.51}$$

Here $\Omega(U, V, N, \xi)$ is the number of quantum states corresponding not simply to the given values of U, V, N but also to the given value of ξ. In the above example we have simply

$$S(\xi) = \boldsymbol{k} \ln \frac{N!}{N^A!\,N^B!} = \boldsymbol{k} \ln \frac{N!}{(N_0^A - \xi)!\,(N_0^B + \xi)!}. \tag{3.52}$$

In an isolated system such as that considered here, the change of entropy must be equal to the production of entropy. Hence on differentiating (3.52), and employing Stirling's approximation, we find

$$dS = d_iS = \boldsymbol{k} \ln \frac{N_0^A - \xi}{N_0^B + \xi}\, d\xi. \tag{3.53}$$

This relation is of the same form as (3.21) and corresponds to an affinity (per mole) of

$$\mathbf{A} = \boldsymbol{R}T \ln \frac{N_0^A - \xi}{N_0^B + \xi}. \tag{3.54}$$

It is easily verified that at equilibrium

$$\xi_e = \frac{N_0^A - N_0^B}{2}\,; \tag{3.55}$$

and that when

$$\mathbf{A} < 0, \quad \xi < \xi_e,$$
$$\mathbf{A} > 0, \quad \xi > \xi_e.$$

* *Cf.* Mayer and Mayer [34], chap. IV ; a careful discussion of the validity of taking the maximum term only is given by Rushbrooke, *loc. cit.*, p. 27.

† *Cf.* Guggenheim [26′], chap. II.

The total entropy produced when the system goes from the initial state to the equilibrium state ξ_e is in this case

$$S(\xi_e) - S(\xi) = \boldsymbol{k} \ln \frac{\left[\left(\frac{N}{2}\right)!\right]^2}{(N_0^A - \xi)!\,(N_0^B + \xi)!} \,. \tag{3.50}$$

We see therefore that in this elementary and rather schematic example, the entropy production can be expressed in a simple statistical mechanical form.

CHAPTER IV

AFFINITY

1. Introduction.

In the last chapter we introduced a precise definition of the affinity of a chemical reaction based upon the creation of entropy. The most important property of the affinity is expressed by the fundamental inequality

$$\mathbf{A}\mathbf{v} \geqslant 0, \tag{4.1}$$

which shows that at any instant the affinity and rate of reaction have the same sign. In this chapter we shall examine the relationship of the affinity to other thermodynamic quantities, as well as the way in which it depends upon the variables which determine the state of the system.

2. Affinity and Heat of Reaction.

Equations (3.25) and (3.26), for the variables T, p, ξ, and equations (3.27) and (3.28), for the variables T, V, ξ give immediately the derivatives of the entropy :

$$\left.\begin{aligned} &\left(\frac{\partial S}{\partial T}\right)_{p,\xi} = \frac{C_{p,\xi}}{T}; && \left(\frac{\partial S}{\partial T}\right)_{V,\xi} = \frac{C_{V,\xi}}{T} \\ &\left(\frac{\partial S}{\partial p}\right)_{T,\xi} = \frac{h_{T,\xi}}{T}; && \left(\frac{\partial S}{\partial V}\right)_{T,\xi} = \frac{l_{T,\xi}}{T} \\ &\left(\frac{\partial S}{\partial \xi}\right)_{T,p} = \frac{\mathbf{A} + (\partial H/\partial\xi)_{T,p}}{T}; && \left(\frac{\partial S}{\partial \xi}\right)_{T,V} = \frac{\mathbf{A} + (\partial U/\partial\xi)_{T,V}}{T} \end{aligned}\right\}. \tag{4.2}$$

In particular we notice the two last formulae which may be written (*cf.* 3.26, 3.28) :

$$-\mathbf{A} = \left(\frac{\partial H}{\partial \xi}\right)_{T,p} - T\left(\frac{\partial S}{\partial \xi}\right)_{T,p}; \quad -\mathbf{A} = \left(\frac{\partial U}{\partial \xi}\right)_{T,V} - T\left(\frac{\partial S}{\partial \xi}\right)_{T,V}. \tag{4.3}$$

These formulae link the affinity with the heats of reaction $(\partial H/\partial\xi)_{T,p}$ and $(\partial U/\partial\xi)_{T,V}$. They show that at sufficiently low temperatures the heat of reaction becomes equal to the affinity ; this will be so when :

$$\left|\left(\frac{\partial U}{\partial \xi}\right)_{T,V}\right| \gg T\left|\left(\frac{\partial S}{\partial \xi}\right)_{T,V}\right|. \tag{4.4}$$

In this case the affinity and the heats of reaction have the same sign, and exothermal reactions $(\partial U/\partial\xi < 0)$ are spontaneous.

Starting from (4.2) and (4.3) and remembering that

$$\frac{\partial^2 S}{\partial T\,\partial \xi} = \frac{\partial^2 S}{\partial \xi\,\partial T}, \tag{4.5}$$

we obtain

$$\frac{1}{T}\left(\frac{\partial C_{p,\xi}}{\partial \xi}\right)_{T,p} = \left[\frac{\partial}{\partial T}\left(\frac{\mathbf{A}}{T}\right)\right]_{p,\xi} + \frac{1}{T}\frac{\partial}{\partial T}\left(\frac{\partial H}{\partial \xi}\right)_{T,p} - \frac{1}{T^2}\left(\frac{\partial H}{\partial \xi}\right)_{T,p}. \tag{4.6}$$

But by Kirchhoff's second equation (2.30),

$$\left(\frac{\partial C_{p,\xi}}{\partial \xi}\right)_{T,p} = \frac{\partial}{\partial T}\left(\frac{\partial H}{\partial \xi}\right)_{T,p}, \tag{4.7}$$

so that (4.6) reduces to

$$\boxed{\left[\frac{\partial}{\partial T}\left(\frac{\mathbf{A}}{T}\right)\right]_{p,\xi} = \frac{1}{T^2}\left(\frac{\partial H}{\partial \xi}\right)_{T,p}}. \tag{4.8}$$

Similarly in the variables V, T, ξ,

$$\boxed{\left[\frac{\partial}{\partial T}\left(\frac{\mathbf{A}}{T}\right)\right]_{V,\xi} = \frac{1}{T^2}\left(\frac{\partial U}{\partial \xi}\right)_{T,V}}. \tag{4.9}$$

The importance of (4.8) lies in the fact that it enables the affinity to be calculated at a temperature T, if its value at some given temperature T_0 is known. Thus if we integrate (4.8) between T_0 and T, at constant p and ξ we have

$$\frac{\mathbf{A}(T, p, \xi)}{T} - \frac{\mathbf{A}(T_0, p, \xi)}{T_0} = \int_{T_0}^{T} \frac{1}{T^2}\left(\frac{\partial H}{\partial \xi}\right)_{T,p} dT. \tag{4.10}$$

It has already been seen (chap. II, § 5) that specific heats may usually be expressed as a power series in T, so that with the aid of Kirchhoff's equation (2.32), $(\partial H/\partial \xi)_{T,p}$ can be expressed in the form :

$$\left(\frac{\partial H}{\partial \xi}\right)_{T,p} = h_{T_0,p} + \alpha_1 T + \alpha_2 T^2 + \alpha_3 T^3 + \ldots, \tag{4.11}$$

which gives

$$\int_{T_0}^{T} \frac{1}{T^2}\left(\frac{\partial H}{\partial \xi}\right)_{T,p} dT = -\frac{h_{T_0,p}}{T} + \alpha_1 \ln T + \alpha_2 T + \tfrac{1}{2}\alpha_3 T^2 \ldots + I, \tag{4.12}$$

where I is a constant given by

$$I = \frac{h_{T_0,p}}{T_0} - \alpha_1 \ln T_0 - \alpha_2 T_0 - \tfrac{1}{2}\alpha_3 T_0^2 \ldots. \tag{4.12'}$$

Table 7.3 p. 92 gives the values of $h_{T_0,p}$, α_1, $\alpha_2 \ldots$ for a number of important reactions.

We now know everything necessary for the calculation of $\mathbf{A}(T, p, \xi)$ from (4.10); the equation takes the form:

$$\mathbf{A} = -h_{T_0, p} + \alpha_1 T \ln T + \alpha_2 T^2 + \tfrac{1}{2}\alpha_3 T^3 \ldots + \left[\frac{\mathbf{A}(T_0, p, \xi)}{T_0} + I\right] T. \qquad (4.13)$$

If in particular, the system is in chemical equilibrium at the temperature T_0 we have $\mathbf{A}(T_0, p, \xi) = 0$, and (4.13) reduces to

$$\mathbf{A} = -h_{T_0, p} + \alpha_1 T \ln T + \alpha_2 T^2 + \tfrac{1}{2}\alpha_3 T^3 + \ldots + IT. \qquad (4.14)$$

3. Affinity as a function of Temperature.

We now calculate the affinity as a function of temperature in the general case by evaluating the integral in (4.10).

From Kirchhoff's equation (2.32) we have first, (using the abbreviation $h_{T,p} = (\partial H / \partial \xi)_{T,p}$),

$$h_{T,p} = h_{T_0, p} + \int_{T_0}^{T} \sum_i \nu_i c_{p,i} dT. \qquad (4.15)$$

Whence

$$\int_{T_0}^{T} \frac{h_{T,p}}{T^2} dT = \int_{T_0}^{T} \frac{h_{T_0,p}}{T^2} dT + \int_{T_0}^{T} \frac{dT}{T^2} \int_{T_0}^{T} \sum_i \nu_i c_{p,i} dT$$

$$= -\frac{h_{T_0,p}}{T} + \frac{h_{T_0,p}}{T_0} + \int_{T_0}^{T} \frac{dT}{T^2} \int_{T_0}^{T} \sum_i \nu_i c_{p,i} dT \qquad (4.16)$$

which on substitution in (4.10) gives

$$\frac{\mathbf{A}}{T} = \frac{\mathbf{A}_0}{T_0} - \frac{h_{T_0,p}}{T} + \frac{h_{T_0,p}}{T_0} + \sum_i \nu_i \int_{T_0}^{T} \frac{dT}{T^2} \int_{T_0}^{T} c_{p,i} dT. \qquad (4.17)$$

We see clearly that to calculate $\mathbf{A}$ at a given temperature T, pressure p, and extent of reaction ξ, we must know

(*a*) the affinity $\mathbf{A}_0$ at one particular temperature T_0 at the pressure p and for the given value of ξ;

(*b*) the heat of reaction at T_0;

(*c*) the partial molar heat capacities of the constituents as a function of temperature throughout the whole range from that at which $\mathbf{A}_0$ and $h_{T_0,p}$ are known, to the temperature at which we wish to calculate $\mathbf{A}$.

Thus, the affinity may be obtained for any given temperature, from a knowledge of its value at any one temperature by the use of purely calorimetric measurements The right hand side of (4.17) may be written in various alternative forms which are often useful.

At T_0, we have from (4.3),

$$-\mathbf{A}_0 = \left(\frac{\partial H}{\partial \xi}\right)_{T_0,p} - T_0 \left(\frac{\partial S}{\partial \xi}\right)_{T_0,p}, \qquad (4.18)$$

whence

$$\frac{\mathbf{A}}{T} = -\frac{1}{T}\left(\frac{\partial H}{\partial \xi}\right)_{T_0,p} + \left(\frac{\partial S}{\partial \xi}\right)_{T_0,p} + \sum_i \nu_i \int_{T_0}^{T} \frac{dT}{T^2} \int_{T_0}^{T} c_{p,i} dT. \qquad (4.19)$$

The double integral, which appears both in (4.17) and (4.19), may be transformed, by integration by parts* to

$$\int_{T_0}^{T}\frac{dT}{T^2}\int_{T_0}^{T}c_{p,i}dT = \frac{1}{T}\int_{T_0}^{T}dT\int_{T_0}^{T}\frac{c_{p,i}}{T}dT = \int_{T_0}^{T}\frac{c_{p,i}}{T}dT - \frac{1}{T}\int_{T_0}^{T}c_{p,i}dT. \quad (4.20)$$

Thus (4.19) may be expressed in the two equivalent forms

$$\mathbf{A} = -\left(\frac{\partial H}{\partial \xi}\right)_{T_0,p} + T\left(\frac{\partial S}{\partial \xi}\right)_{T_0,p} + \sum_i \nu_i \int_{T_0}^{T}dT\int_{T_0}^{T}\frac{c_{p,i}}{T}dT, \quad (4.21)$$

and

$$\mathbf{A} = -\left(\frac{\partial H}{\partial \xi}\right)_{T_0,p} + T\left(\frac{\partial S}{\partial \xi}\right)_{T_0,p} + \sum_i \nu_i \left[T\int_{T_0}^{T}\frac{c_{p,i}}{T}dT - \int_{T_0}^{T}c_{p,i}dT\right]. \quad (4.22)$$

At sufficiently high temperatures, the specific heats may be represented by power series in T, while at low temperatures they are more complicated functions of temperature which we shall consider in detail in chapter X, § 3 and XII, § 5. With the aid of tables of specific heats we can evaluate directly

$$c_{p,i}, \quad \int_{T_0}^{T}c_{p,i}dT, \quad \int_{T_0}^{T}\frac{c_{p,i}}{T}dT$$

for each component taking part in the reaction.

4. Affinity and the Thermodynamic Potentials.

The explicit formula (3.21) for the uncompensated heat gives, on substitution in (3.10), (3.13), (3.17) and (3.18)

$$dU = T\,dS - p\,dV - \mathbf{A}\,d\xi \quad (4.23)$$

$$dH = T\,dS + V\,dp - \mathbf{A}\,d\xi \quad (4.24)$$

$$dF = -S\,dT - p\,dV - \mathbf{A}\,d\xi \quad (4.25)$$

$$dG = -S\,dT + V\,dp - \mathbf{A}\,d\xi \quad (4.26)$$

* The method of integration by parts is based on the formula

$$\int u\,dv = uv - \int v\,du. \quad (a)$$

To show that

$$\int dT\int\frac{c_{p,i}}{T}dT = T\int\frac{c_{p,i}}{T}dT - \int c_{p,i}dT, \quad (b)$$

we write

$$u = \int\frac{c_{p,i}}{T}dT, \quad v = T$$

and substitute in (a).

By putting alternatively

$$u = \int c_{p,i}dT, \quad v = -1/T,$$

it follows that

$$\int\frac{dT}{T^2}\int c_{p,i}dT = -\frac{1}{T}\int c_{p,i}dT + \int\frac{c_{p,i}}{T}dT. \quad (c)$$

Equations (b) and (c) are combined in (4.20).

The thermodynamic functions of state,

$$\left.\begin{aligned} U &= U(S,\ V\ ;\ \xi) \\ H &= H(S,\ p\ ;\ \xi) \\ F &= F(T,\ V\ ;\ \xi) \\ G &= G(T,\ p\ ;\ \xi) \end{aligned}\right\}, \tag{4.27}$$

are called *the thermodynamic potentials relative to the physical variables* S, V ; S, p ; T, V ; T, p respectively (*cf.* chap. III, § 3).

We now compare (4.23), ... , (4.26) with the corresponding total differentials. For that relative to U we have

$$dU = \left(\frac{\partial U}{dS}\right)_{V,\xi} dS + \left(\frac{\partial U}{dV}\right)_{S,\xi} dV + \left(\frac{\partial U}{\partial \xi}\right)_{V,S} d\xi, \tag{4.28}$$

and comparing coefficients we obtain

$$\left.\begin{aligned} \left(\frac{\partial U}{\partial S}\right)_{V,\xi} &= T \\ \left(\frac{\partial U}{\partial V}\right)_{S,\xi} &= -p \\ \left(\frac{\partial U}{\partial \xi}\right)_{S,V} &= -\mathbf{A} \end{aligned}\right\} \qquad \left.\begin{aligned} \left(\frac{\partial H}{\partial S}\right)_{p,\xi} &= T \\ \left(\frac{\partial H}{\partial p}\right)_{S,\xi} &= V \\ \left(\frac{\partial H}{\partial \xi}\right)_{S,p} &= -\mathbf{A} \end{aligned}\right\}$$

$$\left.\begin{aligned} \left(\frac{\partial F}{\partial T}\right)_{V,\xi} &= -S \\ \left(\frac{\partial F}{\partial V}\right)_{T,\xi} &= -p \\ \left(\frac{\partial F}{\partial \xi}\right)_{T,V} &= -\mathbf{A} \end{aligned}\right\} \qquad \left.\begin{aligned} \left(\frac{\partial G}{\partial T}\right)_{p,\xi} &= -S \\ \left(\frac{\partial G}{\partial p}\right)_{T,\xi} &= V \\ \left(\frac{\partial G}{\partial \xi}\right)_{T,p} &= -\mathbf{A} \end{aligned}\right\}. \tag{4.29}$$

We note that the partial derivative of a thermodynamic potential with respect to the *extensive thermal variable* S gives us the *intensive thermal variable* T ; conversely, the partial derivative of a thermodynamic potential with respect to the *intensive thermal variable* gives us S, *with the sign changed.* The same regularity is observed for the pair of *mechanical* variables p and V and the *pair of chemical variables* $\mathbf{A}$ *and* ξ.

Among the sets of equations (4.29) we notice particularly those connecting the affinity with the thermodynamic potentials, namely

$$\mathbf{A} = -\left(\frac{\partial U}{\partial \xi}\right)_{S,V} = -\left(\frac{\partial H}{\partial \xi}\right)_{S,p} = -\left(\frac{\partial F}{\partial \xi}\right)_{T,V} = -\left(\frac{\partial G}{\partial \xi}\right)_{T,p}. \tag{4.30}$$

If we know *one of the thermodynamic potentials as a function of the variables to which it corresponds, we can express all the other thermodynamic variables as a function of this one by using equations* (4.29).

For example suppose that we know G as a function of T, p and ξ. We have now

$$S = -\left(\frac{\partial G}{\partial T}\right)_{p,\xi}, \quad V = \left(\frac{\partial G}{\partial p}\right)_{T,\xi} \quad \text{and} \quad \mathbf{A} = -\left(\frac{\partial G}{\partial \xi}\right)_{T,p}, \tag{4.31}$$

so that:

$$H = G + TS = G - T\left(\frac{\partial G}{\partial T}\right)_{p,\xi},$$

$$F = G - pV = G - p\left(\frac{\partial G}{\partial p}\right)_{T,\xi},$$

and

$$U = G + TS - pV = G - T\left(\frac{\partial G}{\partial T}\right)_{p,\xi} - p\left(\frac{\partial G}{\partial p}\right)_{T,\xi}.$$

In particular we notice the relation between the enthalpy H and G. By a simple transformation this may be written

$$\left[\frac{\partial\left(\frac{G}{T}\right)}{\partial T}\right]_{p,\xi} = -\frac{H}{T^2}. \tag{4.32}$$

Similarly we may obtain the relation between the free energy F and the internal energy U, namely

$$U = F - T\left(\frac{\partial F}{\partial T}\right)_{V,\xi}, \tag{4.33}$$

or

$$\left[\frac{\partial\left(\frac{F}{T}\right)}{\partial T}\right]_{V,\xi} = -\frac{U}{T^2}. \tag{4.34}$$

Equations (4.32), (4.33) and (4.34) are known as the *Gibbs-Helmholtz equations*. We notice that they are of the same form as the relations (4.8) and (4.9) connecting the affinity with the heat of reaction.

We now derive a further set of important relations from (4.29). We have, for example,

$$\frac{\partial^2 U}{\partial S\, \partial V} = \frac{\partial^2 U}{\partial V\, \partial S},$$

whence from the first two equations of (4.29)

$$\left(\frac{\partial T}{\partial V}\right)_{S,\xi} = -\left(\frac{\partial p}{\partial S}\right)_{V,\xi}. \tag{4.35}$$

Proceeding in this way we obtain from the four groups of equations (4.29), four new groups

$$\left.\begin{aligned}\left(\frac{\partial T}{\partial V}\right)_{S,\xi} &= -\left(\frac{\partial p}{\partial S}\right)_{V,\xi}\\ \left(\frac{\partial T}{\partial \xi}\right)_{S,V} &= -\left(\frac{\partial \mathbf{A}}{\partial S}\right)_{V,\xi}\\ \left(\frac{\partial p}{\partial \xi}\right)_{S,V} &= \left(\frac{\partial \mathbf{A}}{\partial V}\right)_{S,\xi}\end{aligned}\right\}, \quad (4.36) \qquad \left.\begin{aligned}\left(\frac{\partial T}{\partial p}\right)_{S,\xi} &= \left(\frac{\partial V}{\partial S}\right)_{p,\xi}\\ \left(\frac{\partial T}{\partial \xi}\right)_{S,p} &= -\left(\frac{\partial \mathbf{A}}{\partial S}\right)_{p,\xi}\\ \left(\frac{\partial V}{\partial \xi}\right)_{S,p} &= -\left(\frac{\partial \mathbf{A}}{\partial p}\right)_{S,\xi}\end{aligned}\right\}, \quad (4.37)$$

$$\left.\begin{aligned}\left(\frac{\partial S}{\partial V}\right)_{T,\xi} &= \left(\frac{\partial p}{\partial T}\right)_{V,\xi}\\ \left(\frac{\partial S}{\partial \xi}\right)_{T,V} &= \left(\frac{\partial \mathbf{A}}{\partial T}\right)_{V,\xi}\\ \left(\frac{\partial p}{\partial \xi}\right)_{T,V} &= \left(\frac{\partial \mathbf{A}}{\partial V}\right)_{T,\xi}\end{aligned}\right\}, \quad (4.38) \qquad \left.\begin{aligned}\left(\frac{\partial S}{\partial p}\right)_{T,\xi} &= -\left(\frac{\partial V}{\partial T}\right)_{p,\xi}\\ \left(\frac{\partial S}{\partial \xi}\right)_{T,p} &= \left(\frac{\partial \mathbf{A}}{\partial T}\right)_{p,\xi}\\ \left(\frac{\partial V}{\partial \xi}\right)_{T,p} &= -\left(\frac{\partial \mathbf{A}}{\partial p}\right)_{T,\xi}\end{aligned}\right\}. \quad (4.39)$$

We take particular note of those relations which give the partial differentials of the affinity. Those in which T is the thermal variable are collected together below :

$$\left.\begin{aligned}\left(\frac{\partial \mathbf{A}}{\partial T}\right)_{V,\xi} &= \left(\frac{\partial S}{\partial \xi}\right)_{T,V} & \qquad \left(\frac{\partial \mathbf{A}}{\partial T}\right)_{p,\xi} &= \left(\frac{\partial S}{\partial \xi}\right)_{T,p}\\ \left(\frac{\partial \mathbf{A}}{\partial V}\right)_{T,\xi} &= \left(\frac{\partial p}{\partial \xi}\right)_{T,V} & \qquad \left(\frac{\partial \mathbf{A}}{\partial p}\right)_{T,\xi} &= -\left(\frac{\partial V}{\partial \xi}\right)_{T,p}\end{aligned}\right\}. \quad (4.40)$$

The general structure of equations (4.36) to (4.39), apart from the sign, can be summarized as follows :

The partial derivative of a *thermal variable* (T or S) with respect to one of the *mechanical variables* (p or V) is equal to the partial derivative of the *conjugate mechanical variable* (V or p) with respect to the *other thermal variable* (S or T). Similar statements hold for the other pairs of variables (T, S) and ($\mathbf{A}$, ξ), and (p, V) and ($\mathbf{A}$, ξ).

The sign of the derivatives can be determined simply by writing down the variables in two rows, the intensive variables above, the extensive variables below so that conjugate pairs are in the same column. The signs attached to the intensive variables are those of the corresponding terms in the fundamental equation (4.23) for the internal energy.

$$\begin{matrix} T & \quad -p & \quad -\mathbf{A} \\ S & \quad V & \quad \xi \end{matrix}$$

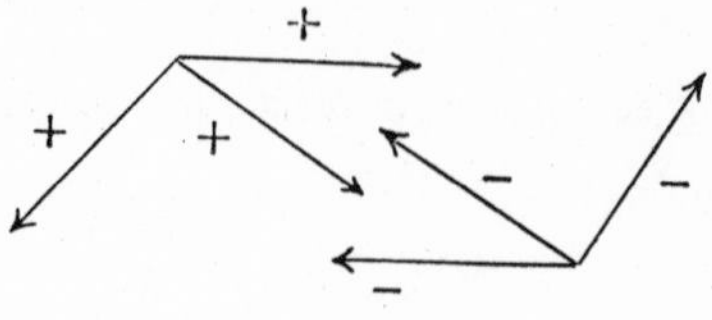

When the variables are taken from this table to form the derivatives the sign attached to the derivative is determined from the vector diagram on the right. Thus for example $\partial T/\partial V$ will have a positive sign, $\partial V/\partial S$ a negative sign.

Each equation obtained using two pairs of variables is valid for constant values of either of the third pair of variables. For example we obtain

$$-\left[\frac{\partial(-\mathbf{A})}{\partial(-p)}\right]_{\xi}=\left(\frac{\partial V}{\partial \xi}\right)_{p}$$

which applies both for constant S and constant T:

$$-\left(\frac{\partial \mathbf{A}}{\partial p}\right)_{S,\xi}=\left(\frac{\partial V}{\partial \xi}\right)_{S,p} \quad \text{and} \quad -\left(\frac{\partial \mathbf{A}}{\partial p}\right)_{T,\xi}=\left(\frac{\partial V}{\partial \xi}\right)_{T,p}.$$

Altogether twenty-four relations follow from these three pairs of variables. If the fundamental equation (4.23) includes other terms corresponding, for example, to the contribution of surface energy to the total energy, then the above scheme can be extended immediately to cover these variables.

These formulae have many applications. For example we have seen (*cf.* 4.2) that

$$\left(\frac{\partial S}{\partial V}\right)_{T,\xi}=\frac{l_{T,\xi}}{T}; \quad \left(\frac{\partial S}{\partial p}\right)_{T,\xi}=\frac{h_{T,\xi}}{T};$$

so that applying the first equations of (4.38) and (4.39) we have

$$l_{T,\xi}=T\left(\frac{\partial p}{\partial T}\right)_{V,\xi}; \tag{4.41}$$

$$h_{T,\xi}=-T\left(\frac{\partial V}{\partial T}\right)_{p,\xi}. \tag{4.42}$$

This provides an indirect method of measuring these two thermal coefficients.

Furthermore, (*cf.* 2.22)

$$C_{p,\xi}-C_{V,\xi}=l_{T,\xi}\left(\frac{\partial V}{\partial T}\right)_{p,\xi}, \tag{4.43}$$

so that using (4.41) we have

$$C_{p,\xi}-C_{V,\xi}=T\left(\frac{\partial p}{\partial T}\right)_{V,\xi}\left(\frac{\partial V}{\partial T}\right)_{p,\xi}; \tag{4.44}$$

and in particular for a pure substance

$$C_{p}-C_{V}=T\left(\frac{\partial p}{\partial T}\right)_{V}\left(\frac{\partial V}{\partial T}\right)_{p}. \tag{4.45}$$

Whenever Mayer's equation (2.26) for a perfect gas

$$C_p - C_V = n\mathbf{R}$$

is not valid, for example for a very imperfect gas, we may calculate $C_p - C_V$ from the isotherms using (4.45). We shall also employ (4.45) in studying the specific heats of solids and liquids (*cf.* chap. XII, § 1).

The last pair of formulae (4.40) are useful because they give the variation of the affinity of reaction with temperature and pressure. The first of them may be written, by differentiating with respect to ξ as in (2.31):

$$\left(\frac{\partial \mathbf{A}}{\partial T}\right)_{p,\xi} = \sum_i \nu_i s_i = \left(\frac{\partial S}{\partial \xi}\right)_{T,p}, \tag{4.46}$$

where s_i is the partial molar entropy of i defined by

$$s_i = \left(\frac{\partial S}{\partial n_i}\right)_{T,p}. \tag{4.47}$$

The second may be put in the form

$$\left(\frac{\partial \mathbf{A}}{\partial p}\right)_{T,\xi} = -\sum_i \nu_i v_i = -\left(\frac{\partial V}{\partial \xi}\right)_{T,p}, \tag{4.48}$$

where $(\partial V/\partial \xi)_{T,p}$, sometimes abbreviated to $v_{T,p}$, is the change in the volume of the system produced by the chemical reaction at constant T and p. We see that *if a reaction results in a positive volume change when the pressure is kept constant, an increase in pressure will reduce the affinity of the reaction.*

*Example**: From equation (4.48), the variation of the affinity of reaction with the pressure is seen to be appreciable only if the reaction is accompanied by a considerable change in volume when it takes place at constant pressure and temperature. This will be the case for gas reactions such as

$$N_2 + 3H_2 \rightleftharpoons 2NH_3$$

in which the total number of molecules changes in the reaction.

For this reaction $(\partial V/\partial \xi)_{T,p} < 0$ and the affinity of the reaction increases with pressure. On the other hand for reactions in condensed phases the effect is usually extremely small. For example the allotropic transformation

C (*graphite*)→C (*diamond*)

has a negative affinity (− 685 cal./g. atom) at ordinary pressures and temperatures and so is impossible. But since the affinity is small, and the reaction is accompanied by a decrease in volume, it is possible that by increasing the pressure sufficiently the sign of the affinity could be reversed. And furthermore, by increasing the temperature to the order of 2000 °C we might also be able to obtain a reasonable rate of reaction.

* *Cf.* Ulich [46], p. 127.

The molar volume of graphite is $v_1 = 5{\cdot}33$ cm.^{3} while that of diamond is $v_2 = 3{\cdot}42$ cm.^{3}; thus

$$(\partial V/\partial \xi)_{T,p} = -1{\cdot}91 \text{ cm.}^3$$

This value is approximately independent of p, so the variation of the affinity with pressure is given by

$$\mathbf{A} - \mathbf{A}_0 = 1{\cdot}91\,(p - p_0).$$

Expressing the affinity in calories and the pressure in atmospheres, this becomes (*cf.* table 2.1):

$$\mathbf{A} - \mathbf{A}_0 = 0{\cdot}0242 \times 1{\cdot}91\,(p - p_0).$$

Now at 2000 °C and 1 atm. it is found that the affinity is $-2{,}000$ cal./g. atom so that to attain equilibrium ($\mathbf{A} = 0$) between the two allotropic modifications of carbon at this temperature a pressure of

$$p - p_0 = \frac{2000}{0{\cdot}0242 \times 1{\cdot}91} \simeq 40{,}000 \text{ atm.}$$

must be applied. Actually Bridgman* has not found any evidence for the allotropic change even at 45,000 atmospheres.

The effect of pressure on the affinity is thus too small to serve as a basis of an industrial process for the synthesis of diamond.

Note: The formulae developed in this chapter can also be applied to the particular case in which no chemical reaction takes place in the system. We then have

$$dQ' = \mathbf{A}\, d\xi = 0,$$

and relations (4.23) to (4.26) may be written

$$\left.\begin{aligned} dU &= T\,dS - p\,dV \\ dH &= T\,dS + V\,dp \\ dF &= -S\,dT - p\,dV \\ dG &= -S\,dT + V\,dp \end{aligned}\right\}. \tag{4.49}$$

The state of the system is then completely defined by two physical variables, for example S and V. From formulae (4.49) we may obtain equations which are the particular cases of the equations obtained in the previous paragraph.

5. Simultaneous Reactions.

We shall now extend the results of the preceding paragraphs to the case in which several reactions may occur in the system. The expression (3.31) for the uncompensated heat is now employed, and may be substituted in (3.10) to give

$$dU = T\,dS - p\,dV - \sum_\rho \mathbf{A}_\rho d\xi_\rho. \tag{4 50}$$

* P. W. Bridgman, *J. Chem. Phys.*, 15, 92 (1947).

Thus
$$\mathbf{A}_\rho = -(\partial U/\partial \xi_\rho)_{S,V}, \tag{4.51}$$
while to the conditions (4.36) for dU to be a total differential we must add the further relations
$$\left(\frac{\partial \mathbf{A}_\rho}{\partial \xi_{\rho'}}\right)_{S,V} = \left(\frac{\partial \mathbf{A}_{\rho'}}{\partial \xi_\rho}\right)_{S,V}, \quad (\rho, \rho' = 1, 2 \ldots r). \tag{4.52}$$
In the same way we have
$$\mathbf{A}_\rho = -\left(\frac{\partial H}{\partial \xi_\rho}\right)_{S,p} = -\left(\frac{\partial F}{\partial \xi_\rho}\right)_{T,V} = -\left(\frac{\partial G}{\partial \xi_\rho}\right)_{T,p}. \tag{4.53}$$

The extension of the other formulae to the more general case follows immediately; in particular we may note that (4.3) may now be written
$$-\mathbf{A}_\rho = \left(\frac{\partial H}{\partial \xi_\rho}\right)_{T,p} - T\left(\frac{\partial S}{\partial \xi_\rho}\right)_{T,p}, \tag{4.54}$$
where $(\partial H/\partial \xi_\rho)_{T,p}$ is the heat change of reaction at constant T and p of the ρth reaction (*cf.* 2.36).

Similarly the important formula (4.8) becomes
$$\left[\frac{\partial\left(\frac{\mathbf{A}_\rho}{T}\right)}{\partial T}\right]_{p,\xi} = \frac{1}{T^2}\left(\frac{\partial H}{\partial \xi_\rho}\right)_{T,p}. \tag{4.55}$$
The subscript ξ on the left hand side of (4.55) means that in the differentiation $\xi_1, \xi_2, \ldots \xi_r$ must remain constant.

Finally, introducing the volume change accompanying the reaction at constant T and p (*cf.* 4.48), we have
$$\left(\frac{\partial V}{\partial \xi_\rho}\right)_{T,p} = \sum_i \nu_{i,\rho} v_i \tag{4.56}$$
and hence
$$\left(\frac{\partial \mathbf{A}_\rho}{\partial p}\right)_{T,\xi} = -\left(\frac{\partial V}{\partial \xi_\rho}\right)_{T,p}. \tag{4.57}$$
This equation gives the effect of pressure on the affinity of the ρth reaction.

6. Total Differential of the Affinity.

The total differential of $\mathbf{A}/T$ in the variables T, p, ξ may be written down and combined with (4.8) and (4.48) to give:
$$\boxed{d\left(\frac{\mathbf{A}}{T}\right) = \frac{1}{T^2}\left(\frac{\partial H}{\partial \xi}\right)_{T,p} dT - \frac{1}{T}\left(\frac{\partial V}{\partial \xi}\right)_{T,p} dp + \frac{1}{T}\left(\frac{\partial \mathbf{A}}{\partial \xi}\right)_{T,p} d\xi}. \tag{4.58}$$

We notice incidentally that, from (4.30),

$$\left(\frac{\partial \mathbf{A}}{\partial \xi}\right)_{T,p} = -\left(\frac{\partial^2 G}{\partial \xi^2}\right)_{T,p} = a_{T,p}. \tag{4.59}$$

Equation (4.58) may be put into the alternative form

$$d\mathbf{A} = \frac{\mathbf{A} + h_{T,p}}{T}\, dT - v_{T,p} dp + a_{T,p} d\xi, \tag{4.60}$$

where we have introduced abbreviations for the derivatives with respect to ξ (*cf.* List of Symbols p. xxv).

In many subsequent applications of this formula (*cf.* chap. XIX) it will be useful to consider $\mathbf{A}$ as an *independent* variable such that ξ becomes a function of the variables T, p and $\mathbf{A}$. If we assume that $a_{T,p} \neq 0$, (4.60) may be written

$$d\xi = -\frac{\mathbf{A} + h_{T,p}}{T a_{T,p}}\, dT + \frac{v_{T,p}}{a_{T,p}}\, dp + \frac{1}{a_{T,p}}\, d\mathbf{A} \tag{4.61}$$

which is the total differential of ξ in the variables T, p, $\mathbf{A}$, and leads immediately to the set of equations :

$$\left(\frac{\partial \xi}{\partial T}\right)_{p,\mathbf{A}} = -\frac{\mathbf{A} + h_{T,p}}{T a_{T,p}}; \quad \left(\frac{\partial \xi}{\partial p}\right)_{T,\mathbf{A}} = \frac{v_{T,p}}{a_{T,p}}; \quad \left(\frac{\partial \xi}{\partial \mathbf{A}}\right)_{T,p} = \frac{1}{a_{T,p}}. \tag{4.62}$$

Analogous formulae may be derived using V as variable in place of p. If we put

$$p_{T,V} = \left(\frac{\partial p}{\partial \xi}\right)_{T,V}; \quad a_{T,V} = \left(\frac{\partial \mathbf{A}}{\partial \xi}\right)_{T,V} = -\left(\frac{\partial^2 F}{d\xi^2}\right)_{T,V}; \tag{4.63}$$

then using (4.9), and the last of (4.38) we have

$$d\left(\frac{\mathbf{A}}{T}\right) = \frac{1}{T^2}\left(\frac{\partial U}{\partial \xi}\right)_{T,V} dT + \frac{1}{T}\left(\frac{\partial p}{\partial \xi}\right)_{T,V} dV + \frac{1}{T}\left(\frac{\partial \mathbf{A}}{\partial \xi}\right)_{T,V} d\xi \tag{4.64}$$

$$= \frac{u_{T,V}}{T^2}\, dT + \frac{p_{T,V}}{T}\, dV + \frac{a_{T,V}}{T}\, d\xi.$$

In the same way we find the total differential of ξ in the variables T, V, $\mathbf{A}$:

$$d\xi = -\frac{\mathbf{A} + u_{T,V}}{T a_{T,V}}\, dT - \frac{p_{T,V}}{a_{T,V}}\, dV + \frac{1}{a_{T,V}}\, d\mathbf{A}. \tag{4.65}$$

Finally we shall derive the relation between $a_{T,p}$ and $a_{T,V}$. The identity

$$\left(\frac{\partial \mathbf{A}}{\partial \xi}\right)_{T,V} = \left(\frac{\partial \mathbf{A}}{\partial \xi}\right)_{T,p} + \left(\frac{\partial \mathbf{A}}{\partial p}\right)_{T,\xi}\left(\frac{\partial p}{\partial \xi}\right)_{T,V} \tag{4.66}$$

may be derived exactly as the identities (2.21). It follows immediately from the last equation of (4.40) that

$$\left(\frac{\partial \mathbf{A}}{\partial \xi}\right)_{T,p} - \left(\frac{\partial \mathbf{A}}{\partial \xi}\right)_{T,V} = \left(\frac{\partial V}{\partial \xi}\right)_{T,p} \left(\frac{\partial p}{\partial \xi}\right)_{T,V}, \tag{4.67}$$

or

$$a_{T,p} - a_{T,V} = v_{T,p} p_{T,V}. \tag{4.67'}$$

Again, we may write (4.67) in a different form by employing the identity

$$\left(\frac{\partial V}{\partial \xi}\right)_{T,V} = 0 = \left(\frac{\partial V}{\partial \xi}\right)_{T,p} + \left(\frac{\partial V}{\partial p}\right)_{T,\xi} \left(\frac{\partial p}{\partial \xi}\right)_{T,V}, \tag{4.68}$$

or

$$\left(\frac{\partial V}{\partial \xi}\right)_{T,p} = -\left(\frac{\partial p}{\partial \xi}\right)_{T,V} \left(\frac{\partial V}{\partial p}\right)_{T,\xi}. \tag{4.69}$$

So that eliminating $(\partial p/\partial \xi)_{T,V}$ from (4.67) we have

$$\left(\frac{\partial \mathbf{A}}{\partial \xi}\right)_{T,p} - \left(\frac{\partial \mathbf{A}}{\partial \xi}\right)_{T,V} = -\frac{(\partial V/\partial \xi)^2_{T,p}}{(\partial V/\partial p)_{T,\xi}}, \tag{4.70}$$

or

$$a_{T,p} - a_{T,V} = -v^2_{T,p}/(\partial V/\partial p)_{T,\xi} \tag{4.70'}$$

This equation is important in the discussion of the stability of chemical equilibria (*cf.* chap. XV).

All these equations are readily extended to the case of several chemical reactions. Thus since

$$\left(\frac{\partial \mathbf{A}_\rho}{\partial \xi_{\rho'}}\right)_{T,p} = -\left(\frac{\partial^2 G}{\partial \xi_\rho \partial \xi_{\rho'}}\right)_{T,p} = \left(\frac{\partial \mathbf{A}_{\rho'}}{\partial \xi_\rho}\right)_{T,p}, \tag{4.71}$$

we have in place of (4.58)

$$d\left(\frac{\mathbf{A}_\rho}{T}\right) = \frac{1}{T^2}\left(\frac{\partial H}{\partial \xi_\rho}\right)_{T,p} dT - \frac{1}{T}\left(\frac{\partial V}{\partial \xi_\rho}\right)_{T,p} dp + \frac{1}{T}\sum_{\rho'}\left(\frac{\partial \mathbf{A}_\rho}{\partial \xi_{\rho'}}\right)_{T,p} d\xi_{\rho'}. \tag{4.72}$$

These equations also are needed for a study of the stability of chemical equilibria, (chap. XV).

CHAPTER V

AVERAGE VALUES OF THE AFFINITY

1. Introduction.

As we have seen the affinity of a reaction is at any instant a function of state of the system, and does not depend upon the conditions under which changes in the system occur. If we consider not the instantaneous value of the affinity but the average value in the course of a reaction, then this average will depend upon the conditions under which the reaction occurs *e.g.* whether at constant T and p, or T and V. In this book we shall employ the instantaneous values of the affinity, but to show the relationship between the present methods, and those introduced by Lewis and Randall we now proceed to express the average values of both heat of reaction and affinity in terms of the thermodynamic functions U, H, F and G.

2. Average values of the Heat of Reaction.

Let us consider a change taking place in a system from state α to state β. We know (*cf.* chap. I, § 9) that all the variables will be functions completely determined by the time. Instead of choosing the time as independent variable we could equally well choose the extent of reaction ξ ; all the variables defining the state of the system will be definite functions of ξ provided we define the conditions under which the reaction takes place.

Let us put

$$q(\xi) = \frac{dQ}{d\xi} \cdot \tag{5.1}$$

The function $q(\xi)$ is called the heat of reaction relative to the physico-chemical change under consideration. The heat absorbed in the change $\alpha\beta$ will be

$$Q_{\alpha\beta} = \int_{\xi_\alpha}^{\xi_\beta} q(\xi)\, d\xi, \tag{5.2}$$

and we shall define the *average heat of reaction* for the change $\alpha\beta$ as

$$\bar{q}_{\alpha\beta} = \frac{Q_{\alpha\beta}}{\xi_\beta - \xi_\alpha}, \tag{5.3}$$

or

$$\bar{q}_{\alpha\beta} = \frac{1}{\xi_\beta - \xi_\alpha} \int_{\xi_\alpha}^{\xi_\beta} q(\xi)\, d\xi. \tag{5.4}$$

If the change $\alpha\beta$ corresponds to one equivalent of reaction, that is if

$$\xi_\beta - \xi_\alpha = 1,$$

equation (5.4) becomes

$$Q_{\alpha\beta} = \bar{q}_{\alpha\beta}. \tag{5.5}$$

Particular Cases :

(*a*) For a reaction taking place *at constant* T *and* V, we have already found in (2.7) and (2.8) that

$$(dQ)_{T,V} = \left(\frac{\partial U}{\partial \xi}\right)_{T,V} d\xi. \tag{5.6}$$

Integrating this from $\xi = 0$ to $\xi = 1$ we have

$$Q_{T,V} = \int_0^1 \left(\frac{\partial U}{\partial \xi}\right)_{T,V} d\xi = (U_1 - U_0)_{T,V} = (\Delta U)_{T,V}, \tag{5.7}$$

where U_1 and U_0 are the internal energies when $\xi = 1$, and $\xi = 0$ respectively.

Thus

$$\bar{q}_{T,V} = (\Delta U)_{T,V}. \tag{5.8}$$

The average heat of reaction at constant T and V is thus equal to the decrease in internal energy in that reaction.

(*b*) For the case of a reaction *at constant* T *and* p a similar argument shows that

$$\bar{q}_{T,p} = (\Delta H)_{T,p}. \tag{5.9}$$

so that the average heat of reaction at constant T and p is equal to the decrease in enthalpy during the reaction.

3. Average values of the Affinity.

From the fundamental inequality (3.21)

$$dQ' = \mathbf{A}\, d\xi \geqslant 0,$$

we have for the change from α to β :

$$Q'_{\alpha\beta} = \int_{\xi_\alpha}^{\xi_\beta} \mathbf{A}(\xi) d\xi > 0. \tag{5.10}$$

The mean affinity during the change is defined by

$$\bar{\mathbf{A}}_{\alpha\beta} = \frac{1}{\xi_\beta - \xi_\alpha} \int_{\xi_\alpha}^{\xi_\beta} \mathbf{A}(\xi) d\xi. \tag{5.11}$$

Thus

$$Q'_{\alpha\beta} = \bar{\mathbf{A}}_{\alpha\beta}(\xi_\beta - \xi_\alpha) > 0. \tag{5.12}$$

If the change $\alpha\beta$ corresponds to one equivalent of reaction ($\xi_\beta - \xi_\alpha = 1$) we have

$$Q'_{\alpha\beta} = \bar{\mathbf{A}}_{\alpha\beta} > 0. \tag{5.13}$$

The average affinity of a change $\alpha\beta$, which corresponds to one equivalent of reaction, is thus equal to the uncompensated heat of that reaction.

Particular Cases :

(*a*) For a reaction at *constant T and V*, we have

$$(dQ')_{T,V} = \mathbf{A}\, d\xi > 0, \tag{5.14}$$

and by virtue of (4.30),

$$(dQ')_{T,V} = -\left(\frac{\partial F}{\partial \xi}\right)_{T,V} d\xi > 0.$$

Integrating from $\xi = 0$ to $\xi = 1$ we have for the reaction

$$Q'_{T,V} = -\int_0^1 \left(\frac{\partial F}{\partial \xi}\right)_{T,V} d\xi = -(F_1 - F_0)_{T,V} = -(\Delta F)_{T,V} > 0, \tag{5.15}$$

and hence

$$\bar{\mathbf{A}}_{T,V} = -(\Delta F)_{T,V} > 0. \tag{5.16}$$

The average value of the affinity for a change at constant T and V is thus equal to the corresponding decrease in the free energy F.

(*b*) Similarly for a reaction at *constant temperature and pressure*

$$\bar{\mathbf{A}}_{T,p} = -(\Delta G)_{T,p} > 0. \tag{5.17}$$

The affinity of a reaction is a function of the instantaneous state of the system. If a reaction is allowed to proceed at a constant T and p the system will pass through a series of states different from those traversed in a reaction at constant T and V, and consequently *the average affinity of a given reaction has, in general, a different value depending upon whether the reaction is carried out at constant T and V, or constant T and p.*

4. Relations between the Heat of Reaction and Average Affinity.

We shall now show that the formulae linking the affinity to the heat of reaction developed in chap. IV, § 2, can be applied also to the average heat and average affinity of reaction.

We return to equation (4.3)

$$-\mathbf{A} = \left(\frac{\partial U}{\partial \xi}\right)_{T,V} - T\left(\frac{\partial S}{\partial \xi}\right)_{T,V}$$

and integrate with respect to ξ from $\xi = 0$ to $\xi = 1$ at constant T and V :

$$-\int_0^1 \mathbf{A}(T, V, \xi)\, d\xi = \int_0^1 \left(\frac{\partial U}{\partial \xi}\right)_{T,V} d\xi - T\int_0^1 \left(\frac{\partial S}{\partial \xi}\right)_{T,V} d\xi. \tag{5.18}$$

Using the definitions (5.3) and (5.11) for $\bar{q}_{T,V}$ and $\bar{\mathbf{A}}_{T,V}$, and introducing

$$(\Delta S)_{T,V} = \int_0^1 \left(\frac{\partial S}{\partial \xi}\right)_{T,V} d\xi = (S_1 - S_0)_{T,V}, \tag{5.19}$$

we then obtain the following relation between the average heat and average affinity of reaction :

$$-\bar{\mathbf{A}}_{T,V} = \bar{q}_{T,V} - T(\Delta S)_{T,V}. \tag{5.20}$$

In the same way for changes at constant T and p we have

$$-\bar{\mathbf{A}}_{T,p} = \bar{q}_{T,p} - T(\Delta S)_{T,p}, \tag{5.21}$$

where $(\Delta S)_{T,p}$ is defined as

$$(\Delta S)_{T,p} = \int_0^1 \left(\frac{\partial S}{\partial \xi}\right)_{T,p} d\xi = (S_1 - S_0)_{T,p}. \tag{5.22}$$

Equations (5.20) and (5.21) allow us to calculate the average value of the affinity for a *change* carried out either with T and V, or T and p constant. They must not be confused with equations (4.3) which give the value of the affinity for a given *instantaneous state* of the system.

Equations (5.20) and (5.21) may be written in another, more familiar, form by using (5.8) and (5.16) on the one hand, and (5.9) and (5.17) on the other.

We obtain

$$(\Delta F)_{T,V} = (\Delta U)_{T,V} - T(\Delta S)_{T,V}, \tag{5.23}$$

$$(\Delta G)_{T,p} = (\Delta H)_{T,p} - T(\Delta S)_{T,p}. \tag{5.24}$$

The latter equation is of great importance as it allows a calculation of the average affinity $-(\Delta G)_{T,p}$ from a knowledge of the average heat $(\Delta H)_{T,p}$ and average entropy of reaction $(\Delta S)_{T,p}$.*

Equations (4.8) and (4.9) can also be written in terms of the average affinity and average heat of reaction. We start from the Gibbs-Helmholtz relation (4.33) and apply this to one state in which $\xi = 1$, and another in which T and V have the same values but $\xi = 0$:

$$U(T, V, 1) - F(T, V, 1) = -T \frac{\partial F(T, V, 1)}{\partial T} \tag{5.25}$$

and

$$U(T, V, 0) - F(T, V, 0) = -T \frac{\partial F(T, V, 0)}{\partial T}, \tag{5.26}$$

where $U(T, V, 1)$ stands for $U(T, V, \xi = 1)$ and so on.

Subtracting (5.26) term by term from (5.25) we have

$$(\Delta U)_{T,V} - (\Delta F)_{T,V} = -T \left[\frac{\partial (\Delta F)_{T,V}}{\partial T}\right]_V \tag{5.27}$$

or

$$\left[\frac{\partial \left(\frac{(\Delta F)_{T,V}}{T}\right)}{\partial T}\right]_V = -\frac{(\Delta U)_{T,V}}{T^2}; \tag{5.28}$$

* *e.g.* Lewis and Randall [32]; Parks and Huffmann [35].

or (*cf.* 5.8 and 5.16)

$$\left[\frac{\partial\left(\dfrac{\bar{\mathbf{A}}_{T,V}}{T}\right)}{\partial T}\right]_V = \frac{\bar{q}_{T,V}}{T^2}. \qquad (5.29)$$

This is the direct relation connecting the average affinity and average heat of reaction.

In the same way we can show that

$$\left[\frac{\partial\left(\dfrac{\bar{\mathbf{A}}_{Tp}}{T}\right)}{\partial T}\right]_p = \frac{\bar{q}_{T,p}}{T^2}. \qquad (5.30)$$

These last two relations have also been used extensively for finding the average affinity of reaction.*

* *Cf.* F. Pollitzer, *Die Berechnung chemischer Affinitäten nach dem Nernstschen Wärmesatz* (Stüttgart 1912); *cf.* also Eucken [17], p. 302.

CHAPTER VI

CHEMICAL POTENTIALS

1. Closed and Open Systems.

So far we have limited ourselves to a study of *closed* systems. We have seen that a closed system is one which cannot exchange matter with its surroundings: the only exchanges which can take place are those of energy.

Let us now extend our study to systems in which the masses $m_1 \dots m_c$ and hence also the number of moles $n_1 \dots n_c$ can vary in an arbitrary manner, as is the case when one can add or remove arbitrary masses of various constituents. The system is now described as *open*.

For closed systems, the first law of thermodynamics establishes the existence of the function of state U. We now *presume* that this function must also exist when *the number of moles varies in an arbitrary manner.*

We write now, quite generally,

$$U = U(T, V; n_1 \dots n_c) \tag{6.1}$$

choosing T and V as the physical variables.

Similarly, the second law establishes the existence of the function of state S for a closed system.

We again presume that this function $S(T, V; n_1 \dots n_c)$ exists *whether the system is closed or not.*

Total differentiation of (6.1), whatever may be the increments δT, δV, $\delta n_1 \dots \delta n_c$, gives

$$\delta U = \left(\frac{\partial U}{\partial T}\right)_{V, n_1, \dots, n_c} \delta T + \left(\frac{\partial U}{\partial V}\right)_{T, n_1, \dots, n_c} \delta V + \sum_i \left(\frac{\partial U}{\partial n_i}\right)_{T, V, n_1, \dots, n_{i-1}, n_{i+1}, \dots, n_c} \delta n_i. \tag{6.2}$$

We have introduced here a new symbol for differentiation δ to emphasize that δn_i is chosen quite arbitrarily. In other words, the δn_i terms represent variations of any kind in the number of moles n_i.

2. Fundamental Theorems.

The two fundamental theorems which follow are valid whatever may be the increments assigned to the independent variables.

1*st Theorem* :

Let us choose S, V ; $n_1 \dots n_c$ as independent variables. Whatever may be the increments δS, δV, $\delta n_1 \dots \delta n_c$ we have

$$\delta U = T\,\delta S - p\,\delta V + \sum_i \left(\frac{\partial U}{\partial n_i}\right)_{S,V,n_j} \delta n_i, \tag{6.3}$$

which is *Gibbs' equation.**

To prove this† we consider U as a function of S, V ; $n_1 \dots n_c$, so that

$$\delta U = \left(\frac{\partial U}{\partial S}\right)_{V,n} \delta S + \left(\frac{\partial U}{\partial V}\right)_{S,n} \delta V + \sum_i \left(\frac{\partial U}{\partial n_i}\right)_{S,V,n_j} \delta n_i. \tag{6.4}$$

The subscript n means that *all* the n_i remain constant during the derivation and the subscript n_j means that all n's except n_i remain constant. When an open system undergoes a change in which all the n_i remain constant, *its state changes exactly as it would in a closed system in which ξ remains constant.*

So that

$$\left(\frac{\partial U}{\partial S}\right)_{V,n} = \left(\frac{\partial U}{\partial S}\right)_{V,\xi} \quad \text{and} \quad \left(\frac{\partial U}{\partial V}\right)_{S,n} = \left(\frac{\partial U}{\partial V}\right)_{S,\xi}. \tag{6.5}$$

But we have already seen (*cf.* 4.29) that for a closed system

$$\left(\frac{\partial U}{\partial S}\right)_{V,\xi} = T \quad \text{and} \quad \left(\frac{\partial U}{\partial V}\right)_{S,\xi} = -p. \tag{6.6}$$

We may now replace the partial derivatives in (6.4) by the values given by (6.6) to obtain

$$\delta U = T\,\delta S - p\,\delta V + \sum_i \left(\frac{\partial U}{\partial n_i}\right)_{S,V,n_j} \delta n_i. \tag{6.7}$$

We can proceed similarly for H, F and G, and obtain the following total differentials :

$$\delta H = \quad T\,\delta S + V\,\delta p + \sum_i \left(\frac{\partial H}{\partial n_i}\right)_{S,p,n_j} \delta n_i, \tag{6.8}$$

$$\delta F = -S\,\delta T - p\,\delta V + \sum_i \left(\frac{\partial F}{\partial n_i}\right)_{T,V,n_j} \delta n_i, \tag{6.9}$$

$$\delta G = -S\,\delta T + V\,\delta p + \sum_i \left(\frac{\partial G}{\partial n_i}\right)_{T,p,n_j} \delta n_i. \tag{6.10}$$

2*nd Theorem* :‡

$$\left(\frac{\partial U}{\partial n_i}\right)_{S,V,n_j} = \left(\frac{\partial H}{\partial n_i}\right)_{S,p,n_j} = \left(\frac{\partial F}{\partial n_i}\right)_{T,V,n_j} = \left(\frac{\partial G}{\partial n_i}\right)_{T,p,n_j}. \tag{6.11}$$

* Gibbs [23], equation (12).

† *Cf.* R. Defay, *Bull. Ac. Roy. Belg.* (*Cl. Sc.*), **15**, 678 (1929).

‡ Gibbs, [23], equation (104).

For from (6.7) and the definitions (3.12), (3.15) and (3.16) of H, F, and G, namely,

$$H \equiv U + pV,$$
$$F \equiv U - TS,$$
$$G \equiv U - TS + pV,$$

we deduce that

$$\delta H = T\,\delta S + V\,\delta p + \sum_i \left(\frac{\partial U}{\partial n_i}\right)_{S,V,n_j} \delta n_i, \tag{6.12}$$

$$\delta F = -S\,\delta T - p\,\delta V + \sum_i \left(\frac{\partial U}{\partial n_i}\right)_{S,V,n_j} \delta n_i, \tag{6.13}$$

$$\delta G = S\,\delta T + V\,\delta p + \sum_i \left(\frac{\partial U}{\partial n_i}\right)_{S,V,n_j} \delta n_i. \tag{6.14}$$

Comparing these with equations (6.8) to (6.10) we see that the relations (6.11) are satisfied.

Following Gibbs we call these common values the chemical potential μ_i of the component i. We thus have (dropping now the subscript n_j) :

$$\boxed{\mu_i \equiv \left(\frac{\partial U}{\partial n_i}\right)_{S,V} = \left(\frac{\partial H}{\partial n_i}\right)_{S,p} = \left(\frac{\partial F}{\partial n_i}\right)_{T,V} = \left(\frac{\partial G}{\partial n_i}\right)_{T,p}} \; ; \tag{6.15}$$

or finally

$$\delta U = T\,\delta S - p\,\delta V + \sum_i \mu_i \delta n_i, \tag{6.16}$$

$$\delta H = T\,\delta S + V\,\delta p + \sum_i \mu_i \delta n_i, \tag{6.17}$$

$$\delta F = -S\,\delta T - p\,\delta V + \sum_i \mu_i \delta n_i, \tag{6.18}$$

$$\delta G = -S\,\delta T + V\,\delta p + \sum_i \mu_i \delta n_i. \tag{6.19}$$

If we consider the equation

$$\mu_i = \left(\frac{\partial G}{\partial n_i}\right)_{T,p} \tag{6.20}$$

we see (*cf.* 1.24) that the chemical potential of i is the partial molar quantity corresponding to the Gibbs free energy G. G is an extensive function, so μ_i is an intensive quantity. We can speak of the chemical potential of a component at each point of the system, just as we can speak of its concentration or mole fraction.

These equations now allow us to express the affinity as a function of the chemical potentials. Equation (4.30) gives us immediately (*cf.* 2.35)

$$\mathbf{A} = -\left(\frac{\partial G}{\partial \xi}\right)_{T,p} = -\sum_i \nu_i \left(\frac{\partial G}{\partial n_i}\right)_{T,p} \tag{6.21}$$

or

$$\mathbf{A} = -\sum_i \nu_i \mu_i. \tag{6.22}$$

The condition of chemical equilibrium $\mathbf{A} = 0$ may thus be expressed very simply in terms of chemical potentials :

$$\sum_i \nu_i \mu_i = 0, \quad \text{at equilibrium.} \tag{6.23}$$

The great advantage following from the use of Gibbs' chemical potentials is that they enable us to write the condition of chemical equilibrium in the form (6.23) which is at once both simple and general.

In the case of several reactions we have in the same way (using 4.53)

$$\mathbf{A}_\rho = -\left(\frac{\partial G}{\partial \xi_\rho}\right)_{T, p} = -\sum_i \nu_{i,\rho} \mu_i \tag{6.22'}$$

and the condition of equilibrium is

$$\sum_i \nu_{i,\rho} \mu_i = 0 \quad (\rho = 1, 2 \ldots r). \tag{6.23'}$$

Example : In the combustion of methane

$$CH_4 + 2O_2 = CO_2 + 2H_2O$$

The affinity is given by

$$\mathbf{A} = \mu_{CH_4} + 2\mu_{O_2} - \mu_{CO_2} - 2\mu_{H_2O}$$

and the condition of equilibrium is

$$\mu_{CH_4} + 2\mu_{O_2} = \mu_{CO_2} + \mu_{H_2O}.$$

Note : In the relations (6.15) we have in each case chosen as independent variables one thermal variable, S or T, and one mechanical variable, V or p. If we choose both thermal variables or both mechanical variables as independent variables we run into difficulties which result in our being unable to define the chemical potential in terms of one of the functions U, H, F or G.

This difficulty can always be avoided by a judicious choice of variables.*

3. The Thermodynamic Potentials as functions of the Chemical Potentials.

The extensive function

$$G(T, p\,;\; n_1 \ldots n_c)$$

is homogeneous of the first degree in $n_1 \ldots n_c$, so that we have immediately (*cf.* 1.25)

$$G = \sum_i n_i \mu_i \,. \tag{6.24}$$

* *Cf.* P. Van Rysselberghe, *C. R.*, 201, 1126 (1935) ; 207, 845 (1938).

The other thermodynamic potentials are then found to be

$$\left.\begin{aligned} U &= \sum_i n_i\mu_i + TS - pV \\ H &= \sum_i n_i\mu_i + TS \\ F &= \sum_i n_i\mu_i - pV \end{aligned}\right\}. \tag{6.25}$$

We showed in § 4 of chap. IV that all the thermodynamic properties of a system are completely determined if we are given

$$G(T, p;\ n_1 \dots n_c).$$

Equation (6.24) shows furthermore that *the thermodynamic properties of a system are uniquely defined if we know the chemical potentials* μ_i *of the i constituents of the system, as functions of the independent variables* T, p, $n_1 \dots n_c$. These c chemical potentials are related among themselves, and to the other thermodynamic variables by formulae which we now proceed to establish.

We take the second partial derivative of G with respect to each of the possible pairs of variables, and recalling equation (2.28), we obtain first the so-called reciprocity relation :

$$\left(\frac{\partial \mu_j}{\partial n_i}\right)_{T,p} = \left(\frac{\partial \mu_i}{\partial n_j}\right)_{T,p} \qquad (i, j = 1, 2 \dots c), \tag{6.26}$$

and also, using (4.29)

$$\left(\frac{\partial \mu_i}{\partial T}\right)_{p,n} = -\left(\frac{\partial S}{\partial n_i}\right)_{T,p} = -s_i; \tag{6.27}$$

$$\left(\frac{\partial \mu_i}{\partial p}\right)_{T,n} = \left(\frac{\partial V}{\partial n_i}\right)_{T,p} = v_i. \tag{6.28}$$

Differentiating $G = U - TS + pV$ with respect to n_i with T and p constant we have

$$\mu_i = u_i - Ts_i + pv_i. \tag{6.29}$$

And similarly, from $H = U + pV$,

$$h_i = u_i + pv_i \tag{6.30}$$

and hence

$$\mu_i = h_i - Ts_i. \tag{6.31}$$

Furthermore

$$\left[\frac{\partial\left(\dfrac{\mu_i}{T}\right)}{\partial T}\right]_{p,n} = \frac{1}{T}\frac{\partial \mu_i}{\partial T} - \frac{\mu_i}{T^2} = -\frac{Ts_i + \mu_i}{T^2} = -\frac{h_i}{T^2}. \tag{6.32}$$

It will be convenient here to collect together the following formulae which have already been derived (*cf.* 2.35, 4.46, 4.48, 6.22):

$$h_{T,p} = \left(\frac{\partial H}{\partial \xi}\right)_{T,p} = \sum_i \nu_i h_i, \tag{6.33}$$

$$v_{T,p} = \left(\frac{\partial V}{\partial \xi}\right)_{T,p} = \sum_i \nu_i v_i, \tag{6.34}$$

$$s_{T,p} = \left(\frac{\partial S}{\partial \xi}\right)_{T,p} = \sum_i \nu_i s_i, \tag{6.35}$$

$$\mathbf{A} = -\left(\frac{\partial G}{\partial \xi}\right)_{T,p} = -\sum_i \nu_i \mu_i. \tag{6.36}$$

All these formulae are of the same structure: they are all the sums of partial molar quantities each of which is multiplied by the corresponding stoichiometric coefficient in the reaction under consideration. As a result these equations have certain properties in common. We have already shown that *heats of reaction can be added together in the same way as chemical reactions.* It is immediately clear that this property is also true of the affinity $\mathbf{A}$, the volume change $v_{T,p}$ and the variation of entropy $s_{T,p}$; in general it is true for all quantities which can be put in the form $(\partial X/\partial \xi)_{T,p}$ where X is any extensive variable.

4. The Gibbs-Duhem Equations.

Finally we shall establish the important *Gibbs-Duhem* equations between the various increments $\delta\mu_i$ of the chemical potentials.

By differentiation of (6.24) we have

$$\delta G = \sum_i n_i \,\delta\mu_i + \sum_i \mu_i \,\delta n_i. \tag{6.37}$$

Comparing this with the corresponding equation (6.19) we see that

$$\boxed{S\,\delta T - V\,\delta p + \sum_i n_i \,\delta\mu_i = 0.} \tag{6.38}$$

This equation is unusual in that the variations occur in the *intensive variables* $T,\ p,\ \mu_1 \ldots \mu_c$, while their coefficients are the *extensive variables* $S,\ V,\ n_i$.

For changes taking place *at constant temperature and pressure*, (6.38) reduces to

$$\boxed{\sum_i n_i \,\delta\mu_i = 0,} \tag{6.39}$$

which is the relation between the variation in the chemical potentials for an isothermal-isobaric change.

For such changes this formula enables us to calculate one of the increments *e.g.* $\delta\mu_1$ when the others are known. If we replace in (6.39) $\delta\mu_i$ by the value

$$\delta\mu_i = \sum_j \left(\frac{\partial\mu_i}{\partial n_j}\right)_{T,p} \delta n_j, \tag{6.39'}$$

we obtain the expression

$$\sum_i \sum_j n_i \left(\frac{\partial\mu_i}{\partial n_j}\right)_{T,p} \delta n_j = 0. \tag{6.40}$$

Since this is true for any arbitrary values of δn_j we must have

$$\sum_i n_i \left(\frac{\partial\mu_i}{\partial n_j}\right)_{T,p} = 0. \tag{6.41}$$

This is simply equation (1.27) corresponding to the partial molar quantity μ_i. Furthermore, from (6.26) we may write, in place of (6.41),

$$\sum_i n_i \left(\frac{\partial\mu_j}{\partial n_i}\right)_{T,p} = 0. \tag{6.42}$$

The properties of the partial molar volume which were studied in chapter I, § 3 transpose immediately to the case of chemical potentials. If we consider a binary mixture and take the mole fraction x_2 as independent variable we have, dropping the subscripts T and p for the rest of this paragraph :

$$\frac{\partial\mu_1}{\partial x_2} = -\frac{n}{x_2}\frac{\partial\mu_1}{\partial n_1}; \quad \frac{\partial\mu_2}{\partial x_2} = -\frac{n}{x_2}\frac{\partial\mu_2}{\partial n_1}; \tag{6.43}$$

and similarly

$$\frac{\partial\mu_1}{\partial x_2} = \frac{n}{x_1}\frac{\partial\mu_1}{\partial n_2}; \quad \frac{\partial\mu_2}{\partial x_2} = \frac{n}{x_1}\frac{\partial\mu_2}{\partial n_2}. \tag{6.44}$$

Thus we can verify (*cf.* 1.34) that

$$x_1 \frac{\partial\mu_1}{\partial x_2} + x_2 \frac{\partial\mu_2}{\partial x_2} = 0. \tag{6.45}$$

Furthermore by considering the Gibbs free energy per mole, and, by applying the same argument as we did to the mean molar volume (*cf.* 1.35), we obtain :

$$g = \frac{G}{n} = \sum_i x_i \mu_i, \tag{6.46}$$

and as before (*cf.* 1.36) for a binary system*

$$\frac{\partial g}{\partial x_2} = \mu_2 - \mu_1. \tag{6.47}$$

Differentiating this with respect to x_2 we have

$$\frac{\partial^2 g}{\partial x_2^2} = \frac{\partial \mu_2}{\partial x_2} - \frac{\partial \mu_1}{\partial x_2}.$$

One or other of the partial derivatives can be eliminated by means of (6.45). Eliminating $(\partial \mu_1/\partial x_2)$ we find that

$$\frac{\partial^2 g}{\partial x_2^2} = \frac{\partial \mu_2}{\partial x_2}\left(1 + \frac{x_2}{x_1}\right); \tag{6.48}$$

or

$$\frac{\partial \mu_2}{\partial x_2} = x_1 \frac{\partial^2 g}{\partial x_2^2}; \tag{6.49}$$

and similarly

$$\frac{\partial \mu_1}{\partial x_2} = -x_2 \frac{\partial^2 g}{\partial x_2^2}. \tag{6.50}$$

Equations (6.49) and (6.50) will be required later when we come to discuss equilibrium displacements.

5. Chemical Potentials and variation of Affinity with the Extent of Reaction.†

We have already seen that the variation of the affinity with the extent of reaction, that is $\partial \mathbf{A}/\partial \xi$, is equal to the second derivative of G with respect to ξ with the sign changed (*cf.* 4.59).

$$a_{T,p} = \frac{\partial \mathbf{A}}{\partial \xi} = -\frac{\partial^2 G}{\partial \xi^2}. \tag{6.51}$$

In view of its application to the stability of chemical equilibria (chap. XV) we shall now evaluate this second derivative as a function of the chemical potentials. We have immediately by differentiation of (6.22) and using (6.39′):

$$-\frac{\partial \mathbf{A}}{\partial \xi} = \sum_i \nu_i \frac{\partial \mu_i}{\partial \xi} = \sum_i \sum_j \nu_i \nu_j \frac{\partial \mu_i}{\partial n_j}. \tag{6.52}$$

* Analogous relations

$$\frac{\partial g}{\partial x_i} = \mu_i - \mu_1 \quad (i = 2 \ldots c) \tag{6.47′}$$

are readily established for a system of c-components; *cf.* R. Haase, *Z. Naturforsch*, **3A**, 285 (1948).

† The results of this paragraph will be needed in studying stability (*cf.* chap. XV) and may be passed over in a first reading.

For brevity we write

$$\frac{\partial \mu_i}{\partial n_j} = \mu_{ij} \tag{6.53}$$

and with this notation (6.42) becomes

$$\sum_i n_i \mu_{ij} = 0, \tag{6.54}$$

whence

$$\mu_{ii} = -\frac{1}{n_i} \sum_j^{(i)} \mu_{ij} n_j, \tag{6.55}$$

where the summation $\sum_j^{(i)}$ extends over all the indices $j = 1, 2 \ldots c$ except $j = i$.

Now equation (6.52) may be rewritten, using (6.55), as

$$\begin{aligned} -\frac{\partial \mathbf{A}}{\partial \xi} = \frac{\partial^2 G}{\partial \xi^2} &= \sum_i \nu_i^2 \mu_{ii} + \sum_i \sum_j^{(i)} \nu_i \nu_j \mu_{ij} \\ &= -\sum_i \sum_j^{(i)} \frac{\nu_i^2}{n_i} \mu_{ij} n_j + \sum_i \sum_j^{(i)} \nu_i \nu_j \mu_{ij} \\ &= \sum_i \nu_i \sum_j^{(i)} \mu_{ij} \left(\frac{n_i \nu_j - n_j \nu_i}{n_i} \right). \end{aligned} \tag{6.56}$$

But since we obtain zero terms in this summation whenever $i = j$, this may be written simply as

$$\frac{\partial^2 G}{\partial \xi^2} = \sum_i \sum_j \frac{\nu_i}{n_i} \mu_{ij} (n_i \nu_j - n_j \nu_i). \tag{6.57}$$

Furthermore the sum is not altered by interchanging i and j so that alternatively

$$\frac{\partial^2 G}{\partial \xi^2} = \sum_j \sum_i \frac{\nu_j}{n_j} \mu_{ji} (n_j \nu_i - n_i \nu_j). \tag{6.58}$$

Adding (6.57) and (6.58), and taking half the sum, remembering that $\mu_{ij} = \mu_{ji}$, we obtain

$$\frac{\partial^2 G}{\partial \xi^2} = \frac{1}{2} \sum_i \sum_j \mu_{ij} \left\{ \frac{\nu_i}{n_i} (n_i \nu_j - n_j \nu_i) + \frac{\nu_j}{n_j} (n_j \nu_i - n_i \nu_j) \right\}$$

which reduces to

$$\frac{\partial^2 G}{\partial \xi^2} = -\frac{1}{2} \sum_i \sum_j \mu_{ij} n_i n_j \left(\frac{\nu_i}{n_i} - \frac{\nu_j}{n_j} \right)^2. \tag{6.59}$$

This equation, which is due to De Donder,* enables us to calculate $\partial^2 G / \partial \xi^2$ with the aid of the μ_{ij}. We shall come across examples of its use later (*e.g.* chap. VII, § 2).

* De Donder [6].

In the case of several simultaneous reactions we may calculate in the same way the quantities $\partial \mathbf{A}_\rho/\partial \xi_{\rho'}$, and $\partial \mathbf{A}_{\rho'}/\partial \xi_\rho$ defined by (4.71). We have

$$\frac{\partial G}{\partial \xi_\rho} = -\mathbf{A}_\rho = \sum_i \nu_{i,\rho}\mu_i, \tag{6.60}$$

and thus

$$\frac{\partial^2 G}{\partial \xi_\rho \partial \xi_{\rho'}} = \frac{\partial \mathbf{A}_\rho}{\partial \xi_{\rho'}} = \sum_i \sum_j \nu_{i,\rho}\nu_{j,\rho'}\mu_{ij}. \tag{6.61}$$

Following through the above steps we obtain

$$\frac{\partial^2 G}{\partial \xi_\rho \partial \xi_{\rho'}} = -\frac{1}{2}\sum_i \sum_j \mu_{ij}\left(\frac{\nu_{i,\rho}}{n_i} - \frac{\nu_{j,\rho}}{n_j}\right)\left(\frac{\nu_{i,\rho'}}{n_i} - \frac{\nu_{j,\rho'}}{n_j}\right). \tag{6.62}$$

This is a generalized form of (6.59) and reduces to the simpler equation when $\rho=\rho'$. This shows that (6.59) is valid even though other reactions are occurring in the system.

6. Systems of Several Phases.

The preceding formulae are easily extended to the case in which the system is composed of many phases. Since the thermodynamic potentials U, H, F, G, are extensive functions, we have, by virtue of (1.32)

$$\left.\begin{aligned} U &= \sum_\alpha U^\alpha, \\ H &= \sum_\alpha H^\alpha, \\ F &= \sum_\alpha F^\alpha, \\ G &= \sum_\alpha G^\alpha. \end{aligned}\right\} \tag{6.63}$$

Every extensive quantity can be related to the corresponding partial molar quantity. Thus the partial molar enthalpy of component i in the phase α will be given by (*cf.* 1.30)

$$h_i^\alpha = \left(\frac{\partial H^\alpha}{\partial n_i^\alpha}\right)_{T,p}. \tag{6.64}$$

Let us now apply Gibbs' two fundamental equations to a system of several phases, choosing S, V, n_1^1, $n_2^1 \dots , n_{c-1}^\phi$, n_c^ϕ as variables. The total differential δU can now be written down using equations (6.6) which, as one can easily verify, are still valid.

$$\delta U = T\,\delta S - p\,\delta V + \sum_\alpha \sum_i \left(\frac{\partial U}{\partial n_i^\alpha}\right)_{S,V} \delta n_i^\alpha, \tag{6.65}$$

and there will be similar expressions for δH, δF and δG. We can then prove, following exactly the method of § 2 (*cf.* 6.11) that

$$\left(\frac{\partial U}{\partial n_i^\alpha}\right)_{S,V} = \left(\frac{\partial H}{\partial n_i^\alpha}\right)_{S,p} = \left(\frac{\partial F}{\partial n_i^\alpha}\right)_{T,V} = \left(\frac{\partial G}{\partial n_i^\alpha}\right)_{T,p} . \tag{6.66}$$

We call this common value the chemical potential μ_i^α of component i in the phase α. In particular we have

$$\mu_i^\alpha = \left(\frac{\partial G}{\partial n_i^\alpha}\right)_{T,p} . \tag{6.67}$$

Making use of the last of equations (6.63) and assuming that by virtue of (1.29) changes in n_i^α affect only G^α it follows that (6.67) may also be written

$$\mu_i^\alpha = \left(\frac{\partial G^\alpha}{\partial n_i^\alpha}\right)_{T,p} . \tag{6.68}$$

μ_i^α is thus the partial molar quantity corresponding to the extensive function G^α.

If a reaction can take place between components partitioned between different phases, its stoichiometric equation may be written in the general form (1.56) :

$$0 = \sum_\alpha \sum_i \nu_i^\alpha M_i .$$

Then, taking account of (1.58) and (6.67), equation (4.30)

$$\mathbf{A} = -\left(\frac{\partial G}{\partial \xi}\right)_{T,p}$$

leads to,

$$\mathbf{A} = -\sum_\alpha \sum_i \nu_i^\alpha \frac{\partial G}{\partial n_i^\alpha} = -\sum_\alpha \sum_i \nu_i^\alpha \mu_i^\alpha . \tag{6.69}$$

The condition of equilibrium thus has a simple form analogous to (6.23) :

$$\sum_\alpha \sum_i \nu_i^\alpha \mu_i^\alpha = 0. \tag{6.70}$$

If several reactions can take place, then the affinity of the ρth reaction is

$$\mathbf{A}_\rho = -\sum_\alpha \sum_i \nu_{i,\rho}^\alpha \mu_i^\alpha , \tag{6.71}$$

and the condition of equilibrium is

$$\sum_\alpha \sum_i \nu_{i,\rho}^\alpha \mu_i^\alpha = 0, \quad (\rho = 1, 2 \ldots r). \tag{6.72}$$

All the other relations obtained in §§ 2-4 may be extended without difficulty to systems of several phases.

Examples :

(*a*) *Passage of one component from one phase to another.*

Here (*cf.* the example on freezing of water p. 16)

$$\nu_i^1 = -1 \text{ and } \nu_i^2 = 1$$

so that,

$$\mathbf{A} = \mu_i^1 - \mu_i^2. \tag{6.73}$$

The condition of equilibrium is

$$\mathbf{A} = 0$$

or

$$\boxed{\mu_i^1 = \mu_i^2}\,. \tag{6.74}$$

We see that *if two phases are in equilibrium, all components capable of passing from one to the other must have the same chemical potential in the two phases.*

(*b*) *Thermal dissociation of calcium carbonate* (*cf.* p. 17).

The equation for this reaction is

$$CaCO_3 \rightleftharpoons CaO + CO_2$$

so that

$$\nu^1{}_{CaCO_3} = -1\,;\ \nu^2{}_{CaO} = +1\,;\ \nu^3{}_{CO_2} = +1.$$

Thus

$$\mathbf{A} = \mu^1{}_{CaCO_3} - \mu^2{}_{CaO} - \mu^3{}_{CO_2}, \tag{6·75}$$

and the equilibrium condition is

$$\mu^1{}_{CaCO_3} = \mu^2{}_{CaO} + \mu^3{}_{CO_2}.$$

At equilibrium the sum of the chemical potentials of CaO and CO_2 is equal to the chemical potential of $CaCO_3$.

CHAPTER VII

IDEAL SYSTEMS AND REFERENCE SYSTEMS

1. Definition of Ideal Systems.

Let us consider the simple case in which the chemical potentials of the c components are all of the form

$$\mu_i = \mu_i^{\ominus}(T, p) + \boldsymbol{R}T \ln x_i, \tag{7.1}$$

where $\mu_i^{\ominus}(T, p)$ is a function only of the variables T and p.

Systems for which μ_i has the form (7.1) possess remarkably simple properties. Moreover these systems are of considerable practical importance since, as we shall show later (*cf.* chap. X, and chap. XX), mixtures of perfect gases and very dilute solutions have just these properties. It is therefore useful to have a collective term to describe systems satisfying (7.1); they are called *ideal systems.*

According to this definition a system is called ideal if the chemical potential of component i varies linearly with the logarithm of the mole fraction of i, with a slope $\boldsymbol{R}T$. This linear relation need not necessarily extend over the whole concentration range, so that the constant $\mu_i^{\ominus}(T, p)$ is, in general, the value of μ_i *extrapolated* to $x_i = 1$ at constant T and p. If the system is ideal in a concentration range which extends to $x_i = 1$, then

$$\mu_i^{\ominus}(T, p) = \mu_i^0(T, p),$$

where μ_i^0 is the chemical potential of the *pure component* i at the temperature and pressure specified.

There are two important cases with which we shall be concerned.

(*a*) The mixture is ideal for all values of x_i and for all i. It is then called a *perfect mixture* and

$$\mu_i^{\ominus}(T, p) = \mu_i^0(T, p) \textit{ for all } i. \tag{7.1'}$$

(*b*) The mixture is ideal when all components but one are present in very small amounts. Such systems are called *ideal dilute solutions.* If the component present in excess (the solvent)is denoted by 1, then

$$\mu_1^{\ominus}(T, p) = \mu_1^0(T, p),$$

but, for all other components

$$\mu_i^{\ominus}(T, p) \neq \mu_i^0(T, p). \tag{7.1''}$$

In the present chapter we shall examine in some detail the properties of ideal systems, and the equations derived will be applied to particular types of ideal system in subsequent chapters.

Different kinds of ideal system are distinguished by the form of the function $\mu_i^{\ominus}(T, p)$. We shall see that for a mixture of perfect gases $\mu_i^{\ominus}(T, p)$ varies logarithmically with the pressure (*cf.* chap. X, § 5) while for liquid and solid solutions we can, to a first approximation, regard $\mu_i^{\ominus}$ as independent of p (*cf.* chap. XX).

When any one of the chemical potentials deviates from the form (7.1) we say that the system is *non-ideal.*

A system consisting of a single component in a single phase may be regarded as a special case of an ideal system in which the mol fraction of the component i is unity. We then have

$$\mu = \mu^0(T, p). \tag{7.2}$$

These definitions can be extended immediately to a system of several phases. We say that such a system is ideal when each of the phases is ideal, and

$$\mu_i^\alpha = \mu_i^{\ominus\alpha}(T, p) + \boldsymbol{R}T \ln x_i^\alpha \tag{7.3}$$

for

$$i = 1, 2 \dots c,$$

$$\alpha = 1, 2 \dots \phi.$$

In particular one or more phases may consist of only a single component. If any one phase is non-ideal, the whole system is said to be non-ideal.

We shall now consider some of the more important thermodynamic properties of ideal systems. To remind ourselves that a particular thermodynamic quantity refers to an ideal system we shall mark it with a superscript "id". Thus μ_i^{id} is the chemical potential of component i in an ideal system.

2. Explicit Expressions for μ_{ij} and $\partial^2 G/\partial\xi^2$.*

We first verify that the chemical potentials in an ideal system satisfy the equations (6.26) and (6.41), which we may write, using the notation of (6.53)

$$\mu_{ij} = \mu_{ji} \tag{7.4}$$

and

$$\sum_i n_i \mu_{ij} = 0. \tag{7.5}$$

We have, from (7.1) and the definition of mol fractions :

$$\mu_i^{\text{id}} = \mu_i^{\ominus}(T, p) + \boldsymbol{R}T \ln \left(\frac{n_i}{n_1 + n_2 + \dots n_c}\right). \tag{7.6}$$

* This paragraph, which is needed for the study of stability, may be omitted in a first reading.

Now, if $i \neq j$,

$$\mu_{ij}^{\text{id}} = \frac{\partial \mu_i^{\text{id}}}{\partial n_j} = - \frac{RT}{n_1 + n_2 + \dots n_c} = - \frac{RT}{n}, \tag{7.7}$$

while for $i = j$

$$\mu_{ii}^{\text{id}} = RT \left(\frac{1}{n_i} - \frac{1}{n} \right). \tag{7.8}$$

The differentials μ_{ij}^{id} thus take on extremely simple forms. Equation (7.7) shows that μ_{ij}^{id} is independent of the indices i and j provided that they are not the same. It follows then that equation (7.4) is obeyed.

We now require to calculate the sum $\sum_i n_i \mu_{ij}$. This summation can be written in the form :

$$\sum_i n_i \mu_{ij} = n_i \mu_{ii} + \sum_j^{(i)} n_j \mu_{ij}, \tag{7.9}$$

where the summation $\sum_j^{(i)}$ extends over all values of j except i. Then, by virtue of (7.8),

$$n_i \mu_{ii}^{\text{id}} = RT \left(1 - \frac{n_i}{n} \right) \tag{7.10}$$

and from (7.7)

$$\sum_j^{(i)} n_j \mu_{ij}^{\text{id}} = - \frac{RT}{n} \sum_j^{(i)} n_j = - \frac{RT}{n} (n - n_i) = - RT \left(1 - \frac{n_i}{n} \right). \tag{7.11}$$

Substituting into (7.9) we have then

$$\sum_i n_i \mu_{ij}^{\text{id}} = 0 \tag{7.12}$$

and hence also (7.5).

We notice that for an ideal system we have always, in view of (7.7) and (7.8) :

$$\mu_{ij}^{\text{id}} < 0 \quad (i \neq j), \tag{7.13}$$

and

$$\mu_{ii}^{\text{id}} > 0. \tag{7.14}$$

The significance of these inequalities will be considered later, (*cf.* chap. XV).

From the values of μ_{ij} derived above we may now calculate the function $\partial^2 G / \partial \xi^2$ for an ideal system (*cf.* chap. VI, § 5). Substituting (7.7) in (6.59) we have :

$$\frac{\partial^2 G^{\text{id}}}{\partial \xi^2} = \frac{RT}{2n} \sum_i \sum_j n_i n_j \left(\frac{\nu_i}{n_i} - \frac{\nu_j}{n_j} \right)^2, \tag{7.15}$$

while if r simultaneous reactions can occur in the system

$$\frac{\partial^2 G^{\text{id}}}{\partial \xi_\rho^2} = \frac{RT}{2n} \sum_i \sum_j n_i n_j \left(\frac{\nu_{i,\rho}}{n_i} - \frac{\nu_{j,\rho}}{n_j} \right)^2, \tag{7.16}$$

and from (6.62)

$$\frac{\partial^2 G^{\text{id}}}{\partial \xi_\rho \, \partial \xi_{\rho'}} = \frac{RT}{2n} \sum_i \sum_j n_i n_j \left(\frac{\nu_{i,\rho}}{n_i} - \frac{\nu_{j,\rho}}{n_j} \right) \left(\frac{\nu_{i,\rho'}}{n_i} - \frac{\nu_{j,\rho'}}{n_j} \right). \tag{7.17}$$

If is of interest to note that for ideal systems we always have

$$\frac{\partial^2 G^{\text{id}}}{\partial \xi^2} > 0 \quad \text{and} \quad \frac{\partial^2 G^{\text{id}}}{\partial \xi_\rho{}^2} > 0. \tag{7.18}$$

We can also establish, by somewhat long but elementary algebra, that

$$\frac{\partial^2 G^{\text{id}}}{\partial \xi_\rho^2} \frac{\partial^2 G^{\text{id}}}{\partial \xi_{\rho'}^2} - \frac{\partial^2 G^{\text{id}}}{\partial \xi_\rho \, \partial \xi_{\rho'}} \frac{\partial^2 G^{\text{id}}}{\partial \xi_{\rho'} \, \partial \xi_\rho} \geqslant 0. \tag{7.19}$$

These inequalities are important in the study of the stability of thermodynamic systems.

3. Partial Molar Quantities.

Starting from the definition (7.1) we shall now establish several important properties of partial molar quantities for an ideal system.

Taking first the partial molar enthalpy, we have, from (6.32),

$$-\frac{h_i^{\text{id}}}{T^2} = \left[\frac{\partial \left(\frac{\mu_i^{\text{id}}}{T} \right)}{\partial T} \right]_{p,n} = \left[\frac{\partial \left(\frac{\mu_i^{\ominus}}{T} \right)}{\partial T} \right]_{p,n} + \left[\frac{\partial \, \boldsymbol{R} \ln x_i}{\partial T} \right]_{p,n} = \left[\frac{\partial \left(\frac{\mu_i^{\ominus}}{T} \right)}{\partial T} \right]_p, \tag{7.20}$$

since the term $\boldsymbol{R} \ln x_i$ is independent of T. Furthermore since $\mu_i^{\ominus}$ is a function of T and p only, we see that the partial molar enthalpy of each constituent i of an ideal system is independent of the composition of the system and depends only upon the temperature and pressure.

The partial molar volumes of the components of an ideal system possess this same property :

$$v_i^{\text{id}} = \left(\frac{\partial \mu_i^{\ominus}}{\partial p} \right)_T, \tag{7.21}$$

while the partial molar entropy depends upon the composition in a very simple way :

$$s_i^{\text{id}} = -\left(\frac{\partial \mu_i^{\ominus}}{\partial T} \right)_p - \boldsymbol{R} \ln x_i. \tag{7.22}$$

From (7.20) we see that the heat of reaction, $(\partial H^{\text{id}}/\partial \xi)_{T,p}$, for a reaction in an ideal system can be written (*cf.* 6.33) :

$$\left(\frac{\partial H^{\text{id}}}{\partial \xi} \right)_{T,p} = -T^2 \sum_i \nu_i \left[\frac{\partial \left(\frac{\mu_i^{\ominus}}{T} \right)}{\partial T} \right]_p. \tag{7.23}$$

The heat of reaction in an ideal system is thus independent of the concentrations and depends only upon T and p.

Similarly, from (7.21) and (6.34), the volume change $(\partial V/\partial \xi)_{T,p}$ is given, for an ideal system, by

$$\left(\frac{\partial V^{\text{id}}}{\partial \xi}\right)_{T,p} = \sum_i \nu_i \left(\frac{\partial \mu_i^{\ominus}}{\partial p}\right)_T \tag{7.24}$$

and is independent of the composition of the system.

Finally the partial derivative $(\partial S/\partial \xi)_{T,p}$ for an ideal system is given, by virtue of (6.35) and (7.22), by :

$$\left(\frac{\partial S^{\text{id}}}{\partial \xi}\right)_{T,p} = -\sum_i \nu_i \left(\frac{\partial \mu_i^{\ominus}}{\partial T}\right)_{T,p} - \mathbf{R} \sum_i \nu_i \ln x_i. \tag{7.25}$$

4. Affinity in a One-Phase Ideal System.

Let us first consider an ideal single phase system. For the affinity $\mathbf{A}^{\text{id}}$ of a reaction occurring in this phase we have, from (6.22) and (7.1)

$$\mathbf{A}^{\text{id}} = -\sum_i \nu_i \mu_i^{\ominus}(T, p) - \sum_i \nu_i \mathbf{R} T \ln x_i. \tag{7.26}$$

This equation can be written in a simple form by setting

$$-\sum_i \nu_i \mu_i^{\ominus}(T, p) = \mathbf{R} T \ln K(T, p), \tag{7.27}$$

and noting that

$$\sum_i \nu_i \mathbf{R} T \ln x_i = \mathbf{R} T \ln x_1^{\nu_1} \ldots x_c^{\nu_c}, \tag{7.28}$$

whence

$$\mathbf{A}^{\text{id}} = \mathbf{R} T \ln K(T, p) - \mathbf{R} T \ln x_1^{\nu_1} \ldots x_c^{\nu_c}; \tag{7.29}$$

or

$$\boxed{\mathbf{A}^{\text{id}} = \mathbf{R} T \ln \frac{K(T, p)}{x_1^{\nu_1} \ldots x_c^{\nu_c}}}\,. \tag{7.30}$$

If there are r simultaneous reactions occurring in the system, then

$$\mathbf{A}_\rho^{\text{id}} = -\sum_i \nu_{i,\rho} \mu_i^{\ominus}(T, p) - \sum_i \nu_{i,\rho} \mathbf{R} T \ln x_i. \tag{7.31}$$

If we put

$$\mathbf{R} T \ln K_\rho(T, p) = -\sum_i \nu_{i,\rho} \mu_i^{\ominus}(T, p), \tag{7.32}$$

then

$$\mathbf{A}_\rho^{\text{id}} = \mathbf{R} T \ln \frac{K_\rho(T, p)}{x_1^{\nu_{1,\rho}} \ldots x_c^{\nu_{c,\rho}}}\,. \tag{7.33}$$

5. Chemical Equilibrium in a One-Phase Ideal System.

The condition for chemical equilibrium is $\mathbf{A}=0$, so that we have immediately from (7.30) :

$$\boxed{K(T, p)=x_1^{\nu_1} \dots x_c^{\nu_c}} \quad . \tag{7.34}$$

This simple equation, which interrelates the mole fractions of the components in the true equilibrium state, is essentially an expression of *Guldberg and Waage's law of mass action.* The quantity $K(T, p)$ is called the *equilibrium constant* of the reaction considered.

We now proceed to find the partial derivatives of $K(T, p)$ with respect to T and p. From the definition (7.27) we have immediately

$$\left(\frac{\partial \ln K(T, p)}{\partial p}\right)_T = -\frac{1}{RT} \sum_i \nu_i \left(\frac{\partial \mu_i^{\ominus}(T, p)}{\partial p}\right)_T , \tag{7.35}$$

and hence from (7.24)

$$\boxed{\left(\frac{\partial \ln K(T, p)}{\partial p}\right)_T = -\frac{1}{RT}\left(\frac{\partial V^{\mathrm{id}}}{\partial \xi}\right)_{T, p}} \quad . \tag{7.36}$$

Thus the partial derivative of the logarithm of K with respect to p is equal to the molar expansion, $\partial V^{\mathrm{id}}/\partial \xi$, with sign reversed, divided by RT. We thus see that an increase in pressure increases the equilibrium constant if the reaction is accompanied by a decrease in volume $(\partial V/\partial \xi < 0)$; and conversely if $\partial V/\partial \xi > 0$ the equilibrium constant is decreased.

This effect of pressure on the equilibrium position of a reaction is a particular case of *Le Chatelier's principle* which will be discussed in chap. XVII. The quantitative expression (7.36) was given later by Planck and van Laar.

Similarly, the partial derivative of $\ln K(T, p)$ with respect to T is given by (*cf.* 7.23)

$$\boxed{\left(\frac{\partial \ln K(T, p)}{\partial T}\right)_p = \frac{1}{RT^2}\left(\frac{\partial H^{\mathrm{id}}}{\partial \xi}\right)_{T, p}} \quad . \tag{7.37}$$

The partial derivative of the logarithm of K with respect to T is equal to the heat of reaction $\partial H^{\mathrm{id}}/\partial \xi$ divided by RT^2. If the reaction is accompanied by an absorption of heat $(\partial H/\partial \xi > 0)$ the equilibrium constant increases with temperature, while for an exothermic reaction ($\partial H/\partial\xi < 0$), it decreases. Equation (7.37) was obtained by van't Hoff.

The above results are easily extended to the case where several simultaneous reactions occur in the system.

6. Ideal Systems of Several Phases.

We now extend the above results to an ideal system of ϕ phases. Using equations (6.69) and (7.3) we have for the affinity of a reaction taking place in the ideal system

$$\mathbf{A}^{\mathrm{id}} = -\sum_{\alpha}\sum_{i} \nu_i^{\alpha}\mu_i^{\ominus,\alpha}(T, p) - \mathbf{R}T\sum_{\alpha}\sum_{i}\nu_i^{\alpha}\ln x_i^{\alpha}. \tag{7.38}$$

Let us first consider a reaction consisting simply of the transfer of a component i from one phase (denoted by $'$) to another (denoted by $''$). We have

$$\nu_i' = -1 \; ; \; \nu_i'' = +1.$$

The general equation (7.38) now gives the affinity of transfer of i :

$$\mathbf{A}^{\mathrm{id}} = \mu_i^{\ominus\prime}(T, p) - \mu_i^{\ominus\prime\prime}(T, p) + \mathbf{R}T\ln x_i' - \mathbf{R}T\ln x_i''. \tag{7.39}$$

Defining the equilibrium constant

$$\mathbf{R}T\ln K_i(T, p) = \mu_i^{\ominus\prime} - \mu_i^{\ominus\prime\prime}, \tag{7.40}$$

we then have

$$\mathbf{A}^{\mathrm{id}} = \mathbf{R}T\ln\frac{K_i(T, p)}{(x_i')^{-1}x_i''} \tag{7.41}$$

which gives the affinity of a reaction consisting simply of the transfer of a component from one phase to another. When equilibrium is attained $\mathbf{A}^{\mathrm{id}} = 0$ and we have

$$\frac{x_i''}{x_i'} = K_i(T, p). \tag{7.42}$$

In an ideal system therefore, the equilibrium ratio of mole fractions of a component in the two phases depends solely upon the temperature and pressure, and is independent of the composition of the system. This is *Nernst's distribution law*, examples of the application of which will be discussed later (chap. XX).

For reactions other than simple phase changes equation (7.38) may be applied directly. One simple example is a reaction in which each component occurs in one phase only; we can then drop the index denoting the phase and write (7.38) in the form

$$\mathbf{A}^{\mathrm{id}} = -\sum_{i}\nu_i\mu_i^{\ominus}(T, p) - \sum_{i}\nu_i\mathbf{R}T\ln x_i, \tag{7.43}$$

where x_i is the mole fraction of i in the phase in which it occurs; $\mu_i^{\ominus}(T, p)$ refers to this same phase. This equation can be written in the alternative form:

$$\mathbf{A}^{\mathrm{id}} = RT \ln \frac{K(T, p)}{x_1^{\nu_1} \dots x_c^{\nu_c}}. \tag{7.44}$$

Example: In the thermal dissociation of calcium carbonate,

$$CaCO_3(s) = CaO(s) + CO_2(g),$$

each constituent occurs in one phase only.

The affinity of the reaction is

$$\mathbf{A} = \mu_{CaCO_3} - \mu_{CaO} - \mu_{CO_2}. \tag{7.45}$$

Since calcium carbonate and calcium oxide are pure phases $x_{CaCO_3} = x_{CaO} = 1$ and (7.44) reduces to

$$\mathbf{A}^{\mathrm{id}} = RT \ln \frac{K(T, p)}{x_{CO_2}}. \tag{7.46}$$

Two cases may arise. If the reaction is studied in the presence of a gas other than CO_2 *e.g.* in air, then the equilibrium condition $\mathbf{A} = 0$ gives:

$$x_{CO_2} = K(T, p) \tag{7.47}$$

which shows that the equilibrium partial pressure of CO_2 depends both upon the total pressure p, and the temperature.

Alternatively, if there is no other gaseous component, $x_{CO_2} = 1$, $p = p_{CO_2}$, and

$$\mathbf{A}^{\mathrm{id}} = RT \ln K(T, p) \tag{7.48}$$

Thus for equilibrium, $\mathbf{A}^{\mathrm{id}} = 0$, and so

$$K(T, p) = 1, \tag{7.49}$$

which shows that, in the absence of air, the equilibrium pressure of carbon dioxide depends only upon the temperature.

7. Standard Thermodynamic Functions.

We have already seen that the thermodynamic properties of a system are defined uniquely when we know the chemical potentials μ_i of the c components as a function of the independent variables T, p, $n_1 \dots n_c$. In the particular case of an ideal system the chemical potentials are given by (7.1).

We notice that the chemical potential may be written as the sum of two functions, the first of which $\mu_i^{\ominus}(T, p)$ is a function of T and p only, while the second $RT \ln x_i$ depends upon the composition.

In general an intensive thermodynamic quantity P in a uniform system:

$$P = P(T, p, x_1 \dots x_c) \tag{7.50}$$

can always be split up into the sum of two functions, the first of which is a function of T and p only, while the second depends also on the mole fractions :

$$P = P^{\ominus}(T, p) + P^{M}(T, p, x_1 \ldots x_c). \tag{7.51}$$

The first of the terms on the right hand side is called the *standard* function, while the second which represents the effect of composition, is often called the function *of mixing*, *e.g.* heat of mixing or entropy of mixing.

This subdivision is not unique, since we can always add any function of T and p to $P^{\ominus}$, and subtract the same function from P^{M}. We must always therefore state precisely how the division is made. For example, for an ideal system

$$\mu_i = \mu_i^{\ominus}(T, p) + \boldsymbol{R}T \ln x_i \tag{7.52}$$

and we write

$$\mu_i^{\ominus} = \mu_i^{\ominus}(T, p)\ ; \quad \mu_i^{M} = \boldsymbol{R}T \ln x_i. \tag{7.53}$$

This method of breaking down intensive thermodynamic quantities can be applied also to any linear combination of partial molar quantities such as $\partial H/\partial \xi$ or $\boldsymbol{A}$. For an ideal system we can make use of the results of §§ 3 and 4 to obtain the relations set out in table 7.1.

TABLE 7.1

Thermodynamic Functions for Ideal Systems

Function	*Standard function*	*Function of mixing*
$\mu_i = \mu_i^{\ominus}(T, p) + \boldsymbol{R}T \ln x_i$	$\mu_i^{\ominus} = \mu_i^{\ominus}(T, p)$	$\mu_i^{M} = \boldsymbol{R}T \ln x_i$
$h_i = -T^2 \dfrac{\partial\left(\frac{\mu_i}{T}\right)}{\partial T} = -T^2 \dfrac{\partial\left(\frac{\mu_i^{\ominus}}{T}\right)}{\partial T}$	$h_i^{\ominus} = -T^2 \dfrac{\partial\left(\frac{\mu_i^{\ominus}}{T}\right)}{\partial T}$	$h_i^{M} = 0$
$s_i = -\dfrac{\partial \mu_i}{\partial T} = -\dfrac{\partial \mu_i^{\ominus}}{\partial T} - \boldsymbol{R} \ln x_i$	$s_i^{\ominus} = -\dfrac{\partial \mu_i^{\ominus}}{\partial T}$	$s_i^{M} = -\boldsymbol{R} \ln x_i$
$v_i = \dfrac{\partial \mu_i}{\partial p} = \dfrac{\partial \mu_i^{\ominus}}{\partial p}$	$v_i^{\ominus} = \dfrac{\partial \mu_i^{\ominus}}{\partial p}$	$v_i^{M} = 0$
$\left(\dfrac{\partial H}{\partial \xi}\right)_{T,p} = \sum\limits_i \nu_i h_i = \sum\limits_i \nu_i h_i^{\ominus}$	$h_{T,p}^{\ominus} = -T^2 \sum\limits_i \nu_i \dfrac{\partial\left(\frac{\mu_i^{\ominus}}{T}\right)}{\partial T}$	$h_{T,p}^{M} = 0$
$\left(\dfrac{\partial S}{\partial \xi}\right)_{T,p} = \sum\limits_i \nu_i s_i$	$s_{T,p}^{\ominus} = -\sum \nu_i \dfrac{\partial \mu_i^{\ominus}}{\partial T}$	$s_{T,p}^{M} = -\boldsymbol{R} \sum\limits_i \nu_i \ln x_i$
$\left(\dfrac{\partial V}{\partial \xi}\right)_{T,p} = \sum\limits_i \nu_i v_i = \sum\limits_i \nu_i v_i^{\ominus}$	$v_{T,p}^{\ominus} = \sum\limits_i \nu_i \dfrac{\partial \mu_i^{\ominus}}{\partial p}$	$v_{T,p}^{M} = 0$
$\boldsymbol{A} = -\sum\limits_i \nu_i \mu_i$	$\boldsymbol{A}^{\ominus} = -\sum\limits_i \nu_i \mu_i^{\ominus}(T, p)$	$\boldsymbol{A}^{M} = -\sum\limits_i \nu_i \boldsymbol{R}T \ln x_i$

The terminology employed in referring to standard functions has in the past not been uniform. Thus, taking the chemical potential as an example, one might apply the term " standard " to any one of three quantities :

(*a*) $\mu_i^{\ominus}(T, p)$, which is the value of μ_i under "standard " conditions of concentration. ;

(*b*) $\mu_i^{\ominus}(T\,;\ p=1$ atm.), in which, in addition, the pressure has been set equal to some "standard " value ;

(*c*) $\mu_i^{\ominus}(T=298{\cdot}16\,;\ p=1$ atm.) where the temperature is also standardized.

Usage (*b*) is common among American authors, following Lewis and Randall, while Prigogine and Defay, in the French edition, adopt convention (*c*). These two usages have in effect been criticized by Guggenheim* on the grounds that unless the standard pressure and standard temperature are universally recognized, then whenever, for example, the term " standard " is employed as in (*c*) some ambiguity exists unless the values of the standard pressure and temperature are stated. For this reason in the present translation the term standard has been restricted to (*a*); any more detailed specification is given in full, for example the "standard chemical potential at one atmosphere and at 600 °K " : $\mu_i^{\ominus}(600$ °K; 1 atm.). The only implication in this is that the composition of the system is to be expressed in mole fractions. As will be seen in chap. XX, when other concentration units are used, a different superscript is employed *e.g.* $\mu_i^m(T, p)$ for molalities and $\mu_i^c(T, p)$ for molar concentrations.

We shall now indicate some important relations between these thermodynamic quantities.

The identity

$$\frac{\partial\left(\dfrac{\mu_i^{\ominus}}{T}\right)}{\partial T}=\frac{1}{T}\frac{\partial\mu_i^{\ominus}}{\partial T}-\frac{\mu_i^{\ominus}}{T^2}$$

enables us to show immediately, from table 7.1, that

$$h_{T,p}^{\ominus}-Ts_{T,p}^{\ominus}=-\mathbf{A}^{\ominus}. \tag{7.54}$$

Thus equation (4.3) remains valid when we consider only the standard quantities ; we must therefore have also :

$$h_{T,p}^{M}-Ts_{T,p}^{M}=-\mathbf{A}^{M}. \tag{7.55}$$

The following equations are also easily verified :

$$\left[\frac{\partial\left(\dfrac{\mathbf{A}^{\ominus}}{T}\right)}{\partial T}\right]_p=-\sum_i \nu_i\left[\frac{\partial\left(\dfrac{\mu_i^{\ominus}}{T}\right)}{\partial T}\right]_p=\frac{h_{T,p}^{\ominus}}{T^2}\,; \tag{7.56}$$

$$\left(\frac{\partial\mathbf{A}^{\ominus}}{\partial p}\right)_T=-\sum_i \nu_i\left(\frac{\partial\mu_i^{\ominus}}{\partial p}\right)_T=-v_{T,p}^{\ominus}. \tag{7.57}$$

* Guggenheim [26′], p. 263.

We note also the following four equations :

$$\left.\begin{array}{l} \mathbf{A}^{\ominus} = -\sum_i \nu_i \mu_i^{\ominus} ; \quad h_{T,p}^{\ominus} = \sum_i \nu_i h_i^{\ominus} ; \\ v_{T,p}^{\ominus} = \sum_i \nu_i v_i^{\ominus} ; \quad s_{T,p}^{\ominus} = \sum_i \nu_i s_i^{\ominus} . \end{array}\right\} . \tag{7.58}$$

from which we can show, by an argument essentially the same as that given previously (*cf.* chap. I, § 6 ; chap. VI, § 3) that *standard affinities, standard heats of reaction, standard expansions and standard entropies of reaction can be added together in the same way as the chemical equations for the reactions themselves.*

8. Reference Systems. Activity and Activity Coefficients.

We consider first a non-ideal system for which the chemical potentials of the various components are given by :

$$\mu_i = \mu_i(T, p, x_1 \dots x_c), \tag{7.59}$$

and secondly a system of the same components but under certain (hypothetical) conditions such that it behaves ideally. This latter system is called the *corresponding ideal system* or the *ideal reference system.* In this system the chemical potentials will be of the form (7.1), and we must suppose that we know the functions $\mu_i^{\ominus}(T, p)$. If we know both the chemical potentials (7.59) for the non-ideal system, and the functions $\mu_i^{\ominus}$ we can write :

$$\mathbf{R}T \ln a_i \equiv \mu_i - \mu_i^{\ominus}(T, p), \tag{7.60}$$

or

$$\boxed{\mu_i = \mu_i^{\ominus}(T, p) + \mathbf{R}T \ln a_i} \ . \tag{7.61}$$

We define a_i as the *activity* of the component i in the non-ideal system, with respect to the particular reference system considered.

We then define the *activity coefficient* γ_i by

$$\gamma_i \equiv \frac{a_i}{x_i}, \tag{7.62}$$

so that the chemical potential (7.61) may now be expressed as

$$\boxed{\mu_i = \mu_i^{\ominus}(T, p) + \mathbf{R}T \ln x_i \gamma_i} \ . \tag{7.63}$$

If we call μ_i^{id} the ideal chemical potential

$$\mu_i^{\text{id}} = \mu_i^{\ominus}(T, p) + \mathbf{R}T \ln x_i, \tag{7.64}$$

then

$$\mu_i = \mu_i^{\text{id}} + \mathbf{R}T \ln \gamma_i. \tag{7.65}$$

The introduction of the activity and activity coefficients enables a comparison to be made quite simply between the properties of a given system and those of the ideal reference system.

By writing the chemical potential of a non-ideal system in the form of equation (7.63) we are able then to extend, in a formal manner, the properties derived in §§ 1-7 for ideal systems. The concepts of activity and activity coefficient were introduced by G. N. Lewis.*

We shall now indicate some general properties of activity coefficients which follow from (7.65). Proceeding exactly as in § 3 we have

$$\left[\frac{\partial\left(\frac{\mu_i}{T}\right)}{\partial T}\right]_p = -\frac{h_i}{T^2} = -\frac{h_i^{\text{id}}}{T^2} + \mathbf{R}\left(\frac{\partial \ln \gamma_i}{\partial T}\right)_p, \tag{7.66}$$

and similarly

$$\left(\frac{\partial \mu_i}{\partial p}\right)_T = v_i = v_i^{\text{id}} + \mathbf{R}T\left(\frac{\partial \ln \gamma_i}{\partial p}\right)_T, \tag{7.67}$$

where we have put

$$\frac{h_i^{\text{id}}}{T^2} = -\left[\frac{\partial\left(\frac{\mu_i^{\text{id}}}{T}\right)}{\partial T}\right]_p \quad \text{and} \quad v_i^{\text{id}} = \left(\frac{\partial \mu_i^{\text{id}}}{\partial p}\right)_T. \tag{7.67'}$$

These equations may be written

$$\left(\frac{\partial \ln \gamma_i}{\partial T}\right)_p = -\frac{h_i - h_i^{\text{id}}}{\mathbf{R}T^2}, \tag{7.68}$$

$$\left(\frac{\partial \ln \gamma_i}{\partial p}\right)_T = \frac{v_i - v_i^{\text{id}}}{\mathbf{R}T}. \tag{7.69}$$

They give the partial derivatives of the activity coefficients in terms of the excess values of h_i and v_i over the ideal values h_i^{id} and v_i^{id}.

The partial derivatives $\mu_{ij} = \left(\frac{\partial \mu_i}{\partial n_j}\right)_{T,p}$ may be written (*cf.* 7.7 and 7.8)

$$\mu_{ij} = -\frac{\mathbf{R}T}{n} + \mathbf{R}T\left(\frac{\partial \ln \gamma_i}{\partial n_j}\right)_{T,p} \quad (i \neq j), \tag{7.70}$$

$$\mu_{ii} = \mathbf{R}T\left(\frac{1}{n_i} - \frac{1}{n}\right) + \mathbf{R}T\left(\frac{\partial \ln \gamma_i}{\partial n_i}\right)_{T,p}. \tag{7.71}$$

The various activity coefficients $\gamma_1 \dots \gamma_c$ are related to one another by

$$\sum_i n_i \frac{\partial \ln \gamma_i}{\partial n_j} = 0, \tag{7.72}$$

which is obtained employing equations (7.5) and (7.12).

* *Cf.* Lewis and Randall [32].

We now wish to see how the activity coefficients enter into the affinity, the heat of reaction and the expansion accompanying the reaction. From (7.65) and (6.22) we see that

$$\mathbf{A} = \mathbf{A}^{\mathrm{id}} - RT \sum_i \nu_i \ln \gamma_i, \tag{7.73}$$

and on replacing $\mathbf{A}^{\mathrm{id}}$ by the value given in (7.30), we have

$$\boxed{\mathbf{A} = RT \ln \frac{K(T, p)}{(x_1\gamma_1)^{\nu_1} \dots (x_c\gamma_c)^{\nu_c}}} \; . \tag{7.74}$$

In particular, at equilibrium $\mathbf{A} = 0$, so that we obtain the *generalization of the law of mass action.*

$$\boxed{K(T, p) = (x_1\gamma_1)^{\nu_1} \dots (x_c\gamma_c)^{\nu_c}} \; . \tag{7.75}$$

From (7.73) (*cf.* (4.8), (4.40)), we obtain for the heat of reaction $(\partial H/\partial \xi)_{T,p}$:

$$h_{Tp} = h^{\mathrm{id}}_{T,p} - RT^2 \sum_i \nu_i \left(\frac{\partial \ln \gamma_i}{\partial T}\right)_{p,\xi}, \tag{7.76}$$

and for the volume change of reaction $(\partial V/\partial \xi)_{T,p}$:

$$v_{T,p} = v^{\mathrm{id}}_{T,p} + RT \sum_i \nu_i \left(\frac{\partial \ln \gamma_i}{\partial p}\right)_{T,\xi}. \tag{7.77}$$

Finally we consider the division into standard functions and functions of mixing introduced in the last paragraph. We see from (7.61) that the chemical potential can be split into two terms, the first $\mu_i^{\ominus}(T, p)$ which depends only upon T and p, while the second $RT \ln a_i$ depends also on the composition, *i.e.*

$$\mu_i^{\ominus} = \mu_i^{\ominus}(T, p)\,; \quad \mu_i^{M} = RT \ln a_i. \tag{7.78}$$

If we compare this with (7.52) we see that the standard chemical potential is the same as before, but the chemical potential of mixing is altered: the activity $a_i = x_i \gamma_i$ replaces the mole fraction x_i. This may be generalized to other thermodynamic quantities. The standard properties of a non-ideal system are the same as those of the corresponding ideal reference system. It is only the quantities dependent upon composition that are altered by the introduction of activity coefficients. This is illustrated by table 7.2 which is to be compared with table 7.1.

TABLE 7.2

Thermodynamic Functions for Non-Ideal Systems

Function	*Standard function*	*Function of mixing*
μ_i	$\mu_i^\ominus = \mu_i^\ominus(T, p)$	$\mu_i^M = \boldsymbol{R}T \ln x_i \gamma_i$
h_i	$h_i^\ominus = -T^2 \dfrac{\partial \left(\dfrac{\mu_i^\ominus}{T}\right)}{\partial T}$	$h_i^M = -\boldsymbol{R}T^2 \dfrac{\partial \ln \gamma_i}{\partial T}$
s_i	$s_i^\ominus = -\dfrac{\partial \mu_i^\ominus}{\partial T}$	$s_i^M = -\boldsymbol{R} \ln x_i \gamma_i - \boldsymbol{R}T \dfrac{\partial \ln \gamma_i}{\partial T}$
v_i	$v_i^\ominus = \dfrac{\partial \mu_i^\ominus}{\partial p}$	$v_i^M = \boldsymbol{R}T \dfrac{\partial \ln \gamma_i}{\partial p}$
$\left(\dfrac{\partial H}{\partial \xi}\right)_{T,p}$	$h_{T,p}^\ominus = -T^2 \sum_i \nu_i \dfrac{\partial \left(\dfrac{\mu^\ominus}{T}\right)}{\partial T}$	$h_{T,p}^M = -\boldsymbol{R}T^2 \sum_i \nu_i \dfrac{\partial \ln \gamma_i}{\partial T}$
$\left(\dfrac{\partial S}{\partial \xi}\right)_{T,p}$	$s_{T,p}^\ominus = -\sum_i \nu_i \dfrac{\partial \mu_i^\ominus}{\partial T}$	$s_{T,p}^M = -\boldsymbol{R} \sum_i \nu_i \ln x_i \gamma_i - \boldsymbol{R}T \sum_i \nu_i \dfrac{\partial \ln \gamma_i}{\partial T}$
$\left(\dfrac{\partial V}{\partial \xi}\right)_{T,p}$	$v_{T,p}^\ominus = \sum_i \nu_i \dfrac{\partial \mu_i^\ominus}{\partial p}$	$v_{T,p}^M = \boldsymbol{R}T \sum_i \nu_i \dfrac{\partial \ln \gamma_i}{\partial p}$
$-\left(\dfrac{\partial G}{\partial \xi}\right)_{T,p}$	$\mathbf{A}^\ominus = -\sum_i \nu_i \mu_i^\ominus$	$\mathbf{A}^M = -\boldsymbol{R}T \sum_i \nu_i \ln x_i \gamma_i$

We note that certain functions of mixing such as h_i^M and v_i^M which are zero for an ideal system are not so in general.

9. Standard Affinity and Equilibrium Constants.

On comparing the definition (7.27) of the equilibrium constant with that of the standard affinity in table 7.2 we see immediately that

$$\mathbf{A}^\ominus = \boldsymbol{R}T \ln K(T, p), \tag{7.79}$$

or

$$\boxed{K(T, p) = \exp[\mathbf{A}^\ominus / \boldsymbol{R}T]}\ . \tag{7.80}$$

When dealing with a reaction which is a linear combination of known reactions, it is advantageous to work with affinities rather than equilibrium constants since the standard affinity is obtained simply by adding together the corresponding standard affinities of the separate reactions in the same linear combination.

Equation (7.80) holds whether a system is ideal or not, for the standard affinity of a reaction in a non-ideal system is the same as that in the corresponding reference system.

The usefulness of these ideas will become apparent in chapter VIII.

10. Variation of Standard Affinity with Temperature.

For an ideal system as shown in table 7.1, the standard heat of reaction $h^{\ominus}_{T,p}$ is identical with the total heat of reaction. At a given pressure we have therefore :

$$h^{\ominus}_{T,p} = h^{\ominus}_{0,p} + \alpha_1 T + \alpha_2 T^2 + \alpha_3 T^3 \ldots . \tag{7.81}$$

If the system is not ideal, $h^{\ominus}_{T,p}$ is different from $h_{T,p}$ but now we may regard $h^{\ominus}_{T,p}$ as the heat of reaction in the corresponding reference system. Thus integrating (7.56) at constant pressure gives

$$\frac{\mathbf{A}^{\ominus}}{T} = -\frac{h^{\ominus}_{0,p}}{T} + \alpha_1 \ln T + \alpha_2 T + \tfrac{1}{2}\alpha_3 T^2 \ldots + I, \tag{7.82}$$

where I is the integration constant.

In table 7.3 are given values (in cal.) of $h^{\ominus}_{0,p}$, α_1, α_2, α_3 and I for various important reactions at atmospheric pressure. These figures are taken from the *Tables annuelles des constantes*.*

TABLE 7.3

Reaction	$h^{\ominus}_{0,p}$	α_1	$10^3\,\alpha_2$	$10^6\,\alpha_3$	I
H_2 (g) + $\frac{1}{2}O_2$ (g)→H_2O (g)	−57 120	+2·75	−0·75	–	− 6·65
$\frac{1}{2}S_2$ (g) + O_2 (g)→SO_2 (g)	−84 905	+3·21	−2·272	+0·32	+ 0·25
C (graphite) + $\frac{1}{2}O_2$ (g)→CO (g)	−27 070	−2·05	+2·25	−0·40	− 7·92
C (graphite) + O_2 (g)→CO_2 (g)	−94 210	+0·30	−0·30	+0·10	− 0·94
Co (s) + $\frac{1}{2}O_2$ (g)→CoO (s)	−57 423	−0·87	+0·25	—	+24·74
Fe (α)→Fe (β)	−20 50	−5·95	+3·4	—	+39·77
PbS (s) + H_2 (g)→Pb (s) + H_2S (g)	+19 660	+1·68	+2·35	−0·74	−26·22

* *Tables Annuelles des Constantes*, J. Guéron and J. P. Mathieu, 3, pp. 10-17 (Paris, 1937), where the bibliography will be found. For data on reactions between hydrocarbons see C. M. Thacker, H. O. Folkins and E. L. Miller, *Ind. Eng. Chem.*, 33, 584 (1941).

CHAPTER VIII

STANDARD AFFINITIES

1. Standard Affinities, Heats and Entropies of Reaction.

In this chapter we shall consider the application of tabulated values of affinities, heats and entropies of reaction to the calculation of equilibrium constants. As we have pointed out already it is much more convenient to consider standard affinities of reaction than equilibrium constants. This is because standard affinities can be added and subtracted in just the same way as stoichiometric equations, so that the standard affinity of a reaction not included in the table is easily calculated. This means, as we shall see, that the only reactions which need to be included are those relating to the formation of compounds from their elements.

Most tables give values of the standard affinities and heats of reaction at a temperature of 298·16 °K and a pressure of 1 atm., and we shall be mainly concerned in this chapter with thermodynamic quantities under these conditions.

2. Standard Affinity of Formation.

The *formation reaction* of a chemical compound is defined as the reaction in which the compound is produced from its elements, these elements being taken in their normal physical state under the specified conditions. Thus if we consider reactions at 298·16 °K and at 1 atm. pressure, chlorine, hydrogen and oxygen are taken in the gas state; mercury and bromine in the liquid state; while carbon is normally taken in the well-defined β-graphite state, and sulphur in the rhombic crystalline state. It is also necessary to specify the physical condition of the compound which is formed, although this need not necessarily be the stable state under the conditions considered.

The *standard affinity of formation* $\mathbf{A}_i^\ominus$, the *standard heat of formation* $(\partial H^\ominus/\partial \xi_i)_{T,p}$ and the *standard entropy change of formation*, $(\partial S^\ominus/\partial \xi_i)_{T,p}$ are then defined as the standard affinity, standard heat and standard entropy of the formation reaction of the compound i. At 25 °C these three quantities are related, *cf.* (7.54), by

$$-\mathbf{A}_i^\ominus = \left(\frac{\partial H^\ominus}{\partial \xi_i}\right)_{T,p} - 298{\cdot}16 \left(\frac{\partial S^\ominus}{\partial \xi_i}\right)_{T,p}. \tag{8.3}$$

In table 8.1 are given $\boldsymbol{A}_i^{\ominus}$ and $(\partial H^{\ominus}/\partial \xi_i)_{T,p}$ for a number of important compounds at 298·16 °K and 1 atm. pressure. The values of $(\partial S^{\ominus}/\partial \xi_i)$ are easily evaluated from (8.3). The table also includes the entropy of the compounds at 25 °C.

The standard values for the formation of an element in the stable physical state are, by definition, zero. For example the reaction for the formation of hydrogen is

$$H_2(g) \rightarrow H_2(g)$$

and its standard affinity is

$$\boldsymbol{A}_{H_2}^{\ominus} = \mu_{H_2}^{\ominus} - \mu_{H_2}^{\ominus}$$

which is identically zero.

On the other hand, the standard affinity of formation of gaseous atomic hydrogen according to the reaction

$$\tfrac{1}{2}H_2\,(g) \rightarrow H\,(g)$$

is given by

$$\boldsymbol{A}_{H}^{\ominus} = \tfrac{1}{2}\mu_{H_2}^{\ominus} - \mu_{H}^{\ominus}$$

which is not zero.

3. Interpretation of Standard Affinities.

The standard affinities of formation of inorganic compounds are usually positive, although we find in the table negative values for compounds such as ozone, NO and NO_2, which are known to be rather unstable. Similarly $\boldsymbol{A}^{\ominus}$ is negative for elements in physical states which are unstable under the standard conditions. This is so, for example, for monoclinic sulphur and gaseous chlorine atoms.

The significance and use of standard affinities may be illustrated by considering the dissociation of chlorine molecules according to the equation

$$\tfrac{1}{2}Cl_2(g) = Cl\,(g), \tag{8.4}$$

for which at 298·16 °K and 1 atm.

$$\boldsymbol{A}^{\ominus} = -25{,}192 \text{ cal./g. atom.}$$

If we assume the system to be ideal, then we have according to equation (7.26) :

$$\boldsymbol{A}^{\text{id}} = -25{,}192 - \sum_i \nu_i \boldsymbol{R}\, 298{\cdot}16 \ln x_i$$
$$= -25{,}192 - \boldsymbol{R}\, 298{\cdot}16 \ln x_{Cl_2}^{-1/2}\, x_{Cl} \tag{8.5}$$

so that at true chemical equilibrium, where $\boldsymbol{A} = 0$,

$$\frac{x_{Cl}}{x_{Cl_2}^{1/2}} = e^{-25{,}192/(298{\cdot}16\boldsymbol{R})} \simeq e^{-40}. \tag{8.6}$$

Thus the large negative value of the standard affinity means that the mole fraction of Cl atoms in equilibrium with Cl_2 molecules at 25 °C and 1 atm. is extremely minute, and for practical purposes may be taken as zero.

If we start with a system containing atomic chlorine in appreciable amounts, then the mole fraction x_{Cl} is greater than that corresponding to equilibrium. The affinity $\mathbf{A}$ will, from (8.5), be negative and in accordance with de Donder's inequality

$$\mathbf{A}\,\mathbf{v} > 0 \tag{8.7}$$

the reaction velocity $\mathbf{v}$ must also be negative. This means in turn that the reaction (8.4) proceeds spontaneously from right to left; that is the atomic chlorine recombines to form molecular chlorine.

Let us consider the formation of HCl (g)

$$\tfrac{1}{2}H_2(g) + \tfrac{1}{2}Cl_2(g) \rightarrow HCl(g). \tag{8.8}$$

For this reaction

$$\nu_{H_2} = -\tfrac{1}{2}; \quad \nu_{Cl_2} = -\tfrac{1}{2}; \quad \nu_{HCl} = +1$$

so that, from (7.34) and (7.80) when true equilibrium is attained at 25 °C and at 1 atm. pressure:

$$\frac{x_{HCl}}{x_{H_2}^{1/2}\ x_{Cl_2}^{1/2}} = \exp\left[\mathbf{A}^{\ominus}/(298{\cdot}16\boldsymbol{R})\right]. \tag{8.9}$$

The standard affinity is given in the table as 22,769 cal./mole so that

$$e^{22{,}769/(298{\cdot}16\boldsymbol{R})} \simeq e^{40}.$$

Because of the large positive value of the standard affinity this reaction is practically complete.

This is not so for the reaction between hydrogen and iodine to form hydrogen iodide:

$$\tfrac{1}{2}H_2(g) + \tfrac{1}{2}I_2(s) \rightarrow HI(g) \tag{8.10}$$

for which the standard affinity at 25 °C and 1 atm. is -310 cal./mole.

Since iodine under these conditions is solid and forms a separate phase, its mole fraction is unity, and the equilibrium constant is

$$\frac{x_{HI}}{x_{H_2}^{1/2}} = K = e^{-310/(298{\cdot}16\boldsymbol{R})} = e^{-0{\cdot}523} = 0{\cdot}593,$$

which gives for the equilibrium mole fractions of hydrogen and hydrogen iodide

$$x_{H_2} = 0{\cdot}558; \quad x_{HI} = 0{\cdot}442.$$

These examples demonstrate the very important relation between the standard affinity and the equilibrium position of a reaction. By measuring the mole fractions of the various components at equilibrium (and their activity coefficients if the system is non-ideal) we can evaluate with the help of (7.34) or (7.75) the equilibrium constant $K(T, p)$ and the standard affinity (7.79). Conversely if the standard affinity is known we can calculate the position of equilibrium.

4. Calculation of the Standard Affinity for a Reaction which does not appear in the Table.

We may take as an example the reaction

$$SO_2(g) + NO_2(g) = SO_3(g) + NO(g).$$

The standard affinity of formation of each of these compounds is given in the table :

$$\text{(i)}\ S_{\text{orthorhombic}} + O_2(g) = SO_2(g);\quad \mathbf{A}^{\ominus}_{SO_2} = 71{,}790 \text{ cal/mole}$$

$$\text{(ii)}\ \tfrac{1}{2}N_2 + O_2(g) = NO_2(g);\quad \mathbf{A}^{\ominus}_{NO_2} = -12{,}390 \text{ cal/mole}$$

$$\text{(iii)}\ S_{\text{orthorhombic}} + \tfrac{3}{2}O_2(g) = SO_3(g);\quad \mathbf{A}^{\ominus}_{SO_3} = 88{,}520 \text{ cal/mole}$$

$$\text{(iv)}\ \tfrac{1}{2}N_2(g) + \tfrac{1}{2}O_2(g) = NO(g);\quad \mathbf{A}^{\ominus}_{NO} = -20{,}719 \text{ cal/mole.}$$

Adding (i) and (ii) we have

$$S + 2O_2 + \tfrac{1}{2}N_2 = SO_2 + NO_2$$

while (iii) and (iv) give

$$S + 2O_2 + \tfrac{1}{2}N_2 = SO_3 + NO.$$

By taking the difference

$$\{\text{(iii)} + \text{(iv)}\} - \{\text{(i)} + \text{(ii)}\}$$

we thus have

$$0 = -SO_2 - NO_2 + SO_3 + NO.$$

This is the stoichiometric equation for the reaction under consideration. The standard affinity for this reaction is therefore given by :

$$\mathbf{A}^{\ominus} = -\mathbf{A}^{\ominus}_{SO_2} - \mathbf{A}^{\ominus}_{NO_2} + \mathbf{A}^{\ominus}_{SO_3} + \mathbf{A}^{\ominus}_{NO} = 8{,}401 \text{ cal./mole.} \tag{8.11}$$

Similarly we can calculate

$$h^{\ominus}_{T,p} = \sum_i \nu_i (h^{\ominus}_{T,p})_i = -(h^{\ominus}_{T,p})_{SO_2} - (h^{\ominus}_{T,p})_{NO_2} + (h^{\ominus}_{T,p})_{SO_3} + (h^{\ominus}_{T,p})_{NO}$$
$$= -9981 \text{ cal./mole,} \tag{8.12}$$

while

$$\left(\frac{\partial S^{\ominus}}{\partial \xi}\right)_{T,p} = s^{\ominus}_{T,p} = \sum_i \nu_i (s^{\ominus}_{T,p})_i = \frac{h^{\ominus}_{T,p} + \mathbf{A}^{\ominus}}{298{\cdot}16} = -5{\cdot}29 \text{ cal./deg. mole.} \tag{8.13}$$

5. Applications of Standard Affinities.

The examples discussed in § 3 and § 4 show clearly the importance of tables of standard affinities and standard heats of formation, since from them we can calculate the thermodynamic behaviour of an almost unlimited number of reactions.

Before going on in § 7 to a detailed consideration of some particular reactions we may illustrate the use of these tables for rather more qualitative considerations.

For example, if we wish to know *qualitatively* whether chlorine tends to displace iodine from its compounds we may take, as a typical reaction,

$$HI(g) + \tfrac{1}{2}Cl_2(g) \rightarrow HCl(g) + \tfrac{1}{2}I_2(g). \qquad (8.14)$$

We find, taking the standard affinities of formation of the molecules involved from table 8.1, and proceeding as in the last paragraph, that

$$\mathbf{A}^{\ominus} = 22{,}769 - \tfrac{1}{2}(4630) + 310 = 20{,}764 \text{ cal.}$$

At chemical equilibrium therefore

$$\frac{x_{HCl}\, x_{I_2}^{1/2}}{x_{HI}\, x_{Cl_2}^{1/2}} = e^{\frac{20{,}764}{298 \cdot 16 \mathbf{R}}} \approx e^{35}.$$

Clearly under these conditions the concentrations of HCl and I_2 will be enormously large compared with those of HI and Cl_2 so that we can conclude that chlorine will displace iodine from hydrogen iodide.

In discussing the stability of compounds we note that a large positive standard affinity of formation means that the compound will not decompose spontaneously into its elements under the standard conditions since the synthesis reaction is practically complete. This does *not* prove however that the compound will not decompose to form a more stable compound.

As an example of this we find that the standard affinity of formation of hydrogen peroxide at 25° C and 1 atm. is 31,470 cal./mole, so that under these conditions hydrogen peroxide will not decompose spontaneously to hydrogen and oxygen. However, hydrogen peroxide does decompose almost completely to form water and oxygen since the standard affinity of the reaction

$$H_2O_2(aq.) = H_2O(l) + \tfrac{1}{2}O_2(g)$$

which is given by

$$\mathbf{A}^{\ominus} = -\mathbf{A}^{\ominus}_{H_2O_2} + \mathbf{A}^{\ominus}_{H_2O} + \tfrac{1}{2}\mathbf{A}^{\ominus}_{O_2} = +25{,}220 \text{ cal./mole},$$

turns out to be large and positive.

Qualitative applications of this kind are particularly important in organic chemistry. It must be stressed however that the fact that thermodynamic considerations show a reaction to be possible, is no proof that it can be carried out in practice. The affinity only indicates the *tendency* of a reaction to proceed and says nothing about the kinetics of the reaction. Furthermore, in organic chemistry we frequently find that a number of different substances can be formed from the same starting materials, so that it is usually necessary to employ a specific catalyst to accelerate the required reaction.

As a general example we may examine the oxidation of acetone. Formic and acetic acids can be formed according to the equation

$$(CH_3)_2CO\,(l) + \tfrac{2}{2}O_2\,(g) \rightarrow HCOOH\,(l) + CH_3COOH\,(l),$$

for which the standard affinity is 139,300 cal.

The reaction can also lead to the formation of carbon monoxide, water and acetic acid :

$$(CH_3)_2CO\,(l) + \tfrac{3}{2}O_2\,(g) \rightarrow H_2O\,(l) + CO\,(g) + CH_3COOH\,(l)$$

with a standard affinity of 146,100 cal. ; or the reaction may proceed further to methane, CO, CO_2 and water :

$$(CH_3)_2CO\,(l) + \tfrac{3}{2}O_2\,(g) \rightarrow H_2O\,(l) + CO\,(g) + CH_4\,(g) + CO_2\,(g)$$

for which $\mathbf{A}^{\ominus}$ is 158,700 cal. All of these reactions will proceed practically to completion on account of their very large affinities. If, however, we wished to carry out one only of the reactions, to the exclusion of the others, it would be necessary to employ a catalyst which is specific for the particular mode of oxidation concerned.

6. Table of Standard Affinities of Formation, Heats of Formation and Standard Entropies.

In the following table are collected together the standard affinities of formation of some of the more important chemical substances, together with the heat content changes accompanying their formation, at 25° C and 1 atm. pressure.

It should be noted that the standard affinity of formation is numerically the same as the standard free energy of the compound, but has the opposite sign.

In the last column the entropies of the compounds are given. These have mostly been determined calorimetrically (*cf.* chap. IX) but in the case of some of the gases they are derived from spectroscopic measurements (*cf.* chap. X, § 3).

In the few cases where the figures given refer to the formation of an aqueous solution the concentration units employed are molalities and not mole fractions ; the calculation of equilibria in solution will be taken up further in chap. XX.

TABLE 8.1

Standard Affinities of Formation, Standard Heats of Formation, and Standard Entropies of Chemical Substances

(in calories)

at $T = 298{\cdot}16°$ K ; $p = 1$ atm.

I. INORGANIC SUBSTANCES

A. *Compounds of metals*

Substance	*State*	$h^{\ominus}_{T,p}$	$\mathbf{A}^{\ominus}$	$s^{\ominus}$
Ag	*s*	0	0	10·21
AgCl	*s*	− 30 362	26 224	22·97
AgI	*s*	− 14 910	15 850	27·3
Ag_2O	*s*	− 7 306	2 586	29·09
AgCN	*s*	+ 34 940	− 39 200	20·0
Ca	*s*	0	0	9·95
$CaCO_3$ (calcite)	*s*	− 288 450	269 780	22·2
— (aragonite)	*s*	− 288 490	269 530	21·2
Cd	*s*	0	0	12·3
—	*g*	+ 26 970	− 18 690	40·067
$CdCl_2$	*s*	− 93 000	81 880	28·3
CdO	*s*	− 60 860	53 790	13·1
CdS	*s*	− 34 500	33 600	17
Cu	*s*	0	0	7·96
CuCl	*s*	− 32 500	28 200	20·2
CuO	*s*	− 37 100	30 400	10·4
$Cu(OH)_2$	*s*	− 106 100	85 090	
$CuSO_4$	*s*	− 184 000	158 200	27·1
Cu_2O	*s*	− 39 840	34 980	24·1
Fe	*s*	0	0	6·49
FeO	*s*	− 63 700	58 400	12·9
Fe_2O_3	*s*	− 196 500	177 100	21·5
Fe_3O_4	*s*	− 267 000	242 400	35·0
Hg	*l*	0	0	18·5
Hg_2	*g*	27 100		
Hg_2Cl_2	*s*	− 63 320	50 350	46·8
Hg_2Br_2	*s*	− 49 420	42 714	50·9
Hg_2I_2 (yellow)	*s*	− 28 910	26 600	57·2
Hg_2SO_4	*s*	− 177 340	149 120	47·98
HgO (red)	*s*	− 21 680	13 990	17·2
— (yellow)	*s*	− 21 560	13 959	17·5
HgS (cinnabar)	*s*	− 13 900	11 670	18·6
— (black)	*s*	− 12 900	11 050	19·9
K	*s*	0	0	15·20
KCl	*s*	− 104 175	97 592	19·76
KBr	*s*	− 93 730	90 630	23·05
KI	*s*	− 78 310	77 030	24·94
KNO_3	*s*	− 117 760	93 960	31·77
$KClO_3$	*s*	− 93 500	69 200	34·17
NH_4Cl	*s*	− 75 380	48 730	22·6
$(NH_4)_2SO_4$	*s*	− 281 860	215 190	52·65
Na	*s*	0	0	12·48

Substance	*State*	$h^{\ominus}_{T,p}$	$\mathbf{A}^{\ominus}$	$s^{\ominus}$
$NaCl$	*s*	− 98 232	91 785	17·3
$NaBr$	*s*	− 86 030	82 660	
NaI	*s*	− 68 840	67 380	
$NaNO_3$	*s*	−101 540	87 450	27·8
Na_2SO_4	*s*	−330 900	302 780	35·73
Pb	*s*	0	0	15·51
$PbCl_2$	*s*	− 85 850	75 040	32·6
$PbSO_4$	*s*	−219 500	193 890	35·2
PbO (red)	*s*	− 52 400	45 250	16·2
— (yellow)	*s*	− 52 070	45 050	16·6
Pb_3O_4	*s*	−175 600	147 600	50·5
PbO_2	*s*	− 66 120	52 340	18·3
Sn	*s*	0	0	12·3
$SnCl_4$	*l*	−130 300	113 300	61·8
SnO	*s*	− 68 400	61 500	13·5
SnO_2	*s*	−138 800	−124 200	12·5
Zn	*s*	0	0	9·95
ZnO	*s*	− 83 170	76 050	10·5
ZnS	*s*	− 48 500	47 400	13·8
$ZnCl_2$	*s*	− 99 400	88 255	25·9
$ZnSO_4$	*s*	−233 880	208 310	29·8
B. *Compounds of non-metals*				
H_2	*g*	0	0	31·211
H	*g*	+ 52 089	−48 575	27·393
F_2	*g*	0	0	48·6
HF	*g*	− 64 200	64 700	41·47
	aq ($m=1$)	− 78 660	66 080	−2·3
Cl_2	*g*	0	0	53·286
Cl	*g*	+ 29 012	−25 192	39·457
HCl	*g*	− 22 063	22 769	44·617
Br_2	*l*	0	0	36·4
	g	+ 7 340	− 751	58·639
Br	*g*	+ 26 710	−19 690	41·805
HBr	*g*	− 8 660	12 720	47·437
I_2	*s*	0	0	27·9
	g	+ 14 876	− 4 630	62·280
I	*g*	+ 25 482	−16 766	43·184
HI	*g*	+ 6 200	− 310	49·314
O_2	*g*	0	0	49·003
O	*g*	+ 59 159	−54 994	38·469
O_3	*g*	+ 34 000	−39 060	56·8
H_2O	*g*	− 57 798	54 635	45·106
	l	− 68 317	56 690	16·716
H_2O_2	*aq* ($m=1$)	− 45 680	31 470	
S (rhombic)	*s*	0	0	7·62
(monoclinic)	*s*	+ 71	− 23	7·78
	g	+ 53 250	−43 570	40·085
H_2S	*g*	− 4 815	7 892	49·15
SO_2	*g*	− 70 960	71 790	59·40
SO_3	*g*	− 94 450	88 520	61·24

Substance	State	$h^{\ominus}_{T,p}$	$\mathbf{A}^{\ominus}$	$s^{\ominus}$
H_2SO_4	*aq* ($m=1$)	−216 900	177 340	4·1
Se (hexagonal)	*s*	0	0	10·00
	g	+ 48 370	− 38 770	42·21
Te	*s*	0	0	11·88
	g	+ 47 600	− 38 100	43·64
	l	− 46 840	28 230	
N_2	*g*	0	0	45·767
N	*g*	+ 85 566	− 81 476	36·615
NH_3	*g*	− 11 040	3 976	46·01
NO	*g*	+ 21 600	− 20 719	50·339
NO_2	*g*	+ 8 091	− 12 390	57·47
N_2O_4	*g*	+ 2 309	− 23 491	72·73
N_2O	*g*	+ 19 490	− 24 760	52·58
HNO_3	*l*	− 41 404	19 100	37·19
P (white)	*s*	0	0	10·6
(red)	*s*	− 4 400		
	g	+ 75 180	− 66 710	39·98
PH_3	*g*	+ 2 210	4 360	50·2
As (grey)	*s*	0	0	8·4
	g	+ 60 640	− 50 740	33·22
As_2O_5	*s*	−218 600	184 600	25·2
As_4O_6 (octahedral)	*s*	−313 940	275 360	51·2
Sb	*s*	0	0	10·5
	g	+ 60 800	− 51 100	43·06
Sb_2O_5	*s*	−234 400	200 500	29·9
Sb_4O_6	*s*	−336 800	298 000	58·8
C (graphite)	*s*	0	0	1·360
(diamond)	*s*	+ 453	− 685	0·583
CO	*g*	− 26 416	32 808	47·301
CO_2	*g*	− 94 052	94 260	51·061
CS_2	*l*	+ 21 000	− 15 200	36·10
HCN	*g*	+ 31 200	− 28 700	48·23
	aq ($m=1$)	+ 25 200	− 26 800	30·8
Si	*s*	0	0	4·47
SiO_2 (quartz)	*s*	−205 400	192 400	10·00
— (cristob.)	*s*	−205 000	192 100	10·19
$SiCl_4$	*l*	−153 000	136 900	57·2

II. ORGANIC SUBSTANCES

Substance	Formula	State	$h^{\ominus}_{T,p}$	$\mathbf{A}^{\ominus}$	$s^{\ominus}$	Ref.
Hydrocarbons						
Methane	CH_4	*g*	− 17 889	12 140	44·50	(a)
Ethane	C_2H_6	*g*	− 20 236	7 860	54·85	(a)
Propane	C_3H_8	*g*	− 24 820	5 614	64·51	(a)
n-Butane	C_4H_{10}	*g*	− 29 812	3 754	74·10	(a)
n-Pentane	C_5H_{12}	*g*	− 35 000	1 960	83·27	(a)
Ethylene	C_2H_4	*g*	+ 12 496	− 16 282	52·45	(a)
Propylene	C_3H_6	*g*	+ 4 879	− 14 990	63·80	(a)

II. ORGANIC SUBSTANCES—*continued*

Substance	*Formula*	*State*	$h^{\ominus}_{T,p}$	$\mathbf{A}^{\ominus}$	$s^{\ominus}$	*Ref.*
1-Butene	C_4H_8	*g*	+ 280	− 17 217	73·48	(a)
cis-2-Butene	—	*g*	− 1 362	− 16 046	71·90	(a)
trans-2-Butene	—	*g*	− 2 405	− 15 315	70·86	(a)
Isobutene	—	*g*	− 3 343	− 14 582	70·17	(a)
1-Pentene	C_5H_{10}	*g*	− 5 000	− 18 787	83·08	(a)
Acetylene	C_2H_2	*g*	+ 54 194	− 50 000	47·997	(a)
Methylacetylene	C_3H_4	*g*	+ 44 319	− 46 313	59·30	(a)
Cyclopentane	C_5H_{10}	*l*	− 25 300	− 8 700	48·82	(a)
Methylcyclopentane	C_6H_{12}	*l*	− 33 070	− 7 530	59·26	(a)
Cyclohexane	C_6H_{12}	*l*	− 37 340	− 6 370	48·85	(a)
Methylcyclohexane	C_7H_{14}	*l*	− 45 450	− 4 860	59·26	(a)
Benzene	C_6H_6	*g*	+ 19 820	− 30 989	64·34	(a)
		l	+ 11 718	− 29 756	41·30	(a)
Toluene	C_7H_8	*g*	+ 11 950	− 29 228	76·42	(a)
		l	+ 2 867	− 27 282	52·48	(a)
o-Xylene	C_8H_{10}	*g*	+ 4 540	− 29 177	84·31	(a)
		l	− 5 841	− 26 370	58·91	(a)
m-Xylene	—	*g*	+ 4 120	− 28 405	85·49	(a)
		l	− 6 075	− 25 730	60·27	(a)
p-Xylene	—	*g*	+ 4 290	− 28 952	84·23	(a)
		l	− 5 838	− 26 310	59·12	(a)
Durene	$C_6H_2(CH_3)_4$	*s*	− 32 570	− 19 000	58·7	(a)
Cumene	$C_6H_5CH(CH_3)_2$	*l*	− 9 848	− 29 708	66·87	(a)
Mesitylene	$C_6H_3(CH_3)_3$	*l*	− 15 184	− 24 832	65·35	(a)
Diphenyl	$C_6H_5\text{-}C_6H_5$	*s*	+ 20 870	− 57 400	49·2	(b)
Diphenylmethane	$C_6H_5\text{-}CH_2\text{-}C_6H_5$	*s*	+ 19 720	− 63 600	57·2	(b)
Triphenylmethane	$(C_6H_5)_3CH$	*s*	+ 41 760	− 101 400	74·6	(b)
Naphthalene	$C_{10}H_8$	*s*	+ 15 960	− 45 200	39·9	(b)
Anthracene	$C_{14}H_{10}$	*s*	+ 27 600	− 64 800	49·6	(b)
Phenanthrene	$C_{14}H_{10}$	*s*	+ 23 100	− 60 000	50·6	(b)
Alcohols						
Methanol	CH_3OH	*g*	− 48 100	38 700	56·8	(a)
		l	− 57 036	39 750	30 3	(a)
Ethanol	C_2H_5OH	*g*	− 56 240	40 300	67·4	(a)
		l	− 66 356	41 770	38·4	(a)
1-propanol	C_3H_7OH	*l*	− 72 860	40 900	46·1	(b)
2-propanol	C_3H_7OH	*l*	− 76 860	44 000	43·0	(b)
1-butanol	C_4H_9OH	*l*	− 79 610	40 400	54·5	(b)
2-methyl-2-propanol	$(CH_3)_3COH$	*l*	− 89 410	47 500	45·3	(b)
1-pentanol	$C_5H_{11}OH$	*l*	− 86 060	39 100	60·9	(c)
2-methyl-2-butanol	$(C_2H_5)COH(CH_3)_2$	*l*	− 96 460	47 700	54·8	(c)
Diphenyl carbinol	$(C_6H_5)_2CHOH$	*s*	− 20 380	− 30 700	57·3	(b)
Triphenyl carbinol	$(C_6H_5)_3COH$	*s*	+ 3 960	− 69 700	78·7	(b)
Cyclohexanol	$C_6H_{11}OH$	*l*	− 85 600	34 300	47·7	(b)
Ethylene glycol	CH_2OHCH_2OH	*l*	− 108 580	77 120	39·9	(a)
Glycerol	$CH_2OHCHOHCH_2OH$	*l*	− 159 160	113 600	49·7	(b)
Phenol	C_6H_5OH	*s*	− 38 370	11 000	34·1	(c)
Thiophenol	C_6H_5SH	*s*			52·6	(f)
Pyrocatechol	$C_6H_4(OH)_2$	*s*	− 85 570	51 400	35·9	(b)
Resorcinol	$C_6H_4(OH)_2$	*s*	− 87 570	53 200	35·3	(b)
Hydroquinone	$C_6H_4(OH)_2$	*s*	− 87 570	52 700	33·5	(b)
Acids						
Formic acid	HCOOH	*l*	− 97 800	82 700	30·8	(a)
Acetic acid	CH_3COOH	*l*	− 116 400	93 800	38·2	(a)
n-Butyric acid	C_3H_7COOH	*l*	− 128 800	91 500	54·1	(b)

II. Organic Substances—*continued*

Substance	*Formula*	*State*	$h^{\ominus}_{T,p}$	$A^{\ominus}$	$s^{\ominus}$	*Ref.*
Palmitic acid	$C_{15}H_{31}COOH$	*s*	− 215 800	80 000	113·7	(b)
dl-Lactic acid	$CH_3CHOH\text{-}COOH$	*l*	− 161 700	124 300	45·9	(g)
Benzoic acid	C_6H_5COOH	*s*	− 93 210	60 100	40·8	(b)
Phthalic acid	$C_6H_4(COOH)_2$	*s*	− 189 150	143 600	49·7	(f)
Oxalic acid	COOH-COOH	*s*	− 197 600	166 800	28·7	(a)
Fumaric acid	COOHCHCHCOOH	*s*	− 194 880	157 230	39·7	(i)
Maleic acid	COOHCHCHCOOH	*s*	− 189 450	151 320	38·1	(i)
Succinic acid	$COOH(CH_2)_2COOH$	*s*	− 225 660	179 360	42·0	(i)
Phthalic anhydride	$C_6H_4(CO)_2O$	*s*	− 110 840	79 800	42·9	(f)
Esters and Ethers						
Methyl Formate	$HCOOCH_3$	*g*		70 850		(b)
Ethyl Acetate	$CH_3COOC_2H_5$	*l*	− 112 200	77 300	62·0	(c)
Ethyl Propionate	$C_2H_5COOC_2H_5$	*l*	− 121 950	79 634	70·04	(j)
Dimethyl ether	$CH_3\text{-}O\text{-}CH_3$	*g*	− 44 300	27 300	63·72	(a)
Diethyl ether	$C_2H_5\text{-}O\text{-}C_2H_5$	*l*	− 66 100	28 300	60·5	(b)
Aldehydes and Ketones						
Formaldehyde	HCHO	*g*	− 27 700	26 200	52·26	(a)
Acetaldehyde	CH_3CHO	*g*	− 39 760	31 960	63·5	(a)
Acetone	$CH_3\text{-}CO\text{-}CH_3$	*l*	− 59 200	37 200	47·9	(b)
Benzophenone	$C_6H_5\text{-}CO\text{-}C_6H_5$	*s*	− 10 000	− 31 400	58·6	(b)
Dibenzoylethane	$(C_6H_5CO)_2C_2H_4$	*s*	− 65 300	2 500	77·6	(b)
Benzoquinone	$C_6H_4O_2$	*s*	− 45 570	21 600	38·9	(b)
Halogen compounds						
Chloromethane	CH_3Cl	*g*	− 19 580	13 960	55·97	(a)
Dichloromethane	CH_2Cl_2	*g*	− 21 000	14 700	64·68	(a)
		l	− 27 900	15 000	42·7	(a)
Trichloromethane	$CHCl_3$	*g*	− 24 000	16 000	70·86	(a)
		l	− 31 500	17 100	48·5	(a)
Tetrachloromethane	CCl_4	*g*	− 25 500	15 350	73·95	(a)
		l	− 33 340	16 430	51·25	(a)
Bromomethane	CH_3Br	*g*	− 8 200	5 900	58·74	(a)
Tribromomethane	$CHBr_3$	*l*	− 21 800	16 300	53·0	(a)
Iodomethane	CH_3I	*g*	+ 4 900	− 5 300	60·85	(a)
		l	− 2 000	4 900	38·9	(a)
Chloroethane	C_2H_5Cl	*g*	− 25 100	12 700	65·90	(a)
1-2 Dichloroethane	$C_2H_4Cl_2$	*l*	− 39 700	19 200	49·84	(a)
Bromoethane	C_2H_5Br	*l*	− 20 400			(a)
1-2 Dibromoethane	$C_2H_4Br_2$	*l*	− 19 300	4 940	53·37	(a)
Tetrafluoromethane	CF_4	*g*	− 162 500	151 800	62·7	(a)
Fluorobenzene	C_6H_5F	*l*	+ 9 585	− 31 600	46·6	(h)
Chlorobenzene	C_6H_5Cl	*l*	+ 26 685	− 46 200	47·2	(h)
Bromobenzene	C_6H_5Br	*l*	+ 10 485	− 26 100	49·7	(h)
Iodobenzene	C_6H_5I	*l*	+ 34 485	− 49 400	49·1	(h)
Phosgene	$COCl_2$	*g*	− 53 300	50 310	69·13	(a)
Nitrogen Compounds						
Methylamine	CH_3NH_2	*g*	− 6 700	− 6 600	57·73	(a)
Dimethylamine	$(CH_3)_2NH$	*g*	− 6 600	− 14 100	65·30	(a)
Acetonitrile	CH_3CN	*l*	+ 12 700	− 24 000	34·5	(a)

II. ORGANIC SUBSTANCES—*continued*

Substance	*Formula*	*State*	$h^{\ominus}_{T,p}$	$A^{\ominus}$	$s^{\ominus}$	*Ref.*
Aminoacetic acid	$CH_2(NH_2)COOH$	*s*	– 126 330	88 619	26·1	(a)
Urea	$CO(NH_2)_2$	*s*	– 79 634	47 120	25·0	(a)
Nitrobenzene	$C_6H_5NO_2$	*l*	+ 2 680	– 33 900	53·6	(f)
Aniline	$C_6H_5NH_2$	*l*	+ 7 340	– 35 400	45·8	(b)
o-nitroaniline	$C_6H_4NH_2(NO_2)$	*s*	– 4 600	– 41 400	42·1	(b)
m-nitroaniline	—	*s*	– 5 600	– 40 400	42·1	(b)
p-nitroaniline	—	*s*	– 9 600	– 36 400	42·1	(b)
o-dinitrobenzene	$C_6H_4(NO_2)_2$	*s*	+ 1 000	– 49 400	51·7	(b)
m-dinitrobenzene	—	*s*	– 5 200	– 42 900	52·8	(b)
Triphenylamine	$(C_6H_5)_3N$	*s*	+ 58 700	– 120 500	73·0	(b)
Cyanogen	C_2N_2	*g*	+ 73 600	– 70 810	57·86	(a)
Carbohydrates						
α-d-Glucose	$C_6H_{12}O_6$	*s*	– 305 730	218 720	50·7	(i)
l-Sorbose	$C_6H_{12}O_6$	*s*	– 303 500	217 100	52·8	(k)
β-Lactose	$C_{12}H_{22}O_{11}$	*s*	– 533 800	373 700	92·3	(l)
α-d-Galactose	$C_6H_{12}O_6$	*s*	– 307 100	219 600	49·1	(k)
Sucrose	$C_{12}H_{22}O_{11}$	*s*	– 533 400	371 600	86·1	(c)
Heterocyclic Compounds						
Pyridine	C_5H_5N	*l*	+ 17 920	– 37 300	42·8	(f)
Quinoline	C_9H_7N	*l*	+ 35 650	– 63 200	51·9	(f)
1-4 Dioxane	$C_4H_8O_2$	*l*	– 95 800	56 300	47·0	(d)
Thiophene	C_5H_5S	*l*	+ 16 400	– 26 300	42·2	(d)
Adenine	$C_5H_3N_4NH_2$	*s*	+ 21 670	– 70 420	36·1	(e)
Hypoxanthine	$C_5H_4N_4O$	*s*	– 27 630	– 17 250	34·8	(e)
Guanine	$C_5H_5N_5O$	*s*	– 45 090	– 10 220	38·3	(e)
Xanthine	$C_5H_4N_4O_2$	*s*	– 91 810	40 730	38·5	(e)
Uric acid	$C_5H_4N_4O_3$	*s*	– 148 980	91 460	41·4	(e)

REFERENCES:

(1) INORGANIC COMPOUNDS

Selected values of chemical thermodynamic properties. Bureau of Standards (Washington, 1947–52).

(2) ORGANIC COMPOUNDS

(*a*) *Selected values of chemical thermodynamic properties*. Bureau of Standards (Washington, 1947–52); *Selected properties of hydrocarbons* (A.P.I. project 44), Bureau of Standards (Washington, 1946–52).

(*b*) G. S. Parks and H. M. Huffman: *The free energies of some organic compounds* (1932) [35].

(*c*) G. S. Parks, H.M. Huffman, M. Barmore: *J. Amer. Chem. Soc.*, **55**, 2733 (1933).

(*d*) C. J. Jacobs and G. S. Parks: *J. Amer. Chem. Soc.*, **56**, 1513 (1934).

(*e*) R. D. Stiehler and H. M. Huffman: *J. Amer. Chem. Soc.*, **57**, 1741 (1935).

(*f*) G. S. Sachs, S. S. Todd, W. A. Moore: *J. Amer. Chem. Soc.*, **58**, 398, (1936).

(*g*) G. S. Parks, S. B. Thomas, D. W. Light: *J. Chem. Phys.*, **4**, 64 (1936).

(*h*) D. R. Stull: *J. Amer. Chem. Soc.*, **59**, 2726 (1937).

(*i*) H. M. Huffman and S. W. Fox: *J. Amer. Chem. Soc.*, **60**, 1400 (1938).

(*j*) H. Essex and M. Sandholzer: *J. Phys. Chem.*, **42**, 317 (1938).

(*k*) G. M. Jack and G. Stegeman: *J. Amer. Chem. Soc.*, **63**, 2121 (1941).

(*l*) A. G.Anderson and G. Stegeman: *J. Amer. Chem. Soc.*, **63**, 2119 (1941).

7. The Decomposition of Hexane.

We conclude this chapter with a detailed quantitative study of the decomposition of hexane.*

* H. S. Taylor and J. Turkevich, *Trans. Faraday Soc.*, **35**, 921 (1939).

Hexane may decompose in a number of different ways ;

(1) $C_6H_{14} \rightarrow CH_4 + C_5H_{10}$

(2) $2C_6H_{14} \rightarrow C_{12}H_{26} + H_2$

(3) $2C_6H_{14} \rightarrow C_7H_{16} + C_5H_{12}$

(4) $C_6H_{14} \rightarrow 6C + 7H_2$

(5) $C_6H_{14} \rightarrow C_6H_{12} + H_2$

(6) $C_6H_{14} \rightarrow \underset{(cyclo)}{C_6H_{12}} + H_2$

(7) $C_6H_{14} \rightarrow \underset{(cyclo)}{C_5H_9} \,.\, CH_3 + H_2$

(8) $C_6H_{14} \rightarrow \underset{(cyclo)}{C_6H_{10}} + 2H_2$

(9) $C_6H_{14} \rightarrow C_6H_6 + 4H_2$

The standard affinity of each of these reactions can be evaluated from a knowledge of the affinities of formation of the compounds involved. If these are known as a function of temperature, then the standard affinity can also be obtained at various temperatures. Thus the standard affinities of formation (in calories) of the hydrocarbons involved in the above reactions are, in the temperature range 300 – 1000 °K ; at 1 atm. pressure :

Methane	$\mathbf{A}^{\ominus} = 19{,}050 - 22{\cdot}6T$
Saturated normal hydrocarbons C_nH_{2n+2}	$\mathbf{A}^{\ominus} = 10{,}550 + 5{,}890n - 25{\cdot}2nT + 2{\cdot}2T$
Ethylene	$\mathbf{A}^{\ominus} = -10{,}770 - 16{\cdot}9T$
Ethylenes C_nH_{2n} with double bond in terminal position	$\mathbf{A}^{\ominus} = -20{,}321 + 5{,}835n + 33{\cdot}26T - 24{\cdot}52nT$
Cyclohexane	$\mathbf{A}^{\ominus} = 32{,}000 - 135{\cdot}5T$
Methylcyclopentane	$\mathbf{A}^{\ominus} = 22{,}600 - 88{\cdot}2T$
Cyclohexene	$\mathbf{A}^{\ominus} = 3{,}300 - 104{\cdot}1T$
Cyclohexadiene	$\mathbf{A}^{\ominus} = -23{,}470 - 72{\cdot}9T$
Benzene	$\mathbf{A}^{\ominus} = -17{,}900 - 41{\cdot}7T$

From these standard affinities of formation we can derive quite readily the standard affinities for reactions (1) to (9). The detailed arithmetic is left as an exercise to familiarize the reader with the general method. The resulting expressions are :

Equation for Standard Affinity	*K(T, p) at 1 atm.*	
	300 °K	700 °K
(1) $\mathbf{A}^{\ominus} = -17{,}986 + 37{\cdot}06T$	1×10^{-5}	3×10^{2}
(2) $\mathbf{A}^{\ominus} = -10{,}550 - 2{\cdot}2T$	$6{\cdot}2 \times 10^{-9}$	$1{\cdot}7 \times 10^{-4}$
(3) $\mathbf{A}^{\ominus} = 0$	1	1
(4) $\mathbf{A}^{\ominus} = -45{,}890 + 149T$	$1{\cdot}4 \times 10^{-1}$	$1{\cdot}7 \times 10^{18}$
(5) $\mathbf{A}^{\ominus} = -31{,}201 + 35{\cdot}13T$	9×10^{-16}	9×10^{-3}
(6) $\mathbf{A}^{\ominus} = -13{,}890 + 13{\cdot}5T$	$6{\cdot}8 \times 10^{-8}$	4×10^{-2}
(7) $\mathbf{A}^{\ominus} = -23{,}290 + 60{\cdot}8T$	2×10^{-4}	1×10^{6}
(8) $\mathbf{A}^{\ominus} = -42{,}590 + 44{\cdot}9T$	$6{\cdot}5 \times 10^{-22}$	$3{\cdot}2 \times 10^{-4}$
(9) $\mathbf{A}^{\ominus} = -63{,}790 + 107{\cdot}3T$	8×10^{-24}	$3{\cdot}5 \times 10^{3}$

It is interesting to know the percentage of hexane decomposed as a function of temperature relative to each mode of reaction. This is readily obtained by calculating the equilibrium constant using equation (7.80), and applying the Guldberg and Waage mass action equation to obtain the percentage dissociation. Thus for reaction (6) at 700 °K we have

$$K(T, p) = \frac{x_{C_6H_{12}(cyclo)}\, x_{H_2}}{x_{C_6H_{14}}} = \frac{\epsilon^2}{1-\epsilon} = 4{\cdot}1 \times 10^{-2}.$$

Hence $\epsilon = 0{\cdot}18.$

We can therefore obtain ϵ as a function of temperature. These results may be represented graphically as in fig. 8.1.

From this figure we conclude that:

(1) Two molecules of a paraffin do not react to form a higher paraffin with the elimination of hydrogen; this agrees with experimental findings.

(2) The conversion of n-hexane to benzene is appreciable at 550 °K, while at 600 °K and atmospheric pressure the equilibrium is completely in favour of benzene.

(3) The dehydrogenation of hexane to hexene or cyclohexane (reactions 5 and 6) only becomes appreciable at temperatures approaching 800 °K. The dehydrogenation to methylcyclopentane however appears to be thermodynamically feasible at temperatures as low as 350 °K. One cannot place too much reliance on this particular result since the affinity of formation of methylcyclopentane is known less accurately than the others. These three reactions, however, scarcely affect the synthesis of aromatic compounds in the reaction since the ethylenes and cycloparaffins are thermodynamically unstable relative to aromatic hydrocarbons above 550 °K, and they decompose spontaneously to form aromatics at this temperature. They can therefore only appear as intermediates in reaction (9) above 550 °K.

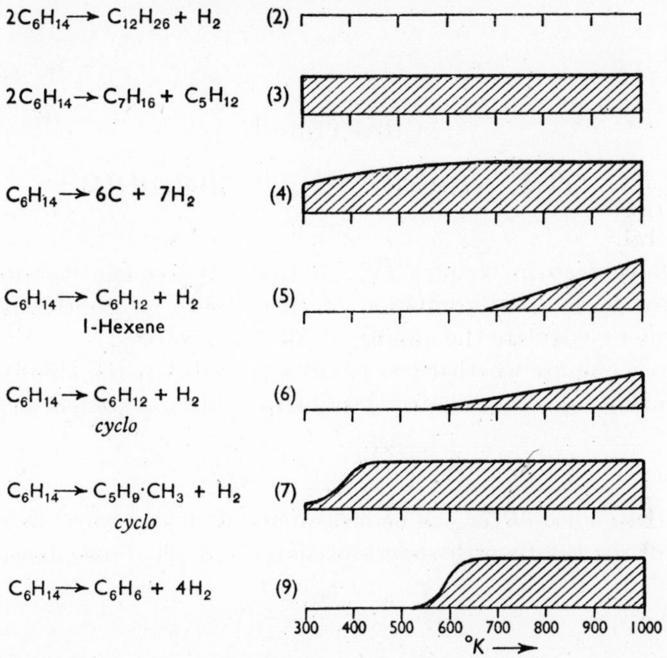

FIG. 8.1. Percentage of hexane dissociated as function of absolute temperature (after H. S. Taylor and J. Turkevich, *Trans. Faraday Soc.*, **35**, 921 (1939)).

(4) Cracking into two paraffins (reaction 3) and decomposition into carbon and hydrogen (reaction 4) can also occur to an appreciable extent in the same temperature range as the conversion to aromatics.

We see, therefore, that in the temperature range 500–700 °K there are, on purely thermodynamic grounds, only *two possibilities* : either the conversion of paraffins to aromatics, or cracking reactions. Thermodynamics cannot tell us which of these reactions will occur in practice, but by suitable choice of catalyst it is in fact possible to direct the reaction into one or other of these two routes.

CHAPTER IX

THE NERNST HEAT THEOREM

1. General.

We have seen in chapter IV, § 3 that calorimetric measurements combined with a determination of the affinity at one temperature, enable us to calculate the affinity at all temperatures.

We now enquire whether it is possible to calculate the affinity at any temperature from calorimetric data alone. From equation (4.3),

$$-\mathbf{A}=\left(\frac{\partial H}{\partial \xi}\right)_{T,p}-T\left(\frac{\partial S}{\partial \xi}\right)_{T,p}, \tag{9.1}$$

we see that, since $\partial H/\partial \xi$ can be measured calorimetrically, the problem is that of the calorimetric determination of $\partial S/\partial \xi$. Since, however,

$$\frac{\partial S}{\partial \xi}=\sum_i \nu_i \frac{\partial S}{\partial n_i}=\sum_i \nu_i s_i, \tag{9.2}$$

where s_i is the partial molar entropy of the substance i, the problem would be completely solved if we could measure calorimetrically the partial molar entropy of each component in the reaction. For most systems we shall consider here the partial molar entropy can be equated to the molar entropy of the compound in the pure state.

2. Calorimetric Determination of Entropy of a Chemical Compound.

We now consider a one-component system whose molar entropy we wish to evaluate calorimetrically. From a consideration of the fundamental equation (3.5),

$$dS=\frac{dQ}{T}+\frac{dQ'}{T}, \tag{9.3}$$

we see that thermodynamics does not allow us to calculate absolute values for the entropy, but only variations in entropy. To assign definite values to the entropy we must have some convention which fixes the zero for the entropy. The conventions which determine the entropy zeros for different substances cannot be completely arbitrary since the sum

$$\sum_i \nu_i s_i=\frac{\partial S}{\partial \xi}$$

must have a value independent of the convention which is chosen.

To give a definite value to the entropy of a substance it is necessary to discuss further the statistical definition of entropy given in chapter III, § 9. We notice first that this definition does not include any arbitrary constant explicitly, and furthermore since the number of quantum states is necessarily greater than or equal to unity, the entropy is always positive.

As the temperature of a substance is lowered, and its internal energy drops, the number of accessible quantum states also decreases. In many cases the number of quantum states falls to unity at the absolute zero, and so, from equation (3.45) we may take the entropy to be zero at 0 °K. The arbitrary constant which seems to be absent from (3.45) is not really eliminated since different criteria can be employed for recognizing distinct quantum states. In the present instance we choose to ignore the quantum states of the atomic nuclei, and those arising from the presence of isotopes. This is justifiable provided that we consider only transformations which do not alter these contributions.*

Thus the entropy of most crystalline substances may be regarded as zero at the absolute zero of temperature. There are a number of exceptions to this generalization, for example in the case of CO (*cf.* p. 196). In the CO crystal the molecules are still able to take up several different orientations even at the lowest experimental temperatures. In the same way, glasses and amorphous solids do not have zero entropy at 0 °K. On the other hand, the entropy of helium at 0 °K is zero even though helium is liquid at this temperature and at 1 atm. pressure.

The fact that we can take the entropy of most substances as zero at 0 °K may be considered as an expression of *Nernst's theorem*. Other more general formulations are possible, based for example on the impossibility of attaining the absolute zero in a finite number of operations, but no use is made of such concepts in the present work and we shall not pursue the matter further. We must remember though, that however Nernst's theorem is formulated, it is necessary to have recourse to the methods of statistical mechanics to examine its domain of validity.†

Equation (9.3) may now be integrated from the absolute zero up to the temperature T to give

$$S = S(0) + \int_0^T \frac{dQ + dQ'}{T}. \tag{9.4}$$

Since the absolute zero is in fact unattainable this integral is really the limit of the integral $\int_{T^*}^{T} \frac{dQ + dQ'}{T}$ as T^* tends to zero.

* *Cf.* Guggenheim [26′], p. 157.

† *Cf.* especially Fowler and Guggenheim [20], chap. V; F. Simon, *Erg. Naturw.*, 9, 222 (1930).

If we assume, as is usually justifiable, that the Nernst theorem is applicable to the compound under consideration we have

$$S(0)=0, \tag{9.5}$$

so that

$$S=\int_0^T \frac{dQ+dQ'}{T}. \tag{9.6}$$

The route by which the integration is made is immaterial since S is a function of state. In general, however, the substance is in a different physical state at T from that at zero temperature so that the integration path must include at least one change of phase. The method of dealing with the integration is outlined below.

As an example let us choose a substance which is liquid at a temperature T and pressure p; let the melting point of the substance at this pressure be T_f.

If we raise the temperature of one mole of the substance at constant pressure from 0 to T_f, then since the system is a homogeneous one phase system dQ' will be zero (*cf.* chap. III, § 4) and

$$\int_0^{T_f} \frac{dQ+dQ'}{T}=\int_0^{T_f} \frac{c_p^s\,dT}{T}, \tag{9.7}$$

where c_p^s is the molar heat capacity of the solid at constant pressure. The substance melts at the temperature T_f. At this temperature, and at pressure p, solid and liquid are in equilibrium, $\mathbf{A}=0$, and hence also $dQ'=0$. On the other hand

$$dQ=\left(\frac{\partial H}{\partial \xi}\right)_{T,p} \partial\xi.$$

If one mole of substance melts we have $\Delta\xi=1$ and the heat adsorbed is equal to $\Delta_f h$ the molar latent heat of fusion of the substance. The corresponding contribution to the entropy is

$$\Delta_f h/T_f. \tag{9.8}$$

Between T_f and T the system again is a homogeneous one component system and the contribution to the entropy on heating through this temperature range is

$$\int_{T_f}^{T} \frac{c_p^l}{T}\,dT \tag{9.9}$$

where c_p^l is the molar heat capacity of the liquid.

The entropy of the liquid will therefore be equal to

$$s^l=\int_0^{T_f} \frac{c_p^s}{T}\,dT+\frac{\Delta_f h}{T_f}+\int_{T_f}^{T} \frac{c_p^l}{T}\,dT. \tag{9.10}$$

Similarly if the compound is in the gaseous state at the given temperature and pressure we must also include the entropy of vaporization so that

$$s^g = \int_0^{T_f} \frac{c_p^s}{T}\, dT + \frac{\Delta_f h}{T_f} + \int_{T_f}^{T_e} \frac{c_p^l}{T}\, dT + \frac{\Delta_e h}{T_e} + \int_{T_e}^{T} \frac{c_p^g}{T}\, dT, \tag{9.11}$$

where $\Delta_e h$ is the latent heat of vaporization, and c_p^g the heat capacity of the gas at constant pressure. If the compound does not form an ideal crystal at the absolute zero an appropriate term $s(0)$ must be added to (9.10) or (9.11).

We now pass on to consider how the various terms appearing in (9.10) and (9.11) may be evaluated.

The latent heats $\Delta_f h$ and $\Delta_e h$ may be measured directly in a calorimeter but the integrals of c_p/T may be obtained in a number of different ways. The method adopted depends to some extent upon the substance under consideration.

(*a*) *Graphical Integration :* if c_p is known as a function of temperature, $\int_0^T \frac{c_p}{T}\, dT$ may be evaluated graphically by plotting c_p/T against T and finding the area under the curve between $T=0$ and $T=T$. Since the lower limit of integration is the absolute zero a slight modification of this method is often employed. This is possible since as $T \to 0$, c_p falls rapidly to zero so that it is possible to evaluate the integral

$$\int_0^T \frac{c_p}{T}\, dT = \int_{-\infty}^{\ln T} c_p \, d \ln T. \tag{9.12}$$

The latter integral has the advantage that T does not figure in the denominator ; this makes the graphical integration much more accurate at small values of T. As an example of this method, fig. 9.1 shows the graph of c_p *vs* $\ln T$ for solid mercury.*

(*b*) *Numerical Method :* If the specific heat c_p can be expressed as a series in ascending powers of T, the integrals are readily calculated. If, for example,

$$c_p = a + bT + cT^2 + \dots$$

we have

$$\int_{T_0}^{T} \frac{c_p}{T}\, dT = a \ln \frac{T}{T_0} + b(T - T_0) + \tfrac{1}{2} c (T^2 - T_0^2) \dots . \tag{9.13}$$

This method is only useful when T and T_0 are both fairly large. It is often employed in the temperature range where the substance is gaseous. We have already given in table 2.2 some examples of the series representing the specific heats of a number of common gases.

* After A. Magnus, *Lehrbuch der Thermodynamik*, (Leipzig, 1929), and Ulich [46], p. 192.

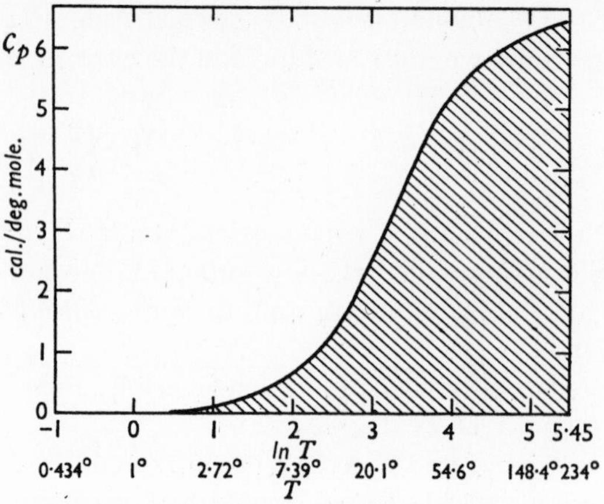

FIG. 9.1. Graphical determination of the entropy of solid mercury.

(c) *Extrapolation :* While it is usually relatively easy to measure specific heats down to about 90 °K, accurate data are much more difficult to obtain at lower temperatures, so that an extrapolation method is often needed to evaluate that part of the integral corresponding to very low temperatures. The general method of doing this will be discussed in chap. XII, but here we may notice a useful empirical method developed by Kelley, Parks and Huffmann* for organic compounds. They found that the specific heats of organic compounds are very closely related to their molecular structure. In particular, they showed that if we know the specific heat c_p^0 of one substance, then that of a substance of analogous molecular structure is given by the equation

$$c_p = (A + BT)c_p^0 \tag{9.14}$$

where A and B are two constants which can be determined by knowing c_p at two temperatures in the range 90 °K to 120 °K. For example, the specific heats, and hence the entropies, of aliphatic hydrocarbons can be calculated with reasonable accuracy when the specific heat of one of them is known down to 20 °K, and the others have been studied at two or more temperatures in the range 90–120 °K.

Examples :

Entropy of gaseous CO_2 *at the sublimation point.*

We wish to calculate the entropy of gaseous CO_2 at 1 atm. at the sublimation temperature 194·67 °K. We have

$$s^g_{CO_2}(T = 194{\cdot}67°,\ p = 1 \text{ atm.}) = \int_0^{194\cdot67°} \frac{c_p^s\,dT}{T} + \frac{\Delta_s h}{194{\cdot}67}$$

* Parks and Huffmann, [35].

where $\Delta_s h$ is the heat of sublimation, which is 6,030 cal./mole at the temperature under consideration. Hence $\Delta_s h/194{\cdot}67 = 30{\cdot}98$ cal./deg. mole.

The integral is taken in two parts :

1. $\int_0^{15} \frac{c_p^s}{T}\, dT$ which has to be evaluated on a theoretical basis outlined in chap. XII, § 5. It is found to equal 0·190 cal./deg. mole

2. $\int_{15}^{194\cdot67} \frac{c_p^s}{T}\, dT$ which is obtained by measuring the specific heat and integrating graphically. The result is 16·33 cal./deg. mole.

Adding these three contributions we find that

$$s^g_{CO_2}(194{\cdot}67^\circ\,;\; 1) = 47{\cdot}50 \pm 0{\cdot}10 \text{ cal./deg. mole}$$

which is the entropy of gaseous CO_2 at a pressure of 1 atm. and temperature 194·67 °K.

If we wish to know the entropy of CO_2 in the perfect gas state a correction term of 0·09 cal./deg. mole must be added to this figure. The method of evaluating this correction is dealt with in chap. XI, § 3. The resulting entropy, 47·59 ±0·10 cal./deg. mole, may be called, following the terminology introduced in chap. VII, the standard entropy of CO_2 at a pressure of 1 atm. and a temperature of 194·67 °K.

Entropy of Gaseous Ethyl Alcohol at its normal boiling point.

The entropy of ethyl alcohol is made up of the following contributions (in cal./deg. mole) :

0 – 16 °K, extrapolation	0·45
16 – 158·5 °K, crystal	16·20
Fusion 1200/158·5	7·57
158·5 – 298·16 °K, liquid	14·18
0 °K (crystal) – 298·16 °K (liq)	38·4 ±0·3
298·16° – 351·5 °K, liquid	4·90 ±0·005
Vaporization 9255/351·5	26·33 ±0·03
Entropy of real gas at b.p. and 1 atm.	69·63 ±0·3
Correction for gas imperfection	0·14
Entropy of ideal gas at b.p. and 1 atm.	69·8 ±0·3 cal./deg. mole.

Entropy of Butane.

The heat capacity of butane has only been determined down to 67 °K so that the evaluation of its entropy involves the application of the Kelley, Parks and Huffmann method.

Between 0 and 67° we employ the equation

$$c_p = (A + BT)c_p^0$$

where A and B are constants and c_p^0 is the heat capacity of the standard aliphatic reference substance.

The entropy of butane can therefore be obtained by summing the following contributions (again in cal./deg. mole) :

0°–67 °K by extrapolation	$7{\cdot}78 \pm 0{\cdot}7$	
67°–134·1 °K crystalline—graphical integration	16·23	$\pm 0{\cdot}2$
Fusion 1,044·3/134·1	7·79	
134·1°–272·5 °K liquid	20·36	
Vaporization 5,324/272·5	$20{\cdot}44 \pm 0{\cdot}2$	
272·5°–298·1 °K (Mean $c_p^g = 21{\cdot}6$)	1·95	
Correction for gas imperfection	0·14	
Total entropy of ideal gas at 1 atm. and 298·1 °K.	$74{\cdot}69 \pm 1{\cdot}0$ cal./deg. mole	

Table 8.1 contains values of the standard entropies of a number of important chemical compounds. These are the molar entropies of the real substances, corrected in the case of gases for gas imperfections, at a pressure of 1 atm. and temperature of 25 °C.

In later chapters (X and XIV) we shall give examples of the application of the Nernst theorem to the calculation of homogeneous and heterogeneous equilibrium constants. We shall also see (chap. X, § 3) how the entropies of simple gaseous molecules may be calculated by statistical methods.

We end this chapter with some rather more qualitative considerations.

3. Approximate Calculations based on Nernst's Theorem.

Let us consider first reactions between solid phases. Even though the standard entropies of the reactants are unknown it is nevertheless possible to obtain a rough approximation by making use of the observation that for the majority of reactions between solids

$$| \partial H/\partial \xi | \gg T \, | \partial S/\partial \xi | \tag{9.15}$$

so that to a crude approximation (9.1) can be written

$$\mathbf{A} \approx -\, \partial H/\partial \xi. \tag{9.16}$$

Examination of table 8.1 shows that the standard entropies of solids are all of roughly the same magnitude so that for reactions between them $298(\partial S/\partial \xi)$ is of the order of thousands of calories per mole, while heats of reaction between solids are usually of the order of tens of thousands of calories. It is thus usually justifiable to employ (9.16) as a rough approximation. It should be noted however, that (9.16) cannot be used for solid reactions such as allotropic changes where the heat of reaction is small.

For reactions involving liquids and gases a quantitative calculation based on (9.1) is clearly impossible in the absence of data on the standard entropies. On general grounds, however, in view of the magnitude of entropies of fusion or sublimation we shall expect $\partial S/\partial \xi$ to be positive for reactions in which solid substances are converted to liquid or gaseous products. This is the reason why the affinity of a reaction such as

$$C + FeO \rightarrow CO + Fe$$

in which a gas is produced, increases with temperature : all metallic oxides are reduced by carbon at a sufficiently high temperature. On the other hand the affinity of a reaction like

$$Fe + \tfrac{1}{2}O_2 \rightarrow FeO$$

decreases with temperature.*

Similarly we notice that $\partial S/\partial \xi$ will, in general, be positive for all dissociation reactions, and for reactions in which the total number of molecules increases. The affinity of such reactions therefore increases with temperature.

Hence if the standard affinity of a reaction is known to be negative at a given temperature, then in a large number of cases it is possible to predict qualitatively whether the reaction can be made feasible by an increase or decrease of temperature.

* For further discussion of the reduction of oxides see Rey [39], *cf.* also C. W. Dannatt and H. J. T. Ellingham, *Discussions of the Faraday Soc.*, **1948,** No. 4, p. 126 ; M. J. N. Pourbaix and C. M. Rorivé-Bouté, *ibid.*, p. 139.

CHAPTER X

PERFECT GASES

1. Equation of State of a Perfect Gas.

We define a *perfect gas* as any gas which obeys the following laws :

Joule's law : the internal energy (u) per mole depends only upon the absolute temperature. The energy of n moles is therefore

$$U = nu(T). \tag{10.1}$$

Boyle's law : at constant temperature the volume V occupied by a given number of moles of gas varies in inverse proportion to the pressure p. That is to say

$$V = n\frac{f(T)}{p}, \tag{10.2}$$

where $f(T)$ is a function independent of the nature of the gas.

We now proceed to show that these two laws lead to the following equation of state for a perfect gas :

$$\boxed{pV = n\mathbf{R}T}, \tag{10.3}$$

where $\mathbf{R}$ is the *gas constant.*

For the moment we shall assume that no chemical reaction can occur in the gas. We can then take the first equation of (4.49) and divide through by the total number of moles of gas (n) to obtain

$$ds = \frac{du + p\,dv}{T} = \frac{c_v}{T}\,dT + \frac{p}{T}\,dv, \tag{10.4}$$

where we have introduced the molar heat capacity at constant volume defined by

$$c_v = \frac{du}{dT}. \tag{10.5}$$

The heat capacity c_v depends, as we see from (10.1), solely upon the temperature. Equation (10.4) is the total differential of s in the independent variables T and v, so that

$$\left(\frac{\partial s}{\partial T}\right)_v = \frac{c_v}{T}; \quad \left(\frac{\partial s}{\partial v}\right)_T = \frac{p}{T},$$

Differentiating the first of these with respect to v, and the second with respect to T, and remembering that the order of differentiation in a second derivative is immaterial we have, using (10.2)

$$\frac{\partial\left(\frac{c_v}{T}\right)}{\partial v}=\frac{\partial\left(\frac{p}{T}\right)}{\partial T}=\frac{\partial\left[\frac{f(T)}{Tv}\right]}{\partial T}.$$

But since c_v/T is independent of v, the first differential is zero and

$$\frac{\partial\left[\frac{f(T)}{T}\right]}{\partial T}=0.$$

Hence $f(T)/T$ must be a constant, called the *gas constant* $\boldsymbol{R}$ which like $f(T)$ is the same for all gases. Replacing $f(T)/T$ by $\boldsymbol{R}$ in (10.2) gives us the perfect gas equation of state (10.3).

The numerical value of the constant $\boldsymbol{R}$ is given in terms of various units below.

$$\begin{aligned}\boldsymbol{R}&=0{\cdot}08205 \text{ litre. atm./deg. mole},\\&=62{,}360 \text{ cm.}^3 \text{ mm. Hg./deg. mole},\\&=8{\cdot}314\times 10^7 \text{ ergs/deg. mole},\\&=1{\cdot}987 \text{ cal./deg. mole}.\end{aligned}$$

2. Thermodynamic Functions of a Perfect Gas.

We have already had occasion to mention some of the simpler properties of a perfect gas (*cf.* chap. II, § 2-4). Among these was the equation for the difference between the molar heat capacities at constant pressure and constant volume :

$$c_p-c_v=\boldsymbol{R}. \tag{10.6}$$

We proceed now to develop the thermodynamic functions for a perfect gas.

Integration of (10.5) from temperature T_0 to T gives for the molar *internal energy* :

$$u(T)-u(T_0)=\int_{T_0}^{T} c_v(T)\,dT. \tag{10.7}$$

Since the specific heat of a gas is readily measured equation (10.7) allows the molar energy to be evaluated, apart from an additive constant.

Similarly by integration of (2.17) we find for the enthalpy,

$$h=u+pv=u+\boldsymbol{R}T,$$

$$h(T)-h(T_0)=\int_{T_0}^{T} c_p(T)\,dT. \tag{10.8}$$

To obtain the *molar entropy* we integrate (10.4) from an initial state (T_0, v_0) to (T, v), making use of (10.3). This gives

$$s(T, v) = \left[s(T_0, v_0) + \int_{T_0}^{T} \frac{c_v(T)}{T} dT - \mathbf{R} \ln v_0 \right] + \mathbf{R} \ln v$$

$$= s^{\ddagger}(T) + \mathbf{R} \ln v. \tag{10.9}$$

where the expression in square brackets has been equated to $s^{\ddagger}(T)$ which is a function of T only, and is the molar entropy of the gas at a molar volume of unity and temperature T.

If we replace v by p using the equation of state (10.3), and c_v by c_p using (10.6) we obtain

$$s(T, p) = \left[s(T_0, p_0) + \int_{T_0}^{T} \frac{c_p(T)}{T} dT + \mathbf{R} \ln p_0 \right] - \mathbf{R} \ln p$$

$$= s^{\dagger}(T) - \mathbf{R} \ln p, \tag{10.10}$$

where $s^{\dagger}(T)$ is the molar entropy of the gas at unit pressure, and $s(T_0, v_0) = s(T_0, p_0)$. By comparing (10.9) and (10.10) we see that

$$s^{\dagger}(T) = s^{\ddagger}(T) + \mathbf{R} \ln \mathbf{R}T. \tag{10.10'}$$

Finally, from (6.31), $\mu_i = h_i - Ts_i$, we obtain for the *chemical potential*

$$\mu(T, p) =$$

$$\left[h(T_0) - Ts(T_0, p_0) + \int_{T_0}^{T} c_p \, dT - T \int_{T_0}^{T} \frac{c_p}{T} dT - \mathbf{R}T \ln p_0 \right] + \mathbf{R}T \ln p;$$

$$\boxed{\mu(T,p) = \mu^{\dagger}(T) + \mathbf{R}T \ln p,} \tag{10.11}$$

where $\mu^{\dagger}(T)$ is the chemical potential of the gas at unit pressure.

The chemical potential of a gas therefore increases logarithmically with the pressure. Comparison of (10.8), (10.10) and (10.11) shows that, for a perfect gas,

$$\mu^{\dagger}(T) = h(T) - Ts^{\dagger}(T), \tag{10.11'}$$

the superscript dagger being unnecessary on the h since the enthalpy of a perfect gas is independent of pressure.

For the molar free energy f of a perfect gas (*cf.* 3.15)

$$f = u(T) - T \, . \, s(T, v)$$

$$= f^{\ddagger}(T) - \mathbf{R}T \ln v, \tag{10.12}$$

where we have put

$$f^{\ddagger}(T) = u(T) - Ts^{\ddagger}(T). \tag{10.12'}$$

Here again we do not need a superscript attached to u.

We notice finally that

$$\mu^{\dagger}(T) - f^{\ddagger}(T) = \boldsymbol{R}T + \boldsymbol{R}T \ln \boldsymbol{R}T. \qquad (10.12'')$$

These equations show that the thermodynamic functions of a perfect gas are determined, apart from additive constants, by the values of the specific heat as a function of temperature.

3. The Heat Capacity of a Perfect Gas. Chemical Constants.

The heat capacities of perfect gases are very closely related to their molecular structures. The exact relations have been derived on the basis of statistical mechanics but here we shall give only a general account of the problem. More detailed accounts will be found in the standard works on statistical mechanics.*

We shall limit ourselves to the case where the mean energy of each molecule is equal to the sum of the energies of translation, of rotation and of vibration. The heat capacity at constant volume c_v (*cf.* 10.5) will also be composed of three terms arising from these three kinds of motion. The contribution from the translational motion is $\frac{3}{2}\boldsymbol{R}$ per mole, and that from rotation is $\boldsymbol{R}$ or $\frac{3}{2}\boldsymbol{R}$ depending upon whether the molecule is linear or not. This last statement is only exact if the rotational motion may be treated by classical, as opposed to quantum, mechanics. This is a good approximation even at low temperatures except for very light molecules such as H_2 and HD. Finally the contribution from vibration of the atoms in a molecule relative to one another is the sum of the contributions from the various modes of vibration. Each mode of vibration is characterized by a fundamental frequency ν_j which is independent of the temperature. It is convenient to relate the fundamental frequency to a characteristic temperature (Θ_j) defined by

$$\Theta_j = \frac{\boldsymbol{h}\nu_j}{\boldsymbol{k}}, \qquad (10.13)$$

where $\boldsymbol{h}$ is Planck's constant ($\boldsymbol{h} = 6{\cdot}624 \times 10^{-27}$ erg. sec.) and $\boldsymbol{k}$ is the Boltzmann constant which is equal to $\boldsymbol{R}$ divided by Avogadro's number ($\boldsymbol{N} = 6{\cdot}023 \times 10^{23}$; $\boldsymbol{k} = 1{\cdot}380 \times 10^{-16}$ erg. deg.$^{-1}$); $\boldsymbol{h}/\boldsymbol{k}$ thus has the value : $4{\cdot}80 \times 10^{-11}$ deg. sec.

The contribution of each vibration to the specific heat increases with increasing temperature and may be written in the form $\boldsymbol{R}P\left(\frac{T}{\Theta_j}\right)$ where

* Fowler, [19], chap. III.
Fowler and Guggenheim [20], chap. III.
Mayer and Mayer [34], chap. V to VIII.

P is a universal function called the Planck-Einstein function, of which an abbreviated table is given in table 10.1.

TABLE 10.1

*Planck-Einstein Function**

T/Θ	$\frac{1}{8}$	$\frac{1}{4}$	$\frac{1}{2}$	1	2	4
$P(T/\Theta)$	0·022	0·303	0·724	0·928	0·979	0·9995

At high temperatures (*i.e.* large T/Θ) this function tends to unity, and the contribution to the specific heat from the vibration tends to $\boldsymbol{R}$ per mole. At low temperatures the function tends to zero.

We may, therefore, write the vibrational contribution to the specific heat as

$$c'(T) = \boldsymbol{R} \sum_j P\left(\frac{T}{\Theta_j}\right). \tag{10.14}$$

Table 10.2 gives the values of Θ for the fundamental vibrations of a number of diatomic molecules.

TABLE 10.2

Characteristic Temperatures for vibration of some Diatomic Molecules.†

	Θ °K		Θ °K
O_2	2 250	Br_2	470
N_2	3 350	I_2	305
NO	2 710	H_2	6 100
CO	3 080	HCl	4 200
Cl_2	810	HBr	3 560

These results may be summarized in terms of c_p in the form

$$c_p = c_p(0) + c'(T), \tag{10.15}$$

with

$$c_p(0) = \tfrac{5}{2}\,\boldsymbol{R} \text{ for monatomic molecules}$$
$$= \tfrac{7}{2}\,\boldsymbol{R} \text{ for linear molecules}$$
$$= 4\boldsymbol{R} \text{ for polyatomic, non-linear molecules.}$$

We must note that equation (10.15) becomes invalid in the vicinity of absolute zero since then the quantization of rotational degrees of freedom cannot be neglected. However, because of the form of the

* For full table of $\boldsymbol{R}P(T/\Theta)$ see H. S. Taylor and S. Glasstone, *A Treatise on Physical Chemistry*, Vol. I (3rd Edn. London, 1942), Appendix I.

† *Cf.* Eucken [17], p. 151.

Planck-Einstein function which occurs in $c'(T)$, it is possible to define a temperature T' such that for most practical purposes

$$c'(T) = 0 \text{ for } T < T'. \tag{10.16}$$

If now in equation (10.11) for the chemical potential, we replace the specific heat by the value given by (10.15) we obtain

$$\frac{\mu(T, p)}{RT} = \left[\frac{h(0)}{RT} - \frac{c_p(0)}{R} \ln T + \frac{1}{RT}\int_{T_0}^{T} c'(T)\,dT - \frac{1}{R}\int_{T_0}^{T} \frac{c'(T)}{T}\,dT - j\right] + \ln p, \tag{10.17}$$

where

$$\left.\begin{aligned} h(0) &\equiv h(T_0) - c_p(0)T_0 \\ j &\equiv \frac{s(T_0, p_0) - c_p(0) - c_p(0)\ln T_0 + R\ln p_0}{R} \end{aligned}\right\}. \tag{10.18}$$

The quantity j is called the *chemical constant* of the perfect gas under consideration. We now proceed to show that the values of $h(0)$ and j are independent of the values chosen for T_0 and p_0, provided that T_0 is a temperature lower than T' as defined by (10.16) and higher than the temperature at which (10.15) breaks down on account of quantization of the rotational motion of the molecule.

We note first that for all values of T_0 lower than T', we can, without altering the value of the integrals in (10.17), extend the domain of integration to 0 °K. Equation (10.17) can then be written in the form:

$$\mu(T, p) = h(T_0) - c_p(0)T_0 - T\,[s(T_0, p_0) - c_p(0) - c_p(0)\ln T_0 + R\ln p_0] - c_p(0)T\ln T + \int_0^T c'(T)\,dT - T\int_0^T \frac{c'(T)}{T}\,dT + RT\ln p. \tag{10.18'}$$

If we choose other initial states T_1, p_1, in place of T_0 and p_0 then we have, providing that T_1, is also lower than T' and within the region of validity of (10.15),

$$\mu(T, p) = h(T_1) - c_p(0)T_1 - T\,[s(T_1, p_1) - c_p(0) - c_p(0)\ln T_1 + R\ln p_1] - c_p(0)T\ln T + \int_0^T c'(T)\,dT - T\int_0^T \frac{c'(T)}{T}\,dT + RT\ln p. \tag{10.18''}$$

The values of μ given by (10.18′) and (10·18″) are the same so that equating the right-hand sides of (10.18′) and (10.18″) and cancelling common terms we obtain

$$h(T_0) - c_p(0)T_0 - T\,[s(T_0, p_0) - c_p(0) - c_p(0)\ln T_0 + R\ln p_0] = h(T_1) - c_p(0)T_1 - T\,[s(T_1, p_1) - c_p(0) - c_p(0)\ln T_1 + R\ln p_1].$$

This can only be true at all temperatures if

$$\text{(i)}\quad h(T_0) - c_p(0)\,T_0 = h(T_1) - c_p(0)\,T_1$$

i.e. $h(0)$ is independent of the choice of T_0,

and (ii) $s(T_0,p_0) - c_p(0) - c_p(0)\ln T_0 + \boldsymbol{R}\ln p_0$

$$= s(T_1,p_1) - c_p(0) - c_p(0)\ln T_1 + \boldsymbol{R}\ln p_1$$

i.e. j is independent of the choice of T_0 and p_0.

We see then that $h(0)$ and j as defined by (10.18) have values independent of the choice of T_0 and p_0, provided T_0 lies between the limits prescribed above. The value of j clearly depends upon the units employed which are normally centigrade degrees, and atmospheres.

Since we assume, in effect, that the heat capacity is constant and equal to $c_p(0)$ in the temperature range 0 to T_0, $h(0)$ is seen to be the enthalpy *extrapolated* to the absolute zero.

Equation (10.17) may be written in a rather more convenient form by employing the transformation (4.20):

$$\frac{\mu(T,p)}{\boldsymbol{R}T} = \left[\frac{h(0)}{\boldsymbol{R}T} - \frac{c_p(0)}{\boldsymbol{R}}\ln T - \frac{1}{\boldsymbol{R}}\int_0^T \frac{dT}{T^2}\int_0^T c'(T)\,dT - j\right] + \ln p, \qquad (10.19)$$

whence (*cf.* 10.11)

$$\mu^{\dagger}(T) = h(0) - c_p(0)\,T\ln T - T\int_0^T \frac{dT}{T^2}\int_0^T c'(T)\,dT - j\,\boldsymbol{R}T. \qquad (10.20)$$

Thermodynamics, although it enables us to define the chemical constant, does not lead to numerical values. These may however be calculated using statistical mechanics which gives the relationships between the chemical constants and the structure of molecules.

Monatomic Gas.

The statistical mechanical equation for the chemical constant reduces, on insertion of the various numerical constants, to

$$j' = \frac{j}{2{\cdot}303} = -1{\cdot}587 + \tfrac{3}{2}\log_{10} M + \log_{10}\pi_0^g. \qquad (10.21)$$

In this equation M is the gram molecular weight of the gas and π_0^g is the statistical weight of the molecule in the lowest quantum state (ground state). The statistical weight may be found from spectroscopic investigations. Thus it is found spectroscopically that the ground state of the inert gases is a ^{1}S state having a statistical weight 1. On the other hand, the ground state of alkali metal atoms in the vapour is a ^{2}S state for which $\pi_0^g = 2$.

Table 10.3 gives the values of the chemical constants of several

TABLE 10.3

*Chemical Constants (j') and Vapour Pressure Constants (i') of some Monatomic Elements**

Element	j'	i'
He	−0·68	−0·626±0·065
Ne	+0·37	+0·396±0·04
A	+0·81	+0·79 ±0·04
Hg	+1·86	+1·95 ±0·06
K	+1·10	+1·11 ±0·3
Na	+0·75	+0·85 ±0·15
Cd	+1·49	+1·57 ±0·10
Zn	+1·18	+1·15 ±0·05
Pb	+1·88	+2·27 ±0·36
Ag	+1·45	+2·10 ±0·40
Cu	+1·11	+1·00 ±0·40
Mg	+0·49	+0·44 ±0·10

monatomic substances. We shall return later to consider the significance of the third column of the table.

Diatomic and Polyatomic Linear Molecules.

For these, statistical mechanics leads to the equation

$$j' = -3{\cdot}185 + \tfrac{3}{2}\log_{10} M + \log_{10}(10^{40} I) + \log_{10}\frac{\varpi_0^g}{\sigma}. \qquad (10.22)$$

In this equation I is the moment of inertia of the molecule in g.cm², σ is a symmetry number which has the simple property of being 2 when a diatomic molecule consists of two identical atoms, and 1 when the atoms are different.

Table 10.4 gives values of j' for various diatomic substances. Again the table includes values of the vapour pressure constant i' which will be considered later (*cf.* chap. XIV, § 2).

Non-linear Polyatomic Molecules.

In this case

$$j' = -3{\cdot}735 + \tfrac{3}{2}\log_{10} M + \tfrac{1}{2}\log_{10}(10^{120} I_A I_B I_C) + \log_{10}\frac{\varpi_0^g}{\sigma}, \qquad (10.23)$$

where I_A, I_B and I_C are the three principal moments of inertia of the molecule; σ is again a symmetry number depending upon the symmetry of the molecule.

We notice finally that the entropy of a perfect gas can be obtained by differentiating equation (10.17) for the chemical potential with respect to temperature (*cf.* 6.27). We can thus calculate the entropy from

* *Cf.* Eucken [17], p. 285.

TABLE 10.4

Chemical Constants (j') and Vapour Pressure Constants (i') of some Diatomic Compounds

Substance	$I \,.\, 10^{10}\, g.cm^2$	π_0^g	σ	j'	i'
H_2	0·46	1	2	−3·357	−3·685
N_2	13·6	1	2	−0·183	−0·153
O_2	19·2	3	2	+0·530	+0·547
Cl_2	108	1	2	+1·30	+1·15
Br_2	347	1	2	+2·35	+2·57
I_2	742	1	2	+2·90	+3·08
HCl	2·64	1	1	−0·420	−0·40
HBr	3·3	1	1	+0·20	+0·24
HI	4·3	1	1	+0·60	+0·65
NO	16·55	2	1	+0·549	+0·52
CO	14·9	1	1	+0·157	−0·075

quantities all of which can be determined spectroscopically (*i.e.* moments of inertia, frequencies of vibration etc.). The statistical evaluation of the entropy allows a fundamental test of the Nernst theorem, for the calculated value should be identical with that obtained calorimetrically on the basis of the Nernst theorem.*

The statistical method is particularly interesting when applied to relatively simple molecules, for in more complicated molecules there is coupling between the various degrees of freedom which renders the statistical formulae much less tractable.†

4. Perfect Gas Mixtures.

In a mixture of gases whether they are perfect or not, we *define* the partial pressure p_i of component i as the product of the total pressure and the mole fraction of i in the mixture :

$$p_i = x_i\, p. \tag{10.24}$$

It follows from this definition that

$$p = \sum_i p_i. \tag{10.25}$$

We say that a mixture of gases in volume V at temperature T, is perfect if the free energy F is equal to the sum of the free energies which the separate constituents would have if each were confined alone in the same volume at the same temperature. We can then apply equation (10.12) to obtain

$$F = \sum_i F_i(T,\, V,\, n_i) = \sum_i n_i f_i = \sum_i n_i \left(f_i^{\ddagger}(T) - \boldsymbol{R}T \ln \frac{V}{n_i} \right). \tag{10.26}$$

* *Cf.* Fowler and Guggenheim [20], chap. V.
† *Cf.* Glasstone [24], chap. VII.

Now since, (4.29),

$$p = -\left(\frac{\partial F}{\partial V}\right)_{T, n_1, \dots n_c},$$

we have for the mixture

$$p = \frac{n\mathbf{R}T}{V}, \tag{10.27}$$

which shows that a mixture of perfect gases obeys the same equation of state as pure gases :

$$pV = n\mathbf{R}T. \tag{10.27'}$$

It follows immediately from (10.24) that

$$p_i = \frac{n_i \mathbf{R}T}{V}. \tag{10.28}$$

The partial pressure of i is thus equal to the pressure which would be exerted by n_i moles of pure i in the same volume, and at the same temperature.

If we employ the molar concentration, $c_i = n_i/V$, this expression can be written

$$p_i = c_i \mathbf{R}T. \tag{10.28'}$$

Formula (10.26) gives the free energy of the mixture in terms of the variables T, V, n_1, ... n_c. All the other properties of the system can therefore be derived from this equation (*cf.* chap. IV, § 4). Thus from (*cf.* 4.29)

$$S = -\left(\frac{\partial F}{\partial T}\right)_{V, n}$$

we obtain, (noting that $\partial f_i^\ddagger(T)/\partial T = -s_i^\ddagger(T)$),

$$S = \sum_i n_i \left(s_i^\ddagger(T) - \mathbf{R} \ln \frac{n_i}{V}\right) = \sum_i S_i(T, V, n_i). \tag{10.29}$$

This is the extension of equation (10.9) to gas mixtures. It shows that the entropy of the mixture in a volume V is equal to the sum of the entropies which the individual components would have if confined separately in the same volume. Similarly by applying (4.34) to (10.26) we obtain for the total energy :

$$U = \sum_i n_i u_i(T) = \sum_i U_i(T, n_i). \tag{10.30}$$

Here the volume does not enter explicitly. The internal energy of the mixture, just as for a single gas, is independent of the volume. The same is also true of the enthalpy which, from (10.27′), is given by

$$H = U + n\mathbf{R}T,$$

If the gases can react together, the heats of reaction are given by

$$\left(\frac{\partial U}{\partial \xi}\right)_{T,V} = \sum_i \nu_i u_i(T),$$

and

$$\left(\frac{\partial H}{\partial \xi}\right)_{T,p} = \sum_i \nu_i h_i(T), \tag{10.30'}$$

and are functions of temperature only.

We now employ the pressure as independent variable. Replacing n_i/V by its value in terms of the total pressure (*cf.* 10.28 and 10.24)

$$n_i/V = p_i/\mathbf{R}T = x_i p/\mathbf{R}T,$$

we find for the entropy

$$S = \sum_i n_i [s_i^\dagger(T) - \mathbf{R} \ln p - \mathbf{R} \ln x_i], \tag{10.31}$$

which is the extension of (10.10) to the case of a mixture. We see that the entropy of the mixture is equal to the sum of the entropies of the components *taken separately at temperature T and pressure p* plus the term

$$S^M = -\sum_i n_i \mathbf{R} \ln x_i > 0, \tag{10.32}$$

which is always positive. This term is called the *entropy of mixing*. It is the sum of the partial molar entropies of mixing as defined in chapter VII (see table 7.1), each multiplied by the appropriate n_i.

5. Chemical Potentials and Affinities in a Perfect Gas Mixture.

We now evaluate the chemical potential by applying (6.15):

$$\mu_i = \left(\frac{\partial F}{\partial n_i}\right)_{T,V}$$

to (10.26). This gives

$$\mu_i = f_i^\ddagger(T) + \mathbf{R}T + \mathbf{R}T \ln \frac{n_i}{V}, \tag{10.33}$$

which may be expressed in terms of the partial pressure :

$$\boxed{\mu_i = \mu_i^\dagger(T) + \mathbf{R}T \ln p_i}, \tag{10.34}$$

in which we have written, (*cf.* 10.12″),

$$\mu_i^\dagger(T) = f_i^\ddagger(T) + \mathbf{R}T + \mathbf{R}T \ln \mathbf{R}T. \tag{10.34'}$$

This function depends solely on the temperature and is seen to be identical with the function $\mu_i^\dagger$ for pure component i as defined in (10.11).

If the substance i is the only component of the system, then p_i will be the total pressure and equation (10.34) becomes identical with (10.11) already established for a single gas.

If we now substitute for p_i in (10.34), its value in terms of the total pressure and mole fraction (10.24) we obtain

$$\boxed{\mu_i = \mu_i^0(T, p) + \boldsymbol{R}T \ln x_i}, \tag{10.35}$$

where

$$\mu_i^0(T, p) = \mu_i^\dagger(T) + \boldsymbol{R}T \ln p, \tag{10.36}$$

is the chemical potential of the *pure gas* at T and p.

We see then that a perfect gas mixture is an ideal system as defined in chapter VII § 1. The properties established generally in that chapter can be applied directly to the present case. Perfect gas mixtures differ from other ideal systems in that the function $\mu^0(T, p)$ depends upon pressure in the simple logarithmic manner given in (10.36).

Finally we express the chemical potential in terms of concentrations. Equation (10.28′) enables us to transform (10.34) into

$$\mu_i = \mu^\dagger(T) + \boldsymbol{R}T \ln \boldsymbol{R}T + \boldsymbol{R}T \ln c_i. \tag{10.37}$$

We can now make use of the above expressions for chemical potentials to calculate the affinity of a reaction in a perfect gas mixture, and to deduce the conditions for chemical equilibrium.

The affinity is given by (6.22)

$$\mathbf{A} = -\sum_i \nu_i \mu_i,$$

and we may substitute into this expression the chemical potentials in each of the three forms (10.34), (10.35), (10.37).

With the substitutions

$$\left.\begin{aligned} -\sum_i \nu_i \mu_i^\dagger(T) \qquad\qquad &= \boldsymbol{R}T \ln K_p(T) \\ -\sum_i \nu_i \mu_i^0(T, p) \qquad\qquad &= \boldsymbol{R}T \ln K_x(T, p) \\ -\sum_i \nu_i \mu_i^\dagger(T) - \nu \boldsymbol{R}T \ln \boldsymbol{R}T &= \boldsymbol{R}T \ln K_c(T), \end{aligned}\right\} \tag{10.38}$$

where ν is the algebraic sum of the stoichiometric coefficients for the reaction, the affinity can be written in the following three equivalent forms :

$$\mathbf{A} = \boldsymbol{R}T \ln \frac{K_p(T)}{p_1^{\nu_1} p_2^{\nu_2} \dots p_c^{\nu_c}}, \tag{10.39}$$

$$\mathbf{A} = \boldsymbol{R}T \ln \frac{K_x(T, p)}{x_1^{\nu_1} x_2^{\nu_2} \dots x_c^{\nu_c}}, \tag{10.40}$$

$$\mathbf{A} = \boldsymbol{R}T \ln \frac{K_c(T)}{c_1^{\nu_1} c_2^{\nu_2} \dots c_c^{\nu_c}}, \tag{10.41}$$

Equation (10.40) will be recognized as the general form for the affinity of reaction in an ideal system.

The three equilibrium constants $K_p(T)$, $K_x(T, p)$ and $K_c(T)$ are related among themselves by the formulae

$$K_x(T, p) = p^{-\nu} K_p(T), \tag{10.42}$$

$$K_c(T) = (\boldsymbol{R}T)^{-\nu} K_p(T), \tag{10.43}$$

and correspond to three forms of the law of mass action. At equilibrium we have :

$$p_1^{\nu_1} p_2^{\nu_2} \dots p_c^{\nu_c} = K_p(T), \tag{10.44}$$

$$x_1^{\nu_1} x_2^{\nu_2} \dots x_c^{\nu_c} = K_x(T, p), \tag{10.45}$$

$$c_1^{\nu_1} c_2^{\nu_2} \dots c_c^{\nu_c} = K_c(T). \tag{10.46}$$

Example :

For the dissociation of water vapour :

$$2H_2O = 2H_2 + O_2$$

we have

$$\nu_{H_2O} = -2 \,; \quad \nu_{H_2} = +2 \,; \quad \nu_{O_2} = +1 \,;$$

and

$$\nu = \Sigma\, \nu_i = +1.$$

At equilibrium

$$x_{H_2O}^{-2}\, x_{H_2}^{2}\, x_{O_2} = K_x(T, p)$$

and the three equilibrium constants are related by

$$K_x(T, p) = \frac{K_p(T)}{p} = \frac{\boldsymbol{R}T}{p} K_c(T).$$

$K_x(T, p)$ is thus inversely proportional to the pressure.

6. Influence of Temperature on Equilibrium Constants.

Since a perfect gas mixture is an ideal system, van't Hoff's equation (7.37) is valid. Because of (10.42) we can replace $K_x(T, p)$ by $K_p(T)$ to give

$$\frac{d \ln K_p(T)}{dT} = \frac{1}{\boldsymbol{R}T^2} \left(\frac{\partial H}{\partial \xi}\right)_{T, p}, \tag{10.47}$$

while in terms of $K_c(T)$,

$$\frac{d \ln K_c(T)}{dT} = \frac{1}{\boldsymbol{R}T^2} \left(\frac{\partial H}{\partial \xi}\right)_{T, p} - \frac{\nu}{T} = \frac{1}{\boldsymbol{R}T^2} \left(\frac{\partial U}{\partial \xi}\right)_{T, V}. \tag{10.48}$$

Integration of (10.47) between T_0 and T gives

$$\ln K_p(T) - \ln K_p(T_0) = \int_{T_0}^{T} \frac{1}{\boldsymbol{R}T^2} \left(\frac{\partial H}{\partial \xi}\right)_{T, p} dT. \tag{10.49}$$

We have already evaluated the righthand side as a function of temperature in connection with the effect of temperature on the reaction affinity (*cf*. chap. II, § 5; chap IV, § 2, 3; chap. VII, § 10). We shall not repeat the detailed results here, but only recall that if the heat of reaction is independent of temperature

$$\ln K_p(T) = -\frac{1}{RT}\left(\frac{\partial H}{\partial \xi}\right)_{T,p} + \text{constant}. \tag{10.50}$$

An example of a reaction for which this equation holds is the dissociation of iodine molecules in the vapour;

$$I_2 = 2I$$

which was first studied by Bodenstein* and more recently by Perlman and Rollefson.† For this equilibrium $\ln K_p$ is a linear function of $1/T$ over a wide temperature range, (*cf*. fig. 10.1).

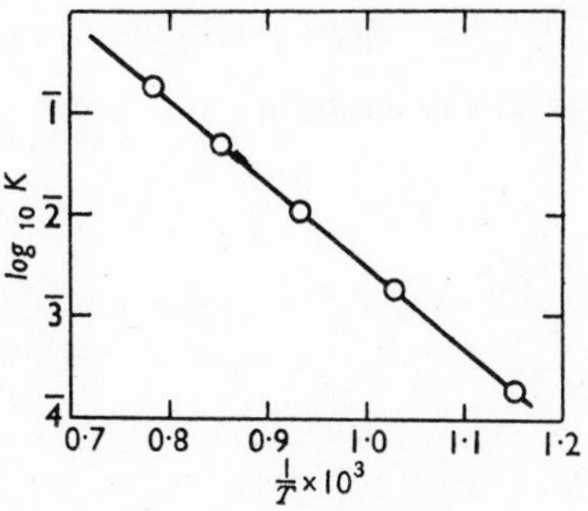

FIG. 10.1. $\log_{10} K$ as a function of $1/T$ for the dissociation of I_2.†

Equation (10.50) is often useful as a first approximation if the temperature range is not too great.

7. Calculation of the Affinity for a given State of a System relative to the Standard Affinity.

It follows from (10.42) that

$$\frac{K(T,p)}{K(T,1)} = p^{-\nu},$$

and since (7.79),‡ $\mathbf{A}^0 = RT \ln K(T,p)$, we have

$$\mathbf{A}^0(T,p) = \mathbf{A}^0(T,1) - RT \ln p^{\nu},$$

and the affinity $\mathbf{A}$ is then given by (10.40):

$$\mathbf{A}(T,p) = \mathbf{A}^0(T,1) - RT \ln p^{\nu} - RT \ln x_1^{\nu_1} x_2^{\nu_2} \dots x_c^{\nu_c}. \tag{10.50'}$$

This equation enables us to calculate the affinity for any values of T, p, $x_1 \dots x_c$ when $\mathbf{A}^\circ(T,1)$ is known.

Example: Synthesis of Ammonia.

$$N_2 + 3H_2 = 2NH_3.$$

We assume that the gas mixture obeys the perfect gas laws. By reference to table 8.1 we find that the standard affinity of this reaction at 298·16 °K and 1 atm. is equal to

$$\mathbf{A}^0 = 2 \times 3{,}976 = 7{,}952 \text{ cal./mole of } N_2.$$

* *Cf*. Eucken [17], p. 307.
† M. L. Perlman and G. K. Rollefson, *J. Chem. Phys.*, **9**, 362 (1941).
‡ Perfect gas mixtures are ideal over the whole concentration range so that $\mathbf{A}^{\ominus} = \mathbf{A}^0$.

We have also seen (*cf.* 2.33′) that the heat of reaction for this synthesis is given by

$$(\partial H/\partial \xi)_{T,p} = -18250 - 15{\cdot}10T + 7{\cdot}954 \times 10^{-3}T^2 - 1{\cdot}34 \times 10^{-6}T^3$$

Thus

$$\frac{d\left(\dfrac{\mathbf{A}^0}{T}\right)}{dT} = -\frac{18250}{T^2} - \frac{15{\cdot}10}{T} + 7{\cdot}954 \times 10^{-3} - 1{\cdot}34 \times 10^{-6}T$$

and on integration

$$\frac{\mathbf{A}^0(T,p)}{T} = \frac{18250}{T} - 15{\cdot}10 \ln T + 7{\cdot}954 \times 10^{-3}T - 0{\cdot}67 \times 10^{-6}T^2 + I(p)$$

where $I(p)$ is the integration constant and may depend upon p.

Changing to decadic logarithms we obtain

$$\mathbf{A}^0(T,p) = 18250 - 34{\cdot}78T \log_{10} T + 7{\cdot}954 \times 10^{-3}T^2 - 0{\cdot}67 \times 10^{-6}T^3 + I(p)T$$

When $T = 298{\cdot}16$ °K and $p = 1$ atm. this equation must give $\mathbf{A}^0(298{\cdot}16$, 1 atm.$) = 7{,}952$ cal.; the integration constant at 1 atm. is therefore

$$I = 49{\cdot}18$$

giving

$$\mathbf{A}^0(T,1) = 18250 - 34{\cdot}78T \log_{10} T + 7{\cdot}954 \times 10^{-3}T^2 - 0{\cdot}67 \times 10^{-6}T^3 + 49{\cdot}18T.$$

Using (10.50′) we can now calculate, for example, the affinity at 400 °C ($T = 673$ °K) for $p = 100$ atm., in a gas mixture of composition

$$x_{NH_3} = 0{\cdot}2,\ x_{N_2} = 0{\cdot}2,\ x_{H_2} = 0{\cdot}6.$$

We find that

$$\mathbf{A}(673\ °\text{K}, 100\ \text{atm.}) = -11447 - 2{\cdot}303\,\mathbf{R}T \log_{10}(100)^{-2}$$
$$- 2{\cdot}303\,\mathbf{R}T \log_{10}(0{\cdot}6)^{-3}(0{\cdot}2)^{-1}(0{\cdot}2)^2,$$

which gives

$$\mathbf{A}(673\ °\text{K}, 100\ \text{atm.}) = 968\ \text{cal./mole of } N_2.$$

The affinity is thus positive under these conditions and further reaction will occur to increase the concentration of ammonia. The low value of the affinity shows, however, that the composition considered is not far removed from equilibrium. We can show quite easily that the mixture will attain equilibrium at 400 °C and 100 atm. when $x_{NH_3} = 0{\cdot}251$, $x_{N_2} = 0{\cdot}188$, $x_{H_2} = 0{\cdot}562$, since for this composition $\mathbf{A} = 0$. These figures are confirmed experimentally.

8. Calculation of Equilibrium Constants from Entropies and Heats of Formation.

The standard affinity of reaction is given in terms of heat and entropy changes by (7.54).

For ideal systems however the standard heat of reaction is equal to the total heat of reaction (*cf.* chap. VII, § 7) so that we may replace

$h^0_{T,p}$ by $h_{T,p} = (\partial H/\partial \xi)$. Furthermore the standard affinity and equilibrium constant are related by $\mathbf{A}^0 = RT \ln K_x(T, p)$ so that

$$\ln K_x(T, p) = -\frac{1}{RT}\left(\frac{\partial H}{\partial \xi}\right)_{T,p} + \frac{1}{R}\left(\frac{\partial S^0}{\partial \xi}\right)_{T,p} = -\frac{h_{T,p}}{RT} + \frac{s^0_{T,p}}{R}. \qquad (10.51)$$

If the temperature is not too far removed from 298·16 °K we may, to a first approximation, replace the heat and entropy terms in (10.51) by their standard values at 298·16° which may be calculated from the data in table 8.1. Thus we have, approximately, at 1 atm. pressure,

$$\ln K_x(T, 1) = -\frac{h^0_{298\cdot 1,1}}{RT} + \frac{s^0_{298\cdot 1,1}}{R}, \qquad (10.52)$$

This equation has the same form as 10.50, but we have now expressed the integration constant explicitly.

To obtain a more accurate equation we must take account of the fact that both $h_{T,p}$ and $s_{T,p}$ depend upon the temperature. The variation of $h_{T,p}$ with temperature is given by Kirchhoff's equation (2.32) so that

$$h_{T,p} = h_{298\cdot 1,p} + \int_{298\cdot 1}^{T} \sum_i \nu_i c_{p,i} \, dT.$$

Furthermore, from (4.2),

$$\frac{\partial}{\partial T}\left(\frac{\partial S}{\partial \xi}\right)_{T,p} = \frac{\partial}{\partial \xi}\left(\frac{\partial S}{\partial T}\right)_{p,\xi} = \frac{\partial}{\partial \xi}\frac{C_p}{T} = \frac{\sum_i \nu_i c_{p,i}}{T}. \qquad (10.53)$$

Thus (10.51) can now be written in the accurate form, at unit pressure,

$$\ln K_x(T, 1) = \ln K_p(T) = -\frac{h^0_{298\cdot 1,1} + \int_{298\cdot 1}^{T} \sum_i \nu_i c_{p,i} \, dT}{RT} + \frac{1}{R}\left[s^0_{298\cdot 1,1} + \int_{298\cdot 1}^{T} \frac{\sum_i \nu_i c_{p,i}}{T} \, dT\right]. \qquad (10.54)$$

In the simplest case $\sum_i \nu_i c_{p,i}$ can be assumed constant in the temperature range concerned so that

$$\ln K_p(T) = -\frac{h^0_{298\cdot 1,1}}{RT} + \frac{s^0_{298\cdot 1,1}}{R} + \frac{1}{R}\sum_i \nu_i c_{p,i}\left[\ln \frac{T}{298} - 1 + \frac{298}{T}\right]. \qquad (10.55)$$

This equation was derived by Ulich* who also pointed out that, within an accuracy of a few per cent and over a wide temperature range the term in square brackets can be replaced by $(0{\cdot}0007T - 0{\cdot}20)$.

Example : Dissociation of Water Vapour.†

Let us consider the reaction

$$2H_2O(g) \rightarrow 2H_2(g) + O_2(g).$$

* Ulich [46], p. 222 ; *cf.* Rey [39], p. 71.

† *Cf.* Eucken [17], p. 329 ; for other examples see E. Briner, *Helv. Chim. Acta*, **25**, 1515, (1942).

The standard entropies are given in table 8.1 and from them we calculate :

$$s^0_{298\cdot1,1} = 2 \times 31\cdot2 + 49 - 2 \times 45\cdot1 = 21\cdot2 \text{ cal./deg.}$$

The standard heat of reaction is calculated also from the tables as

$$h^0_{298\cdot1,1} = -115{,}600 \text{ cal.}$$

Hence the equilibrium constant is given approximately by

$$\log_{10} K_p(T) = -\frac{25250}{T} + 4\cdot63. \tag{10.56}$$

Table 10.5 gives the observed values of $\log_{10} K$ and those calculated by the above formula based on (10.52). The deviation between the two sets of values increases as we move away from 298 °K.

We now apply the more accurate equation (10.55), using the following approximate specific heats ;

$$c_{p,\,H_2O} \simeq 9\cdot25\ ;\ c_{p,\,H_2} \simeq 7\cdot25\ ;\ c_{p,\,O_2} \simeq 7\cdot5 \text{ cal./deg. mole.}$$

These give

$$\sum_i \nu_i c_{p,\,i} \simeq 3\cdot5 \text{ cal./deg.}$$

so that a more accurate equation is

$$\log_{10} K_p(T) = -\frac{25250}{T} + 4\cdot63 + \frac{3\cdot5}{4\cdot573}(0\cdot0007T - 0\cdot20). \tag{10.57}$$

As shown by the figures in the last column of table 10.5, this equation is in much closer agreement with the observed equilibrium constants.

TABLE 10.5

T	$\log_{10} K$ (*obs.*)	$\log_{10} K$ (*calc.*) (10·52)	$\log_{10} K$ (*calc.*) (10·55)
290	−82·17	−82·53	−82·53
1 300	−14·01	−14·79	−14·25
1 500	−11·42	−12·22	−11·57
1 705	− 9·28	−10·63	− 9·41

9. Equilibrium Constants and Chemical Constants.

Returning to equation (10.38)

$$\ln K_p(T) = -\sum_i \nu_i \frac{\mu^\dagger(T)}{RT},$$

and recalling that $\mu^\dagger(T)$ is given in terms of the chemical constant j by (10.20), we see that the equilibrium constant can be put into the form :

$$\ln K_p(T) = -\frac{h_{0,\,p}}{RT} + \frac{1}{R}\sum_i \nu_i c_{p,\,i}(0) \ln T + \frac{1}{R}\int_0^T \frac{dT}{T^2}\int_0^T \sum_i \nu_i c_i'(T)\, dT + J, \tag{10.58}$$

where we have put

$$J = \sum_i \nu_i j_i, \tag{10.59}$$

while

$$h_{0,p} = \sum_i \nu_i h_i(0) \tag{10.60}$$

is effectively the heat of reaction extrapolated to the absolute zero (*cf.* p. 122).

Equation (10.58) shows how the chemical constants, which determine the value of J, enter into the equilibrium constant. An experimental determination of J for a given reaction can therefore be compared with the value deduced from the various chemical constants as calculated on the basis of statistical mechanics (Tables 10.3 and 10.4). In practice, when using decadic logarithms, it is more convenient to use the integration constant

$$J' = \frac{J}{2{\cdot}303} = \Sigma\, \nu_i j_i'.$$

Thus for the reaction $H_2 + Cl_2 = 2HCl$ we find that the chemical constants j' for the species involved are

$$j'_{H_2} = -3{\cdot}36\ ;\ j'_{Cl_2} = 1{\cdot}30\ ;\ j'_{HCl} = -0{\cdot}42$$

so that $J' = 1{\cdot}22$.

The experimental data indicate a value lying between 0·92 and 1·32.

In table 10.6 are collected the observed and calculated values of J' for several simple gas reactions. The agreement is satisfactory and within the rather large experimental error.

Table 10.6

Observed and Calculated Values of

$$J' = \sum_i \nu_i j_i'$$

Reaction	*J′ calc.*	*J′ obs. lies between the extreme values*	
$2NH_3 \rightarrow 3H_2 + N_2$	−7·16	−6·94	−7·14
$2H_2O \rightarrow 2H_2 + O_2$	−2·64	−2·35	−2·55
$2HCl \rightarrow H_2 + Cl_2$	−1·22	−0·92	−1·32
$2HI \rightarrow H_2 + I_2$	−1·57	−1·38	−1·62
$2NO \rightarrow N_2 + O_2$	+0·75	+0·65	+1·25
$2CO_2 \rightarrow 2CO + O_2$	−0·62	−0·55	−1·05
$H_2 + CO_2 \rightarrow CO + H_2O$	+0·91	+0·70	+0·94
$2H_2O + 2Cl_2 \rightarrow 4HCl + O_2$	−0·24	−0·06	−0·34
$CH_4 + 2H_2O \rightarrow 4H_2 + CO_2$	−7·18	−6·75	−7·25

10. Maximum Yield from a Reaction.

Let us consider a system containing initially n_1^0, n_2^0 ... n_c^0 moles of the various components. The concentration of a given component is (*cf.* 1.41)

$$c_i = \frac{n_i}{V} = \frac{n_i^0 + \nu_i \xi}{V}, \tag{10.61}$$

so that at equilibrium, (10.46) becomes

$$(n_1^0 + \nu_1 \xi)^{\nu_1} (n_2^0 + \nu_2 \xi)^{\nu_2} \dots (n_c^0 + \nu_c \xi)^{\nu_c} = V^{\nu} K_c(T). \tag{10.62}$$

Thus if we know the initial concentrations we can calculate ξ the extent of reaction at equilibrium. The stoichiometric coefficients of the reactants may be written $\nu_1 \dots \nu_j$; these are all negative, while for the products we have $\nu_{j+1} \dots \nu_c$ which are positive. Let us suppose we choose $n_{j+1}^0 \dots n_c^0$ to be zero and we wish to find the initial concentrations of the reactants which will give the greatest value of ξ, that is the greatest yield of products. For the moment we fix only the total number of molecules initially present in a given volume V at temperature T:

$$\sum_{i=1}^{i=j} n_i^0 = n. \tag{10.63}$$

Taking logarithms in (10.62) we obtain,

$$\sum_{i=1}^{i=c} \nu_i \ln (n_i^0 + \nu_i \xi) = constant, \tag{10.64}$$

whence taking the differential of (10.64)

$$\sum_{i=1}^{i=c} \frac{\nu_i}{n_i^0 + \nu_i \xi} \nu_i \, \delta\xi + \sum_{i=1}^{i=j} \frac{\nu_i}{n_i^0 + \nu_i \xi} \delta n_i^0 = 0. \tag{10.65}$$

If ξ is a maximum the differential $\delta\xi$ of the function $\xi(n_1^0 \dots n_j^0)$ is zero and (10.65) reduces to

$$\sum_{i=1}^{i=j} \frac{\nu_i}{n_i^0 + \nu_i \xi} \delta n_i^0 = 0. \tag{10.66}$$

We have specified however that the total initial number of molecules is n so that

$$\sum_{i=1}^{i=j} \delta n_i^0 = 0. \tag{10.67}$$

To find the condition that (10.66) and (10.67) are simultaneously satisfied for all values of $\delta n_1^0 \ldots \delta n_j^0$ we employ Lagrange's method of undetermined multipliers* which gives

$$\sum_{i=1}^{i=j} \frac{\nu_i}{n_i^0 + \nu_i \xi} \delta n_i^0 + \lambda \sum_{i=1}^{i=j} \delta n_i^0 = 0, \tag{10.68}$$

where λ is the undetermined multiplier.

For (10.68) to be satisfied for all $\delta n_1^0 \ldots \delta n_j^0$ we must have the j conditions

$$\frac{\nu_i}{n_i^0 + \nu_i \xi} + \lambda = 0 \quad (i = 1, \ldots j) \tag{10.69}$$

satisfied. Since the coefficients $\nu_1 \ldots \nu_j$ are negative these conditions may be written

$$\frac{n_1^0}{|\nu_1|} = \frac{n_2^0}{|\nu_2|} = \ldots = \frac{n_j^0}{|\nu_j|} = \frac{1}{\lambda} + \xi. \tag{10.70}$$

Thus to obtain a maximum value of ξ corresponding to equilibrium, the initial number of moles $n_1^0 \ldots n_j^0$ must be chosen proportional to the corresponding stoichiometric coefficients $\nu_1 \ldots \nu_j$.†

By taking the sum (10.63) we see that

$$n = \{|\nu_1| + |\nu_2| + \ldots + |\nu_j|\} \left(\frac{1}{\lambda} + \xi\right)$$

or

$$\frac{1}{\lambda} + \xi = \frac{n}{|\nu_1| + |\nu_2| + \ldots + |\nu_j|}.$$

Thus the initial composition leading to the maximum yield in the reaction is given by

$$\left.\begin{aligned} n_1^0 &= \frac{\nu_1 n}{|\nu_1| + |\nu_2| + \ldots + |\nu_j|}, \\ &\vdots \\ n_j^0 &= \frac{\nu_j n}{|\nu_1| + |\nu_2| + \ldots + |\nu_j|}, \\ n_{j+1}^0 &= 0, \\ &\vdots \\ n_c^0 &= 0. \end{aligned}\right\} \tag{10.71}$$

* *Cf. e.g.* G. S. Rushbrooke, *Introduction to Statistical Mechanics*, (Oxford, 1949) Appendix III.

† Th. De Donder and G. van Lerberghe, *Bull. Ac. Roy. Belg.* (*Cl. Sc.*), (5), **12**, 151 (1926).

11. Partial Molar Quantities in a Mixture and in a Pure Gas.

The partial molar quantities in a perfect gas mixture are given by

$$u_i = \left(\frac{\partial U}{\partial n_i}\right)_{T,p} ; \quad s_i = \left(\frac{\partial S}{\partial n_i}\right)_{T,p} ; \quad h_i = \left(\frac{\partial H}{\partial n_i}\right)_{T,p} ; \quad \mu_i = \left(\frac{\partial G}{\partial n_i}\right)_{T,p} . \tag{10.72}$$

Now consider the partial (mean) molar quantities of i if n_i moles are placed *alone* in the same volume V and at the same temperature T. If we call these $(u_i)_s$, $(s_i)_s$, $(h_i)_s$ and $(\mu_i)_s$, then we wish to show that

$$u_i = (u_i)_s ; \quad \mu_i = (\mu_i)_s ; \tag{10.73}$$

$$h_i = (h_i)_s ; \quad s_i = (s_i)_s . \tag{10.74}$$

This property does not apply to all partial molar quantities, for

$$v_i \neq (v_i)_s. \tag{10.75}$$

This is seen immediately since in the mixture

$$\left.\begin{aligned} &v_i = (\partial V/\partial n_i)_{T,p} = RT/p, \\ &\text{while in the pure gas} \quad (v_i)_s = RT/p_i. \end{aligned}\right\} \tag{10.76}$$

The first formula in (10.73) is obtained by differentiating (10.30). The second follows from (10.34) since, when the component is alone in the volume V, it exerts a pressure p_i.

Furthermore

$$h_i = u_i + pv_i \quad \text{and} \quad (h_i)_s = (u_i)_s + p_i(v_i)_s.$$

so that, from (10.76) and since $u_i = (u_i)_s$,

$$h_i = (h_i)_s.$$

Finally, since

$$\mu_i = h_i - Ts_i ; \quad (\mu_i)_s = (h_i)_s - T(s_i)_s,$$

it follows also that

$$s_i = (s_i)_s.$$

CHAPTER XI

REAL GASES

1. Evaluation of Thermodynamic Functions from the Equation of State.

The equation of state of a gas can be obtained provided that we know one or other of the thermodynamic potentials F or G. Thus if we know $F(T, V, n_1, \dots n_c)$ then equation (4.29),

$$p = -\frac{\partial F}{\partial V}, \tag{11.1}$$

gives the required relation between the pressure and $T, V, n_1, \dots n_c$. Similarly, if $G(T, p, n_1, \dots n_c)$ is known, then from

$$V = \frac{\partial G}{\partial p}, \tag{11.2}$$

we obtain V as a function of $T, p, n_1, \dots n_c$.

Thus, for example, if we could show that the free energy of a perfect gas was of the form (*cf.* 10.12)

$$F(T, V) = n\left[f^{\ddagger}(T) + \boldsymbol{R}T \ln \frac{n}{V}\right], \tag{11.3}$$

we could obtain the equation of state

$$p = \frac{n\boldsymbol{R}T}{V} \tag{11.4}$$

by differentiating in accordance with (11.1).

In practice of course, F and G are not susceptible to direct experimental determination. The easily observable properties of a gas are usually summarized in the form of an equation of state.* We must therefore develop a method of using the equation of state to calculate the thermodynamic functions of the gas.†

Let us consider a mixture of real gases described by the variables $T, V, n_1 \dots n_c$. By integrating (11.1) between V_0 and V we have

$$F(T, V, n_1, \dots n_c) = F(T, V_0, n_1, \dots n_c) - \int_{V_0}^{V} p\, dV.$$

* *Cf.* J. Otto, *Handbuch der Experimentalphysik*, VIII 2 (1929); for high pressure determinations *cf.* P. W. Bridgman, *Rev. Mod. Phys.* **18**, 1 (1948); for helium *cf.* W. H. Keesom, *Helium* (London, 1942).

† L. J. Gillespie, *J. Amer. Chem. Soc.*, **47**, 305, (1925); Th. De Donder, *C. R.*, **130**, 1922 (1925); for a general review *cf.* J. A. Beattie, *Chem. Rev.* **44**, 141 (1949). This latter paper contains a very complete bibliography of the thermodynamics of real gases.

Now if $V_0 \to \infty$, then $F(T, V_0, n_1 \dots n_c)$ tends towards the free energy of the corresponding perfect gas, so that we may write

$$F(T, V, n_1, \dots n_c) = \lim_{V_0 \to \infty} F^{\text{id}}(T, V_0, n_1, \dots n_c) - \lim_{V_0 \to \infty} \int_{V_0}^{V} p\, dV, \quad (11.5)$$

where the superscript " id " denotes, as before, a function corresponding to a perfect, or ideal, gas mixture.

For a perfect gas (11.5) takes the form

$$F^{\text{id}}(T, V, n_1, \dots n_c) = \lim_{V_0 \to \infty} F^{\text{id}}(T, V_0, n_1, \dots n_c) - \lim_{V_0 \to \infty} \int_{V_0}^{V} p^{\text{id}}\, dV \quad (11.6)$$

where p^{id} is the pressure exerted by a perfect gas mixture under the specified conditions of $T, V, n_1, \dots n_c$.

By subtraction of (11.6) from (11.5)

$$F(T, V, n_1, \dots n_c) = F^{\text{id}}(T, V, n_1, \dots n_c) - \lim_{V_0 \to \infty} \int_{V_0}^{V} (p - p^{\text{id}})\, dV. \quad (11.7)$$

This equation allows us to calculate F if we know the equation of state in the form of p as a fuuction of $T, V, n_1 \dots n_c$ and also the free energy of the corresponding perfect gas.

Similarly we find

$$G(T, p, n_1, \dots n_c) = G^{\text{id}}(T, p, n_1, \dots n_c) - \lim_{p_0 \to 0} \int_{p_0}^{p} (V - V^{\text{id}})\, dp, \quad (11.8)$$

which enables us to obtain G when we know the equation of state $V(T, p, n_1, \dots n_c)$ and the Gibbs free energy of the corresponding perfect gas.

The chemical potential of component i is obtained by differentiating (11.8) with respect to n_i at constant T, p (*cf.* 6.15) :

$$\mu_i = \mu_i^{\text{id}} + \lim_{p_0 \to 0} \int_{p_0}^{p} (v_i - v_i^{\text{id}})\, dp, \quad (11.9)$$

where for the perfect gas,

$$v_i^{\text{id}} = \boldsymbol{R}T/p.$$

Equation (11.9) shows how the equation of state affects the chemical potential, and enables us to calculate the influence of deviations from the perfect gas laws upon the position of chemical equilibrium. This is most readily achieved by substituting into equation (6.22), which gives the affinity in terms of the chemical potentials :

$$\mathbf{A} = \mathbf{A}^{\text{id}} - \sum_i \nu_i \int_0^p (v_i - v_i^{\text{id}})\, dp, \quad (11.10)$$

where to simplify the notation we have written the lower limit of integration as zero. The same equation is obtained if we differentiate (11.8) with respect to ξ, the extent of reaction.

We may now define an equilibrium parameter K by the equation

$$\mathbf{A} = RT \ln \frac{K}{p_1^{\nu_1} p_2^{\nu_2} \dots p_c^{\nu_c}} \tag{11.11}$$

where $p_i = px_i$ is the partial pressure of component i, (*cf.* 10.24). If the gas were perfect the value of K would be $K_p^{\mathrm{id}}(T)$ and would be independent of the initial gas composition ; the relation between K and $K_p^{\mathrm{id}}(T)$ is given by

$$\mathbf{A} - \mathbf{A}^{\mathrm{id}} = RT \ln \frac{K}{K_p^{\mathrm{id}}(T)} = -\sum_i \nu_i \int_0^p (v_i - v_i^{\mathrm{id}})\, dp. \tag{11.12}$$

This formula shows clearly the influence of the equation of state on the position of chemical equilibrium ; we shall work out an example later in this chapter. We note that the parameter K, which is a " pseudo-constant " of equilibrium, is a function not only of T and p, but also of the mole fractions of the various components.

2. Virial Coefficients.

In the first place we shall restrict our discussion to pure gases, and later indicate the extension to mixed gases.

The pressure of a gas can be represented with a high degree of accuracy by a series in powers of $1/v$, where v is the molar volume V/n :

$$p = \frac{RT}{v}\left(1 + \frac{B}{v} + \frac{C}{v^2} + \dots\right), \tag{11.13}$$

in which $B, C, \dots$ are functions of temperature only. The number of terms needed to represent the experimental data within the accuracy of the measurements varies from two to four depending upon the temperature, and upon the pressure range examined. The coefficients $B, C, \dots$ are called the second, third, ... virial coefficients.

For a slightly imperfect gas we need only retain the first two terms of the expansion giving

$$p = \frac{nRT}{V}\left(1 + \frac{Bn}{V}\right). \tag{11.14}$$

The second virial coefficient has the dimensions of a volume per mole. The unit often chosen is the *Amagat unit* which is by definition the molar volume of the gas at 0 °C and 1 atm. The exact value of this unit depends upon the gas considered but is approximately equal to $2{\cdot}24 \times 10^4$ cm.^{3}/mole. Alternatively, it is now becoming customary to give B directly in terms of cm.^{3}/mole.

The following table gives the second virial coefficient B as a function of temperature for several common gases.

TABLE 11.1

Second Virial Coefficient in Amagat Units★

T °K	$10^4 . B$ in Amagat units				
	He	Ne	A	H_2	N_2
65·1	—	−9·35	—	−8·18	—
71·5	4·58	—	—	—	—
89·9	4·81	—	—	—	—
90·0	4·73	—	—	−2·47	—
90·5	—	−3·65	—	—	—
123	—	0·04	—	1·31	—
126·5	5·53	—	—	—	—
143	—	—	—	—	−35·6
169·7	5·89	—	—	—	—
173	—	2·88	−28·7	4·08	−23·1
223	—	4·06	−16·9	5·39	−11·8
273	5·29	4·75	− 9·86	6·24	− 4·61
323	5·23	—	− 4·92	6·76	− 0·11
373	5·10	5·29	− 1·92	6·94	2·74
423	—	—	0·52	—	5·14
473	4·93	5·82	2·08	7·00	6·85
573	4·69	6·14	5·01	—	9·21
673	4·54	6·12	6·83	—	10·5

The second virial coefficient is negative at low temperatures but increases and becomes positive at higher temperatures. The transition temperature at which $B=0$ is called the *Boyle temperature*.

Statistical mechanics enables us to express the virial coefficients in terms of integrals which depend upon the law of interaction between the molecules of the gas.† The potential energy of interaction $\epsilon(r)$ between two molecules is shown schematically in fig. 11.1 as a function of the distance r between their centres of gravity. As the molecules move together the potential energy first decreases, corresponding to an attraction, passes through a minimum at $r=r^*$ and then increases rapidly toward infinity as the molecules come even closer together and repel one another. The analytical form of the potential energy curve can be represented approximately by the superposition of an attractive potential which varies as r^{-6}, and a repulsive potential varying very rapidly with r, as r^{-12} or e^{-kr}. In view of the very rapid increase in the

★ See Fowler and Guggenheim, [20], p. 283 for the bibliography.
† *Cf.* Mayer and Mayer, [34].

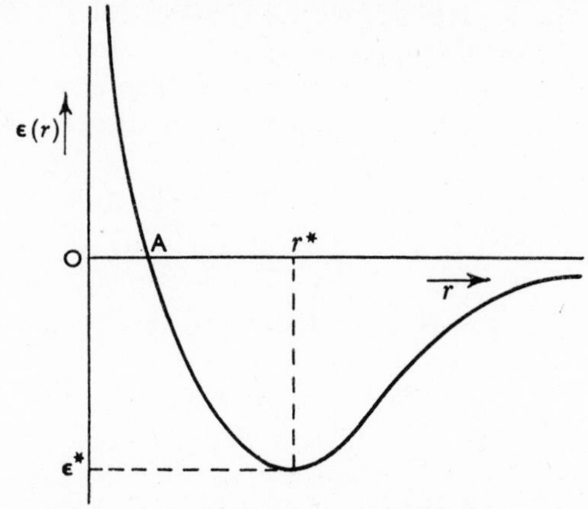

FIG. 11.1. Schematic representation of potential energy of molecular interaction, as function of intermolecular distance r.

repulsive potential at close distances of approach it is possible, for approximate calculations, to replace it by a potential which is zero for $r > D$ and infinite for $r < D$. D is thus the diameter of the molecules which are to be regarded as rigid spheres. The potential energy thus has the form shown in fig. 11.2.

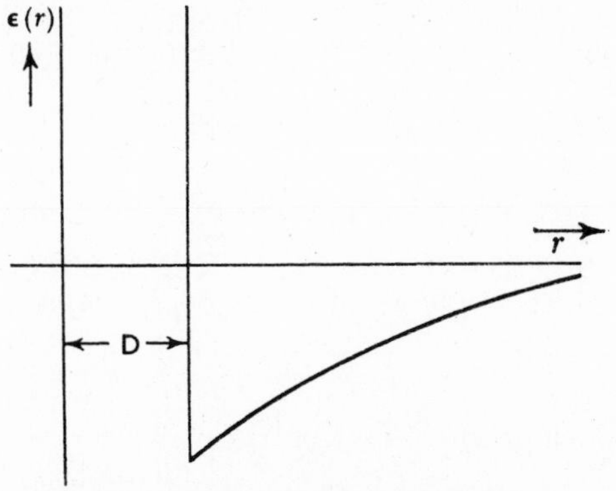

FIG. 11.2. Schematic representation of potential energy of molecular interaction (rigid spheres approximation).

The equation, which may be derived on the basis of statistical mechanics, between the second virial coefficient and the interaction energy has the simple form

$$B(T) = \frac{N}{2} \int_{\infty}^{0} (1 - e^{-\epsilon(r)/kT})\, 4\pi r^2\, dr, \tag{11.15}$$

where N is Avogadro's Number. This enables us either to calculate the second virial coefficient from a knowledge of a theoretical form of

$\epsilon(r)$; or to evaluate $\epsilon(r)$ and more particularly the r^* and the depth of the minimum ϵ^* from measurements of $B(T)$ at a series of temperatures.* The fact that $B(T)$ is negative at low temperatures and positive at higher temperatures shows that at low temperatures it is the values of r for which $\epsilon(r)$ is negative which determine the value of the integral (11.15), while at high temperatures the range in which $\epsilon(r)$ is positive plays a more important part. It is also possible to express the other virial coefficients in terms of $\epsilon(r)$. For example, expressions for the third virial coefficient have been derived by de Boer,† and by Montroll and Mayer.‡

The free energy of a slightly imperfect gas may be evaluated easily in terms of the second virial coefficient. Using (11.14) in (11.7) we obtain

$$F = F^{\text{id}} + n^2 \frac{\boldsymbol{R}TB}{V}, \tag{11.16}$$

and

$$\mu = \left(\frac{\partial F}{\partial n}\right)_{T,V} = \mu^{\text{id}}(T, V, n) + \frac{2\boldsymbol{R}TBn}{V}. \tag{11.17}$$

The chemical potential of a perfect gas was obtained in equation (10.11) as

$$\mu^{\text{id}} = \mu^{\dagger}(T) + \boldsymbol{R}T \ln p^{\text{id}},$$

where p^{id} represents the pressure exerted by n molecules of a perfect gas in a volume V, that is $p^{\text{id}} = n\boldsymbol{R}T/V$. Substituting in (11.17) we have

$$\mu = \mu^{\dagger}(T) + \boldsymbol{R}T \ln \frac{n\boldsymbol{R}T}{V} + \frac{2\boldsymbol{R}TBn}{V}. \tag{11.18}$$

The molar entropy of the gas is given by

$$s = \frac{S}{n} = -\frac{1}{n}\left(\frac{\partial F}{\partial T}\right)_{V,n} = s^{\text{id}} - \frac{n\boldsymbol{R}}{V}\left(B + T\frac{dB}{dT}\right); \tag{11.19}$$

s^{id} is the entropy which the gas would have at the same T and V if it behaved as a perfect gas, and can be calculated from (11.19) if we measure s calorimetrically (*cf.* chap. IX) and know the equation of state. The corrections employed in the numerical calculations in chap. IX were evaluated in a similar way.

Alternatively instead of expanding the pressure of a gas as a power series in $1/V$, we may express the volume as a power series in p:

$$V = \frac{n\boldsymbol{R}T}{p}(1 + B'p + C'p^2 + \dots), \tag{11.20}$$

where B', C' ... are functions of temperature.

* *Cf.* Mayer and Mayer, *loc. cit.*; Fowler and Guggenheim [20], chap. VII.
† J. de Boer, *Thesis* (Amsterdam, 1940).
‡ E. W. Montroll and J. E. Mayer, *J. Chem. Phys.* 9, 626 (1941).

Again for a slightly imperfect gas we can neglect terms in p^2 and calculate the Gibbs free energy.

Since $V^{id} = nRT/p$, we have

$$V - V^{id} = nRTB'$$

and from (11.8)

$$G(T, p, n) = G^{id}(T, p, n) + \lim_{p_0 \to 0} \int_{p_0}^{p} nRTB'\, dp$$

$$= G^{id}(T, p, n) + nRTB'p. \tag{11.21}$$

Since for one component system

$$G = n\mu, \tag{11.22}$$

$$\mu(T, p) = \mu^{id}(T, p) + RTB'p. \tag{11.23}$$

Replacing $\mu^{id}(T, p)$ by the value given by (10.11) we have

$$\mu = \mu^{\dagger}(T) + RT \ln p + B'RTp. \tag{11.24}$$

The coefficients B', C' ... introduced in (11.20) can be expressed in terms of the virial coefficients in (11.13). This is readily seen for the second virial coefficient since from (11.13)

$$\frac{pv}{RT} = 1 + \frac{B}{v} + \ldots$$

while from (11.20)

$$\frac{pv}{RT} = 1 + B'p + \ldots$$

so that neglecting higher terms,

$$B = B'pv.$$

To a close approximation we have therefore

$$B = B'RT. \tag{11.25}$$

Instead of (11.20) we can thus write, to this approximation,

$$v = \frac{RT}{p}\left(1 + \frac{B}{RT}\, p\right) \tag{11.25'}$$

or

$$v = v^{id} + B. \tag{11.25''}$$

The second virial coefficient is thus approximately equal to the difference between the molar volume of a real gas, and the ideal molar volume at the same temperature and pressure.

Finally we consider a mixture of two slightly imperfect non-reacting gases. Since we now have to take account of interactions both between like and unlike molecules, equation (11.14) may be written in the more general form :

$$p=\frac{n_1+n_2}{V}RT+\frac{RT}{V^2}(B_{11}n_1^2+2B_{12}n_1n_2+B_{22}n_2^2). \qquad (11.26)$$

The coefficient B_{11} is related to the mutual interaction between molecules of type 1 ; B_{12} to interaction between unlike molecules and B_{22} to that between type 2 molecules. In terms of mole fractions this becomes

$$p=\frac{nRT}{V}+\frac{RTn^2}{V^2}(B_{11}x_1^2+2B_{12}x_1x_2+B_{22}x_2^2). \qquad (11.27)$$

Comparing this expression with (11.14) we see that we can define the second virial coefficient of the mixture by

$$B=B_{11}x_1^2+2B_{12}x_1x_2+B_{22}x_2^2, \qquad (11.28)$$

which is a quadratic function of the mole fractions. It should be observed that to obtain the virial coefficient of a mixture, it is not enough to know the virial coefficients of each of the pure gases, but we must also know B_{12}.

The equation for the coefficient B_{12} derived from statistical mechanics is analogous to (11.15) :*

$$B_{12}(T)=\frac{N}{2}\int_{\infty}^{0}(1-e^{-\epsilon_{12}(r)/kT})\,4\pi r^2\,dr \qquad (11.29)$$

where $\epsilon_{12}(r)$ is the interaction energy between molecules of types 1 and 2 separated by a distance r between their centres. Thus a study of the virial coefficients of a binary gas mixture enables one, in principle at least, to determine not only the energies ϵ_{11} and ϵ_{22}, between like molecules, but also ϵ_{12}. Very little work has, however, been carried out along these lines.†

The free energy can be obtained as before and takes the form

$$F=F^{\mathrm{id}}+RT\,\frac{B_{11}n_1^2+2B_{12}n_1n_2+B_{22}n_2^2}{V} \qquad (11.30)$$

while the chemical potentials of the two components are

$$\left.\begin{aligned}\mu_1&=\left(\frac{\partial F}{\partial n_1}\right)_{T,V,n_2}=\mu_1^{\mathrm{id}}+2RT\,\frac{B_{11}n_1+B_{12}n_2}{V},\\ \mu_2&=\left(\frac{\partial F}{\partial n_2}\right)_{T,V,n_1}=\mu_2^{\mathrm{id}}+2RT\,\frac{B_{12}n_1+B_{22}n_2}{V}\end{aligned}\right\}. \qquad (11.31)$$

* *Cf.* Fowler and Guggenheim, [20], p. 265.

† *Cf.* D. M. Newitt, *The Design of High Pressure Plants*, (Oxford, 1940); J. A. Beattie and W. H. Stockmayer, *J. Chem. Phys.*, **10**, 473 (1942) ; R. J. Lunbeck and A. J. H. Boerboom, *Physica*, **17**, 76 (1951).

Alternatively, using (10.34) these equations can be written

$$\left.\begin{aligned}\mu_1&=\mu_1^\dagger(T)+RT\ln\frac{n_1RT}{V}+2RT\,\frac{B_{11}n_1+B_{12}n_2}{V},\\ \mu_2&=\mu_2^\dagger(T)+RT\ln\frac{n_2RT}{V}+2RT\,\frac{B_{12}n_1+B_{22}n_2}{V}\end{aligned}\right\}. \qquad (11.32)$$

3. The van der Waals Equation of State.

The van der Waals equation of state may be written

$$p=\frac{RT}{v-b}-\frac{a}{v^2} \qquad (11.33)$$

where a and b are constants called respectively the *cohesion* and the *covolume* of the gas. For a slightly imperfect gas we may expand $1/(v-b)$ in terms of b/v. If we neglect terms in $(b/v)^2$ and higher powers we have

$$p=\frac{RT}{v}\left(1+\frac{b-\dfrac{a}{RT}}{v}\right). \qquad (11.34)$$

Comparing this with (11.14) we see that the second virial coefficient has the form

$$B(T)=b-\frac{a}{RT}, \qquad (11.35)$$

while the Boyle temperature at which B is zero is given by

$$T_B=\frac{a}{Rb}. \qquad (11.36)$$

The free energy F of a van der Waals gas is obtained by substituting (11.33) into (11.7) to give

$$F(T,V,n)=F^{\text{id}}(T,V,n)-\lim_{V_0\to\infty}\int_{V_0}^{V}\left(\frac{nRT}{V-nb}-\frac{n^2a}{V^2}-\frac{nRT}{V}\right)dV \qquad (11.37)$$

$$=F^{\text{id}}(T,V,n)-nRT\ln\frac{V-nb}{V}-\frac{n^2a}{V}. \qquad (11.38)$$

We can now evaluate all the thermodynamic functions of a van der Waals gas.

The entropy is given by

$$S=-\left(\frac{\partial F}{\partial T}\right)_V=S^{\text{id}}+nR\ln\frac{V-nb}{V}. \qquad (11.39)$$

The entropy of the ideal gas at the same temperature and volume is the observed entropy less the term $nR\ln(V-nb)/V$. It may be noted that if (11.35) is inserted in (11.19) we obtain the difference between the real and ideal entropy as n^2Rb/V. The apparent discrepancy arises from the fact that in obtaining the second virial coefficient we neglected powers of b/V greater than the first.

The internal energy may be obtained using the Gibbs-Helmholtz equation

$$U = -T^2 \left[\frac{\partial \left(\frac{F}{T}\right)}{\partial T} \right]_V = U^{\text{id}} - \frac{n^2 a}{V}, \tag{11.40}$$

while the heat capacity at constant volume is

$$C_V = \left(\frac{\partial U}{\partial T}\right) = C_V^{\text{id}}(T). \tag{11.41}$$

Thus a van der Waals gas has the same specific heat at constant volume as the perfect gas at the same temperature. This result is common to all equations of state in which the pressure is linearly related to the temperature. This can be shown quite generally since (*cf.* 4.2)

$$\frac{1}{T}\left(\frac{\partial C_V}{\partial V}\right)_T = \frac{\partial^2 S}{\partial V\, \partial T}.$$

The right hand side can be transformed using the first equation of (4.38)

$$\frac{\partial}{\partial T}\left(\frac{\partial S}{\partial V}\right)_T = \frac{\partial}{\partial T}\left(\frac{\partial p}{\partial T}\right)_V$$

so that

$$\left(\frac{\partial C_V}{\partial V}\right)_T = T\left(\frac{\partial^2 p}{\partial T^2}\right)_V. \tag{11.42}$$

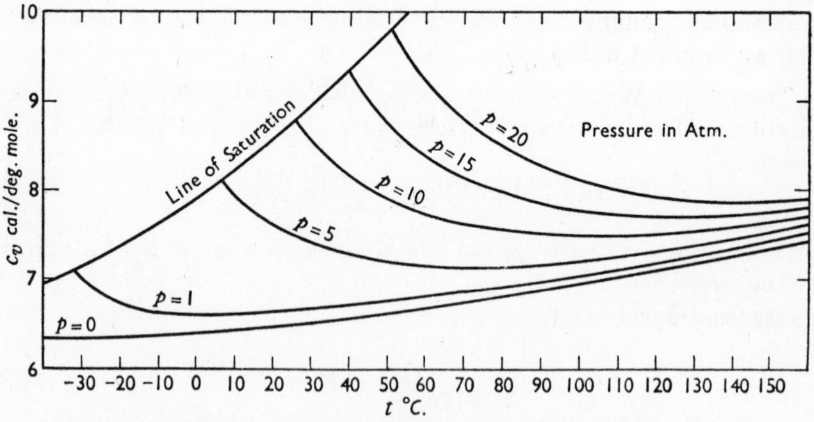

FIG. 11.3. Molar heat capacity c_v of ammonia as function of T and p.*

* *Cf.* Eucken [17] p. 100.

Thus for all equations of state in which the pressure is linearly related to the temperature

$$\frac{\partial C_V}{\partial V}=0. \qquad (11.43)$$

In fact we find that real gases do not exhibit this behaviour and the specific heat is not equal to that of the perfect gas. For example, fig. 11.3 shows the molar heat capacity c_V of ammonia as a function of T and p.

The van der Waals equation is thus mainly of qualitative interest. Its quantitative shortcomings are illustrated by the data in table 11.2 which gives the product pv calculated for CO_2 at 40 °C compared with the observed values.

TABLE 11.2*

(*p in atm.; v in cm.*^{3} *mole*$^{-1}$).

p	pv (*obs.*)	pv (*calc.*)
1	25 574	25 597
10	24 485	24 713
25	22 500	23 060
50	19 000	19 750
80	9 500	10 700
100	6 930	8 890
200	10 500	14 100
500	22 000	29 700
1000	40 000	54 200

The agreement with experiment can be improved considerably if we assume that the coefficients a and b are themselves functions of temperature and volume,† but these corrections are of an empirical nature and we shall not discuss them further here.

The van der Waals equation can be extended quite readily to binary mixtures. The coefficients a and b are quadratic functions of the mole fractions :‡

$$\left.\begin{aligned} a&=a_1x_1^2+2a_{12}x_1x_2+a_2x_2^2,\\ b&=b_1x_1^2+2b_{12}x_1x_2+b_2x_2^2\end{aligned}\right\}. \qquad (11.44)$$

The coefficient a_{12} is related to the forces between the unlike molecules. London § has shown that to a first approximation we may write

$$a_{12}=\sqrt{a_1a_2}, \qquad (11.45)$$

* *Cf.* van Laar, [48].
† *Cf.* especially van Laar, [48].
‡ K. A. Lorentz, *Ann. Physik*, 12, 122, 660 (1881).
§ F. London, *Trans. Faraday Soc.*, 33, 19 (1937).

while since b is related to the volume occupied by the molecules themselves we can, for rough calculations, write it as a linear function of the mole fractions. With these simplifications we have

$$a=(\sqrt{a_1}x_1+\sqrt{a_2}x_2)^2, \tag{11.46}$$

$$b=b_1x_1+b_2x_2. \tag{11.47}$$

These simplified formulae can easily be extended to systems of more than two components, and we shall make use of them in the next paragraph.

For further discussions on the range of validity of van der Waals' equation the reader is referred to the work of Boltzmann* and Rocard.†

4. The Effect of Gas Imperfection on Chemical Equilibrium.

The equations derived in the preceding paragraph can be used to calculate the effect of pressure upon the affinity and equilibrium constant in a mixture of reacting gases.

We begin by calculating the Gibbs free energy of an imperfect gas mixture. Employing the van der Waals equation and inserting the virial coefficient (11.35) into (11.21), remembering that $B'=B/RT$, we have

$$G=G^{\mathrm{id}}+np\left(b-\frac{a}{RT}\right). \tag{11.48}$$

The coefficients a and b may be replaced by the approximate values (11.46) and (11.47) to yield

$$G=G^{\mathrm{id}}+\frac{p}{RT}\left[RT\sum_i b_in_i-\frac{1}{n}(\sum_i\sqrt{a_i}n_i)^2\right]. \tag{11.49}$$

The affinity of the reaction is obtained simply by differentiating with respect to ξ (*cf.* 4.30):

$$\mathbf{A}=\mathbf{A}^{\mathrm{id}}-\frac{p}{RT}[RT\sum_i b_i\nu_i-2(\sum_i\sqrt{a_i}x_i)(\sum_i\sqrt{a_i}\nu_i)+\nu(\sum_i\sqrt{a_i}x_i)^2]. \tag{11.50}$$

Following the method employed in § 1 of this chapter we introduce an equilibrium parameter K defined by (11.11), whence

$$\ln\frac{K}{K_p^{\mathrm{id}}(T)}$$

$$=-\frac{p}{(RT)^2}[RT\sum_i b_i\nu_i-2(\sum_i\sqrt{a_i}x_i)(\sum_i\sqrt{a_i}\nu_i)+\nu(\sum_i\sqrt{a_i}x_i)^2]. \tag{11.51}$$

* L. Boltzmann, *Vorlesungen über Gastheorie*, 3rd Edition (Leipzig, 1923).
† Y. Rocard, *Ann. Phys.*, [2], **8**, 5 (1927).

This equation gives the effect of gas imperfection on the equilibrium constant ; we notice that as $p \to 0$, K reduces to $K_p^{\mathrm{id}}(T)$.

*Example : Synthesis of Ammonia.**

If the gas mixture could be considered as a mixture of perfect gases, then we should have

$$\frac{p^2_{\mathrm{NH_3}}}{p^3_{\mathrm{H_2}}\,p_{\mathrm{N_2}}} = K_p^{\mathrm{id}}(T) \tag{11.52}$$

where K_p^{id} is a function of temperature but not of pressure. It is found experimentally that the product of the partial pressures at equilibrium does in fact vary markedly with total pressure. We shall employ (11.51) to calculate K/K_p^{id} and compare the results with the experimental observations. The covolumes and cohesions of the various components are known from measurements of the critical constants ; they are given below

$$b_{\mathrm{N_2}} = 40{\cdot}5 \text{ cm.}^3\text{/mole}, \qquad \sqrt{a_{\mathrm{N_2}}} = 1{\cdot}135 \times 10^3 \text{ atm.}^{\frac{1}{2}} \text{ cm.}^3\text{/mole},$$

$$b_{\mathrm{H_2}} = 19{\cdot}4 \text{ cm.}^3\text{/mole}, \qquad \sqrt{a_{\mathrm{H_2}}} = 0{\cdot}3987 \times 10^3 \text{ atm.}^{\frac{1}{2}} \text{ cm.}^3\text{/mole},$$

$$b_{\mathrm{NH_3}} = 40{\cdot}87 \text{ cm.}^3\text{/mole}, \qquad \sqrt{a_{\mathrm{NH_3}}} = 1{\cdot}935 \times 10^3 \text{ atm.}^{\frac{1}{2}} \text{ cm.}^3\text{/mole}.$$

If the initial amounts of N_2 and H_2 are chemically equivalent we have one relation between $x_{\mathrm{N_2}}$, $x_{\mathrm{H_2}}$ and $x_{\mathrm{NH_3}}$ and from a value of K_p^{id} we can calculate, by successive approximations if necessary, the equilibrium values of the mole fractions at equilibrium and hence K/K_p^{id}. The observed and calculated values at 450 °C are given below :

TABLE 11.3

p (atm.)	K/K_p^{id} (*obs.*)	K/K_p^{id} (*calc.*)
100	1·11	1·056
300	1·355	1·257
600	1·985	1·798
1 000	3·566	3·301

The above method thus gives remarkably satisfactory results up to a pressure of 1,000 atmospheres. No better agreement can be expected from the use of van der Waals' equation to represent the gas imperfection.

5. Fugacity of a Real Gas.

The effects of intermolecular forces upon the thermodynamic properties of a gas can be conveniently summarized in terms of the fugacity of the gas.§

We have already seen, (10.11), that for a perfect gas

$$\mu = \mu^\dagger(T) + RT \ln p.$$

* F. G. Keyes, *The Nucleus*, **19**, 204 (1942).

§ G. N. Lewis, *Proc. Amer. Acad.*, **37**, 49 (1901) ; *Z. physik. Chem.*, **38**, 205 (1901).

We shall now write, for any real gas, the analogous equation

$$\boxed{\mu = \mu^\dagger(T) + RT \ln p^*(T, p)} \tag{11.53}$$

where $\mu^\dagger(T)$ is the same function as for the perfect gas. Because of molecular interactions p^*, called the *fugacity*, is a function of both T and p. This form of equation has the advantage of retaining the chemical potential of a real gas in the same general form as for a perfect gas except that p^* replaces p. We note that p^*, like p, is an intensive variable.

At sufficiently low pressures all gases are perfect and the fugacity becomes equal to the pressure :

$$\lim_{p\to 0} \frac{p^*}{p} = 1. \tag{11.54}$$

The relationships between p^* and other thermodynamic properties are obtained as follows.

Since $[\partial(\mu/T)/\partial T]_p = -h/T^2$ we have from (11.53)

$$\frac{\partial\left(\frac{\mu^\dagger}{T}\right)}{\partial T} + R\frac{\partial \ln p^*}{\partial T} = -\frac{h}{T^2}. \tag{11.55}$$

Now for a perfect gas $p^* = p$ and (11.55) reduces to

$$\frac{\partial\left(\frac{\mu^\dagger}{T}\right)}{\partial T} = -\frac{h^{\mathrm{id}}}{T^2}. \tag{11.56}$$

Thus by subtracting (11.56) from (11.55)

$$\frac{\partial \ln p^*}{\partial T} = -\frac{h - h^{\mathrm{id}}}{RT^2}. \tag{11.57}$$

Similarly from (6.28)

$$\frac{\partial \ln p^*}{\partial p} = \frac{v}{RT}. \tag{11.58}$$

The fugacity may be calculated directly since (11.9) can be rewritten, using (11.53), in the form

$$RT \ln \frac{p^*}{p} = \lim_{p_0\to 0} \int_{p_0}^{p} (v - v^{\mathrm{id}})\, dp. \tag{11.59}$$

The integral can be evaluated either graphically, or analytically using an equation of state. For example if we use the equation of state in the form (11.20), we have

$$\ln \frac{p^*}{p} = B'p + \tfrac{1}{2}C'p^2 + \tfrac{1}{3}D'p^3 + \dots \tag{11.60}$$

The relationship between the fugacity and the second virial coefficient of a slightly imperfect gas may be expressed in several ways.

If we set C', D' . . . equal to zero in (11.60) and write B' in terms of B, the second virial coefficient, we have

$$\ln \frac{p^*}{p} = \frac{Bp}{RT}. \tag{11.61}$$

Alternatively comparing (11.18) with (11.53) we see that

$$\begin{aligned} \ln p^* &= \ln \frac{nRT}{V} + \frac{2Bn}{V} \\ &= \ln p^{\mathrm{id}} + 2B/v. \end{aligned} \tag{11.62}$$

If $2Bn/V$ is small compared with unity, we may write this

$$\ln p^* = \ln \frac{nRT}{V} + \ln\left(1 + \frac{2Bn}{V}\right) \tag{11.63}$$

since on expanding the logarithm we may neglect all powers of Bn/V greater than the first.

Thus

$$p^* = \frac{nRT}{V}\left(1 + \frac{2Bn}{V}\right), \tag{11.64}$$

provided that the gas is only slightly imperfect.

Now the equation of state of the gas may be written (11.14)

$$p = \frac{nRT}{V}\left(1 + \frac{Bn}{V}\right) \tag{11.65}$$

which on comparison with (11.64) gives

$$p^* - p = \frac{nRT}{V} \cdot \frac{Bn}{V} = p - p^{\mathrm{id}}. \tag{11.66}$$

Examples :

(*a*) The second virial coefficient of benzene vapour at 75 °C is 1000 cm.³/mole. The fugacity of benzene vapour at a pressure of 0·75 atm. and 75 °C is thus given by (11.61)

$$\ln p^* = \ln(0{\cdot}75) - (1000 \times 0{\cdot}75)/(82{\cdot}07 \times 348{\cdot}1)\,;\, p^* = 0{\cdot}73 \text{ atm.}$$

(*b*) The saturation vapour pressure of fluorobenzene at $T = 382{\cdot}0$ °K is 1·974 atm. The molar volume of the vapour is

$$v = V/n = 15{,}000 \text{ cm.}^3\text{/mole.}$$

Hence

$$p^{\text{id}} = \frac{nRT}{V} = \frac{82{\cdot}07 \times 382{\cdot}1}{15{,}000} = 2{\cdot}085 \text{ atm.}$$

Thus $$p - p^{\text{id}} = 1{\cdot}974 - 2{\cdot}085 = -0{\cdot}111 \text{ atm.}$$

The fugacity of the saturated vapour is therefore obtained from (11.66) as

$$p^* = p - 0{\cdot}111 = 1{\cdot}86 \text{ atm.}$$

6. Fugacities in a Mixture of Real Gases.

The definition of partial pressures (10.24) applies both to real and perfect gases.

We have already seen (10.34) that in a mixture of *perfect gases*

$$\mu_i = \mu_i^\dagger(T) + RT \ln p_i.$$

By analogy, we write for a mixture of real gases

$$\boxed{\mu_i = \mu_i^\dagger(T) + RT \ln p_i^*}, \tag{11.67}$$

where $\mu_i^\dagger(T)$ is the same function as for the perfect gas, while all the effects of molecular interaction are included in the p_i^*'s which are functions of T and the partial pressures, or of T, p, n_1, ... n_c. Equation (11.67) is the definition of the function p_i^*.

Again we see that this equation preserves the general form of the equation for perfect gases, with the fugacities replacing partial pressures. For example, for a binary mixture, for which the equation of state is (11.26), we have by comparing (11.32) with (11.67)

$$\left.\begin{aligned} \ln p_1^* &= \ln \frac{n_1 RT}{V} + 2\,\frac{B_{11}n_1 + B_{12}n_2}{V}, \\ \ln p_2^* &= \ln \frac{n_2 RT}{V} + 2\,\frac{B_{12}n_1 + B_{22}n_2}{V} \end{aligned}\right\}. \tag{11.68}$$

The arguments of the preceding paragraph apply without alteration to the case of a mixture. Thus, just as for a single gas, the fugacity may be calculated from (*cf.* 11.59).

$$RT \ln \frac{p_i^*}{p} = \lim_{p_0 \to 0} \int_{p_0}^{p} (v_i - v_i^{\text{id}})\, dp. \tag{11.69}$$

We only require to know the partial molar volumes as a function of pressure to evaluate the fugacity of each component at a given temperature. We can use either directly determined values or an equation of state such as that derived from the van der Waals equation in § 4 of this chapter. Alternatively we can make use of *Lewis' rule* which assumes that

$$p_i^* = (p_i^*)^0 x_i \tag{11.70}$$

where $(p_i^*)^0$ is the fugacity of component i if it is alone at temperature T and pressure p. This rule gives results which are qualitatively interesting,* but since, in effect, it ignores all cross terms in the virial coefficients it cannot hold with any accuracy.

The affinity of reaction is readily expressed in terms of the fugacities. We have immediately from the definition (11.67), that

$$\mathbf{A} = RT \ln \frac{K_p(T)}{(p_1^*)^{\nu_1} \dots (p_c^*)^{\nu_c}}, \tag{11.71}$$

where $K_p(T)$ has the same value as for the perfect gas mixture. Chemical equilibrium is characterized by the state in which

$$\boxed{K_p(T) = (p_1^*)^{\nu_1} \dots (p_c^*)^{\nu_c}} \; . \tag{11.72}$$

This is the extension to real gases of the Guldberg and Waage law of mass action. By introducing fugacities we have been able to preserve, for all real gases, the same form for the equations for the affinity and the law of mass action as in the case of perfect gases.

7. Activities and Activity Coefficients in a Mixture of Real Gases.

Instead of starting from the equation for perfect gases

$$\mu_i = \mu_i^\dagger(T) + RT \ln p_i,$$

and extending it to real gases by the introduction of fugacities, we can equally well begin from (10.35)

$$\mu_i = \mu_i^0(T, p) + RT \ln x_i,$$

where x_i is the mole fraction of i. To extend this to real gases we write

$$\boxed{\mu_i = \mu_i^0(T, p) + RT \ln a_i} \; , \tag{11.73}$$

where μ_i^0 is the same function as in (10.35). All the effects arising from interaction are contained in $a_i(T, p, n_1, \dots n_c)$ which is called the *activity* of component i. As the total pressure is reduced, the activity of each component approaches its mole fraction. We have then

$$\lim_{p \to 0} \frac{a_i(T, p, n_1, \dots n_c)}{x_i} = 1. \tag{11.74}$$

It should be noticed that a_i, like x_i, is an intensive variable.

* *Cf.* I. R. Krichevsky, *J. Amer. Chem. Soc.*, **59**, 2733 (1937); R. H. Ewell, *Ind. Eng. Chem.*, **32**, 147 (1940).

Here then we have a non-ideal system (*cf.* chap. VII, § 8) which may be compared with an ideal reference system consisting of a gas mixture of the same composition, and at the same temperature T but at a pressure sufficiently low that the mixture behaves as a perfect mixture.

We can therefore apply all the formulae established in § 8 of chap. VII. In particular we may introduce activity coefficients γ defined by

$$\gamma_i = \frac{a_i}{x_i}, \tag{11.75}$$

with the property that

$$\lim_{p \to 0} \gamma_i = 1. \tag{11.76}$$

For a perfect gas mixture all the activity coefficients are unity; the values of $1 - \gamma_i$ or $\ln \gamma_i$ may be used as measures of deviations from the perfect gas laws.

We also find that

$$\frac{p_i^*}{p_i} = \gamma_i. \tag{11.77}$$

This follows from (10.36) and (11.73) which on combination give

$$\mu_i = \mu_i^\dagger(T) + \boldsymbol{R}T \ln p + \boldsymbol{R}T \ln x_i \gamma_i ;$$

whence $$\mu_i = \mu_i^\dagger(T) + \boldsymbol{R}T \ln p_i \gamma_i.$$

Comparing this with (11.67) we obtain (11.77).

Activity coefficients may be calculated in essentially the same way as fugacities. Since $\gamma_i = p_i^*/p_i$, (11.69) gives immediately

$$\boldsymbol{R}T \ln \gamma_i = \lim_{p_0 \to 0} \int_{p_0}^{p} (v_i - v_i^{\text{id}})\, dp. \tag{11.78}$$

If we employ, for example, an equation of state in the form

$$v_i = \frac{\boldsymbol{R}T}{p}(1 + B_i' p) \tag{11.79}$$

analogous to (11.25′), we obtain

$$\ln \gamma_i = B_i' p. \tag{11.80}$$

We may also deduce activity coefficients directly from (11.49); for by virtue of (7.65) and (6.15) we have

$$\boldsymbol{R}T \ln \gamma_i = \frac{p}{\boldsymbol{R}T}\left[\boldsymbol{R}T\, b_i + \frac{1}{n^2}\left(\sum_i \sqrt{a_i}\, n_i\right)^2 - \frac{2}{n}\sqrt{a_i}\left(\sum_i \sqrt{a_i}\, n_i\right)\right]$$

$$= \frac{p}{\boldsymbol{R}T}\,[\boldsymbol{R}T\, b_i + (\sum_i \sqrt{a_i}\, x_i)^2 - 2\sqrt{a_i}(\sum_i \sqrt{a_i}\, x_i)] \tag{11.81}$$

which gives the activity coefficient of the component i of a gas mixture obeying van der Waals' equation.

We have already, in chapter VII, derived expressions for the affinity and conditions of chemical equilibrium in terms of activity coefficients. We shall not repeat these results here, but simply draw attention to the fact that the equilibrium condition (7.75),

$$K(T,p)=(x_1\gamma_1)^{\nu_1} \dots (x_c\gamma_c)^{\nu_c} \tag{11.82}$$

can be transformed into

$$K_p(T)=(p_1\gamma_1)^{\nu_1} \dots (p_c\gamma_c)^{\nu_c} \tag{11.83}$$

since $p_i=px_i$ and $K(T,p)=K_p(T)p^{-\nu}$ (*cf.* 10.42).

Furthermore the equilibrium parameter K which we employed in (11.11) and (11.51):

$$K=p_1^{\nu_1} \dots p_c^{\nu_c}$$

is related to $K_p(T)$ by

$$K=\frac{K_p(T)}{\gamma_1^{\nu_1} \dots \gamma_c^{\nu_c}}\,. \tag{11.84}$$

Thus the variation of K with the composition of the system is determined by the dependence of the various activity coefficients upon composition.

In a real gas mixture, the standard quantities (table 7.2) all have the same values as for a perfect gas at the same temperature and pressure. This results immediately from the use of the same function $\mu^0(T, p)$ for both real and perfect gases. The standard affinities are also equal in the two cases.

CHAPTER XII

CONDENSED PHASES

In this chapter we shall be concerned with condensed phases (solid or liquid) consisting of a single component; solutions will be studied in later chapters.

1. Coefficients of Expansion and Compressibility.

The coefficients of thermal expansion (α) *and of compressibility* (κ) are defined in terms of the molar volume $v(T, p)$ by the equations

$$\alpha = \frac{1}{v}\left(\frac{\partial v}{\partial T}\right)_p ; \quad \kappa = -\frac{1}{v}\left(\frac{\partial v}{\partial p}\right)_T . \tag{12.1}$$

We shall also make use of the pressure coefficient (β) defined by

$$\beta = \frac{1}{p}\left(\frac{\partial p}{\partial T}\right)_V . \tag{12.2}$$

The mathematical identity

$$\left(\frac{\partial v}{\partial p}\right)_T \left(\frac{\partial p}{\partial T}\right)_V + \left(\frac{\partial v}{\partial T}\right)_p = 0 \tag{12.3}$$

shows immediately that

$$\beta = \frac{1}{p}\,\frac{\alpha}{\kappa} . \tag{12.4}$$

This relation enables β to be calculated from a knowledge of α and κ.

In table 12.1 are given values of v, α and κ for copper as a function of temperature and at a pressure of one atmosphere.

TABLE 12.1

T °K	$\alpha \,.\, 10^6$ *deg.*$^{-1}$	$\kappa \,.\, 10^{12}$ *dynes*$^{-1}$ *cm.*^{2}	v *cm.*^{3}*/mole*
103	31·2	0·72	7·04
123	36·3	0·72	7·04
143	39·3	0·73	7·05
183	44·1	0·74	7·06
223	46·7	0·75	7·07
283	48·9	0·77	7·10
585	55·8	0·86	7·23

We see that the coefficient of expansion falls rapidly as the temperature is lowered. Studies of the properties of solids at low temperatures show that this behaviour is quite general and that the coefficient of thermal expansion approaches a constant value at high temperatures and tends to zero as the temperature approaches the absolute zero. This follows from Nernst's theorem (*cf.* chap. IX), for by virtue of (4.39),

$$\left(\frac{\partial V}{\partial T}\right)_p = -\left(\frac{\partial S}{\partial p}\right)_T ,$$

and at sufficiently low temperatures S tends to zero whatever the pressure. Hence both $\partial S/\partial p$ and $\partial V/\partial T$ must tend to zero. This behaviour is illustrated for a number of crystals in fig. 12.1.*

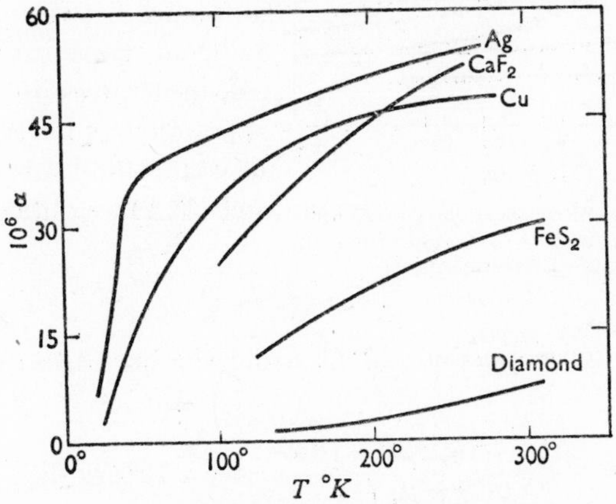

FIG. 12.1. Coefficients of expansion of various crystals as a function of temperature.*

The compressibility also decreases with temperature but at absolute zero it tends to a well defined limit and not to zero. Thus for copper the value of κ extrapolated to $T=0$ is $0{\cdot}71 \times 10^{-6}$ atm.$^{-1}$ or about $0{\cdot}71 \times 10^{-12}$ dyne^{-1} cm.^{2} (*cf.* table 12.1).

The compressibility also varies with pressure,† although here again, as shown for example in fig. 12.2, the variation is not important unless we consider ranges of pressure amounting to hundreds of atmospheres.

The coefficients of compressibility of liquids are about one hundred times greater than those of solids ($\kappa \sim 10^{-4}$ atm.$^{-1}$). This difference is however small compared with that between the compressibility of liquids and gases. For a perfect gas we have

$$\kappa = -\frac{1}{v}\frac{\partial}{\partial p}\left(\frac{RT}{p}\right) = \frac{1}{p}$$

* *Cf.* F. E. Simon, *Erg. Naturw.*, 9, 239 (1930).
† *Cf.* P. W. Bridgman, *Rev. Mod. Phys.*, 18, 1 (1948).

so that κ is of the order of 1 atm.$^{-1}$ which is 10^4 times greater than the compressibility of a liquid. The relatively low compressibility of solids is illustrated by Bridgman's experiments at very high pressures: to reduce the volume of an alkali metal by fifty per cent a pressure of some 45,000 atm. is needed.

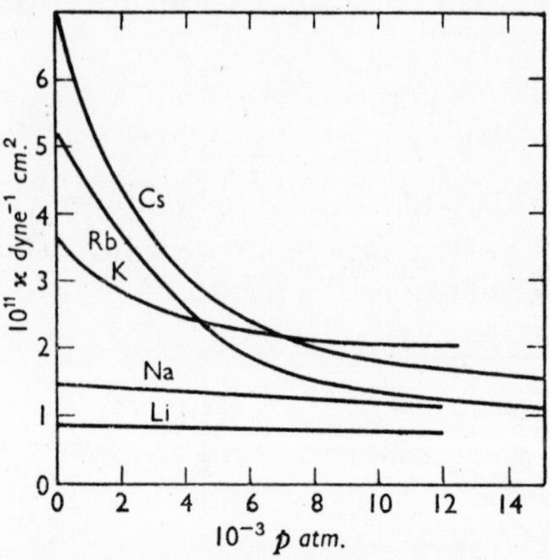

FIG. 12.2. Coefficients of compressibility of the alkaline metals as a function of pressure. (1 atm.$\sim 10^6$ dyne/cm.$^{-2}$)

The coefficients of expansion and compressibility of condensed phases are important also because they are related to the difference between the heat capacity at constant volume and constant pressure. By writing equation (4.45) for one mole of substance, and substituting (12.1) and (12.2) we obtain the relation

$$c_p - c_v = T\,\frac{v\alpha^2}{\kappa}. \qquad (12.5)$$

For example, for copper at 25 °C, using the data from table 12.1 we have

$$c_p - c_v = \frac{293 \times 7{\cdot}1(49{\cdot}2)^2 \times 10^{-12}}{0{\cdot}77 \times 10^{-12}} = 6{\cdot}5 \times 10^6 \text{ erg/deg. mole.}$$

$$= 0{\cdot}15 \text{ cal./deg. mole.}$$

Since c_v is about 6 cal./deg. mole, the difference between the heat capacities is small for solids. For liquids the difference may be quite large, thus for mercury at 630 °C $c_p = 6{\cdot}72$, $c_v = 5{\cdot}29$ cal./deg. mole.

The effect of pressure on c_p is also related to the thermal expansion. If we take equation (4.39):

$$\left(\frac{\partial S}{\partial p}\right)_T = -\left(\frac{\partial V}{\partial T}\right)_p \qquad (12.6)$$

and differentiate with respect to T, remembering that, (4.2),

$$\left(\frac{\partial S}{\partial T}\right)_p = \frac{C_p}{T}, \qquad (12.7)$$

we have for one mole

$$\left(\frac{\partial c_p}{\partial p}\right)_T = -T\left(\frac{\partial^2 v}{\partial T^2}\right)_p. \qquad (12.8)$$

Employing (12.1) this becomes

$$\frac{\partial c_p}{\partial p} = -Tv\left[\frac{\partial \alpha}{\partial T} + \alpha^2\right] \simeq -Tv\frac{\partial \alpha}{\partial T} \tag{12.9}$$

since α^2 is negligible in comparison with $\partial\alpha/\partial T$ (*cf.* table 12.1).

The magnitude of the variation of c_p with pressure is thus determined by the variation of α with temperature. Since $\partial\alpha/\partial T$ is always positive, the heat capacity at constant pressure decreases with increased pressure, but the effect becomes small at high temperatures since $\partial\alpha/\partial T$ falls off more rapidly than T increases (*cf.* fig. 12.1). A similar formula is readily obtained for the effect of volume on c_v.

2. Equation of State of Condensed Phases.

First we consider the case where the external pressure is not too large (<100 atm.) so that the compressibility can be taken as independent of pressure. The second equation of (12.1) can then be integrated with respect to p to give

$$v(T, p) = v(T, 0)e^{-\kappa p} \simeq v(T, 0)(1-\kappa p), \tag{12.10}$$

where $v(T, 0)$ is the molar volume extrapolated to $p=0$; $v(T, 0)$ therefore depends only on the temperature.

Equation (12.10) is the equation of state at ordinary pressures and remains valid provided that

$$\kappa p \ll 1. \tag{12.11}$$

This condition is satisfied for $p \sim 100$ atm. since κ is of the order 10^{-6} or 10^{-4} atm.$^{-1}$ depending on whether we are dealing with solids or liquids.

If we wish to extend the equation of state to cover wide ranges of pressure we may express the equation as a series expansion

$$v(T, p) = v(0, 0)(1 + a_0 + a_1 p + \dots) \tag{12.12}$$

where $v(0, 0)$ is the molar volume extrapolated to $T=0$ and $p=0$ and where a_0, $a_1 \dots$ are functions of temperature only. The volume $v(T, 0)$ in equation (12.10) corresponds to $p=0$ at a temperature T so that

$$v(T, 0) = v(0, 0)(1 + a_0). \tag{12.13}$$

We notice of course that the function $a_0(T)$ must become zero when $T=0$. At normal temperatures a_0 is usually very small compared with unity because of the smallness of the coefficient of expansion (*cf.* table 12.1).

The coefficient of thermal expansion is now given by

$$\alpha = \frac{\dfrac{da_0}{dT} + p\,\dfrac{da_1}{dT} + \dots}{1 + a_0 + a_1 p + \dots}, \tag{12.14}$$

which to a first approximation is

$$\alpha = \frac{da_0}{dT}, \tag{12.15}$$

while the coefficient of compressibility is

$$\kappa = \frac{-a_1 - 2a_2 p - \dots}{1 + a_0 + a_1 p + \dots} \tag{12.16}$$

the approximate value being

$$\kappa = -a_1. \tag{12.17}$$

Instead of expanding the volume v as a series in terms of p, we may expand the pressure p in terms of $\{v(0, 0) - v\}/v$ that is the relative change in volume.

Thus

$$p = b_0 - b_1 \left(\frac{v(0, 0) - v}{v}\right) + b_2 \left(\frac{v(0, 0) - v}{v}\right)^2 + \dots \tag{12.18}$$

where b_0, b_1, b_2, ... are functions of temperature only. The relations between these coefficients and a_0, a_1, a_2, ... of (12.12) are easily obtained by calculating $\{v(0, 0) - v\}/v$ from (12.12), substituting in (12.18) and equating coefficients of p on the two sides. If we neglect terms higher than the second order we obtain

$$b_0 = -\frac{a_0}{a_1}\left(1 + \frac{a_0 a_2}{a_1^2}\right);\ b_1 = -\frac{1}{a_1}\left(1 + \frac{2a_0 a_2}{a_1^2}\right);\ b_2 = -\frac{a_2}{a_1^3}. \tag{12.19}$$

Neglecting the second order terms we have approximately

$$b_0 = -\frac{a_0}{a_1};\quad b_1 = -\frac{1}{a_1};$$

so that

$$b_0 = \frac{a_0}{\kappa} \quad \text{and} \quad b_1 = \frac{1}{\kappa}. \tag{12.20}$$

At high temperatures, α and κ can be taken as nearly independent of temperature. Thus, since, (12.15), $\alpha = da_0/dT$, a_0 is a linear function of temperature; furthermore since $a_0 = 0$ when $T = 0$ it must be proportional to temperature. The same must also be true of b_0 if κ is independent of temperature.

3. Influence of Temperature and Pressure on the Thermodynamic Functions of Condensed Phases.

We now proceed to calculate the thermodynamic functions of a condensed phase. First, by taking the temperature and pressure as independent variables, we may evaluate the molar enthalpy.

From equations (2.17) and (4.42) we have

$$\left(\frac{\partial h}{\partial T}\right)_p = c_p; \quad \left(\frac{\partial h}{\partial p}\right)_T = v - T\left(\frac{\partial v}{\partial T}\right)_p. \tag{12.21}$$

To integrate h from $(T=0,\ p=0)$ to (T, p) we may integrate first at constant p from $(T=0,\ p=0)$ to $(T,\ p=0)$ and then at constant T from $(T,\ p=0)$ to (T, p).

Thus

$$\begin{aligned} h &= h(0, 0) + \int_0^T c_p(T, 0)\,dT + \int_0^p \left[v - T\left(\frac{\partial v}{\partial T}\right)_p\right] dp \\ &= h(0, 0) + \int_0^T c_p(T, 0)\,dT + \int_0^p v(1-\alpha T)\,dp, \end{aligned} \tag{12.22}$$

where $h(0, 0)$ is the enthalpy extrapolated to $T=0,\ p=0$; and $c_p(T, 0)$ is the heat capacity c_p at temperature T extrapolated to $p=0$.

If we limit ourselves to low pressures we may make use of the approximate equation (12.10). Assuming that α and κ are independent of temperature, (12.22) then becomes

$$h = h(0, 0) + \int_0^T c_p(T, 0)\,dT + pv(T, 0)(1-\alpha T)(1-\tfrac{1}{2}\kappa p). \tag{12.23}$$

Now the condition for the applicability of (12.10) is that $\kappa p \ll 1$, so that h varies linearly with pressure and the magnitude of the variation is determined by the term $pv(T, 0)$. This product is however very small. For example if $v=20$ cm.^{3}/mole. and $p=1$ atm.; $pv \simeq 2\times 10^{-2}$ litre atm./mole. $\simeq 0{\cdot}48$ cal./mole.

On the other hand h varies quite rapidly with temperature since the specific heat is of the order of 6 cal./deg. mole. Thus except at extremely low temperatures or very high pressures the second term on the right hand side of (12.23) is overwhelmingly large compared with the third term. For most purposes then *the enthalpy may be taken as independent of pressure* and is given by

$$\boxed{h = h(0, 0) + \int_0^T c_p(T, 0)\,dT}. \tag{12.24}$$

It is of course important to remember that if any phase changes involving a latent heat occur between 0 and T, the latent heats must also be added to equation (12.24).

The *molar energy* of a condensed phase is readily obtained since $u = h - pv$; in view of what has been said above about the magnitude of pv, the difference between h and u is quite small for condensed phases.

The *molar entropy* may be calculated as a function of T and p by using equations (12.6) and (12.7) ; whence

$$s = s(0, 0) + \int_0^T \frac{c_p(T, 0)}{T} \, dT - \int_0^p \left(\frac{\partial v}{\partial T}\right)_p dp. \tag{12.25}$$

Now if the condensed phase is a perfect crystal at absolute zero we may equate $s(0, 0)$ to zero (Nernst's theorem, chap. IX). Furthermore as $T \to 0$ the specific heat tends to zero sufficiently rapidly for the integral $\int_0^T \frac{c_p}{T} \, dT$ to converge to a finite value. Again if we assume that (12.10) is a sufficient approximation to the equation of state, and assuming α to be independent of pressure, we obtain

$$s = s(0, 0) + \int_0^T \frac{c_p(T, 0)}{T} \, dT - \alpha p v(T, 0)(1 - \tfrac{1}{2}\kappa p). \tag{12.26}$$

Also, since κp is negligible compared with unity, the variation of entropy with pressure is linear, and is given by the term $\alpha p v(T, 0)$. This term is so small compared with the integral that we may regard *the entropy as independent of pressure* and given by

$$\boxed{s = s(0, 0) + \int_0^T \frac{c_p(T, 0)}{T} \, dT} \, . \tag{12.27}$$

Here again entropy changes accompanying changes of phase between 0 and T must be included in (12.27) (*cf.* chap. IX, p. 110).

Finally, we shall calculate the *chemical potential* as a function of T and p. Since h and s have already been evaluated this is easily done since $\mu = h - Ts$. We obtain, using (12.23) and (12.26),

$$\mu = h(0, 0) - Ts(0, 0) + \int_0^T c_p(T, 0) \, dT - T \int_0^T \frac{c_p(T, 0)}{T} \, dT + pv(T, 0)(1 - \tfrac{1}{2}\kappa p). \tag{12.28}$$

We notice that this equation is independent of any phase changes which occur in the range 0–T since the terms introduced in (12.23) and (12.26) to take account of them will cancel out. This is obvious also from the fact that at the transition temperature the two phases are in equilibrium and transformation from one to the other involves no change in chemical potential.

The two integrals can be replaced by a double integral in just the same way as in chap. IV (*cf.* p. 51) to give

$$\mu=\left[h(0,0)-Ts(0,0)-T\int_0^T\frac{dT}{T^2}\int_0^T c_p(T,0)\,dT\right] +pv(T,0)(1-\tfrac{1}{2}\kappa p). \quad (12.29)$$

If we equate the term in square brackets to $\mu^\dagger(T)$ we have

$$\mu=\mu^\dagger(T)+pv(T,0)(1-\tfrac{1}{2}\kappa p). \quad (12.30)$$

The function $\mu^\dagger(T)$ which we have introduced is analogous to that introduced in the theory of perfect gases (*cf.* 10.11), except that here the standard pressure is zero instead of unity. The way in which the chemical potential of a condensed phase varies with pressure is, however, quite different from the logarithmic variation of μ with p in the case of a perfect gas. Here we see that, since $(1-\frac{1}{2}\kappa p)\sim 1$ the variation of μ with p is linear and is given by the term $pv(T, 0)$. As we have seen this term is quite negligible under ordinary conditions so that the *chemical potential is independent of pressure* and

$$\boxed{\mu=\mu^\dagger(T)}\text{, for solids and liquids.} \quad (12.31)$$

The effects of large pressure changes upon the thermodynamic functions can, of course, be examined by using the more general equation of state (12.12); a rather more interesting discussion of this case follows, however, if we regard the volume instead of the pressure as independent variable.

4. Influence of Temperature and Volume on the Thermodynamic Functions of Condensed Phases.

We now proceed to calculate the thermodynamic functions in terms of temperature and volume as independent variables. Since the pressures needed to change the volume of a condensed phase appreciably (*e.g.* by 10 per cent) are extremely high we cannot now use the approximate equation of state, but must employ the full equation (12.18).

The *internal energy* is obtained by combining equations (2.8) and (4.41) and integrating:

$$\left(\frac{\partial u}{\partial T}\right)_v=c_v;\quad \left(\frac{\partial u}{\partial v}\right)_T=T\left(\frac{\partial p}{\partial T}\right)_v-p. \quad (12.32)$$

We carry out the integration in two stages, first from $(T=0, v=v(0, 0))$ to $(T, v(0, 0))$, and then to (T, v), where $v(0, 0)$ is the molar volume at zero pressure and at the absolute zero of temperature :

$$u=u(0, 0)+\int_0^T c_v(T, 0)\,dT+\int_{v(0,0)}^{v}\left[T\left(\frac{\partial p}{\partial T}\right)_v-p\right]dv. \tag{12.33}$$

In this equation $u(0, 0)$ is the internal energy at $T=0$, $v=v(0, 0)$, and $c_v(T, 0)$ is the heat capacity at a constant volume equal to $v(0, 0)$. We may now replace p and $\partial p/\partial T$ by the values derived from the equation of state (12.18), to obtain

$$\begin{aligned}u=u(0, 0)+\int_0^T c_v(T, 0)\,dT-v(0, 0)\Bigg[&\left(T\frac{db_0}{dT}-b_0\right)\left(\frac{v(0, 0)-v}{v(0, 0)}\right)\\&+\tfrac{1}{2}\left(T\frac{db_1}{dT}-b_1\right)\left(\frac{v(0, 0)-v}{v(0, 0)}\right)^2\\&+\tfrac{1}{3}\left(T\frac{db_2}{dT}-b_2\right)\left(\frac{v(0, 0)-v}{v(0, 0)}\right)^3+\dots\Bigg].\end{aligned} \tag{12.34}$$

We saw, at the end of paragraph 2 that b_0 is approximately proportional to temperature so that $\{T(db_0/dT)-b_0\}$ is very small. On the other hand b_1 is almost independent of temperature so that $\{T(db_1/dT)-b_1\}$ is approximately equal to $-b_1$. Thus, approximately,

$$u=u(0, 0)+\int_0^T c_v(T, 0)\,dT+\tfrac{1}{2}b_1 v(0, 0)\left(\frac{v(0, 0)-v}{v(0, 0)}\right)^2.$$

The internal energy should thus be a minimum,

$$u(0, 0)+\int_0^T c_v(T, 0)\,dT$$

when $v=v(0, 0)$ and should increase parabolically both for v greater and less than $v(0, 0)$, *i.e.*, corresponding to the application of both positive and negative pressures. An example of this behaviour is shown in fig. 12.3 where the internal energy of solid sodium is shown as a function of volume at various temperatures; the dotted line joins points of zero pressure *i.e.* $v(T, 0)$.

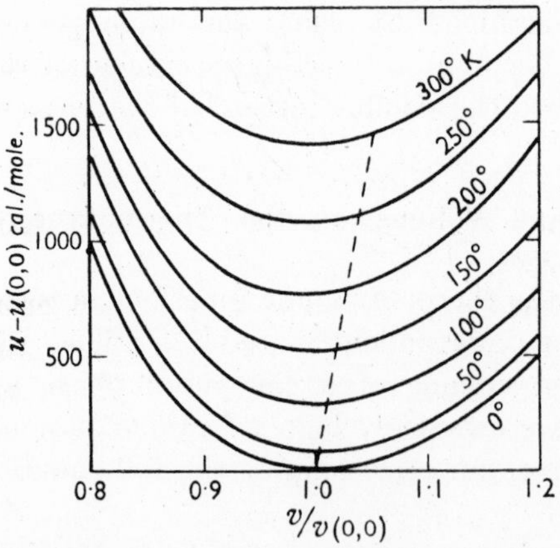

FIG. 12.3. Internal energy of solid sodium as a function of volume at different temperatures.*

* After Slater, [43], p. 206.

An expression for the *entropy* follows from equations (4.2) and (4.38) :

$$\left(\frac{\partial s}{\partial T}\right)_v = \frac{c_v}{T}; \quad \left(\frac{\partial s}{\partial v}\right)_T = \left(\frac{\partial p}{\partial T}\right)_v. \tag{12.35}$$

We have seen, however, (*cf.* (12.2) and (12.4)) that

$$\left(\frac{\partial p}{\partial T}\right)_v = \frac{\alpha}{\kappa} = \left(\frac{\partial s}{\partial v}\right)_T. \tag{12.36}$$

Thus the ratio of the coefficient of thermal expansion to coefficient of compressibility is equal to the derivative of the entropy with respect to volume. This ratio is easily measured. It is found (*cf.* table 12.1) that as $T \to 0$, $\alpha \to 0$, while κ remains finite, so that at low temperatures the entropy becomes independent of volume, in conformity with the Nernst theorem.

By integrating (12.35) we obtain

$$s = s(0, 0) + \int_0^T \frac{c_v(T, 0)}{T}\, dT + \int_{v(0,0)}^{v} \left(\frac{\partial p}{\partial T}\right)_v dv. \tag{12.37}$$

The second integral may be evaluated as before using (12.18).

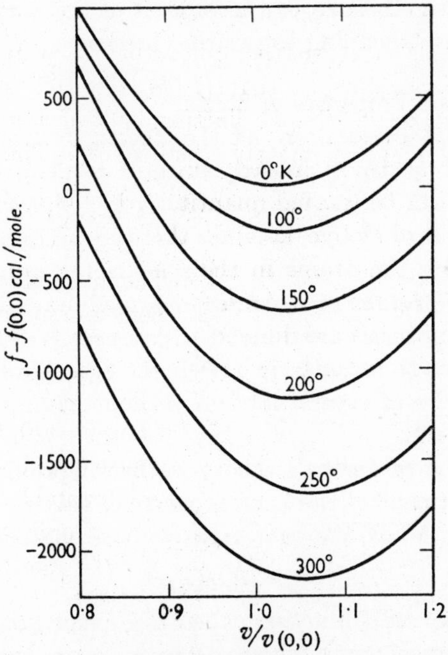

FIG. 12.4. Free energy of solid sodium as a function of volume at different temperatures.*

Finally the Helmholtz free energy per mole is obtained from the relation

$$f = u - Ts. \tag{12.38}$$

* Slater [43], p 209.

Combining (12.33) and (12.37) we find on rewriting the integrals as a double integral (*cf.* 4.20),

$$f=f(0,0)-\int_0^T dT\int_0^T \frac{c_v(T,0)}{T}\,dT$$
$$+v(0,0)\left[b_0\left(\frac{v(0,0)-v}{v(0,0)}\right)+\tfrac{1}{2}b_1\left(\frac{v(0,0)-v}{v(0,0)}\right)^2+\dots\right]. \qquad (12.39)$$

The value of $f-f(0,0)$ for sodium is shown in fig. 12.4 as a function of volume. We note that from (4.29) the derivatives of f with respect to T and v are

$$\left(\frac{\partial f}{\partial T}\right)_v=-s\,;\quad \left(\frac{\partial f}{\partial v}\right)_T=-p\,; \qquad (12.40)$$

so that the minima in the f *vs* v curves correspond to zero pressure; the corresponding values of v are the equilibrium volumes at zero pressure at the various temperatures. The position of the minimum moves to higher values of v as the temperature increases, corresponding of course to thermal expansion. We note finally that we can only attach physical significance to those parts of the curves to the left of the minimum corresponding to positive pressures.

5. Thermodynamic Properties of Solids.

The theoretical calculation of the thermodynamic properties of condensed phases is still in an early stage of development and only the simplest models can be treated quantitatively. For solids the simplest useful theory, that of Debye, assumes that the distribution of vibration frequencies among the atoms in the solid is the same as that of the frequencies of vibration of a continuous medium. The errors introduced by this hypothesis are difficult to estimate.* Some progress has, however, been made recently in the direct evaluation of the thermodynamic properties of crystal lattices without having to liken them to continuous media.†

The main value of Debye's theory is that it provides a reasonably satisfactory treatment of the heat capacity of solids.

For *monatomic solids*, the heat capacity c_v is of the form

$$c_v=3RD(T/\Theta) \qquad (12.41)$$

where D is a universal function called the *Debye function*, and Θ is a characteristic temperature which depends upon both the chemical nature of the solid and, to a much smaller extent, upon the pressure.

* *Cf.* Fowler and Guggenheim, [20], chap. IV; Mayer and Mayer, [34], chap. XI.

† M. Born and M. Bradburn, *Proc. Camb. Phil. Soc.*, 39, 113 (1943); W. V. Houston, *Rev. Mod. Phys.*, 20, 101 (1948); R. B. Leighton, *ibid.*, 20, 165 (1948); E. W. Montroll, *Quart. App. Math.*, 5, 223 (1947); M. Blackman, *Proc. Roy. Soc.*, **A159**, 417 (1937), *cf.* also M. Blackman, *Rep. Prog. Phys.*, 8 (1941).

Values of the characteristic temperatures for a number of solids at ordinary pressures are collected together in table 12.2.

TABLE 12.2

*Characteristic Temperatures of some Solid Elements at Ordinary Pressures**

Element	Θ	*Element*	Θ
Pb	88	Ag	215
Tl	96	Ca	226
Hg	97	Zn	235
I	106	Cu	315
Cd	168	Al	398
Na	172	Fe	453
		C (diamond)	1 860

A selection of values of the Debye function are tabulated in table 12.3. As T increases $D(T/\Theta)$ tends to unity, so that at temperatures above the characteristic temperature we have a theoretical justification of the empirical rule of Dulong and Petit, namely that $c_v \simeq 3R$ for atomic solids. On the other hand at low temperatures $D(T/\Theta)$ tends to zero, and for $T/\Theta < 0{\cdot}1$ we have the simple approximate formula

$$D(T/\Theta) = \frac{4\pi^4}{5}\left(\frac{T}{\Theta}\right)^3. \tag{12.42}$$

TABLE 12.3†

The Debye Function

T/Θ	$D(T/\Theta)$	T/Θ	$D(T/\Theta)$
∞	1·0000	1/13	0·03535
1	0·9517	1/14	0·02835
1/2	0·8254	1/15	0·02307
1/3	0·6628	1/16	0·01902
1/4	0·5031	1/17	0·01586
1/5	0·3686	1/18	0·01336
1/6	0·2656	1/19	0·01136
1/7	0·1909	1/20	0·009741
1/8	0·1382	1/21	0·008415
1/9	0·1015	1/22	0·007318
1/10	0·07582	1/23	0·006405
1/11	0·05773	1/24	0·005637
1/12	0·04478	for $T/\Theta < 1/24$	$D(T/\Theta) =$ $77{\cdot}92727\,(T/\Theta)^3$

* *Cf.* Fowler and Guggenheim, [20], p. 145.

† J. A. Beattie, *J. of Math. and Phys. Mass. Inst. Techn.*, 6, 1 (1926–1927 ; see also H. S. Taylor and S. Glasstone, *A Treatise on Physical Chemistry*, Vol. I (3rd Edn. London, 1942), Appendix IV.

The heat capacity c_v *thus becomes proportional to the cube of the absolute temperature* near the absolute zero. This was predicted by Debye and has been confirmed experimentally in many instances.

For solids composed of polyatomic molecules or ions it is also found that the T^3-law holds at sufficiently low temperatures ; it can therefore be employed, as foreshadowed in chap. IX, for the extrapolation of c_v to the absolute zero. In a few simple cases it has indeed been found that (12.41) is applicable over a wide temperature range to polyatomic solids.

In applying the Debye formulae to the calculation of heat capacities we require values of the double integral

$$\int_0^T \frac{dT}{T^2} \int_0^T D\left(\frac{T}{\Theta}\right) dT\,;$$

these are available in tabular form.* We may notice incidentally that the fact that the specific heat at low temperatures is proportional to T^3 ensures that the integral converges.

6. Thermodynamic Properties of Liquids.

The theoretical calculation of the thermodynamic properties of liquids presents an even more difficult problem than that of solids, for in a liquid the molecules are in a state of disorder intermediate between the random motion of a gas, and the long range order of a solid. We must therefore be content with an even cruder approximation than for solids.† A model which leads to a useful semi-quantitative correlation is based upon the idea of the *free volume.*

According to this model the free energy of the liquid differs from that of a perfect gas for two main reasons : (*a*) the actual volume of the molecules, or the repulsive forces which come into play when two molecules come close to one another, means that the centre of gravity of a given molecule cannot move freely over the whole volume v of the liquid, but is only free to move in a smaller volume v_f which is called the *free volume*, and is regarded as a function of v ; (*b*) the attractions between the molecules give rise to a potential energy which contributes to the free energy of the liquid. This is also a function of v.

Now for a perfect gas the free energy is of the form

$$f^{\text{id}} = f^{\ddagger}(T) - \boldsymbol{R}T \ln v.$$

For the free-volume model of a liquid we assume that the free energy is of the analogous form

$$f = f^{\ddagger}(T) - \boldsymbol{R}T \ln v_f(v) - \Lambda(v), \tag{12.43}$$

* *Cf. Landolt-Börnstein Tabellen :* Eg. I, 702 (Berlin, 1927).
† *Cf. e.g.* Frenkel [21].

where $\Lambda(v)$ is the contribution from intermolecular forces. Thus

$$f - f^{\text{id}} = -\boldsymbol{R}T \ln \frac{v_f(v)}{v} - \Lambda(v). \tag{12.43'}$$

The physical interpretation of Λ becomes apparent by applying equation (4.34) to (12.43′):

$$\left[\frac{\partial (f - f^{\text{id}})/T}{\partial T}\right]_v = \frac{\Lambda(v)}{T^2} = -\frac{u - u^{\text{id}}}{T^2},$$

so that

$$u - u^{\text{id}} = -\Lambda(v). \tag{12.44}$$

The term Λ is therefore the difference between the internal energy of liquid and perfect gas in the same volume : it is in effect the energy of vaporization.

Furthermore, (12.40) applied to (12.43′) gives

$$s - s^{\text{id}} = \boldsymbol{R} \ln \frac{v_f}{v}. \tag{12.45}$$

The pressure may now be obtained from (12.43) and (12.40), giving the equation of state

$$p = \boldsymbol{R}T\left(\frac{\partial \ln v_f}{\partial v} + \frac{1}{\boldsymbol{R}T}\frac{\partial \Lambda}{\partial v}\right). \tag{12.46}$$

The magnitude of the free volume may be estimated from a knowledge of the coefficients of expansion and compressibility.* As we have seen earlier in this chapter, (12.36),

$$\frac{\partial s}{\partial v} = \frac{\alpha}{\kappa},$$

so that differentiating (12.45) with respect to volume, and employing (10.9) for the entropy of a perfect gas, we obtain

$$\boldsymbol{R}\frac{\partial \ln v_f}{\partial v} = \frac{\alpha}{\kappa} \tag{12.47}$$

or

$$v_f = \frac{\boldsymbol{R}\kappa}{\alpha}\frac{\partial v_f}{\partial v}. \tag{12.47'}$$

To obtain a numerical estimate of v_f we must employ some simple model to indicate the dependence of v_f on v. Two such models lend themselves to simple discussion.

If we compare (11.38) with (12.43′) we see that the free energy of a

* H. Eyring and J. Hirschfelder, *J. Phys. Chem.*, **41**, 249 (1937) ; *cf.* J. Hirschfelder, D. Stevenson and H. Eyring, *J. Chem. Phys.*, **5**, 896 (1937).

system obeying the equation of state of van der Waals is of the same general form as (12.43) with

$$v_f = v - b,$$

$$\Lambda = \frac{a}{v}. \tag{12.48}$$

This is easily verified by substituting these values in (12.46) when the van der Waals equation is recovered. The van der Waals equation may thus be employed as an approximation to the equation of state for a liquid provided suitable values of a and b are inserted.

Since for most liquids $\Lambda \sim 10\boldsymbol{R}T$, the term a/v^2 in the equation of state (11.33) will be of the order 2×10^4 atm., so that at ordinary pressures p may be neglected and we have approximately

$$v_f = v - b = \boldsymbol{R}Tv^2/\Lambda. \tag{12.49}$$

Inserting the above approximate value for Λ we have, therefore,

$$v_f \approx v/10. \tag{12.50}$$

The free volume of a liquid, on the basis of this model is thus roughly one tenth of the geometric volume. Alternatively we may write $v_f = v - b$ in (12.47) whence

$$v_f = \boldsymbol{R}\kappa/\alpha. \tag{12.51}$$

Insertion of numerical values of κ and α leads to values of v_f of the same order of magnitude as those predicted by (12.50). The agreement between these two estimates of v_f indicates that the model exhibits a fair degree of self consistency.

An alternative model of a liquid, which leads to v_f and Λ in a rather different form, is based on the following ideas.*

In a liquid far away from the critical point the intermolecular distances are only a little greater than those corresponding to contact between the molecules. We may therefore regard each molecule as oscillating under the influence of an average force field in a " cage " or " cell " formed by its neighbours.

The free volume of a molecule in this picture is to be taken as the geometric volume available to a given molecule contained in its " cage ". This volume is readily calculated in terms of the average distance separating two molecules (d) and their diameter (D). We find that

$$v_f = \mathbf{N}\frac{4\pi}{3}(d - D)^3, \tag{12.52}$$

* H. Eyring and J. Hirschfelder, *loc. cit.*, J. E. Lennard-Jones and A. F. Devonshire, *Proc. Roy. Soc.*, **A163**, 59 (1937); H. S. Frank, *J. Chem. Phys.*, **13**, 478, 493 (1945); H. S. Frank and M. W. Evans, *J. Chem. Phys.*, 13, 587 (1945); I. Prigogine and G. Garikian, *J. Chim. Phys.*, **45**, 273 (1948).

where N is Avogadro's Number. The distance d is related, as assumed above, to the molar volume by an equation of the type

$$Nd^3 = \gamma v, \tag{12.53}$$

where γ is a constant depending upon the geometrical arrangement of the particles ; it has a value of $\sqrt{2}$ for a face-centred cubic lattice. We can, therefore, rewrite (12.52) in the form

$$v_f = \frac{4\pi}{3} \gamma \left(v^{\frac{1}{3}} - v_0^{\frac{1}{3}}\right)^3 \tag{12.54}$$

where we have put

$$ND^3 = \gamma v_0. \tag{12.55}$$

We now turn to the evaluation of the energy of vaporization $\Lambda(v)$. We shall assume that the energy of interaction $\epsilon(r)$ between two molecules (*cf.* chap. XI, § 2) is of the form

$$\epsilon(r) = -\frac{\mu}{r^6} + \frac{\nu}{r^{12}} \tag{12.56}$$

where $-\mu r^{-6}$ represents an attraction and νr^{-12} is the repulsive energy. This equation is found to be adequate to interpret the virial coefficients of rare gas atoms.

This equation may be put into a more useful form for the present purpose by expressing it not in terms of the parameters μ and ν, but in terms of r^* and ϵ^*, the co-ordinates of the minimum in the curve of ϵ against r (*cf.* fig. 11.1). At the minimum

$$\left(\frac{d\epsilon}{dr}\right)_{r=r^*} = \frac{6\mu}{r^{*7}} - \frac{12\nu}{r^{*13}} = 0. \tag{12.57}$$

Hence the energy at the minimum is

$$\epsilon^* = -\frac{\mu}{r^{*6}} + \frac{1}{2}\frac{\mu}{r^{*6}} = -\frac{1}{2}\frac{\mu}{r^{*6}}. \tag{12.58}$$

We can therefore rewrite (12.56) in the form

$$\epsilon(r) = -|\epsilon^*|\left[2\left(\frac{r^*}{r}\right)^6 - \left(\frac{r^*}{r}\right)^{12}\right]. \tag{12.59}$$

To calculate $\Lambda(v)$ we assume that all molecules are located at the centre of their cells. If each molecule has z nearest neighbours, and if d is the radius of the cell, then, taking account only of nearest neighbour interactions,

$$\Lambda(v) = -\frac{zN}{2}|\epsilon^*|\left[2\left(\frac{r^*}{d}\right)^6 - \left(\frac{r^*}{d}\right)^{12}\right] \text{per mole.} \tag{12.60}$$

We now substitute, (*cf.* 12.53),

$$Nr^{*3} = \gamma v^* \tag{12.61}$$

and

$$\Lambda^* = z \mid \epsilon^* \mid \tag{12.62}$$

whence,

$$\Lambda(v) = \frac{N}{2}\Lambda^*\left[\left(\frac{v^*}{v}\right)^4 - 2\left(\frac{v^*}{v}\right)^2\right]. \tag{12.63}$$

If we also include interactions with more distant molecules a slightly different equation is obtained*

$$\Lambda(v) = \frac{N}{2}\Lambda^*\left[1{\cdot}011\left(\frac{v^*}{v}\right)^4 - 2{\cdot}410\left(\frac{v^*}{v}\right)^2\right]. \tag{12.64}$$

We now have to find the diameter of the molecules, D, in terms of the interaction law. The diameter can be defined roughly as the distance apart of a pair of molecules at which $\epsilon(r)$ is zero. We find therefore

$$D = \frac{r^*}{2^{\frac{1}{6}}} \quad \text{or} \quad v_0 = \frac{v^*}{2^{\frac{1}{2}}}. \tag{12.65}$$

Substituting (12.54) and (12.64) into (12.46), the equation of state at sufficiently low pressures ($p \sim 0$) becomes†

$$\frac{\Lambda^*}{kT} = \frac{1}{2\left(\frac{v^*}{v}\right)^2\left\{1 - \frac{1}{2^{\frac{1}{6}}}\left(\frac{v^*}{v}\right)^{\frac{1}{3}}\right\}\left\{1{\cdot}205 - 1{\cdot}011\left(\frac{v^*}{v}\right)^2\right\}}. \tag{12.66}$$

The important feature of such an equation of state is that it contains only quantities which can be obtained from the law of interaction, and enables the properties of liquids to be calculated from well defined molecular constants.

We shall make further use of this model in chap. XXV, when discussing the relationship between the thermodynamic properties of solutions and intermolecular forces.

Since as we have already seen, the heat capacities of solids can be accounted for theoretically, it is of interest to examine whether the heat capacities of liquids can also be predicted in a similar way. We observe in the first place, that in the neighbourhood of the melting point the specific heats of simple solids and liquids are generally nearly equal.‡ Thus for solid mercury at 234 °K, $c_p = 6{\cdot}77$ cal./deg. mole. while for

* R. H. Wentorf, R. J. Buehler, J. O. Hirschfelder and C. F. Curtiss, *J. Chem. Phys.*, 18, 1484 (1950).

† I. Prigogine and V. Mathot, *J. Chem. Phys.*, 20, 49 (1952).

‡ *Cf.* Frenkel, [21].

the liquid at 236 °K it is 6·80. Similarly for potassium $c_p = 7{\cdot}81$ at 232° (solid) and 7·96 at 341° (liquid). However, at higher temperatures the heat capacity deviates widely from the value at the melting point.

For argon, for example,* the heat capacity c_v at the melting point is equal to that for the solid, *i.e.* ≈ 6 cal./mole. As the temperature is raised, c_v at first remains approximately constant and then decreases rapidly approaching, near the critical point, a value corresponding to a gas. Thus the specific heat of a liquid is a complex function of temperature which cannot be interpreted by means of the models we have considered. This is most easily seen by calculating c_v from the entropy given by (12.45). Since the free volume depends on temperature only through v, the variation of the right-hand side of (12.45) with respect to temperature at constant volume is zero and we have

$$c_v = T\left(\frac{\partial s}{\partial T}\right)_v = T\left(\frac{\partial s^{\text{id}}}{\partial T}\right)_v = c_v^{\text{id}}(T), \tag{12.67}$$

which shows that, according to these models, the specific heat of a liquid should be equal to that of a perfect gas. However, if in the second model we take account of the exact form of $\epsilon(r)$ at small distances we obtain for the free volume an expression which depends both upon volume and temperature.† This temperature dependence is small, yet is enough to explain the general behaviour of the heat capacity.‡

* A. Eucken and F. Hauck, *Z. physik. Chem.*, **134**, 161 (1928).

† J. E. Lennard-Jones and A. F. Devonshire, *Proc. Roy. Soc.*, **A163**, 53 (1937), **A165**, 1, (1938); Fowler and Guggenheim [20], p. 336.

‡ A. F. Devonshire, *Proc. Roy. Soc.*, **A174**, 102 (1940); I. Prigogine and S. Raulier, *Physica*, 9, 396 (1942); I. Prigogine and G. Garikian, *loc. cit.*

CHAPTER XIII

GIBBS' PHASE RULE AND DUHEM'S THEOREM

1. The Phase Rule.

If a system consists of c components, and ϕ phases at a temperature T, and pressure p, and if the components can undergo r' distinct chemical reactions, omitting those which consist solely of the passage of a chemical species from one phase to another, then Gibbs' phase rule gives the answer to the following question : *when the system is in equilibrium, how many intensive variables can be fixed arbitrarily?*

The phase rule is not concerned with the quantities of the various phases, but only with *intensive variables.* From this point of view the state of the system is completely determined if we know the temperature, the pressure and the chemical composition of each phase, that is if we know the values of the $(2+c\phi)$ variables :

$$T, p, x_1^1, \dots x_c^1 \dots x_1^\phi \dots x_c^\phi, \tag{13.1}$$

where x_i^α denotes the mole fraction of i in the phase α.

We notice, however, that the variables in (13.1) are not all independent, for in each phase the sum of the mole fractions must always be unity. Thus, we have

$$\sum_i x_i^\alpha = 1 \quad (\alpha = 1, \dots \phi). \tag{13.2}$$

There are ϕ relations of this type.

We must now examine the relations among these variables when the system is in equilibrium. We have first to consider the equilibrium partition of each component among the various phases. For component i the equilibrium conditions are

$$\mu_i^1 = \mu_i^2 = \dots = \mu_i^\phi. \tag{13.3}$$

These are equivalent to $(\phi - 1)$ separate equations for each component. The number of conditions arising in this way is thus $c(\phi - 1)$ for the whole system.

Secondly, we have to state the conditions of equilibrium for the r' chemical reactions which can take place in the system. These are

$$\mathbf{A}_\rho = 0 \; (\rho = 1, \dots r'). \tag{13.4}$$

The number of equations between the variables is thus ϕ from (13.2), $c(\phi-1)$ from (13.3) and r' from (13.4), a total of

$$\phi+c(\phi-1)+r'$$

relations among $2+c\phi$ intensive variables (13.1).

The *number of independent intensive variables*, the *variance*, or the *number of degrees of freedom w*, is thus given by

$$w=2+c\phi-\{\phi+c(\phi-1)+r'\}$$

or

$$\boxed{w=2+(c-r')-\phi} \quad . \tag{13.5}$$

This is the Gibbs phase rule.*

Most older statements of the phase rule employ the term " number of independent components " (c') ; this is the total number of components less the number of reactions which can occur between them. Thus

$$c'=c-r' \tag{13.6}$$

so that

$$\boxed{w=2+c'-\phi} \quad . \tag{13.7}$$

In writing equation (13.3) we have implied that each component is present in each phase. However, our conclusions are not affected even though a component (i say) is insoluble in one of the phases (α say). For although one of the equations in (13.3) drops out, say,

$$\mu_i^1=\mu_i^\alpha$$

we have to introduce another condition expressing the insolubility of i in the phase α, *i.e.*

$$x_i^\alpha=0. \tag{13.8}$$

For each condition of insolubility like (13.8) which we introduce, we lose a condition like (13.3). Thus the total number of conditions is unaltered, and the phase rule (13.5) remains valid.

2. One-Component Systems.

We have $c=1,\ r'=0,$

so that the phase rule can take the following forms :

(i) if the system consists of only *one phase* (vapour, liquid or solid) $\phi=1$ and so $w=2$. The system is thus *divariant* and within certain

* Gibbs [23], p. 96 ; P. Duhem, *J. Phys. Chem.*, **2**, 1, 91 (1898) ; *cf.* also De Donder [5], p. 125 ; E. Jouguet, *J. Ec. Polyt.*, 2nd series, **21**, 62 (1921) ; S. T. Bowden, *The Phase Rule and Phase Reactions* (London, 1945).

limits both the temperature and pressure can be fixed arbitrarily. Thus if we plot the pressure p as ordinate and T as abscissa, the representative point of the system can take up any position in the area covered by the diagram.

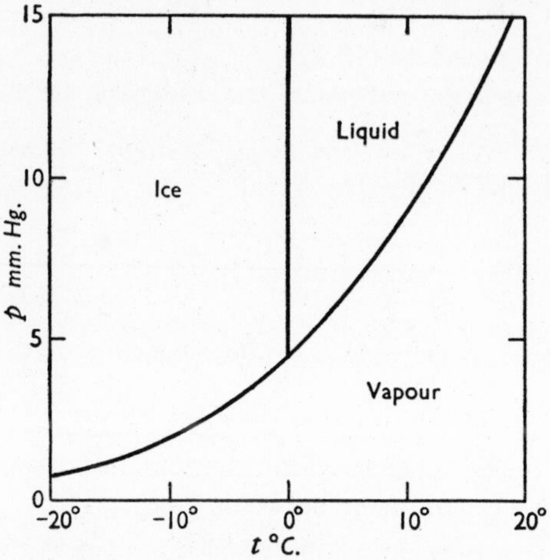

FIG. 13.1. Phase diagram of water at low pressures.

(ii) if the system contains *two phases* (liquid and vapour, liquid and solid, or solid and vapour) then

$$\phi = 2 \quad \text{and} \quad w = 1.$$

The system is said to be *monovariant.* We can, for example, fix the temperature arbitrarily, but the equilibrium pressure exerted by the two phases will then be a function of the chosen temperature. The representative points of two phase systems will thus be grouped along *lines.* At each point on the line the affinity of passage of the substance from one phase to the other is zero.

(iii) if three phases are present in the system (vapour, liquid and solid)

$$\phi = 3 \quad \text{and} \quad w = 0.$$

The system is *invariant.* We cannot fix either T or p arbitrarily. Experimentally we find indeed that equilibrium between the three states of a substance can only exist at well defined values of the temperature and pressure. This point at which pure solid, liquid and vapour are in equilibrium is called the *triple point.*

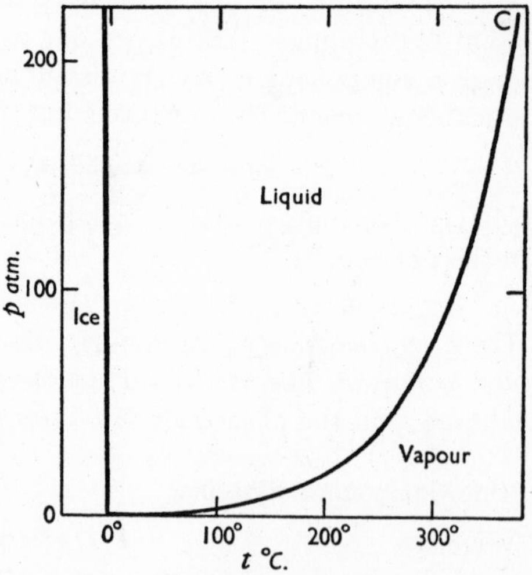

FIG. 13.2. Phase diagram of water at moderate pressures.

For water, the coexistence of the three phases occurs at a temperature of $+0{\cdot}0076$ °C and a pressure of $4{\cdot}6$ mm. of mercury. The phase diagram for water at low pressures (a few mm. of mercury) is shown in fig. 13.1. The three curves which meet at the triple point are the vapour pressure curve of ice, the vapour pressure curve of liquid water and the curve of coexistence of ice and liquid water ; the latter is practically vertical. Fig. 13.2 refers to pressures reaching up to several hundred atmospheres and shows the critical point (C) above which liquid and vapour cannot be distinguished. Finally, fig. 13.3 shows the phase diagram of water up to 30,000 atm.* At very high pressures we see that various polymorphic forms of ice can exist. Any two of these are separated by a line along which they can coexist, while there are also several triple points corresponding to the coexistence of three forms of ice, for example ice II, ice III and ice V.

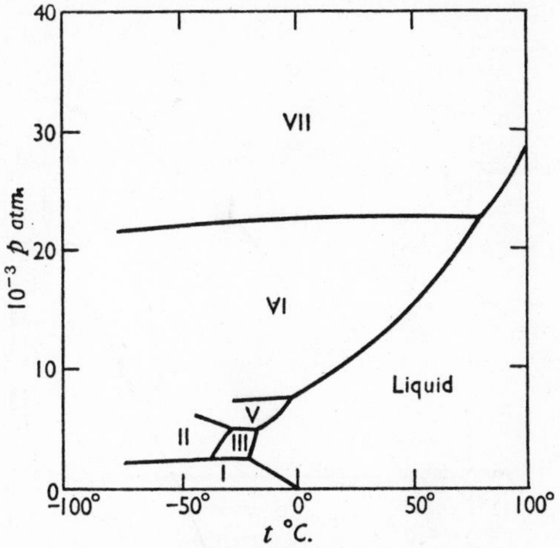

FIG. 13.3. Phase diagram of water at very high pressures.*

3. Binary Systems.

Melting point curves : Eutectics.

For the moment we shall consider a system of two components A and B which do not form a solid solution. The pressure applied to the system is always assumed to be greater than the vapour pressure of the liquid mixture. The only phases which can be present are therefore the liquid solution A + B, the solid A and the solid B. We also assume that A and B do not react with one another chemically.

Consider first the two phase system, solution + solid. Here we have $c=2$, $\phi=2$, $r'=0$ so that the phase rule gives $w=2$, *i.e.* the system is divariant. We can therefore fix two of the intensive variables arbitrarily, for example the mole fraction x_B in the solution and the pressure p. The temperature at which equilibrium is established is then a function of these two variables. For many purposes we may consider systems at constant pressure (for example atmospheric pressure). The equilibrium diagram can then be represented in two dimensions as in fig. 13.4 in which CE gives the equilibrium temperature T between solution and solid A as a function of the concentration of the solution x_B. Similarly DE corresponds to equilibrium between the solution

* P. W. Bridgman, *J. Chem. Phys.*, **5**, 964 (1937).

and solid B. At the point of intersection E of these two curves the solution is in equilibrium with both crystals of A and crystals of B.

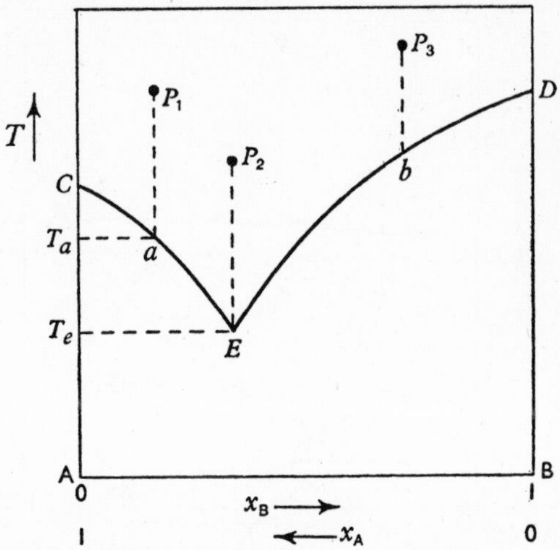

FIG. 13.4. Freezing point curves of a binary system which forms an eutectic. (p = constant).

The point E is called the *eutectic point*, and at this point the system has the *eutectic composition* at the *eutectic temperature*. Since a binary system containing three phases (solution, solid A and solid B) is univariant, the position of the eutectic point is a function only of the applied pressure. In fact, of course, in view of the small influence which the applied pressure has upon the properties of liquids and solids (*cf.* chap. XII) the eutectic point is very little affected by changes of pressure (but see chap. XXII, § 5).

All points on the diagram lying above the curve CED represent conditions under which the solution can exist alone at the given pressure p : the one phase system is a trivariant system and all the variables T, p and x_B can be varied arbitrarily.

If a solution represented by the point P_1 is cooled, the representative point moves along the line P_1a : the temperature falls while the composition remains the same. At a crystals of A begin to separate and the concentration of B in the solution increases. The system can now only exist in equilibrium when the state of the liquid phase follows the line aE. At E both A and B crystallize out and since the composition of the solution must now remain constant, the two solid phases must be produced in just the same mole fractions as exist in the eutectic liquid.*

Solidification of the solution thus begins at a temperature T_a at a, and is completed at the eutectic temperature T_e.

Similarly a solution represented by P_3 follows the route P_3bE on cooling : solidification sets in at b, the composition and temperature change along bE and the last portions of solid have the eutectic composition and separate at the eutectic temperature. Finally, a solution such as P_2 whose composition is the same as the eutectic composition freezes completely at the eutectic temperature.

* Eutectic, derived from the Greek, means "well interwoven" and signifies that at this concentration the solid which is formed is an intimate mixture of crystals of A and B.

The cooling curves, of temperature against time, corresponding to initial liquids of composition P_1, P_2 and P_3 are shown in fig. 13.5. In the case of P_1 and P_3 the curve exhibits a break at T_a and T_b respectively, while the temperature remains steady at the eutectic

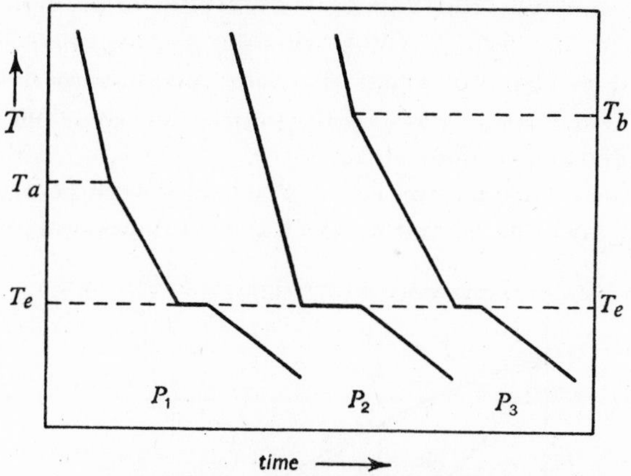

FIG. 13.5. Cooling curves of liquid of composition P_1 (Fig. 13.4), P_2, P_3 as a function of time (t).

temperature until the whole system is solid. A study of cooling curves of liquids covering the whole range of composition enables the phase diagram to be obtained experimentally.

Compound formation in Binary Systems.

If A and B can react together to form an addition compound C, then $c=3$ and $r'=1$ so that $c-r'=2$ as in the previous example. Thus the existence of an addition compound does not affect the variance of the system, the behaviour of which can be represented by curves analogous to those discussed above, but a little more complicated. This case will be examined in more detail in chaps. XXIII and XXIX.

Experiments carried out in the presence of air.

We have supposed in the preceding discussion that the experiments have been carried out in the absence of a vapour phase. We come to the same general conclusion however if air is present since the variance of a system is not altered if we add both a new phase (the vapour phase) and a new constituent (air). We note that air can be regarded as a single component since its composition remains constant throughout (aside from the vapours derived from the solution).

Vapour Pressure of a Binary Liquid.

We now consider a liquid mixture composed of A and B in the presence of a vapour phase also consisting of A and B. Again we suppose that A and B do not react together chemically. We have $c=2$, $r'=0$, $\phi=2$

so that $w=2$, and the system is divariant. We can therefore vary two intensive variables arbitrarily and study the variation of the other variables in terms of them. In this example we shall be interested in two cases, first that in which we fix the temperature and study the variation of pressure and vapour composition in terms of the mole fraction x_B^l in the liquid, which we take as the other independent variable; and secondly where the total pressure is fixed and the equilibrium temperature and vapour composition are given as functions of the liquid concentration.

In fig. 13.6 we consider first curve (I) where the temperature has been taken as constant (30 °C) and in which the total pressure over mixtures

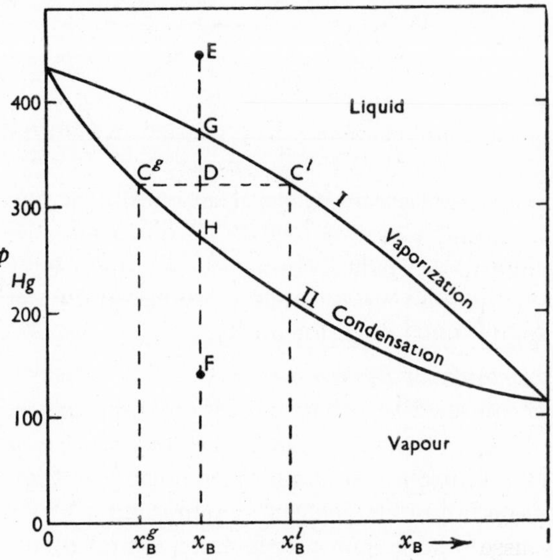

FIG. 13.6. Total vapour pressures of mixtures of carbon disulphide (A) and benzene (B) at 30 °C.

of carbon disulphide (A) and benzene (B) is given as a function of the mole fraction of B in the liquid phase, x_B^l. Alternatively we may take the vapour composition (x_B^g) as independent variable and plot a curve (II) of p against x_B^g. The first important property of this diagram is that when a horizontal line cuts curves I and II at C^l and C^g (say), then these points, corresponding to the same pressure, give the composition of the liquid x_B^l and the vapour x_B^g which are in equilibrium with one another at the pressure p. Curve I is called the *vaporization curve*, and curve II the *condensation curve*.

A point E situated above curve I corresponds to liquid of composition x_B at a pressure too high to allow the presence of vapour phase.

Similarly F represents a vapour phase of the same composition. Finally a point D within the area enclosed by the two curves represents a two-phase system consisting of liquid C^l and vapour C^g in such proportions that the *overall* composition of the whole system is x_B. The concentrations in the two phases are, as explained above, x_B^l and x_B^g. The ratio of the amounts of the two phases can be calculated as follows. Let n be the total number of moles in the system while x_B is the overall mole fraction of B. Then

$$x_B = \frac{n_B^l + n_B^g}{n_B^l + n_B^g + n_A^l + n_A^g}.$$

Now

$$(n^l + n^g)\,x_B = n^l x_B^l + n^g x_B^g$$

or

$$\frac{n^l}{n^g} = \frac{x_B^g - x_B}{x_B - x_B^l}.$$

The ratio of the number of moles contained in the liquid and vapour phases is therefore equal to the inverse ratio of DC^l to C^gD.

Thus if D is close to the vaporization curve, the system will nearly all be in the liquid phase, while as D approaches the condensation curve more and more of the system will be vaporized.

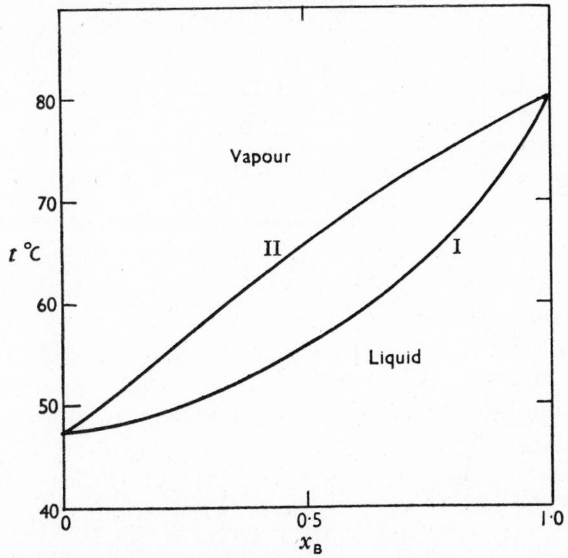

FIG. 13.7. Curves of temperature against composition at constant p (1 atm.) for mixtures of carbon disulphide (A) and benzene (B).

An alternative method of representing the behaviour of a system of this kind is to consider it under conditions of constant pressure, (fig. 13.7) we then obtain curve I, the boiling point as a function of liquid composition x_B^l; and curve II, the composition of vapour x_B^g in equilibrium with liquid at a given temperature.

Melting point curves where Solid Solutions are formed.

If, contrary to what was assumed in (*a*), the two solids A and B can form solid solutions, then the phase diagram is similar in many respects to that for the vapour pressure of binary liquids. Thus if the applied pressure is fixed the diagram has the general form shown in fig. 13.8;

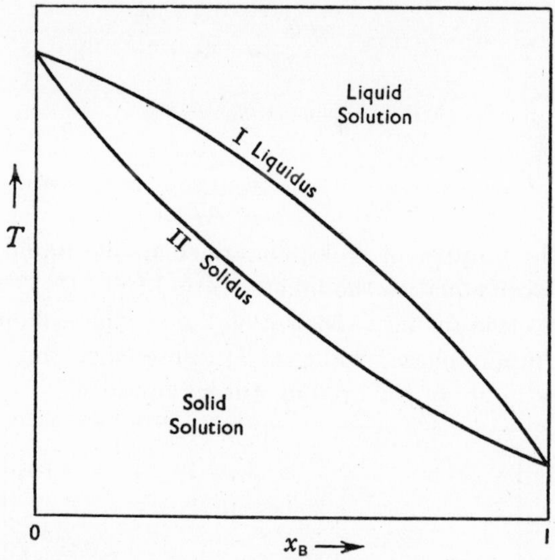

FIG. 13.8. Curves of temperature against composition for solid-liquid equilibrium where solid solutions are formed (p = constant).

curve I, called the *liquidus*, gives the temperatures at which solutions of varying composition commence to crystallize, while curve II, the *solidus*, gives the composition of solid which is deposited from the liquid at the same temperature.

4. Ternary Systems.*

As first pointed out by Gibbs the composition of a solution containing three components may be represented by a point in an equilateral triangle whose vertices A, B and C represent the three pure components. If the side of the triangle is taken as unity, then the mole fractions x_A, x_B and x_C in the solution under consideration are given by the distances, measured along lines parallel to the sides of the triangle,

* There is a vast literature on ternary systems; in particular, mention should be made of the work of H. W. Bakhuis Roozeboom, *Die Heterogenen Gleichgewichte* (Amsterdam, 1901–1911), work continued by F. A. H. Schreinemakers and R. Vogel [50]. See also the work of Findlay and of Bancroft; *Cf.* esp. G. Masing, *Ternäre Systeme* (Leipzig, 1933). Eng. Trans. by B. A. Rogers (London, 1944).

of the point P from the sides of the triangle remote from A, B and C respectively (fig. 13.9 (a)). This representation ensures automatically that

$$x_A + x_B + x_C = 1.$$

This is easily shown by reference to fig. 13.9 (b), from which it is seen that the sum of the three lengths which represent x_A, x_B and x_C is equal to the side of the triangle, *i.e.* to unity.

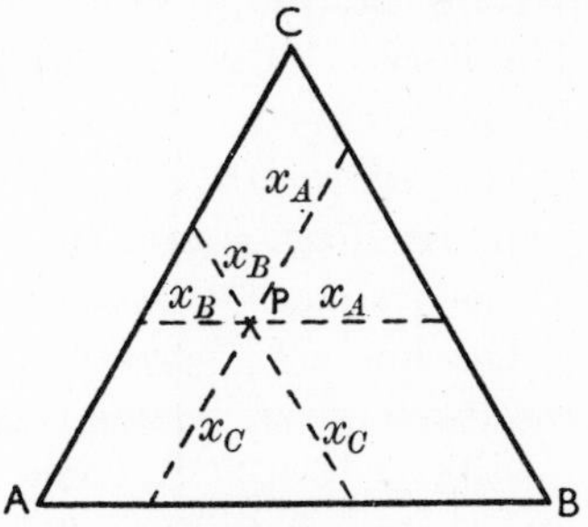

FIG. 13.9 (a).

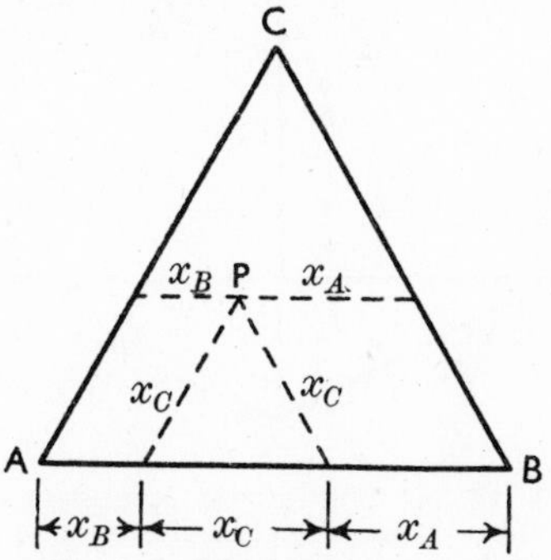

FIG. 13.9 (b).

Representation of ternary systems in triangular co-ordinates.

Furthermore we see that the sides of the triangle represent the binary systems (A + B), (B + C) and (C + A) ; and the vertices represent pure components.

We see then that

(i) any line drawn parallel to a side of a triangle corresponds to a series of ternary systems in which one of the mole fractions remains constant, and

(ii) any line drawn through an apex represents a series of systems in which the mole fractions of two components remain in a constant ratio.

To represent the variation in some property of a solution which is a function of the composition we employ a three-dimensional diagram the base of which is a triangle : the height of the representative point above the base is proportional to the property under consideration.

Solidification of a Ternary System.

Let us consider a solution of three substances A, B and C which do not react together, and suppose the solution is in equilibrium with one of the solid components. Then $c = 3$, $r' = 0$, $\phi = 2$ whence $w = 3$ and the system is trivariant. We can thus consider the pressure and composition of the solution (p, x_A, x_B) and see how the equilibrium temperature changes with these variables. Let us take the pressure as constant, then we may construct a diagram like fig. 13.10 in which the equilibrium temperature between liquid and one of the solid phases is shown as a function of composition (x_A, x_B). The surface $B'k_2Kk_1$ is the equilibrium surface for the system solution + crystals of B; $C'k_2Kk_3$ corresponds to solution + crystals of C, while $A'k_1Kk_3$ is for the system solution + crystals of A. The curve $A'k_1B'$ is clearly the solidification curve for the binary system AB, with a eutectic k_1; similarly $B'k_2C'$ and $C'k_3A'$ refer to the systems BC and CA.

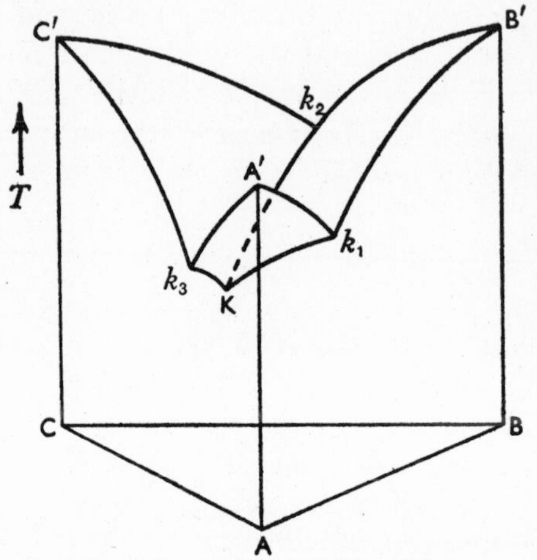

FIG. 13.10. Solid-liquid equilibrium surfaces for Ternary System forming eutectic (p = constant).

The line Kk_1 corresponds to the three phase system solution + solid A + solid B; this is a divariant system but when p is fixed the representative points for the solution lie on a line.

The three lines k_1K, k_2K and k_3K meet at K which is the ternary eutectic point at which the four phases, liquid, solid A, solid B and solid C are in equilibrium. This system is monovariant, but at a given pressure there is only one point representing this state, namely K.

Experiments carried out in the presence of air.

As before we can show easily that experiments carried out in the presence of air at constant pressure can be represented in the same way. We may consider air as an extra component, but we also add a new phase (vapour) so that the variance of the system is unaltered.

Evolution of a representative point.

If we project the lines Kk_1, Kk_2 and Kk_3 in fig. 13.10 on to the base of the diagram we obtain the triangular diagram shown in fig. 13.11. Suppose we consider what happens when a solution of composition P is cooled from a temperature above the melting point of the system. Crystallization begins when the perpendicular from P meets the surface $B'k_1Kk_2$; initially

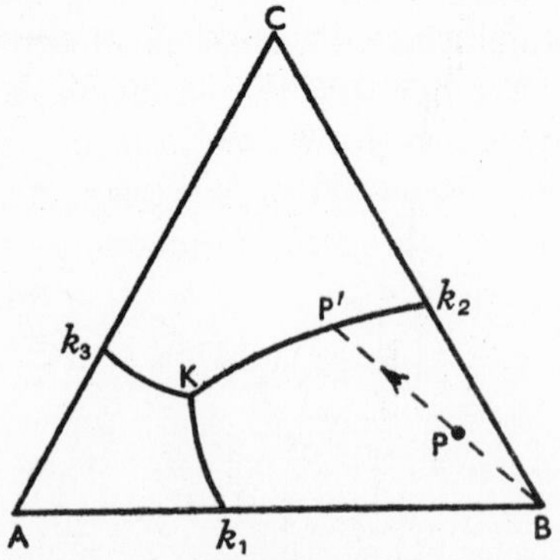

FIG. 13.11. Solidification of a ternary system forming eutectic.

B crystallizes out and the concentrations of A and C in the solution increase. Since the concentrations of A and C must remain in a constant ratio the composition changes along the line PP' which radiates from B. When the point P' is reached crystallization of C begins as well, and as the temperature falls the composition of liquid follows the line $P'K$ until at K all three components crystallize out in the eutectic proportions until the system is completely solid. Whatever the initial composition of the system the eutectic is reached when the system is cooled sufficiently.

As an example of a ternary system exhibiting this type of behaviour we may quote the alloy system Bi + Pb + Sn.

Bi : M.P. 268 °C. Pb : M.P. 325 °C. Sn : M.P. 232 °C.

Bi + Pb	Binary eutectic (55 weight per cent Bi)	: 127 °C
Pb + Sn	Binary eutectic (63 weight per cent Sn)	: 182 °C
Bi + Sn	Binary eutectic (58 weight per cent Bi)	: 133 °C
Bi + Pb + Sn	Ternary eutectic (52 weight per cent Bi ; 32 weight per cent Pb ; 16 weight per cent Sn)	: 96 °C

More complicated diagrams are of course obtained when the various components can form solid solutions in one another.

Ternary Systems in which the three Components are linked by a Chemical Reaction.

Here the variance is reduced by one so that the behaviour is simplified. One example of a system of this kind is the calcium carbonate, lime, carbon dioxide system in which the reaction

$$CaCO_3 \rightleftharpoons CaO + CO_2$$

can occur. We have three phases so that with $c = 3$ and $r' = 1$, there is only one degree of freedom. The system is monovariant and, at equilibrium, its state is completely specified when the temperature is fixed. Thus the pressures of carbon dioxide at equilibrium at a series of temperatures are :

725 °C	71·2 mm. Hg.
750 °C	100 mm. Hg.
815 °C	230 mm. Hg.
860 °C	420 mm. Hg.

5. Conditions of Enclosure.

In the preceding paragraphs we have been concerned with conditions governing the *intensive variables*. The phase rule is concerned only with the physico-chemical state of the phases which are present, the state being characterized by the values of the intensive variables. The phase rule can thus be applied both to open systems, where transfer of matter to or from the system can occur, as well as to closed systems.

In what follows we shall extend our considerations to cover a complete specification of the state of a system in terms of both intensive and extensive variables. To do this we must consider closed systems and ask ourselves how many variables must be fixed to *determine completely* the equilibrium state of the system, that is to determine the intensive and extensive variables characterizing each phase.

Let us consider a closed system of c components and ϕ phases. We have already seen that in a *closed* system in which r' distinct reactions can occur, the increase in the number of moles of component i in the whole system is given by (*cf.* 1.64′)

$$dn_i = \sum_{\rho=1}^{r'} \nu_{i,\rho}\, d\xi_\rho, \tag{13.9}$$

where the summation includes all reactions, except those which consist simply of passage of a substance from one phase to another and which cannot therefore alter the total mass of the substance in the system.

If the initial numbers of moles of the various components are $n_1^0, \ldots n_c^0$ at $t=0$, and if we measure the extents of reaction from this initial state (*i.e.* we put $\xi_1^0=0, \ldots \xi_{r'}^0=0$), then (13.9) can be integrated to give

$$n_i = n_i^0 + \sum_{\rho=1}^{r'} \nu_{i,\rho}\xi_\rho, \quad (i=1 \ldots c). \tag{13.10}$$

By putting i successively 1, 2 ... c we thus obtain c equations which give the final state of a closed system in terms of the initial state. These are called the *conditions of enclosure*.

By multiplying (13.10) by M_i, the molecular weight of i, we can write these conditions in the form

$$m_i = m_i^0 + \sum_{\rho=1}^{r'} \nu_{i,\rho} M_i \xi_\rho, \tag{13.10′}$$

in which we are concerned with the total mass of each component in the system.

The total number n^α of moles in each phase can be introduced into these equations since

$$n_i = \sum_\alpha n_i^\alpha = \sum_\alpha x_i^\alpha n^\alpha$$

so that (13.10) can also be put in the form

$$\sum_\alpha x_i^\alpha n^\alpha - \sum_{\rho=1}^{r'} \nu_{i,\rho}\xi_\rho = n_i^0. \tag{13.11}$$

Alternatively, if we wish to consider the total mass of each phase we can do so by using (13.10′) and introducing weight fractions.

$$w_i^\alpha = \frac{m_i^\alpha}{m^\alpha} \qquad (13.12)$$

where m^α is the mass of phase α. This gives us the equation

$$\sum_\alpha w_i^\alpha m^\alpha - \sum_{\rho=1}^{r'} \nu_{i,\rho} M_i \xi_\rho = m_i^0. \qquad (13.13)$$

6. Duhem's Theorem.

We shall say that the state of a system is *completely determined* when we know :

(i) The physico-chemical state of each phase, defined for example by the intensive variables

$$T, p, w_1^1 \dots w_c^\phi. \qquad (13.14)$$

(ii) The extensive variables for each phase. We may take as the independent extensive variables the masses

$$m^1 \dots m^\phi \qquad (13.15)$$

of the phases of the system. If we know the intensive variables and the masses of the various phases we can calculate the other extensive variables.

Thus the volume is

$$V = \sum_\alpha m^\alpha \underline{v}^\alpha \qquad (13.16)$$

where $\underline{v}^\alpha$ is the specific volume of phase α, which can be expressed in terms of $T, p, w_1^\alpha \dots w_c^\alpha$.

Let us now consider a closed system, characterized by some given initial state, and enquire how many variables must be given to determine completely the final equilibrium state of the system.

The number of variables is $2 + c\phi$ from (13.14) and ϕ from (13.15) giving a total of $(2 + c\phi + \phi)$. These are related by the following equations :

(i) the ϕ relations

$$\sum_i w_i^\alpha = 1 \quad (\alpha = 1, \dots \phi), \qquad (13.17)$$

(ii) the $c(\phi - 1)$ conditions of equilibrium for partition of each component among the ϕ phases

$$\mu_i^1 = \mu_i^2 = \dots = \mu_i^\phi \quad (i = 1, \dots c), \qquad (13.18)$$

(iii) the r' conditions of equilibrium for the chemical reactions

$$\mathsf{A}_\rho = \sum_i \nu_{i,\rho} \mu_i = 0 \quad (\rho = 1, \dots r), \qquad (13.19)$$

(iv) the c conditions of enclosure (13.13) which introduce at the same time r' new variables $\xi_1, \ldots \xi_{r'}$.

We thus have

$$2 + c\phi + \phi + r' \quad \text{variables,}$$

$$\text{and} \quad \phi + c(\phi - 1) + r' + c \quad \text{equations;}$$

the difference between them thus gives *two* as the number of independent variables. *Duhem's theorem** therefore states that :

Whatever the number of phases, of components or of chemical reactions, the equilibrium state of a closed system, for which we know the initial masses $m_1^0 \ldots m_c^0$, is completely determined by two independent variables.

7. Choice of Independent Variables.

The phase rule as we have already seen, limits the number of *intensive* variables which we can fix arbitrarily for a system in equilibrium. This will clearly influence our freedom of choice of the variables completely determining the state of a closed system. The various cases which arise may be summarized as follows :

(*a*) If, in the sense of the phase rule, the system is *invariant*, we cannot employ any intensive variable to specify the final state of the system. We must therefore fix two extensive variables ; these may be for example the masses of two phases, or the mass of one phase and the total volume of the system.

To fix our ideas let us consider conditions at the triple point of water. The initial mass m of water is given, so that we can choose arbitrarily the mass m^s of ice, and m^l of liquid ; the rest of the water must be in the vapour phase (m^g). The total volume of the system is also completely determined since

$$V = m^s \underline{v}^s + m^l \underline{v}^l + m^g \underline{v}^g.$$

The various specific volumes are functions of temperature and pressure but T and p are already fixed at the triple point temperature and pressure.

Alternatively, if the total volume and the mass of one of the phases is given, the masses of the other two can be calculated from the two simultaneous equations :

$$m = m^s + m^l + m^g,$$

$$V = m^s \underline{v}^s + m^l \underline{v}^l + m^g \underline{v}^g.$$

(*b*) If the system is *monovariant* we can clearly choose one intensive variable arbitrarily, for example the temperature. The second variable

* Duhem, [15], vol. IV.

must then be an extensive variable, for example the mass of one of the phases or the total volume.

A given monovariant closed system thus has the remarkable property that its state is completely determined when, in addition to one intensive variable, we know the total volume: in particular the mass of each phase is determined.

For example, let us consider the monovariant equilibrium between liquid water and its vapour. Suppose the total mass of the system (given initially) is 1,000 g. We wish to see how the state of the system is completely determined if we know one intensive variable (T), and the total volume: let us take $T = 199$ °C and $V = 2$ litres. The pressure exerted in the system is now determined—it is the vapour pressure of water at 199 °C *i.e.* 15 atm. Under these conditions the specific volumes of steam and water are 129·3 cm.³/g. and 1·15 cm.³/g. respectively. The total volume of the system can therefore be expressed in terms of the mass m^l of the liquid phase:

$$m^l \times 1{\cdot}15 + (1000 - m^l) \times 129{\cdot}3 = 2000,$$

whence

$$m^l = 993{\cdot}37 \text{ g. and } m^g = 6{\cdot}63 \text{ g.}$$

(*c*) If the system is *polyvariant* we can clearly choose two intensive variables, for example T and p, as the variables in Duhem's theorem. These two variables are sufficient, in general, to determine completely the equilibrium state in a closed system of this kind.

As an example of this behaviour we may take the divariant system composed of a mixture of carbon disulphide and benzene and their vapours. The total masses of the two components in the closed system are given initially. We know from the phase rule that if T and p are fixed the physico-chemical state of the system is determined, that is to say the mole fractions or weight fractions of the components in both liquid and vapour phase are determined. As we have seen these weight fractions are, in general, different. If we know these weight fractions and the initial masses of the components m_A^0 and m_B^0 we can calculate the masses of the two phases from the equations

$$\left.\begin{aligned} w_A^l m^l + w_A^g m^g &= m_A^0, \\ w_B^l m^l + w_B^g m^g &= m_B^0 \end{aligned}\right\}. \tag{13.20}$$

When the mass of each phase is known the other extensive properties are readily calculated (*e.g.* the volume of each phase, and the total volume).

In the same way we can determine the state completely from a knowledge of one extensive variable and one intensive variable (*e.g.* V and T) or from two extensive variables (*e.g.* m^l and m^g).

8. Note on Azeotropic Systems and Indifferent States.

We must mention however, that in certain special cases—called *indifferent states*—the choice of variables T and p is not convenient in the sense that for these systems these two variables do not suffice to calculate all the others. We indicate below the way in which this state of affairs arises, but a detailed examination is deferred until chap. XXIX.

Let us consider, to fix our ideas, a mixture of water and alcohol in the presence of the two vapours. This system, of two phases and two components, is *divariant*. Suppose we choose some fixed pressure (say 1 atm.) and study the composition of the system at equilibrium as a

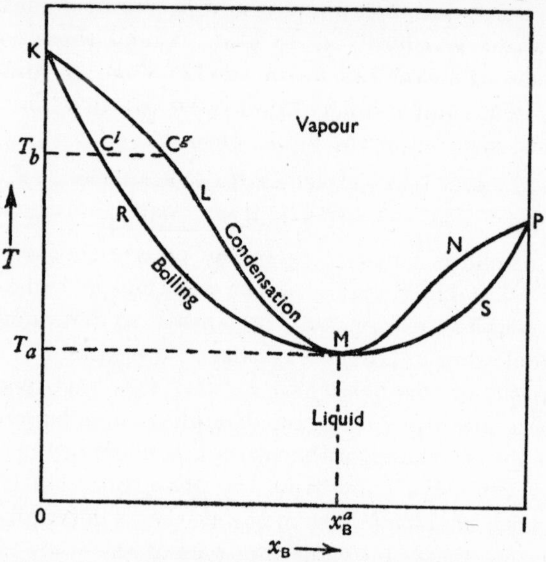

FIG. 13.12. Vapour-liquid equilibrium in a binary system forming an azeotrope (p = constant).

function of temperature, then the experimental results will be as shown, schematically, in fig. 13.12. The vapour curve *KLMNP* gives the composition of the vapour as a function of temperature T, and the liquid curve *KRMSP* gives the composition of the liquid as a function of temperature. These two curves have a common point M.

The state represented by M is that in which the two states, vapour and liquid have the same composition x_B^a on the mole fraction scale. Because of the special properties associated with systems in this state, the point M is called an *azeotropic point*, and the system is said to form an *azeotrope*.

Now we consider a system, at a pressure of 1 atm., and at a temperature T_b. The compositions of the two phases at equilibrium are given by the mole fractions corresponding to the two points C^l and C^g. If however we consider the temperature T_a corresponding to the point M, then the two phases have the same composition and therefore

$$\left.\begin{aligned} w_A^l &= w_A^g, \\ w_B^l &= w_B^g \end{aligned}\right\}, \tag{13.21}$$

and hence the two equations (13.20) are indeterminate. There are thus an infinity of values of m^l which satisfy these equations.

We see therefore, that for values of T and p for which the liquid and vapour compositions are equal, there are an infinite number of equilibrium states which differ from one another only in the amounts of liquid and vapour which are present. In an azeotropic system, one phase may be transformed to the other *at constant temperature, pressure and composition* without affecting the equilibrium state.*

This means that *in the case of a system which forms an azeotrope, Duhem's theorem ceases to be valid if the temperature and pressure are chosen corresponding to the point at which the compositions of the two phases are equal.* If instead of T and p we choose T and V as the variables then these systems do not present any anomaly.

The above property for the divariant system water + alcohol can be generalized for polyvariant systems. For any system which, for a certain set of values of the intensive variables T, p, $w_1^1 \dots w_c^\phi$, leads to a set of c equations

$$\left.\begin{aligned} \sum_\alpha w_1^\alpha m^\alpha - \sum_\rho \nu_{1,\rho} M_1 \xi_\rho &= m_1^0 \\ \cdot \quad \cdot \quad \cdot \quad \cdot \quad & \cdot \\ \sum_\alpha w_c^\alpha m^\alpha - \sum_\rho \nu_{c,\rho} M_c \xi_\rho &= m_c^0 \end{aligned}\right\} \tag{13.22}$$

which are indeterminate in the variables $m^1 \dots m^\phi$; $\xi_1 \dots \xi_r$, the masses of the various phases present will be indeterminate.

The state of a system for which the intensive variables have values $T, p, w_1^1 \dots w_c^\phi$ such that the equations (13.22) are indeterminate, is called an *indifferent state*. This name was introduced by Duhem.†

The point M in fig. 13.12 represents a particular case of an indifferent state. A more extensive study of indifferent states will be given in chap. XXIX.

* This property justifies the name *azeotropy* which means a system which boils unchanged. The term " azeotropic mixtures " was introduced by J. Wade and R. W. Merriman (*J. Chem. Soc.*, 99, 1004 (1911)), while " azeotropism " was used by M. Lecat, *cf.* [31] ; more recently J. J. van Laar introduced the term " azeotropy ". (*Cf. Tables annuelles des constantes*, Vol. 10, 1st ed., (Paris, 1934)).

† P. Duhem, *J. Phys. Chem.*, 2, 31 (1898).

CHAPTER XIV

PHASE CHANGES

1. The Clausius-Clapeyron Equation.

In the last chapter we established two powerful general theorems, those of Gibbs and Duhem, relating to heterogeneous systems. We shall now consider in more detail the quantitative behaviour of some simple systems, beginning with a study of the phase changes of a pure substance. A study of more complex heterogeneous systems will follow in later chapters after we have discussed the thermodynamic conditions of stability.

We consider first a single component system in two phases. The chemical potential of the substance will be determined solely by the temperature and pressure; so also will the affinity of the phase change. At equilibrium we must of course have

$$\mathbf{A}(T, p) = 0 \qquad (14.1)$$

so that if either of the intensive variables T or p is given, the value of the other at equilibrium can be calculated. This is in agreement with the phase rule (13.5) which shows that such a system ($c=1$, $r'=0$, $\phi=2$) is monovariant. We can therefore show on a graph of T and p, the line $\mathbf{A}=0$ corresponding to equilibrium (fig. 14.1).

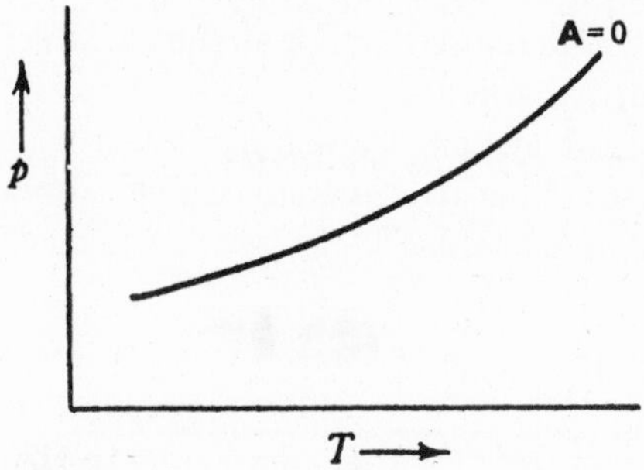

FIG. 14.1.

The differential equation which this line satisfies can be derived easily, since in any displacement along the line the affinity remains zero.

Hence, along this line, for any arbitrary change

$$\delta \mathbf{A} = 0. \qquad (14.2)$$

We may now employ equation (4.58) or (4.60), remembering that $\mathbf{A}$ depends only on T and p, to obtain

$$-\frac{1}{T}\left(\frac{\partial H}{\partial \xi}\right)_{T,p} \delta T + \left(\frac{\partial V}{\partial \xi}\right)_{T,p} \delta p = 0, \qquad (14.3)$$

or

$$\frac{\delta p}{\delta T} = \frac{(\partial H/\partial \xi)_{T,p}}{T(\partial V/\partial \xi)_{T,p}}. \qquad (14.4)$$

This is the *Clausius-Clapeyron equation*.

Evaporation of a Liquid.

If the phase change under consideration consists of the evaporation of a liquid or a solid, then the latent heat of evaporation $\Delta_e h$, which is by definition equal to the heat of reaction $\partial H/\partial \xi$ corresponding to the phase change, can be evaluated from equation (14.4) which can be written

$$\boxed{\frac{\delta p}{\delta T}=\frac{\Delta_e h}{T\Delta_e v}}, \tag{14.5}$$

where $\Delta_e v$ is the volume change of evaporation per mole.

This equation can be put in a simpler approximate form if it is assumed that the vapour phase behaves as a perfect gas, and if the molar volume of the condensed phase is neglected in comparison with that of the vapour. With those assumptions

$$\Delta_e v = v^g - v^{cond} \simeq v^g = RT/p \tag{14.6}$$

so that (14.5) becomes

$$\frac{\delta \ln p}{\delta T}=\frac{\Delta_e h}{RT^2}. \tag{14.7}$$

Making the further assumption that $\Delta_e h$ is independent of temperature in the interval considered, (14.7) may be integrated to give the approximate equation

$$\ln p = -\frac{\Delta_e h}{RT}+C, \tag{14.8}$$

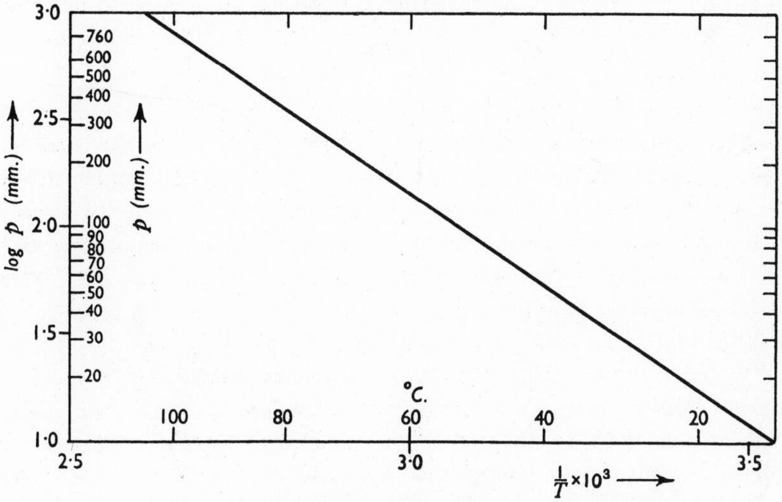

FIG. 14.2. Vapour pressure of water as function of temperature: $\log_{10} p$ against $1/T$.

where C is a constant independent of temperature. Thus a graph of $\ln p$ against $1/T$ should be a straight line. Fig. 14.2 shows this graph in the case of the evaporation of water.

*Example : Vaporization of Water.**

Let us consider the evaporation of water at 100 °C and at a pressure of 1 atm. ; $\delta p/\delta T$ may be obtained either by differentiation of an empirical equation which represents the vapour pressure accurately as a function of temperature, or from accurate measurements in the range considered.

Thus at 99·90 °C it is found that $p = 757{\cdot}29$ mm. Hg, while at 100·10 °C, $p = 762{\cdot}72$ mm. Hg. Hence

$$\frac{\delta p}{\delta T} = \frac{762{\cdot}72 - 757{\cdot}92}{0{\cdot}20} = 27{\cdot}2 \text{ mm. Hg/ °C} = 0{\cdot}0358 \text{ atm./ °C.}$$

Also

$$\Delta_e v = v^g - v^l,$$

where v^g and v^l are the molar volumes of the two phases at 1 atm. and at 100 °C. These are

$$v^g = 18{\cdot}0 \times 1{\cdot}67 \text{ litre/mole,}$$

$$v^l = 18{\cdot}0 \times 0{\cdot}00104 \text{ litre/mole.}$$

Hence, from (14.8)

$$\Delta_e h = T\Delta_e v \,.\, \frac{\delta p}{\delta T} = 373 \times 0{\cdot}0358 \times 18{\cdot}0 \times 1{\cdot}67$$

$$= 401 \text{ litre atm./mole} = 9{,}710 \text{ cal./mole.}$$

$$= 40{,}600 \text{ joules/mole.}$$

Direct calorimetric measurements give values lying between 9,709 and 9,738 cal./mole, with a probable value of 9,714 cal./mole in good agreement with the calculated value.

Melting of a Solid.

If we consider the melting point of a solid as a function of applied pressure, then we are more interested in the reciprocal of the coefficient in (14.4) *i.e.* in $\delta T/\delta p$. This must be equal to $T\Delta_f v/\Delta_f h$ where $\Delta_f v$ and $\Delta_f h$ are the volume change and latent heat of fusion respectively. If therefore we measure the volume change which accompanies melting and also the slope of the curve of m.p. against pressure, we can evaluate the latent heat of fusion $\Delta_f h$.

Table 14.1 gives some results obtained by Bridgman† for sodium.

We notice that despite the very high pressures employed, the latent heat of fusion varies very little with pressure, although the melting point is considerably affected. The change in volume on fusion decreases steadily as the pressure is increased.

* Eucken [17], p. 278.

† P. W. Bridgman, *Phys. Rev.*, 3, 127, (1914) ; 6, 1, (1915) ; *cf.* also Vogel, [50], p. 45.

TABLE 14.1

Effect of Pressure on Melting of a Solid

p (*kg./cm.*^{2})	*M. P.* °C	$\Delta_f v \cdot 10^5$ (*cm.*^{3}/*g.*)	$\Delta_f h$ (*joule/g.*)
1	97·6	2787	126·5
2000	114·2	2362	119·3
4000	129·8	2072	117·0
6000	142·5	1873	117·6
8000	154·8	1711	119·8
10000	166·7	1556	122·4
12000	177·2	1398	124·7

This behaviour may be compared with that for the evaporation process where as we move along the line of coexistence of liquid and vapour both the change of volume on evaporation, and the latent heat of evaporation tend to zero. At the critical point the value of $\delta p/\delta T$ becomes indeterminate and the line of coexistence ends. It appears that there is no solid-liquid critical point with analogous properties.

2. Vapour Pressure Constants and Chemical Constants.

The condition of equilibrium between a solid and its vapour is (*cf.* 6.74)

$$\mu^s = \mu^g. \tag{14.9}$$

General expressions for the chemical potentials of gases and solids have been derived in chapters X and XII, so that using equations (10.19) and (12.29) and neglecting the effect of pressure on the chemical potential of the solid, we have

$$\ln p = j - \frac{s^s(0, 0)}{R} - \frac{\Delta_e h(0, 0)}{RT} + \frac{c_p^g(0)}{R} \ln T + \frac{1}{R}\int_0^T \frac{dT}{T^2}\int_0^T [c'(T) - c_p^s(T, 0)]\, dT, \tag{14.10}$$

where we have put

$$h^s(0, 0) - h^g(0) = -\Delta_e h(0, 0). \tag{14.11}$$

This notation is justified by the fact that, as we saw in chap. X, $h^g(0)$ may be regarded as the enthalpy of the gas extrapolated to the absolute zero ; $\Delta_e h(0, 0)$ is therefore the heat of evaporation (*i.e.* reaction of phase change) extrapolated to $T=0$ and $p=0$.

We now put

$$i = j - \frac{s^s(0, 0)}{R}, \tag{14.12}$$

where i is called the *vapour pressure constant.*

Thus if we know the heat of evaporation, the specific heats and the vapour pressure we can calculate the vapour pressure constant i.

TABLE 14.2

*Difference between Chemical Constants (j') and Vapour Pressure Constants (i') for some Monatomic Solids**

He	+0·058	±0·065
Ne	+0·026	±0·04
A	−0·02	±0·04
Hg	+0·09	±0·06
K	+0·01	±0·3
Na	+0·10	±0·15
Cd	−0·08	±0·10
Zn	−0·03	±0·05
Pb	+0·39	±0·36
Ag	+0·65	±0.40
Cu	−0·11	±0·40
Mg	+0·05	±0·10

Equation (14.12) enables us to make a direct test of the Nernst heat theorem, for if this is valid then $s(0, 0)$ is zero and

$$i = j \tag{14.13}$$

i.e. the vapour pressure constant and the chemical constant are equal. In tables 10.3 and 10.4 we gave values of both i and j. As shown in table 14.2, the differences between the figures given are usually within the experimental error. There are, however, a number of instances, for example for carbon monoxide, where the difference is certainly real. In the case of carbon monoxide the non-zero entropy of the crystal in the region of absolute zero appears to arise from the different orientations of the carbon monoxide molecules relative to one another which may persist at the lowest temperatures studied experimentally.†

3. Vapour Pressure and Entropy of Vaporization.

We shall now derive an equation for the vapour pressure of a condensed phase in a form which stresses the significance of the entropy of vaporization.

For this purpose we start from (4.3), where in this case,

$$\left(\frac{\partial S}{\partial \xi}\right)_{T,p} = s^g - s^c, \tag{14.14}$$

where s^g and s^c are the molar entropies of the gas and condensed phase

* Eucken, [17], p. 285.

† For a more detailed statistical discussion see Fowler and Guggenheim, [20] chap. V.

respectively. If we assume the gas to be perfect, then we have from (10.10),

$$s^g = s^{\dagger,g}(T) - R \ln p. \tag{14.15}$$

For the condensed phase we have, neglecting the effect of pressure, (*cf.* 12.27) :

$$s^c = s^{\dagger,c}(T). \tag{14.16}$$

If we designate the difference $s^{\dagger,g} - s^{\dagger,c}$ by $\Delta_e s^\dagger$, and $h^g - h^c$ by $\Delta_e h$, we obtain

$$\mathbf{A} = -\Delta_e h + T\Delta_e s^\dagger - RT \ln p, \tag{14.17}$$

so that at equilibrium ($\mathbf{A} = 0$)

$$\ln p = -\frac{\Delta_e h}{RT} + \frac{\Delta_e s^\dagger}{R}. \tag{14.18}$$

We notice that $\Delta_e s^\dagger$ is simply the entropy of evaporation for $p = 1$ atm. and is identical with the standard entropy change ($\Delta_e s^0$).

Thus at $T = 298{\cdot}1$ °K,

$$\ln p = -\frac{\Delta_e h(298{\cdot}1)}{R298{\cdot}1} + \frac{\Delta_e s^\dagger(298{\cdot}1)}{R}. \tag{14.19}$$

This equation is analogous to (10.52).

TABLE 14.3

*Trouton's Rule**

Substance	T_b (°K)	$\Delta_e h$ (*cal./mole*)	$\Delta_e h/T_b$ *cal./deg. mole*
Ne	27·2	415	15·3
N_2	77·5	1360	17·6
A	87·5	1500	17·2
O_2	90·6	1660	18·3
$(C_2H_5)_2O$	307	6470	21·1
CS_2	319	6490	20·4
$CHCl_3$	334	6970	20·8
CCl_4	350	7140	20·4
C_6H_6	353	7350	20·8
Methyl salicylate	497	11000	22·2
Normal organic compounds (mean)	—	—	20–23
CH_3OH	337·7	8380	24·8
CH_3COOH	373·6	5540	14·8

If T is not too different from 298·1 °K we may as an approximation

* *Cf.* Fowler and Guggenheim, [20], p. 334.

equate $\Delta_e h$ and $\Delta_e s^\dagger$ to the values at this temperature. We may therefore extend (14.19) to these temperatures and obtain the approximate equation

$$\ln p = -\frac{\Delta_e h(298{\cdot}1)}{RT} + \frac{\Delta_e s^\dagger(298{\cdot}1)}{R}, \tag{14.20}$$

which is of just the same form as (14.8) except that the constant now has a precise physical meaning.

If we wish to take account of the variation of $\Delta_e h$ and $\Delta_e s^\dagger$ with temperature we proceed exactly as in chap. X, § 8.

It often happens that we do not know the standard entropies of vapour and condensed phase, and in such cases we may, for approximate calculations, employ an empirical rule to estimate the value of $\Delta_e s^\dagger$ at atmospheric pressure. The most important of these is *Trouton's rule*,* which states that the entropy of vaporization at the normal boiling point T_b (*i.e.* when liquid and vapour co-exist at 1 atm. pressure) has a value of about 20 cal./deg. mole. Thus

$$\frac{\Delta_e h}{T_b} \approx 20 \text{ cal./deg. mole.} \tag{14.21}$$

Data to illustrate this rule are given in table 14.3. They show that Trouton's rule only gives the order of magnitude of the entropy of vaporization.†

We notice in particular the low value of the entropy of vaporization of acetic acid which is related to the fact that acetic acid is associated not only in the liquid state but also in the vapour. As a result the increase in the number of complexions (and hence the increase in entropy) on vaporization is much less than, for example, in the case of ethyl alcohol which is associated only in the liquid state.

Besides Trouton's rule we must also mention the modification introduced by Hildebrand,‡ who suggested that the entropies of vaporization should be taken not at the boiling point, but at a temperature such that the concentration ($c = p/RT$) in the vapour phase is a constant. In general, Hildebrand's rule holds more accurately than Trouton's rule. It should be noted, however, that neither of these rules follows from the law of corresponding states, according to which the entropies should be the same at corresponding temperatures, that is to say for a definite value of the ratio T/T_c.§

* F. T. Trouton, *Phil. Mag.*, 18, 54 (1884).

† *Cf.* I. M. Barclay and J. A. V. Butler, *Trans. Faraday Soc.*, 34, 1445 (1938).

‡ J. H. Hildebrand, *J. Amer. Chem. Soc.*, 37, 970 (1915); *ibid.*, 40, 45 (1918); *J. Chem. Phys.*, 7, 233 (1939); J. H. Hildebrand and T. S. Gilman, *ibid.* 15, 229 (1947).

§ E. A. Guggenheim, *J. Chem. Phys.*, 13, 253 (1945).

4. Vapour Pressure and Free Volume.

We shall now examine briefly the calculation of the vapour pressure on the basis of statistical models of the solid and liquid states. Debye's model of the solid state, which we have discussed briefly in chapter XII, § 5, allows us to evaluate the vapour pressure of a solid, but the agreement with experiment is very poor. We obtain only a rough order of magnitude.*

Application of Born's model† does not improve the value obtained for the vapour pressure.|| It is useful, however, to examine a little more closely the idea of free volume introduced in chap. XII, § 6. The fundamental equation

$$G = F + pV$$

gives for a one component system

$$\mu = f + pv \tag{14.22}$$

where f is the free energy per mole.

Now the free energy of a liquid is given by (12.43) so that the chemical potential of the liquid is

$$\mu^l = f^{\ddagger}(T) - RT \ln v_f - \Lambda + pv^l. \tag{14.23}$$

For the same substance in the perfect gas state (10.12) gives

$$\mu^g = f^{\ddagger}(T) - RT \ln \frac{RT}{p} + RT. \tag{14.24}$$

At equilibrium the chemical potentials will be equal and, neglecting pv^l in comparison with RT, we obtain for the vapour pressure

$$p = \frac{RT}{v_f} e^{-\frac{\Lambda + RT}{RT}}. \tag{14.25}$$

This equation shows how the vapour pressure of a liquid is affected by the free volume and the energy of vaporization.

To proceed further it is necessary to employ some particular model. For example if we use the van der Waals model and replace v_f by $(v-b)$ and Λ by a/v (*cf.* 12.48) we have

$$p = \frac{RT}{v-b} e^{-\left(1 + \frac{a}{bRT}\right)}. \tag{14.26}$$

For sufficiently low pressures the molar volume of the liquid can be calculated from (12.49). This is a quadratic equation in v, but at low temperatures

$$v \simeq b\left(1 - \frac{RTb}{a}\right) \tag{14.27}$$

* H. S. Frank, *J. Chem. Phys.*, **13**, 478 (1945).
† M. Born and M. Bradburn, *Proc. Camb. Phil. Soc.*, **39**, 113 (1943).
|| I. Prigogine and G. Garikian (unpublished calculations).

so that (14.26) becomes

$$p = \frac{a}{b^2} e^{-\left(1+\frac{a}{bRT}\right)}, \tag{14.28}$$

or

$$\ln p = \ln \frac{a}{b^2} - 1 - \frac{a}{bRT}. \tag{14.29}$$

This equation is of the correct form (*cf.* 14.8) but if we test it, for example in the case of argon, by inserting values of a and b calculated from the critical constants, we obtain*

$$\log_{10} p_{\text{atm.}} = 3{\cdot}0 - \frac{175}{T},$$

while the experimental values to the same approximation, are given by

$$\log_{10} p_{\text{atm.}} = 4{\cdot}0 - \frac{350}{T}.$$

The agreement is not good.

Alternatively Λ and v_f may be calculated on the basis of the cage-model from equations (12.64) and (12.54), but no better agreement is achieved. It appears that the actual entropy of the liquid is greater than that given by the cage-model, but less than that corresponding to the van der Waals model.

Furthermore the energy of evaporation according to the van der Waals equation is proportional to the density of the liquid (12.48), while the cage-model in its simplest form indicates a proportionality to the square of the density. Equation (12.64) corresponds to a similar but more complicated dependence. Benson† has shown that the experimental data are consistent with a proportionality between Λ and the square of the density.

Finally we mention that the free-volume concept leads to an interpretation of the Trouton and Hildebrand rules.‡

5. Entropy of Fusion.

The entropy of fusion, $\Delta_f h/T_f$, like the entropy of vaporization, exhibits some interesting regularities.

For elements the entropy of fusion lies in the region of $\boldsymbol{R}$, as shown in table 14.4, while for compounds it appears to depend very largely on the molecular shape.

* *Cf.* I. Prigogine and G. Garikian, *J. Chim. Phys.*, **45**, 273 (1948); *cf.* also I. Prigogine, *J. Phys. Rad.*, **5**, 16 (1944).

† S. W. Benson, *J. Chem. Phys.*, **15**, 367 (1947).

‡ H. Eyring and J. O. Hirschfelder, *J. Phys. Chem.*, **41**, 249 (1937). H. S. Frank, *loc. cit.*; I. Prigogine and G. Garikian, *loc. cit.*

Molecules which are roughly spherical have values of $\Delta_f s$ which are approximately the same as for the elements, as is shown in table 14.5, while for straight chain molecules the entropy of fusion increases steadily with the chain length. Thus, in table 14.6, we see that for methane the entropy of fusion corresponds to its spherical shape, while for ethane which is a long ellipsoid the value is over twice as great. Similarly for *n*-octane which melts at 216 °K, $\Delta_f h$ is 4,930 cal./mole so that $\Delta_f s = 22{\cdot}8$ cal./deg. mole.; while its isomer hexamethylethane which is nearly spherical melts at 377 °K with $\Delta_f h = 1{,}700$ cal./mole, and an entropy of fusion of only 4·5 cal./deg. mole. There are many other examples of this kind of behaviour.* The interpretation of the small entropy of fusion of spherical molecules is related to the fact that these compounds acquire free rotation while still in the solid state.†

In general, however, rotation and translation of the molecules are degrees of freedom which are acquired simultaneously on fusion, although sometimes only translational freedom is acquired. This happens, for example, in the case of very long molecules where rotation is prevented by steric factors (anisotropic liquids), and also when the intermolecular forces are powerful and anisotropic as for associated liquids. In these instances the freedom of rotation is achieved progressively as the temperature is raised above the melting point. This is in contrast to spherical molecules which, because of their shape and the symmetry of their force fields, begin to rotate freely in the solid state.

We must however notice that abnormally low values of the entropy of fusion are also encountered with some non-spherical molecules. table 14.7 indicates that some substances classed as " associated " appear to acquire rotational degrees of freedom before melting.

Finally, we see from the data in table 14.8 how the spherical shape of molecules reduces very considerably the domain of existence of the liquid phase.‡ The fusion of hexachloroethane cannot be observed at atmospheric pressure as the substance sublimes directly; fusion can only occur at higher pressures. On the other hand, pentachloroethane which is not symmetrical exists as a liquid for a range of nearly 200 degrees.

* *Cf.* J. Pirsch, *Ber.*, **70**, 1, 12 (1937); L. O. Fischer, *Bull. Soc. Chim. Belg.*, **49**, 129 (1940).

† J. Timmermans, *Physico-chemical Constants of Pure Organic Compounds*, (New York, Amsterdam, London, 1950). For a further discussion of this question see in particular Frenkel, [21].

‡ Among the work devoted to spherical molecules, see J. Pirsch, *loc. cit.*; J. Becker, *Chem. Weekbl.* **29**, 46, (1932); J. Timmermans, *J. Chim. Phys.*, **35**, 311 (1938).

TABLE 14.4

*Entropies of Fusion of some Elements**

Element	$\Delta_f h$ *cal./mole*	T_f (°K)	$\Delta_f s = \frac{\Delta_f h}{T_f}$ *cal./deg. mole*
Li	830	459	1·80
Na	630	370	1·70
K	570	335	1·70
Rb	520	311	1·70
Cs	500	299	3.4
Cu	2750	1356	2·0
Ag	2630	1233	2·2
Au	3180	1336	2·4
Zn	1700	692	2·4
Cd	1500	594	2·5
Hg	560	234	2·4
Al	1910	933	2·0
Ga	1320	303	4·4
Tl	1470	580	2·6
Pb	1120	590	1·90
Ne	80·1	24·5	1·66
A	281	83·8	1·68
K	390·7	116	1·70

TABLE 14.5

Entropies of Fusion of some Spherical Molecules†

Substance	T_f (°C)	$\Delta_f h$ *cal./mole*	$\frac{\Delta_f h}{T_f}$ *cal./deg. mole*
Tetramethylmethane	− 16·7	778	3·0
Tertiary butyl chloride	− 27·1	560	1·9
CF_4	−188·6	167·6	2·0
CCl_4	− 22·9	647	2·6
CBr_4	− 92·3	878	2·4
2·2 dimethylbutane	−101	111	0·6
Hexamethylethane	−104	1700	4·5
Cyclohexene	−104·1	786	4·6
Cyclohexane	6·2	623	2·2
Cyclohexanol	23·9	406	1·3

* *Cf.* Fowler and Guggenheim, [20], p. 330 ; K. Clusius, *Zeit. physik. Chem.*, 31, 456 (1936).

† *Cf.* J. Timmermans and L. Deffet, *Le polymorphisme des composés organiques*. (Paris, 1939). *Cf.* also L. O. Fischer, *Bull. Soc. Chim. Belg.* 49, 129 (1940).

TABLE 14.6

Entropies of Fusion of some Saturated Hydrocarbons and normal Primary Alcohols

Substance	T_f °K	$\Delta_f h$ *cal./mole*	$\frac{\Delta_f h}{T_f}$ *cal./deg. mole*	*Ref.*
CH_4	91·5	224	2·45	(*a*)
C_2H_6	101·4	668	6·57	(*a*)
C_4H_{10}	134	1050	7·85	(*a*)
C_5H_{12}	143·3	2000	13·9	(*a*)
C_6H_{14}	118	3110	17·5	(*a*)
C_8H_{18}	216	4930	22·8	(*a*)
$C_{18}H_{38}$	573·1	10000	33·3	(*a*)
CH_3OH	175·7	757	4·30	(*b*)
C_2H_5OH	156·2	1105	7·05	(*b*)
C_3H_7OH	146·9	1241	8·47	(*b*)
C_4H_9OH	183·9	2215	12·1	(*b*)
$C_5H_{11}OH$	194·1	2348	12·1	(*b*)
$C_6H_{13}OH$	225·9	3678	16·7	(*b*)
$C_{18}H_{37}OH$	331	11700	35·4	(*b*)

(*a*) G. S. Parks and H. M. Huffmann, *Ind. Eng. Chem.*, 23, 1138 (1931); Fischer, *loc. cit.*

(*b*) For bibliography, *cf.* Fischer, *loc. cit.*, p. 149.

TABLE 14.7

Entropies of Fusion of some Associated Substances

Substance	*Entropy of fusion (cal./deg. mole)*
H_2O	5·0
$C(CH_3)_3OH$	5·4
$C(CH_3)_3CH_2OH$	4·0
CCl_3COOH	4·2
$C(CH_3)_3COOH$	2·6
Urea	2·2
Cyclohexanol	1·4

TABLE 14.8

Range of existence of liquid state at atmospheric pressure

Substance	T_f (°C)	T_b (°C)
	Spherical molecules	
Cyclohexane	+ 6	+ 81
Hexachloroethane	+186·8	+185·5
Camphor	+178	+205
Tetramethylmethane	− 16·5	+ 9·5
	Non-spherical molecules	
Methylcyclohexane	−126	+101
Pentachloroethane	− 29·5	+162
Fenchone	+ 6·0	+193
Pentane	−130	+ 36

CHAPTER XV

THERMODYNAMIC STABILITY

1. Production of Entropy during a Perturbation.

Let us consider a system in a state P characterized by physical variables x and y (*e.g.* T and p), together with the extent of reaction ξ_P. Suppose a change takes place such that the system moves to a state P' characterized by $\xi_{P'}$. Then the uncompensated heat corresponding to this change (*cf.* 3.21) is

$$Q'_{PP'} = \int_{\xi_P}^{\xi_{P'}} \mathbf{A}(\xi)\, d\xi, \tag{15.1}$$

and as we have seen, this is closely related to the entropy production (chap. III, § 2).

We remember (chap. I, § 9) that for a specified process we may regard x and y as functions completely determined by ξ. The affinity may now be developed in the form of a Taylor series in the interval ξ_P to $\xi_{P'}$:

$$\mathbf{A}(\xi) = \mathbf{A}_P + \left(\frac{d\mathbf{A}}{d\xi}\right)_P (\xi - \xi_P) + \tfrac{1}{2}\left(\frac{d^2\mathbf{A}}{d\xi^2}\right)_P (\xi - \xi_P)^2 + \dots, \tag{15.2}$$

where we have put $\mathbf{A}_P = \mathbf{A}(\xi_P)$ and where

$$\left(\frac{d\mathbf{A}}{d\xi}\right) = \left(\frac{\partial \mathbf{A}}{\partial \xi}\right)_{x,y} + \left(\frac{\partial \mathbf{A}}{\partial x}\right)_{\xi,y} \frac{dx}{d\xi} + \left(\frac{\partial \mathbf{A}}{\partial y}\right)_{\xi,x} \frac{dy}{d\xi}, \tag{15.3}$$

and similarly for the higher differential coefficients.
Substituting (15.2) into (15.1) with

$$\Delta\xi = \xi_{P'} - \xi_P, \tag{15.4}$$

and integrating term by term, we have

$$Q'_{PP'} = \mathbf{A}_P \Delta\xi + \tfrac{1}{2}\left(\frac{d\mathbf{A}}{d\xi}\right)_P (\Delta\xi)^2 + \dots + \frac{1}{n!} \cdot \frac{d^{(n-1)}\mathbf{A}}{d\xi^{(n-1)}} (\Delta\xi)^n. \tag{15.5}$$

If now we consider a very small change we can limit ourselves to the lowest power of $\Delta\xi$ and

$$Q'_{PP'} = \mathbf{A}_P\, \delta\xi, \quad \text{if} \quad \mathbf{A}_P \neq 0, \tag{15.6}$$

or

$$Q'_{PP'} = \tfrac{1}{2}\left(\frac{d\mathbf{A}}{d\xi}\right)_P (\delta\xi)^2, \quad \text{if} \quad \mathbf{A}_P = 0, \ \left(\frac{d\mathbf{A}}{d\xi}\right)_P \neq 0. \tag{15.7}$$

We now use the symbol $\delta\xi$ instead of $\Delta\xi$ to remind ourselves that the change is an infinitesimal one.

If the state P of the system is an equilibrium state, then the transformation we have considered is called a *perturbation* of the system. The above equations will be applicable to this case and will give the entropy production associated with the perturbation.

We notice finally that in most examples considered below, the physical variables x and y remain constant during the perturbation so that the total derivatives of $\mathbf{A}$ with respect to ξ may be replaced by partial derivatives. Equation (15.7) then becomes

$$Q'_{PP'} = \frac{1}{2}\left(\frac{\partial \mathbf{A}}{\partial \xi}\right)_{x,y,P} (\delta\xi)^2. \tag{15.8}$$

2. Criterion of Stability.

Suppose we have a system in a state P which is perturbed to a neighbouring state P'. The state P is said to be stable with respect to this transformation if the production of entropy accompanying it is *negative*. The criterion of stability is thus

$$\boxed{Q'_{PP'} < 0}\,. \tag{15.9}$$

The inverse process, that is the change from P' to P, is a spontaneous process accompanied by a positive production of entropy.

The perturbation is characterized in the first place by the change $\delta\xi$ in the extent of transformation ξ, and secondly by the conditions under which it is carried out. We may for example consider a change in which x and y (*e.g.* T and p) are maintained constant, or we may study the stability with respect to an adiabatic change.

The great advantage of the method outlined above over the original Gibbs method is that the condition for stability is expressed in a form independent of the conditions under which the perturbation takes place (*cf.* § 14). The nature of the parameter ξ which defines the perturbation may be very varied : it may refer to the appearance of a small amount of a new phase in an existing phase (*cf.* § 4), a perturbation of a chemical equilibrium (*cf.* § 7), the appearance of a slight heterogeneity in a phase which is initially uniform (*cf.* § 12), or a perturbation of the internal configuration of the phase under consideration (*cf.* chap. XIX, § 6).

We distinguish between two kinds of perturbation : those in which ξ can have only one sign (*unilateral perturbations*) and those in which ξ can be either positive or negative (*bilateral perturbations*). An example of a unilateral perturbation is the appearance of a very small amount of solid phase in a system which was initially completely liquid. The importance of these conditions of stability, which we shall consider in the following paragraphs, lies in the fact that they tell us what happens to a system when it is perturbed. If it is stable, it reverts to the initial equilibrium position ; if unstable, the perturbation proceeds to a finite extent.

It is important to realize that a perturbation is not necessarily related to any external action on the system. Molecular fluctuations lead inevitably to small variations of the macroscopic quantities from their equilibrium values. There is in fact a relation between the probability of a fluctuation and the production of entropy which accompanies it but we shall defer full discussion of this problem until we examine irreversible processes in greater detail.

3. Stability with respect to Unilateral Perturbations.

Before embarking on a study of stability in general, it is instructive to begin by finding the condition of equilibrium of a system with respect to a parameter ξ which can only vary unilaterally. Let us consider, to fix our ideas, $\delta\xi > 0$. To find the condition of equilibrium we must find the conditions under which the rate of reaction is zero in the state P. Because of the nature of $\delta\xi$, the rate of reaction $d\xi/dt$ must either be zero or positive. From De Donder's inequality (3.21)

$$dQ' = \mathbf{A}\,d\xi \geqslant 0,$$

which characterizes a spontaneous process it follows that the system will be in equilibrium provided that

$$\mathbf{A} \leqslant 0. \tag{15.10}$$

This equilibrium condition is much less restrictive than that obtained for bilateral changes for which, as we have already seen (chap. III, § 6),

$$\mathbf{A} = 0. \tag{15.11}$$

The system may therefore be stable at P if either

$$\mathbf{A}_P < 0,$$

or

$$\mathbf{A}_P = 0.$$

In the first case (*i.e.* $\mathbf{A}_P \neq 0$) combination of (15.9) with (15.6) leads back to

$$\mathbf{A}_P < 0\,; \tag{15.12}$$

while in the second, since

$$Q'_{PP'} < 0.$$

(15.7) leads to

$$\left(\frac{d\mathbf{A}}{d\xi}\right)_P < 0. \tag{15.13}$$

In the particular case of a perturbation from the state P at constant x and y (15.13) may be written

$$\left(\frac{\partial \mathbf{A}}{\partial \xi}\right)_{x,y,P} < 0. \tag{15.14}$$

These conditions of stability with respect to unilateral perturbations may also be expressed in terms of the thermodynamic potentials U, H, F, G. For example, in terms of U we have from (4.30) and (15.12)

$$\left(\frac{\partial U}{\partial \xi}\right)_{V,S,P} > 0. \tag{15.15}$$

If we consider U as a function of ξ only, which is permissible when V and S are maintained constant, the condition (15.12) means that, if P is a stable equilibrium state, U increases in the perturbation (*cf.* fig. 15.1).

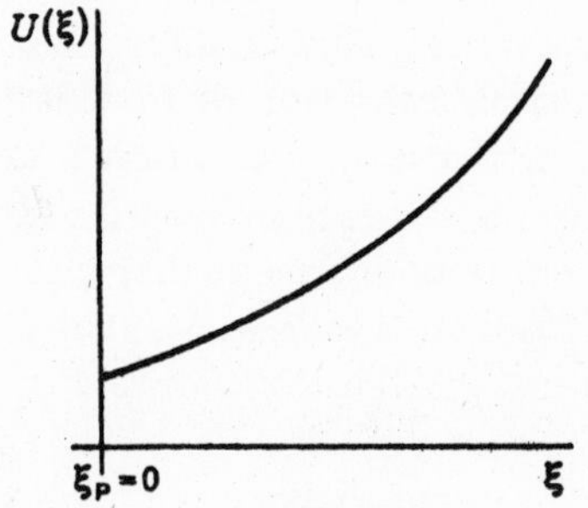

FIG. 15.1.

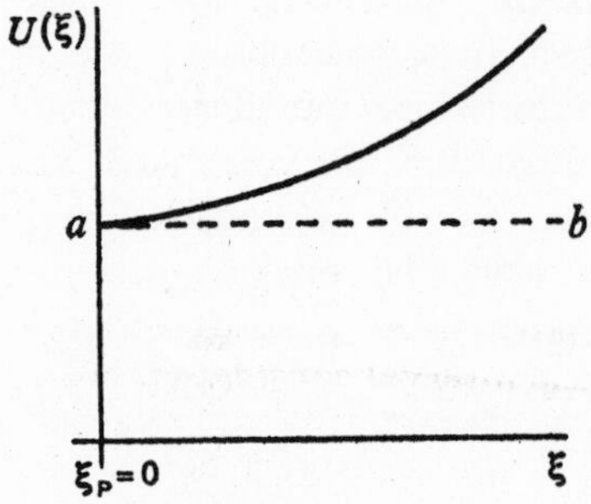

FIG. 15.2.

The interpretation of equation (15.14) is analogous, but in this case

$$\mathbf{A}_P = 0 \quad \text{and} \quad \left(\frac{\partial \mathbf{A}}{\partial \xi}\right)_{x,y,P} < 0$$

so that, by virtue of (4.30)

$$\left(\frac{\partial U}{\partial \xi}\right)_{V,S,P} = 0; \quad \left(\frac{\partial^2 U}{\partial \xi^2}\right)_{V,S,P} > 0. \tag{15.16}$$

In this case the thermodynamic potential has a horizontal tangent at P (fig. 15.2). Here again U increases during a perturbation if P is a stable equilibrium state.

4. Stability of Phases.

These considerations may be applied to the problem of the stability of phases. First of all we must state quite clearly the exact nature of the perturbation considered. The *unperturbed* system consists of a *single phase*, while the *perturbed system* contains, in addition to the original phase, a small amount of a *new phase*.

We must also specify carefully the *nature of the new phase*. Either the intensive properties of this new phase (partial molar volume, composition *etc.*), differ but infinitesimally from those of the original phase, or they differ from them by a finite, non-zero, amount.

We can then consider the following possibilities :

(i) The initial phase is *stable* with respect to all other phases whether infinitesimally different from it or not.

(ii) The initial phase is *stable* with respect to all phases infinitesimally different from it, but there is at least one other phase with respect to which it is not stable.

(iii) The initial phase is *unstable* with respect to phases infinitesimally different from it.

In the first case we say that the phase is *stable*, in the second *metastable* and in the third *unstable*.

If a phase is *unstable* with respect to phases infinitesimally different from it, then it will disappear and give rise to one or more neighbouring phases. This process will be repeated until we arrive at a phase which is stable with respect to adjacent phases. In fact, since all matter undergoes molecular fluctuations, small amounts of phases infinitesimally different from the initial phase will be formed continuously, and so by means of such fluctuations, the system will be transformed spontaneously into a perturbed state. If a phase is not stable with respect to the perturbed state, then the phase will disappear.

In the case of *metastable* phases the system may remain indefinitely in equilibrium without the appearance of a new phase. On the other hand if nuclei of a new, more stable, phase are introduced the system changes over into this phase. This is, for example, what happens in the case of supercooled liquids which can remain unchanged indefinitely but crystallize when seeded with crystals of the solid phase.

Finally a phase *stable* with respect to all other phases, whether adjacent or not, can never give rise spontaneously to a new phase in macroscopic amounts. Very often we describe both stable and metastable phases as stable, since both have certain properties in common which distinguish them from unstable phases.

5. Conditions of Thermal and Mechanical Stability.

A phase consisting of a single component must satisfy certain conditions if it is to be stable with respect to adjacent phases. These may be derived by studying the variation in the entropy S when, under conditions of constant U and V, the system in one phase is perturbed by the formation of a phase infinitesimally different from it.

If we denote the initial phase by a prime, and the new phase by a double prime then the unperturbed system will be characterized by the following values of the variables :

$$n'_P = n, \; n''_P = 0, \; V \text{ and } U,$$

where n is the total number of moles of the substance considered. For the perturbed system we shall have

$$n'_{P'} = n - \delta\xi, \; n''_{P'} = \delta\xi, \; V \text{ and } U.$$

If v and u are respectively the molar volume and molar energy of the system in the initial state, then the corresponding quantities v'' and u'' for the newly formed phase will differ only infinitesimally from the initial values :

$$v'' = v + \delta'' v \; ; \; u'' = u + \delta'' u. \tag{15.17}$$

The molar volume of the original phase in the perturbed state will also be changed slightly by $\delta' v$ since the total volume has been maintained constant. In effect, the total volume of the unperturbed system is given by

$$V_P = nv, \tag{15.18}$$

while after the perturbation

$$V_{P'} = (n - \delta\xi)(v + \delta' v) + \delta\xi(v + \delta'' v). \tag{15.19}$$

But

$$V_P = V_{P'}, \tag{15.20}$$

so that we must have

$$(n - \delta\xi)\delta' v + \delta\xi \, \delta'' v = 0. \tag{15.21}$$

Similarly, since the energy remains constant

$$U_P = U_{P'}, \tag{15.22}$$

we have a similar formula for the change in molar energy

$$(n - \delta\xi) \, \delta' u + \delta\xi \, \delta'' u = 0. \tag{15.23}$$

Now suppose we express the molar entropy of a phase in terms of u and v, then for the unperturbed system

$$S_P = ns(u, v). \tag{15.24}$$

After the perturbation let the molar entropy of the original phase be s', then the appropriate Taylor series becomes

$$s' = s + \left(\frac{\partial s}{\partial v}\right)_u \delta' v + \left(\frac{\partial s}{\partial u}\right)_v \delta' u$$
$$+ \tfrac{1}{2}\left\{\left(\frac{\partial^2 s}{\partial v^2}\right)_u (\delta' v)^2 + 2\frac{\partial^2 s}{\partial v \, \partial u}\delta' v \, \delta' u + \left(\frac{\partial^2 s}{\partial u^2}\right)_v (\delta' u)^2\right\} + \dots, \tag{15.25}$$

and similarly for the new phase produced by the perturbation :

$$s'' = s + \left(\frac{\partial s}{\partial v}\right)_u \delta'' v + \left(\frac{\partial s}{\partial u}\right)_v \delta'' u$$
$$+ \tfrac{1}{2}\left\{\left(\frac{\partial^2 s}{\partial v^2}\right)_u (\delta'' v)^2 + 2\,\frac{\partial^2 s}{\partial v\,\partial u}\,\delta'' v\,\delta'' u + \left(\frac{\partial^2 s}{\partial u^2}\right)_v (\delta'' u)^2\right\} + \ldots \quad (15.26)$$

The total entropy after the perturbation will be

$$S_{P'} = (n - \delta\xi)s' + \delta\xi s'', \quad (15.27)$$

and the increase in entropy resulting from the perturbation

$$\delta S = (n - \delta\xi)\,s' + \delta\xi s'' - ns. \quad (15.28)$$

We now have in (15.25) and (15.26) expressions for s' and s'' while (15.21) and (15.23) give $\delta' v$ in terms of $\delta'' v$ and $\delta' u$ in terms of $\delta'' u$. Substituting into (15.28) we obtain

$$\delta S = \tfrac{1}{2}\,\frac{n\,\delta\xi}{(n - \delta\xi)}\left\{\frac{\partial^2 s}{\partial v^2}(\delta'' v)^2 + 2\,\frac{\partial^2 s}{\partial v\,\partial u}\,\delta'' v\,\delta'' u + \frac{\partial^2 s}{\partial u^2}(\delta'' u)^2\right\} \quad (15.29)$$

and by dividing by $\delta\xi$, and allowing $\delta\xi$ to tend to zero :

$$\mathbf{A}_P = T\left(\frac{\partial S}{\partial \xi}\right)_{U,V,P} = \tfrac{1}{2}T\left\{\frac{\partial^2 s}{\partial v^2}(\delta'' v)^2 + 2\,\frac{\partial^2 s}{\partial v\,\partial u}\,\delta'' v\,\delta'' u + \frac{\partial^2 s}{\partial u^2}(\delta'' u)^2\right\}. \quad (15.30)$$

If the second differentials which appear in (15.30) are not all zero, then (15.12) tells us that the sum of the three terms in the bracket must be negative whatever values (positive or negative) we give to $\delta'' v$ and $\delta'' u$.

This can only be so* if

$$\frac{\partial^2 s}{\partial u^2} < 0, \quad (15.31)$$

and

$$\frac{\partial^2 s}{\partial v^2}\,\frac{\partial^2 s}{\partial u^2} > \left(\frac{\partial^2 s}{\partial v\,\partial u}\right)^2. \quad (15.32)$$

Now since, (4.49),

$$ds = \frac{du}{T} + \frac{p}{T}\,dv$$

$$\left(\frac{\partial s}{\partial u}\right)_v = \frac{1}{T}, \quad (15.33)$$

while, (2.8),

$$\left(\frac{\partial u}{\partial T}\right)_v = c_v,$$

* See W. L. Ferrar, *Algebra* (Oxford, 1941) chap. XI, pp. 135–143.

the first of the above conditions leads to

$$\left(\frac{\partial^2 s}{\partial u^2}\right)_v = \frac{\partial}{\partial u}\left(\frac{1}{T}\right) = -\frac{1}{T^2}\left(\frac{\partial T}{\partial u}\right)_v = -\frac{1}{T^2 c_v} < 0$$

or

$$\boxed{c_v > 0}\ . \tag{15.34}$$

The heat capacity at constant volume of all stable phases (stable and metastable) *is necessarily positive.* This is *the condition of thermal stability.*

Furthermore, to apply the second inequality we observe that from (15.33)

$$\left(\frac{\partial^2 s}{\partial v^2}\right)_u = \frac{\partial}{\partial v}\left(\frac{p}{T}\right) = \frac{1}{T}\left(\frac{\partial p}{\partial v}\right)_u - \frac{p}{T^2}\left(\frac{\partial T}{\partial v}\right)_u . \tag{15.35}$$

We also have the identity

$$\left(\frac{\partial p}{\partial v}\right)_u = \left(\frac{\partial p}{\partial v}\right)_T + \left(\frac{\partial p}{\partial T}\right)_v \left(\frac{\partial T}{\partial v}\right)_u , \tag{15.36}$$

while equations (2.6) and (2.8) give for a change in a single component at constant energy

$$0 = (l_T - p)\, dv + c_v\, dT,$$

or (*cf.* 4.41)

$$\left(\frac{\partial T}{\partial v}\right)_u = -\frac{l_T - p}{c_v} = -\frac{1}{c_v}\left\{T\left(\frac{\partial p}{\partial T}\right)_v - p\right\}. \tag{15.37}$$

Substituting back in (15.35) we obtain

$$\left(\frac{\partial^2 s}{\partial v^2}\right)_u = \frac{1}{T}\left(\frac{\partial p}{\partial v}\right)_T - \left\{\frac{1}{T}\left(\frac{\partial p}{\partial T}\right)_v - \frac{p}{T^2}\right\}^2 \frac{T^2}{c_v}. \tag{15.38}$$

Finally

$$\frac{\partial^2 s}{\partial v\, \partial u} = \frac{\partial}{\partial v}\frac{1}{T} = -\frac{1}{T^2}\left(\frac{\partial T}{\partial v}\right)_u , \tag{15.39}$$

and this is given by (15.37).

We now have the values of the various terms in the second inequality of (15.32), which on substitution lead to

$$-\frac{1}{T^2 c_v}\left[\frac{1}{T}\left(\frac{\partial p}{\partial v}\right)_T - \frac{T^2}{c_v}\left\{\frac{1}{T}\left(\frac{\partial p}{\partial T}\right)_v - \frac{p}{T^2}\right\}^2\right] > \frac{1}{c_v^{\,2}}\left\{\frac{1}{T}\left(\frac{\partial p}{\partial T}\right)_v - \frac{p}{T^2}\right\}^2 , \tag{15.40}$$

which reduces simply to

$$\boxed{-\left(\frac{\partial p}{\partial v}\right)_T > 0} \tag{15.41}$$

The coefficient of compressibility is thus always positive for all stable phases (stable or metastable). This is *the condition of mechanical stability.*

The inequalities (15.34) and (15.41) give us the *necessary* and *sufficient* conditions for a phase to be stable with respect to all immediately adjacent phases.

We may note here that for a phase composed of several constituents these conditions of stability are necessary, but not sufficient. For in this case we must also consider the stability with respect to immediately adjacent phases which differ in composition from the initial phase. We shall consider this problem in § 12 below.

It may also be observed that, because of the relation between heat capacities at constant volume and constant pressure (12.5), conditions (15.34) and (15.41) imply also that

$$c_p > 0. \tag{15.42}$$

The heat capacity at constant pressure is therefore also positive.

So far we have considered only the stability of a phase with respect to perturbations at constant U and V. A similar calculation may be made keeping T and V constant. In this case, instead of calculating the perturbation of the entropy we consider the Helmholtz free energy, F, and write the molar free energy f as a function of T and v. The molar volumes are perturbed by $\delta' v$ and $\delta'' v$ as in (15.21) but since the perturbation is isothermal $\delta' T = \delta'' T = 0$. We then obtain a formula

$$\mathbf{A}_P = -\left(\frac{\partial F}{\partial \xi}\right)_{T,V,P} = -\tfrac{1}{2}\left(\frac{\partial^2 f}{\partial v^2}\right)(\delta'' v)^2 \tag{15.43}$$

analogous to (15.30), which, by virtue of (4.29) and (15.12) leads once again to the condition of mechanical stability

$$-\left(\frac{\partial p}{\partial v}\right)_T > 0.$$

In this case we obtain just one condition of stability instead of the two obtained previously. This means that we have considered a more restricted class of perturbations. In the first case we considered perturbations such that the *total energy* of the system was constant, while in the second we specify that the temperature *at each point* remains constant.

6. Conditions of higher order Mechanical Stability.

Suppose in some state P we have

$$\left(\frac{\partial p}{\partial v}\right)_P = 0. \tag{15.44}$$

In these circumstances we cannot limit ourselves to quadratic terms in the series expansion used in (15.25) and (15.26). Let us consider, for simplicity, perturbations at constant T and V. Instead of (15.43) we have

$$\mathbf{A}_P = -\left(\frac{\partial F}{\partial \xi}\right)_{T,V,P} = -\frac{1}{2!}\left(\frac{\partial^2 f}{\partial v^2}\right)_P (\delta'' v)^2 - \frac{1}{3!}\left(\frac{\partial^3 f}{\partial v^3}\right)(\delta'' v)^3 - \frac{1}{4!}\left(\frac{\partial^4 f}{\partial v^4}\right)(\delta'' v)^4. \tag{15.45}$$

If

$$\mathbf{A}_P < 0$$

whatever the sign of $\delta'' v$ it is necessary that

$$\left(\frac{\partial^3 f}{\partial v^3}\right)_P = 0\,;\quad \left(\frac{\partial^4 f}{\partial v^4}\right)_P > 0, \tag{15.46}$$

or, since $(\partial f/\partial v) = -p$,

$$\left(\frac{\partial^2 p}{\partial v^2}\right)_P = 0,\quad \left(\frac{\partial^3 p}{\partial v^3}\right)_P < 0. \tag{15.47}$$

These are the higher order conditions for mechanical stability, which, as we shall see in chap. XVI, are satisfied at the critical point of a substance.

7. Triple Points and Multiple Points.*

The distinction between stable and metastable phases enables us to give a physical interpretation of the points of intersection of curves relating to heterogeneous equilibria.

We first consider the vaporization of a liquid. The affinity of this reaction is given by

$$\mathbf{A}_1 = \mu^l - \mu^g, \tag{15.48}$$

and the condition for true equilibrium $\mathbf{A}_1 = 0$ will be satisfied at all points on the vapour pressure curve of the liquid, as shown schematically in fig. 15.3.

Similarly for the fusion process of the substance the affinity is

$$\mathbf{A}_2 = \mu^s - \mu^l. \tag{15.49}$$

Here again the conditions of true equilibrium $\mathbf{A}_2 = 0$ will be satisfied at all points on the melting point curve (*cf.* fig. 15.3).

If these two curves intersect at t, then the line $\mathbf{A}_1 = 0$ is cut into two portions at and tb. We proceed to show that only one of these segments corresponds to stable equilibrium between liquid and vapour, while the other corresponds to metastable equilibrium states. If the state of co-existence of vapour and liquid is to be stable then solid must not appear either spontaneously or following the introduction of crystal

* *Cf.* Duhem [15], vol. IV, p. 317 and Jouguet [30].

nuclei. It follows therefore that the affinities of fusion and of sublimation of the solid must both be positive. The chemical potentials of the liquid and gaseous phases are equal all along the curve $\mathbf{A}_1$, so that we only need to consider the affinity of fusion $\mathbf{A}_2$. Points on the curve $\mathbf{A}_1=0$ will correspond to states of stable equilibrium only if in addition

$$\mathbf{A}_2>0 \tag{15.50}$$

so that we have to find the region in which this condition is satisfied. We observe that, from (4.48),

$$\left(\frac{\partial \mathbf{A}_2}{\partial p}\right)_T = -\left(\frac{\partial V}{\partial \xi_2}\right)_{T,p}.$$

Hence on moving up from the curve $\mathbf{A}_2=0$ parallel to the pressure axis we enter a region

$$\mathbf{A}_2>0$$

if $(\partial V/\partial \xi)_{T,p}$ is negative; conversely if $(\partial V/\partial \xi)_{T,p}$ is positive we must drop below the curve $\mathbf{A}_2=0$ to enter the region where $\mathbf{A}_2>0$. It follows, however, from the Clausius-Clapeyron equation (14.4) that since $\partial H/\partial \xi_2$ is positive for fusion, the slope of the equilibrium curve $\mathbf{A}_2=0$ has the same sign as $\partial V/\partial \xi_2$. In both cases therefore the true equilibrium condition is satisfied to the right of the equilibrium curve $\mathbf{A}_2=0$; the region in which the condition is not satisfied is indicated by the shading to the left of this line in fig. 15.3. We see, therefore, that only the segment *at* corresponds to stable equilibrium, while *bt* represents a state of metastable equilibrium characterized by the fact that the liquid and vapour phases will change to the solid, if not spontaneously, then on the introduction of solid nuclei.

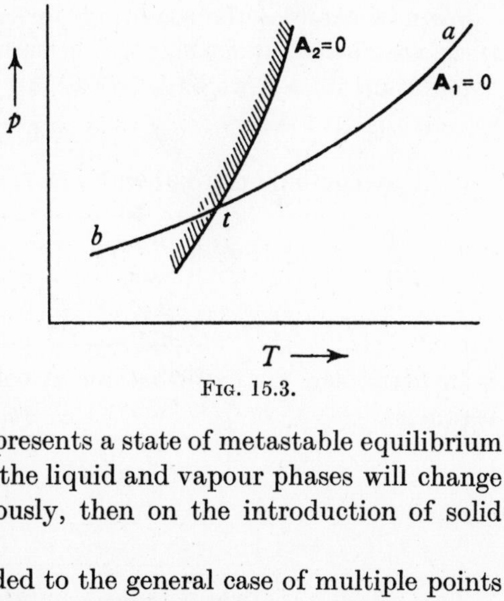

FIG. 15.3.

This property can be extended to the general case of multiple points in systems of several components. At a multiple point the variance is zero and the number of coexisting phases is

$$\phi = 2 + (c - r').$$

If three phases coexist the point is called a triple point, if four, a quadruple point and so on.

A quadruple point is the point of intersection of four equilibrium curves, each of which corresponds to equilibrium between three

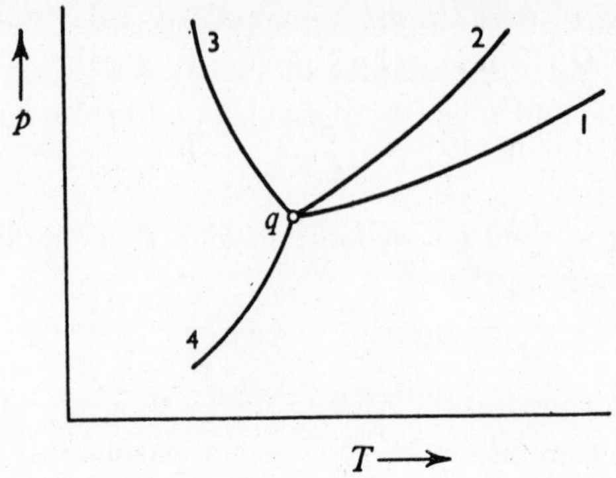

FIG. 15.4. Schematic representation of a quadruple point.

phases. Each of these curves is divided into a stable and a metastable branch, and the stable branches form a star at the quadruple point (fig. 15.4).

8. Stability with respect to Bilateral Perturbations.

We now examine the conditions for equilibrium when the perturbations are such that $\delta\xi$ may be either positive or negative. For an equilibrium state P we have (*cf.* 15.11)

$$\mathbf{A}_P = 0, \tag{15.51}$$

so that by combining (15.9) with (15.7)

$$\boxed{\left(\frac{d\mathbf{A}}{d\xi}\right)_P < 0} \; . \tag{15.52}$$

In particular, for perturbations at constant x and y, this condition becomes

$$\boxed{\left(\frac{\partial \mathbf{A}}{\partial \xi}\right)_{x, y, P} < 0} \; . \tag{15.53}$$

The relation between these conditions and the thermodynamic potentials is easily seen. Thus if we choose T and p as physical variables, then

$$\left.\begin{aligned} \mathbf{A} &= -(\partial G/\partial \xi)_{T,p} = 0, \\ \text{and} \quad a_{T,p} &= -(\partial^2 G/\partial \xi^2)_{T,p} < 0. \end{aligned}\right\} \tag{15.54}$$

These conditions express the fact that if P is stable at constant T and p, G is a minimum at this point.

The conditions of equilibrium are similarly related to the physical variables T, V; U, V or S, p by the following pairs of equations:

$$\left.\begin{aligned}\left(\frac{\partial F}{\partial \xi}\right)_{T,V}&=0\\ a_{T,V}=-\left(\frac{\partial^2 F}{\partial \xi^2}\right)_{T,V}&<0\end{aligned}\right\};\quad \left.\begin{aligned}\left(\frac{\partial U}{\partial \xi}\right)_{S,V}&=0\\ -\left(\frac{\partial^2 U}{\partial \xi^2}\right)_{S,V}&<0\end{aligned}\right\};\quad \left.\begin{aligned}\left(\frac{\partial H}{\partial \xi}\right)_{S,p}&=0\\ -\left(\frac{\partial^2 H}{\partial \xi^2}\right)_{S,p}&<0\end{aligned}\right\}. \tag{15.55}$$

Thus stability at constant T, V corresponds to a minimum in F; that at constant S, V to a minimum in U; and at constant S, p a minimum in H.

The role played by the chemical potentials in determining equilibrium at constant T and p is seen by replacing $a_{T,p}$ in (15.54), by its value (6.59) in terms of chemical potentials:

$$a_{T,p}=-\left(\frac{\partial^2 G}{\partial \xi^2}\right)_{T,p}=-\sum_i\sum_j \mu_{ij}\nu_i\nu_j=\tfrac{1}{2}\sum_i\sum_j \mu_{ij}n_i n_j\left(\frac{\nu_i}{n_i}-\frac{\nu_j}{n_j}\right)^2<0. \tag{15.56}$$

For this condition to be satisfied it is sufficient for μ_{ij} to be negative for all $i\neq j$. We have already seen that this condition is always satisfied by ideal systems (*cf.* 7.13). This means that all stable states ($\mathbf{A}=0$) of an ideal system are stable equilibrium states at constant T and p.

9. Relation between Stable Equilibrium at constant (T, p) and at constant (T, V).*

We have seen earlier (4.70′) that $a_{T,V}$ and $a_{T,p}$ are related by the following equation:

$$a_{T,p}-a_{T,V}=-(v_{T,p})^2/(\partial V/\partial p)_{T,\xi}. \tag{15.57}$$

Let us suppose that the system is in stable chemical equilibrium, then from (15.41)

$$(\partial V/\partial p)_{T,\xi}<0$$

and hence also

$$a_{T,p}-a_{T,V}>0. \tag{15.58}$$

But if the system is in stable equilibrium at constant T, p, then $a_{T,p}$ is negative from (15.54); therefore $a_{T,V}$ is also negative (and of greater magnitude than $a_{T,p}$). The system must therefore also be in stable equilibrium with respect to changes at constant T, V.

* G. Homès, *Bull. Ac. Roy. Belg.* (*Cl. Sc.*), 11, 724 (1925).

On the other hand, stability at constant T, V does not necessarily ensure stability at constant T, p. Stability in the second case is only found if

$$(v_{T,p})^2 < \left| a_{T,V} \left(\frac{\partial V}{\partial p}\right)_{T,\xi} \right| . \tag{15.59}$$

This latter condition is not necessarily satisfied, but as we now show, is always satisfied for a perfect gas.

For all ideal systems we have (*cf.* 7.15)

$$a_{T,p} = -\frac{RT}{2n} \sum_i \sum_j n_i n_j \left(\frac{\nu_i}{n_i} - \frac{\nu_j}{n_j}\right)^2 < 0, \tag{15.60}$$

which simplifies to

$$a_{T,p} = -RT \left(\sum_i \frac{\nu_i^2}{n_i} - \frac{\nu^2}{n}\right) < 0. \tag{15.61}$$

Now for a mixture of perfect gases, for which $V = nRT/p$,

$$v_{T,p} = \left(\frac{\partial V}{\partial \xi}\right)_{T,p} = \nu \frac{RT}{p} \tag{15.62}$$

and

$$\left(\frac{\partial V}{\partial p}\right)_{T,\xi} = -\frac{nRT}{p^2}. \tag{15.63}$$

So that, on substitution in (15.57), we find

$$a_{T,V} = -RT \sum_i \frac{\nu_i^2}{n_i}, \tag{15.64}$$

and (15.59) reduces to the condition

$$\sum_i \frac{\nu_i^2}{n_i} - \frac{\nu^2}{n} > 0. \tag{15.65}$$

Equation (15.61) shows that this condition is always satisfied in an ideal system so that in a perfect gas mixture, stable equilibrium with respect to changes at constant T, V, also implies stability at constant T, p.

10. Stability with respect to Adiabatic Perturbations.

As an example of the application of the most general condition of stability (15.52) we now consider adiabatic perturbations at constant pressure. From (2.13)

$$dQ = C_{p,\xi}\, dT + h_{T,p}\, d\xi = 0,$$

whence

$$\frac{dT}{d\xi} = -\frac{h_{T,p}}{C_{p,\xi}}. \tag{15.66}$$

For a transformation of this kind, therefore, the condition of stability (15.52) may be written (*cf.* 15.3)

$$\left(\frac{\partial \mathbf{A}}{\partial \xi}\right)_{T,p} + \left(\frac{\partial \mathbf{A}}{\partial T}\right)_{p,\xi} \frac{dT}{d\xi} < 0. \tag{15.67}$$

This may be expressed more explicitly by substituting from (4.59), (4.8), (15.66) and (15.51) to give

$$a_{T,p} - \frac{h_{T,p}^2}{TC_{p,\xi}} < 0. \tag{15.68}$$

Provided that the system is in stable thermal equilibrium (C_p positive), and is stable with respect to changes at constant T, p ($a_{T,p}$ negative), then it is also stable with respect to adiabatic perturbations at constant pressure.

11. Conditions of higher order Stability.

So far we have only considered stability in the two cases in which either

$$\mathbf{A}_P \neq 0$$

or

$$\mathbf{A}_P = 0 \quad \text{but} \quad (d\mathbf{A}/d\xi)_P \neq 0.$$

It may happen, however, that at P, all the successive differentials of $\mathbf{A}$ with respect to ξ up to the $(n-2)$th are zero. The uncompensated heat is therefore given according to (15.5) by

$$Q'_{PP'} = \frac{1}{n!}\left(\frac{d^{(n-1)}\mathbf{A}}{d\xi^{(n-1)}}\right)_P (\delta\xi)^n. \tag{15.69}$$

We now have to distinguish between two cases. *If n is odd*, then the criterion of stability (15.9) can only be satisfied for unilateral perturbations, since $(\delta\xi)^n$ will change sign with $\delta\xi$. The phase will be stable with respect to unilateral perturbations ($\delta\xi > 0$) provided that

$$\left(\frac{d^{(n-1)}\mathbf{A}}{d\xi^{(n-1)}}\right)_P < 0, \tag{15.70}$$

but will be unstable with respect to bilateral perturbations. *If n is even*, then the condition of stability with respect to both unilateral and bilateral perturbations is

$$\left(\frac{d^{(n-1)}\mathbf{A}}{d\xi^{(n-1)}}\right)_P < 0. \tag{15.71}$$

As an example of these conditions of higher order stability we may mention the order-disorder transformation in the alloy of equimolecular proportions of gold and copper. The affinity of the change is given by the approximate equation (*cf.* 19.55)

$$\mathbf{A} = \tfrac{1}{2} w\epsilon - \frac{kT}{2} \ln \frac{1+\epsilon}{1-\epsilon}, \tag{15.72}$$

where ϵ is a parameter related to the long-distance order, and plays a part analogous to ξ. As we shall see (p. 304) at the Curie point,

$$\epsilon = 0 \quad \text{and} \quad T = w/2k. \tag{15.73}$$

It is easily verified also that, at this point,

$$\mathbf{A} = 0\,; \quad \left(\frac{\partial \mathbf{A}}{\partial \epsilon}\right)_{T,p} = 0\,; \quad \left(\frac{\partial^2 \mathbf{A}}{\partial \epsilon^2}\right)_{T,p} = 0\,; \quad \left(\frac{\partial^3 \mathbf{A}}{\partial \epsilon^3}\right)_{T,p} = -2kT < 0. \tag{15.74}$$

The Curie point thus corresponds to an equilibrium state which is stable with respect to perturbations of ξ (or ϵ) at constant T and p.

12. Stability with respect to Diffusion in a Binary System.

The results of the preceding paragraph may now be applied to a perturbation which consists of the appearance of a heterogeneity in the composition of a binary system which is initially uniform. Stability with respect to perturbations of this kind will be called *stability with respect to diffusion*.

Consider a system P which is homogeneous, and characterized by the variables T, p and the mole fraction x_A, and let us direct attention to two elements of volume a and b in the system. The extent of change is denoted by ξ and corresponds to the passage of a molecule of component A from a to b, together with the passage of an arbitrary number (ν) of molecules B from b to a. We then have (*cf.* chap. I, § 7)

$$\frac{dn_A^a}{-1} = \frac{dn_A^b}{+1} = \frac{dn_B^a}{+\nu} = \frac{dn_B^b}{-\nu} = d\xi, \tag{15.75}$$

and the corresponding affinity is

$$\mathbf{A} = (\mu_A^a - \mu_A^b) + \nu(\mu_B^b - \mu_B^a). \tag{15.76}$$

Since the system is in equilibrium $\mathbf{A}_P = 0$, and the chemical potentials have the same values independent of the choice of the volume elements a and b. Furthermore, at constant T and p

$$\frac{\partial \mathbf{A}}{\partial \xi} = \left(\frac{\partial \mu_A^a}{\partial x_A^a} - \nu \frac{\partial \mu_B^a}{\partial x_A^a}\right)\frac{\partial x_A^a}{\partial \xi} - \left(\frac{\partial \mu_A^b}{\partial x_A^b} - \nu \frac{\partial \mu_B^b}{\partial x_A^b}\right)\frac{\partial x_A^b}{\partial \xi}\,. \tag{15.77}$$

Now

$$\left.\begin{aligned} x_A^a &= \frac{n_A^a}{n_A^a + n_B^a} = \frac{n_A^a(0) - \xi}{n_A^a(0) + n_B^a(0) + (\nu - 1)\xi}, \\ x_A^b &= \frac{n_A^b(0) + \xi}{n_A^b(0) + n_B^b(0) - (\nu - 1)\xi} \end{aligned}\right\} . \tag{15.78}$$

so that

$$\left.\begin{aligned} \frac{\partial x_A^a}{\partial \xi} &= -\frac{1}{n^a}[1 + (\nu - 1)x_A^a], \\ \frac{\partial x_A^b}{\partial \xi} &= \frac{1}{n^b}[1 + (\nu - 1)x_A^b] \end{aligned}\right\} . \tag{15.79}$$

We may also replace the partial derivatives of the chemical potentials in (15.77) by their values in terms of the mean molar Gibbs free energy, g (*cf*. 6.49 and 6.50). Hence we obtain

$$\frac{\partial \mathbf{A}}{\partial \xi} = -\frac{\partial^2 g^a}{\partial (x_A^a)^2}\frac{[1 + (\nu - 1)x_A^a]^2}{n^a} - \frac{\partial^2 g^b}{\partial (x_A^b)^2}\frac{[1 + (\nu - 1)x_A^b]^2}{n^b} . \tag{15.80}$$

Since the system P is homogeneous, there is no need to retain the indices a and b and we find for the condition of stability

$$\frac{\partial \mathbf{A}}{\partial \xi} = -2\left(\frac{\partial^2 g}{\partial x_A^2}\right)_P \frac{[1 + (\nu - 1)x_A]^2}{n} < 0. \tag{15.81}$$

For all stable systems therefore

$$\frac{\partial^2 g}{\partial x_A^2} > 0, \tag{15.82}$$

and this is the required condition for stability with respect to diffusion processes. We notice that this condition ensures stability with respect to any diffusion process, since the number ν in equation (15.75) may be chosen quite arbitrarily.

Furthermore, using (6.49) and (6.50) this condition is equivalent to

$$\frac{\partial \mu_B}{\partial x_B} > 0 \quad \text{or} \quad \frac{\partial \mu_B}{\partial x_A} < 0. \tag{15.83}$$

In the next chapter we shall show that at the critical solution point of a binary system

$$\left(\frac{\partial^2 g}{\partial x_A^2}\right)_c = 0, \quad \left(\frac{\partial^3 g}{\partial x_A^3}\right)_c = 0, \tag{15.84}$$

and it is found that, from (15.80),

$$\left(\frac{\partial \mathbf{A}}{\partial \xi}\right)_c = 0. \tag{15.85}$$

To obtain the condition of stability at the critical point we must therefore calculate the higher order derivatives of **A** with respect to ξ. Taking account of the first condition of (15.84) we have

$$\frac{\partial^2 \mathbf{A}}{\partial \xi^2} = \left[\frac{\partial^2 \mu_A^a}{\partial (x_A^a)^2} - \nu \frac{\partial^2 \mu_B^a}{\partial (x_A^a)^2}\right]\left(\frac{\partial x_A^a}{\partial \xi}\right)^2 - \left[\frac{\partial^2 \mu_A^b}{\partial (x_A^b)^2} - \nu \frac{\partial^2 \mu_B^b}{\partial (x_A^b)^2}\right]\left(\frac{\partial x_A^b}{\partial \xi}\right)^2$$

$$= \frac{\partial^3 g^a}{\partial (x_A^a)^3} \frac{[1+(\nu-1)x_A^a]^3}{(n^a)^2} - \frac{\partial^3 g^b}{\partial (x_A^b)^3} \frac{[1+(\nu-1)x_A^b]^3}{(n^b)^2}. \quad (15.86)$$

But because of the second condition of (15.84) we find at the critical point

$$\left(\frac{\partial^2 \mathbf{A}}{\partial \xi^2}\right)_c = 0. \quad (15.87)$$

It is necessary, therefore, to examine the next higher derivative which has the value

$$\frac{\partial^3 \mathbf{A}}{\partial \xi^3} = -\frac{\partial^4 g^a}{\partial (x_A^a)^4} \frac{[1+(\nu-1)x_A^a]^4}{(n^a)^3} - \frac{\partial^4 g^b}{\partial (x_A^b)^4} \frac{[1+(\nu-1)x_A^b]^4}{(n^b)^3}. \quad (15.88)$$

The stability condition $(\partial^3 \mathbf{A}/\partial \xi^3)_c < 0$ then gives directly

$$\left(\frac{\partial^4 g}{\partial x_A^4}\right)_c > 0 \quad (15.89)$$

and this is the condition for stability at the critical point.

13. Simultaneous Reactions.*

The arguments developed in the preceding paragraphs can be extended immediately to systems where r simultaneous reactions can take place. Suppose that we characterize these reactions by the parameters $\xi_1, \xi_2, \dots \xi_r$, and consider at once the case of bilateral perturbations ; that is $\delta\xi_1, \delta\xi_2 \dots \delta\xi_r$ can each be either positive or negative. Then any equilibrium state will be given by (*cf.* 3.36)

$$\mathbf{A}_{1,P} = 0\ ;\ \mathbf{A}_{2,P} = 0 \dots \mathbf{A}_{r,P} = 0. \quad (15.90)$$

Furthermore we shall consider perturbations in which the variables x and y are maintained constant. Now the course of a given perturbation can be expressed by considering $\xi_1, \dots \xi_r$ as functions of a parameter τ. That is to say we write

$$\xi_1 = \xi_1(\tau), \dots \xi_r = \xi_r(\tau).$$

This parameter varies from τ_P to $\tau_{P'}$, during the perturbation. If the difference $\tau_{P'} - \tau_P$ is sufficiently small, we may write

$$\xi_\rho = \xi_{\rho,P} + \left(\frac{d\xi_\rho}{d\tau}\right)_P (\tau - \tau_P).$$

* The rest of this chapter is required only for §§ 11–13 of chap. XVI and may be omitted on first reading.

Similarly, since $\mathbf{A}_{\rho,P}=0$, the affinities may be written (*cf.* 472) :

$$\mathbf{A}_\rho = \sum_{\rho'} \left(\frac{\partial \mathbf{A}_\rho}{\partial \xi_{\rho'}}\right)_P \left(\frac{d\xi_{\rho'}}{d\tau}\right)_P (\tau - \tau_P).$$

The uncompensated heat for the transformation is then

$$Q'_{PP'} = \sum_\rho \int_{\tau_P}^{\tau_{P'}} \mathbf{A}_\rho \frac{d\xi_\rho}{d\tau} \,.\, d\tau.$$

Whence, neglecting terms of higher orders,

$$Q'_{PP'} = \sum_\rho \sum_{\rho'} \left(\frac{\partial \mathbf{A}_\rho}{\partial \xi_{\rho'}}\right)_P \left(\frac{d\xi_{\rho'}}{d\tau}\right)_P \left(\frac{d\xi_\rho}{d\tau}\right)_P \int_{\tau_P}^{\tau_{P'}} (\tau - \tau_P)\, d\tau$$

$$= \sum_\rho \sum_{\rho'} \left(\frac{\partial \mathbf{A}_\rho}{\partial \xi_{\rho'}}\right)_P \left(\frac{d\xi_{\rho'}}{d\tau}\right)_P \left(\frac{d\xi_\rho}{d\tau}\right)_P \frac{(\tau_{P'} - \tau_P)^2}{2}.$$

Now the difference $\delta\xi_\rho$ is given by

$$\delta\xi_\rho = \xi_{\rho,P'} - \xi_{\rho,P} = \left(\frac{d\xi_\rho}{d\tau}\right)_P (\tau_{P'} - \tau_P),$$

and we can simplify the equation for the uncompensated heat to

$$Q'_{PP'} = \tfrac{1}{2} \sum_\rho \sum_{\rho'} \left(\frac{\partial \mathbf{A}_\rho}{\partial \xi_{\rho'}}\right)_{x,y,P} \delta\xi_\rho \, \delta\xi_{\rho'}. \tag{15.91}$$

The condition for stability thus gives us the inequality

$$\sum_\rho \sum_{\rho'} \left(\frac{\partial \mathbf{A}_\rho}{\partial \xi_{\rho'}}\right)_{x,y,P} \delta\xi_\rho \, \delta\xi_{\rho'} < 0. \tag{15.92}$$

The conditions under which this quadratic form is negative are well known.*

The conditions are :

1. That

$$\left(\frac{\partial \mathbf{A}_1}{\partial \xi_1}\right)_P < 0, \ldots \left(\frac{\partial \mathbf{A}_r}{\partial \xi_r}\right)_P < 0, \tag{15.93}$$

2. That the minors of *odd order*, constructed on the principal diagonal of the determinant of the $(\partial \mathbf{A}_\rho / \partial \xi_{\rho'})$, must be negative or zero.

3. That the minors of *even order* such as

$$\begin{vmatrix} \dfrac{\partial \mathbf{A}_1}{\partial \xi_1} & \dfrac{\partial \mathbf{A}_1}{\partial \xi_2} \\[2ex] \dfrac{\partial \mathbf{A}_2}{\partial \xi_1} & \dfrac{\partial \mathbf{A}_2}{\partial \xi_2} \end{vmatrix}, \quad \begin{vmatrix} \dfrac{\partial \mathbf{A}_1}{\partial \xi_1} & \dfrac{\partial \mathbf{A}_1}{\partial \xi_3} \\[2ex] \dfrac{\partial \mathbf{A}_3}{\partial \xi_1} & \dfrac{\partial \mathbf{A}_3}{\partial \xi_3} \end{vmatrix},$$

must be positive or zero.

* *Cf.* Ferrar *loc. cit.*, p. 141.

Thus for two reactions, the conditions of equilibrium become

$$\left.\begin{array}{lll} \mathbf{A}_{1,P}=0 & \mathbf{A}_{2,P}=0 & (a) \\ \left(\frac{\partial \mathbf{A}_1}{\partial \xi_1}\right)_P<0 & \left(\frac{\partial \mathbf{A}_2}{\partial \xi_2}\right)_P<0 & (b) \\ \left(\frac{\partial \mathbf{A}_1}{\partial \xi_1}\right)_P\left(\frac{\partial \mathbf{A}_2}{\partial \xi_2}\right)_P-\left(\frac{\partial \mathbf{A}_1}{\partial \xi_2}\right)_P\left(\frac{\partial \mathbf{A}_2}{\partial \xi_1}\right)_P \geqslant 0 & & (c) \end{array}\right\}. \tag{15.94}$$

We have already proved that, (4.52),

$$\left(\frac{\partial \mathbf{A}_\rho}{\partial \xi_{\rho'}}\right)_{x,y}=\left(\frac{\partial \mathbf{A}_{\rho'}}{\partial \xi_\rho}\right)_{x,y}, \tag{15.95}$$

while the relationship of these differentials to the thermodynamic potentials has been derived in § 8.

If we choose T and p as physical variables then the conditions of stability become :

$$\left.\begin{array}{lll} \left(\frac{\partial G}{\partial \xi_1}\right)_{T,p}=0, & \left(\frac{\partial G}{\partial \xi_2}\right)_{T,p}=0\,; & (a) \\ \left(\frac{\partial^2 G}{\partial \xi_1{}^2}\right)_{T,p}>0, & \left(\frac{\partial^2 G}{\partial \xi_2{}^2}\right)_{T,p}>0\,; & (b) \\ \left(\frac{\partial^2 G}{\partial \xi_1{}^2}\right)_{T,p}\left(\frac{\partial^2 G}{\partial \xi_2{}^2}\right)_{T,p}-\left(\frac{\partial^2 G}{\partial \xi_1 \partial \xi_2}\right)_{T,p}\left(\frac{\partial^2 G}{\partial \xi_2 \partial \xi_1}\right)_{T,p}\geqslant 0. & & (c) \end{array}\right\}. \tag{15.96}$$

These conditions again express the fact that, at constant T and p, the thermodynamic potential G is a minimum at P. We have already seen (*cf.* 7.18, 7.19) that the conditions (*b*) and (*c*) are always satisfied in an ideal system, so that equilibria in ideal systems are always stable.

14. Stability with respect to Diffusion in a c-Component System.

We return to the problem of stability with respect to diffusion studied in § 12, but now we consider the case of a system containing any number of components. To achieve the greatest symmetry we introduce as many reaction variables $\xi_1 \ldots \xi_c$ as there are components. Each extent of change ξ_i corresponds to passage of component i from the volume element a to b.

The conditions of equilibrium (15.90) now reduce simply to

$$\mathbf{A}_{i,P}=\mu_i^a-\mu_i^b=0, \quad (i=1, \ldots c), \tag{15.97}$$

and express the condition that in the unperturbed system P the chemical potential of each component is constant independent of the choice of a and b.

On the other hand the chemical potentials μ_i^a and μ_i^b may be expressed as functions of T, p and the numbers of moles of the various components. Because of (15.75) we see that μ_i^a $(T, p, n_1^a, \dots n_c^a)$ depends on ξ_j only through n_j^a, and μ_i^b through n_j^b. Whence

$$\left(\frac{\partial \mathbf{A}_i}{\partial \xi_j}\right)_{T,p,P} = \frac{\partial \mu_i^a}{\partial \xi_j} - \frac{\partial \mu_i^b}{\partial \xi_j} = \frac{\partial \mu_i^a}{\partial n_j^a}\frac{\partial n_j^a}{\partial \xi_j} - \frac{\partial \mu_i^b}{\partial n_j^b}\frac{\partial n_j^b}{\partial \xi_j}. \tag{15.98}$$

Then from (15.75), putting for simplicity $\nu = 1$,

$$\frac{\partial n_j^a}{\partial \xi_j} = -1; \quad \frac{\partial n_j^b}{\partial \xi_j} = +1. \tag{15.99}$$

Using the notation (6.53)

$$\mu_{ij} = \frac{\partial \mu_i}{\partial n_j} = \frac{\partial \mu_j}{\partial n_i}$$

we now write equation (15.98) in the form :

$$\left(\frac{\partial \mathbf{A}_i}{\partial \xi_j}\right)_{T,p,P} = -\mu_{ij}^a - \mu_{ij}^b. \tag{15.99'}$$

But since P is homogeneous, the value of μ_{ij} is independent of the element of volume chosen, so that (15.99′) becomes

$$\left(\frac{\partial \mathbf{A}_i}{\partial \xi_j}\right)_{T,p,P} = -2\mu_{ij}. \tag{15.100}$$

The condition of stability of the equilibrium (15.92) may therefore be written :

$$\sum_i \sum_j \mu_{ij}\, \delta\xi_i\, \delta\xi_j > 0. \tag{15.101}$$

For this inequality to be satisfied, it is necessary and sufficient that $\mu_{11}, \mu_{22} \dots \mu_{cc}$ are positive *and* that all the other minors, of both odd and even order, constructed on the principal diagonal of the determinant of the μ_{ij} are positive or zero.

In the case of *binary systems*, the conditions are

$$\mu_{11} > 0; \quad \mu_{22} > 0; \quad \begin{vmatrix} \mu_{11} & \mu_{21} \\ \mu_{12} & \mu_{22} \end{vmatrix} \geqslant 0. \tag{15.102}$$

Now we have already seen in (6.26) and (6.41) that

$$\left.\begin{aligned} \mu_{12} &= \mu_{21}, \\ n_1\mu_{11} + n_2\mu_{12} &= 0, \\ n_1\mu_{12} + n_2\mu_{22} &= 0 \end{aligned}\right\}. \tag{15.103}$$

and

The last two equations show that the determinant in (15.102) is always zero, so that we need only specify the first two inequalities in (15.102). Furthermore eliminating $\mu_{12} = \mu_{21}$ from (15.103) we have

$$n_2^2\mu_{22} = n_1^2\mu_{11} \tag{15.104}$$

so that the first two inequalities of (15.102) are equivalent ; we need therefore only specify one of them.

We note also that this condition also implies that

$$\mu_{12} = \mu_{21} < 0. \tag{15.105}$$

These conditions are identical with those obtained in § 12, *cf.* (15.83).

In the case of *ternary systems* the conditions for stability are

$$\mu_{11} > 0 \; ; \; \mu_{22} > 0 \; ; \; \mu_{33} > 0 \; ; \tag{15.106}$$

$$\begin{vmatrix} \mu_{11} & \mu_{12} \\ \mu_{21} & \mu_{22} \end{vmatrix} \geqslant 0 \; ; \quad \begin{vmatrix} \mu_{11} & \mu_{31} \\ \mu_{13} & \mu_{33} \end{vmatrix} \geqslant 0 \; ; \quad \begin{vmatrix} \mu_{22} & \mu_{32} \\ \mu_{23} & \mu_{33} \end{vmatrix} \geqslant 0 \; ; \tag{15.107}$$

$$\begin{vmatrix} \mu_{11} & \mu_{21} & \mu_{31} \\ \mu_{12} & \mu_{22} & \mu_{32} \\ \mu_{13} & \mu_{23} & \mu_{33} \end{vmatrix} \geqslant 0. \tag{15.108}$$

Here again, because of the relations (6.41) the determinant (15.108) must be zero, and the conditions reduce to those in (15.106) and (15.107).

The conditions (15.101) are both necessary and sufficient for the system to be stable with respect to diffusion. However, the *sufficient* conditions may be expressed in a very much simpler form.

We proceed along the same lines as in § 5 of chap. VI and find that (*cf.* 6.59)

$$\sum_i \sum_j \mu_{ij} \, \delta\xi_i \, \delta\xi = -\tfrac{1}{2} \sum_i \sum_j \mu_{ij} \left(\frac{\delta\xi_i}{n_i} - \frac{\delta\xi_j}{n_j} \right)^2 n_i n_j. \tag{15.109}$$

The condition of stability (15.101) can then be written :

$$\sum_i \sum_j \mu_{ij} \left(\frac{\delta\xi_i}{n_i} - \frac{\delta\xi_j}{n_j} \right)^2 n_i n_j < 0, \tag{15.110}$$

and this inequality will be satisfied by the very simple condition

$$\mu_{ij} < 0, \quad i \neq j. \tag{15.111}$$

We now confirm for a ternary system, that if the inequalities (15.111) are satisfied then the inequalities (15.106), (15.107) and (15.108) are also satisfied. Equations (6.42) are, in this case :

$$\left.\begin{aligned} n_1\mu_{11} + n_2\mu_{12} + n_3\mu_{13} &= 0, \\ n_1\mu_{21} + n_2\mu_{22} + n_3\mu_{23} &= 0, \\ n_1\mu_{31} + n_2\mu_{32} + n_3\mu_{33} &= 0 \end{aligned}\right\}. \tag{15.112}$$

If, as specified by (15.111), μ_{12}, μ_{21}, μ_{13} ... are all negative, then for these equations to be satisfied μ_{11}, μ_{22} and μ_{33} must be positive. This is the condition specified by (15.106).

Furthermore the first determinant of (15.107) has the value

$$\mu_{11}\mu_{22} - \mu_{12}^2$$

and this must be positive because both μ_{11} and μ_{22} are positive. The same must also be true of the other determinants of (15.107). Finally the determinant (15.108) is zero because of (15.112).

We have now shown that the sufficient conditions (15.111) ensure the validity of the conditions (15.106) to (15.108). The inverse is however not true, and (15.111) is therefore a more restrictive condition than the other set. This is readily shown since $\mu_{11}>0$; $\mu_{22}>0$; $\mu_{11}\mu_{22}-\mu_{12}^2 \geqslant 0$ does not necessarily imply $\mu_{12}<0$ but merely that $\mu_{12} \leqslant \sqrt{\mu_{11}\mu_{22}}$.

The sufficient conditions (15.111) are always satisfied for an ideal system (*cf.* 7.13). *An ideal system is thus always stable with respect to diffusion.*

Finally we shall prove that the three inequalities (15.107) are equivalent, and that it is sufficient to consider any one of them, and that only two of the three conditions (15.106) are independent.

We have the identities

$$\mu_{ij}=\mu_{ji}, \quad \text{all } i, j; \tag{15.113}$$

while the Gibbs-Duhem formulae (15.112) give us

$$\left.\begin{aligned} \mu_{23} &= -\frac{n_1}{n_3}\mu_{21} - \frac{n_2}{n_3}\mu_{22}, \\ \mu_{33} &= \frac{n_1^2}{n_3^2}\mu_{11} + 2\frac{n_1 n_2}{n_3^2}\mu_{12} + \frac{n_2^2}{n_3^2}\mu_{22} \end{aligned}\right\}. \tag{15.114}$$

We now consider the expression $\mu_{22}\mu_{33}-\mu_{23}\mu_{32}$ and substitute from (15.113) and (15.114) for μ_{23} and μ_{33}; this gives

$$\mu_{22}\mu_{33}-\mu_{23}^2 = \frac{n_1^2}{n_3^2}(\mu_{22}\mu_{11}-\mu_{12}^2), \tag{15.115}$$

which shows clearly the equivalence of the first and third inequalities of (15.107). The equivalence of the first and second inequalities may be demonstrated in a similar way.

Furthermore, we may also notice that by virtue of the second equation of (15.114), the inequality $\mu_{33}>0$ is a direct consequence of $\mu_{11}>0$, $\mu_{22}>0$ and $\mu_{11}\mu_{22}-\mu_{12}^2\geqslant 0$. It is therefore quite sufficient to consider only three inequalities, two of them from (15.106) and one of (15.107) for example

$$\mu_{11}>0; \quad \mu_{22}>0; \quad \mu_{11}\mu_{22}-\mu_{12}^2 \geqslant 0. \tag{15.116}$$

15. Chemical Equilibrium in a Stable Phase.

We now show that all true chemical equilibria ($\boldsymbol{A}=0$) in a phase which is stable with respect to diffusion, are also states of stable equilibrium at constant T and p.

The phase being stable, the inequality (15.101) must be satisfied whatever the values of $\delta\xi_i$ and $\delta\xi_j$. Let us take, in particular, $\delta\xi_i$ as equal to the stoichiometric coefficient of component i in the reaction under consideration, then (15.101) becomes

$$\sum_i \sum_j \nu_i \nu_j \mu_{ij} > 0.$$

But this is just the condition (15.56) for chemical equilibrium for this reaction. Hence we conclude that if the system is stable with respect to diffusion, then it is also in chemical equilibrium. This theorem is due to Duhem and Jouguet.*

The stability of chemical equilibrium may be considered as a consequence of the stability of diffusion equilibrium. On the other hand, the stability of internal equilibria of a condensed system leads to independent conditions for diffusion stability, (*cf.* chap. XIX, § 6).

16. Comparison of the present treatment with that of Gibbs.

The study of thermodynamic stability owes a very great deal to Gibbs, who first realized its importance. Gibbs' method was later examined in detail by Duhem† who clarified several aspects of the treatment.

The discussions of stability given by Gibbs and Duhem are based upon the behaviour of the thermodynamic potentials U, H, F and G. The link between their methods and that adopted here is seen immediately, for we know that for a change at constant T and p, the uncompensated heat is equal to the decrease in free energy G (*cf.* 3.20). Hence a study of the uncompensated heat during a perturbation at constant T and p reduces essentially to a study of the behaviour of G.

The inconvenience of Gibbs' method is that it only allows a study of stability to be made when the perturbation takes place at constant values of one of the four groups of variables S, V ; S, p ; T, V or T, p.‡

On the other hand the method adopted in this chapter is more powerful because it is based upon the direct evaluation of the production of entropy in the course of a perturbation, and so permits a discussion of stability with respect to any kind of perturbation. As an example of this greater flexibility we gave in § 10 a discussion of stability with respect to an adiabatic perturbation.

* P. Duhem : L'equilibre et le mouvement des fluides mélanges, *Travaux et Mémoires des Facultés de Lille*, vol. IIIB, 1893 ; [15], *cf. esp.* vol. III, p. 7, *cf.* also Jouguet [30].

† P. Duhem, [16], chap. XVI.

‡ P. Duhem, [15], vol. II, p. 337.

CHAPTER XVI

STABILITY AND CRITICAL PHENOMENA

1. Isotherms of a Pure Substance: Maxwell's Theorem.

Let us consider the family of isotherms of a pure substance such, for example, as those shown in fig. 16.1 for carbon dioxide.* At suffi-

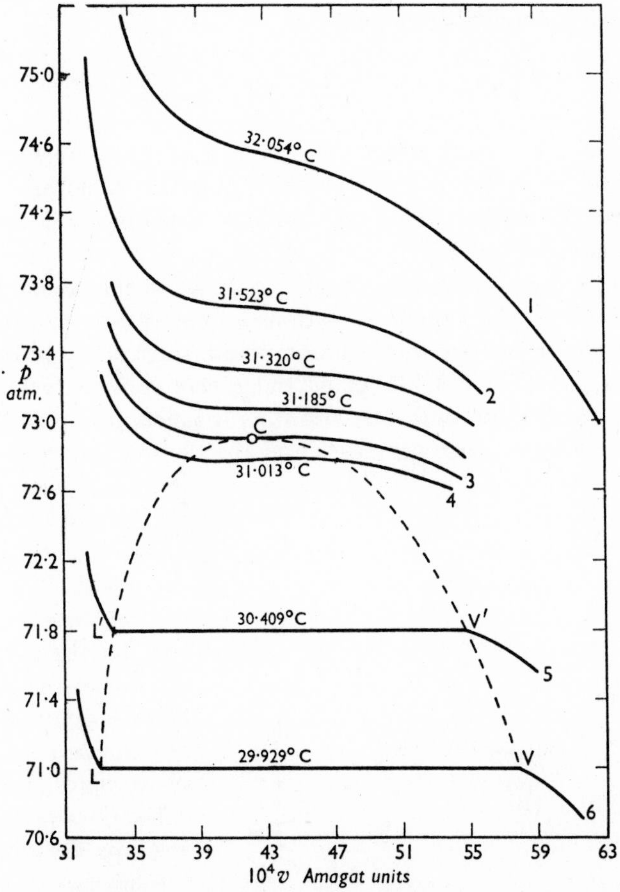

FIG. 16.1. Isotherms of CO_2 in the neighbourhood of the critical point. (1 Amagat unit of volume $= 2{\cdot}24 \times 10^4$ cm.^{3}/mole)

ciently high temperatures each isotherm is a continuous curve, but at low temperatures the isotherm consists of three portions. The first

* A. Michels, B. Blaisse and C. Michels, *Proc. Roy. Soc.*, **A160**, 367 (1937).

section of the curve at high pressures corresponds to the liquid state, while that at low pressures refers to the gaseous state. These two curves are joined by a horizontal line corresponding to the simultaneous presence of two phases, liquid and gas.

The isotherm numbered 3 in the figure represents the transition between isotherms corresponding to the gas phase only, and those including a horizontal portion corresponding to a liquid–gas equilibrium. In this isotherm the horizontal segment has contracted to a single point of inflexion C. This is the *critical point* of the system. It is characterized by the conditions for the existence of a point of inflexion with a horizontal tangent :

$$\left(\frac{\partial p}{\partial V}\right)_{T_c} = 0\,; \quad \left(\frac{\partial^2 p}{\partial V^2}\right)_{T_c} = 0\,; \quad \left(\frac{\partial^3 p}{\partial V^3}\right)_{T_c} < 0\,; \qquad (16.1)$$

where T_c is the critical temperature ; that is the temperature corresponding to the isotherm which passes through C. The third condition shows that the critical point represents a phase in stable mechanical equilibrium (*cf.* chap. XV).

The curve $LL'C$ gives the molar volumes of the liquid phases in equilibrium with the vapour at various temperatures, as a function of p. As the temperature rises the molar volume increases and the density diminishes. Similarly $VV'C$ gives the molar volume of the gaseous phases in equilibrium with the liquid as a function of p. The molar volume of the gas phase decreases and the density increases with rise in temperature until at the critical point the molar volumes of gas and liquid are equal. In general, a critical state is characterized by the fact that *the two coexistent phases* (*in this case liquid and vapour*) *are identical.* The complete curve $VV'CL'L$ is called the *saturation curve.*

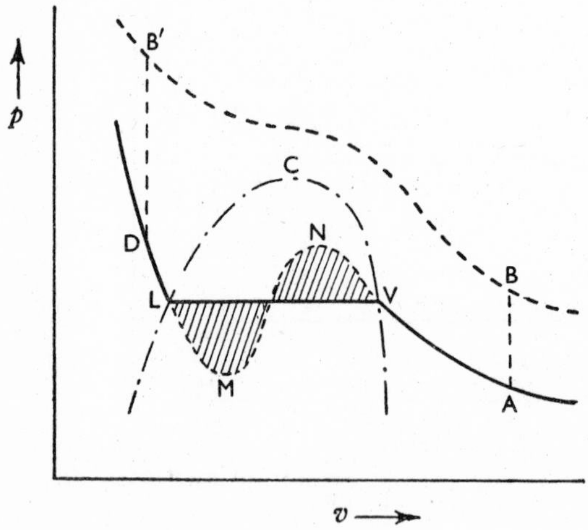

FIG. 16.2

Above the critical point the substance can exist in true equilibrium only in the gaseous state. The critical temperature is thus the highest temperature at which the liquid and vapour can coexist in true equilibrium. The existence of a critical point makes it possible to pass from one physical state to another without at any stage observing the appearance of a new phase. This may be done, for example, by starting with gas at A (fig. 16.2), raising the temperature maintaining the volume constant (AB) to above the critical temperature, then compressing the system maintaining the temperature above T_c (BB'), and finally reducing the temperature at constant v. We may thus pass in a continuous way from the gas state A to the liquid state at D.

The continuity of state which results from the existence of a critical point was first pointed out by James Thomson. In a certain sense the gaseous and liquid states appear as two different aspects of the same physical state, and it was natural that Thomson should have further suggested that the segments AV and LD of the isotherm were really two parts of a single continuous curve such as $AVNMLD$. This idea was taken up and developed extensively by van der Waals and his school; its validity is discussed in § 3.

The various parts of the continuous curve $AVNMLD$ have distinct physical significance. First of all we see that between N and M

$$\left(\frac{\partial p}{\partial V}\right)_T > 0, \tag{16.2}$$

which (*cf.* 15.41) means that these states, although possible equilibrium states, are unstable and therefore are not realizable in practice.

The portion VN corresponds to a supersaturated vapour, which may exist but is metastable and disappears spontaneously if condensation nuclei are introduced into the system. Similarly ML corresponds to an over-expanded liquid, which again is a metastable state. The points M and N are thus boundary points between metastable and unstable states of the system. If we take the loci of the points M and N of a series of isotherms we obtain the curves aC and bC (*cf.* fig. 16.3) characterized by the equation

$$\left(\frac{\partial p}{\partial V}\right)_T = 0. \tag{16.3}$$

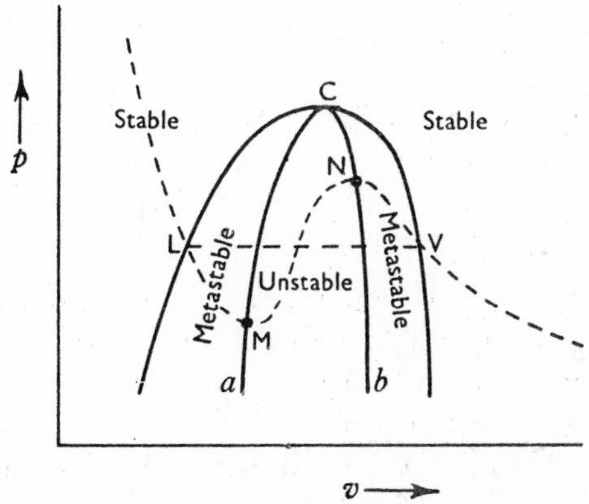

Fig. 16.3. Stable, metastable and unstable states in the vaporization of a pure substance.

This curve, together with the saturation curve LCV, divides the figure into areas corresponding to stable, metastable and unstable states.

Let us now return to fig. 16.2 and consider the liquid L in true equilibrium with the vapour V. The equilibrium condition,

$$\mu^l = \mu^g, \tag{16.4}$$

may be written in an interesting form due to Maxwell. We see from (6.28) that, by integrating along the curve $VNML$,

$$\mu^g - \mu^l = \int_{VNML} \left(\frac{\partial \mu}{\partial p}\right)_T dp = \int_{VNML} v\, dp\ ; \tag{16.5}$$

and since the chemical potentials of the two phases are equal

$$\boxed{\int_{VNML} v\, dp = 0}\ . \tag{16.6}$$

The two conditions of equilibrium, namely $p^g = p^l$ representing mechanical equilibrium, and $\mu^g = \mu^l$ representing chemical equilibrium, are both satisfied when the two shaded areas in fig. 16.2 are equal.

2. Geometrical representation of Stability in terms of the Free Energy F.

The preceding results relating to the critical point and to the co-existence of liquid and vapour may be represented geometrically in a very elegant manner in terms of the Helmholtz free energy.*

We have, from (4.29),

$$\left(\frac{\partial F}{\partial V}\right)_T = -p \tag{16.7}$$

and hence

$$\left(\frac{\partial^2 F}{\partial V^2}\right)_T = -\left(\frac{\partial p}{\partial V}\right)_T. \tag{16.8}$$

The condition of mechanical stability, $-(\partial p/\partial V)_T > 0$, thus means that

$$\left(\frac{\partial^2 F}{\partial V^2}\right)_T > 0. \tag{16.9}$$

If we plot F as a function of V at constant temperature, the curve *decreases* steadily because of (16.7) and is *convex downwards* for all stable states because of (16.9).† Above the critical temperature the free energy F is represented by a curve such as 1 in fig. 16.4, and the system is stable for all values of the volume.

On the other hand, below the critical temperature the curve is of the form 2.‡ At the points of inflexion C and D

$$\frac{\partial^2 F}{\partial V^2} = -\frac{\partial p}{\partial V} = 0, \tag{16.10}$$

* *Cf.* van der Waals and Kohnstamm, [47].

† The convexity or concavity of the curve $y = y(x)$ is determined by the sign of d^2y/dx^2.

‡ The assumption that a unique function F exists with the properties 16.7, 16.8, for both stable and unstable states, is equivalent to our assumption that the isotherm $AVNMLD$ (fig. 16.2) exists.

and we see that between them the curve is concave downwards, and the system is unstable.

In addition to the points C and D there are also two points A and B

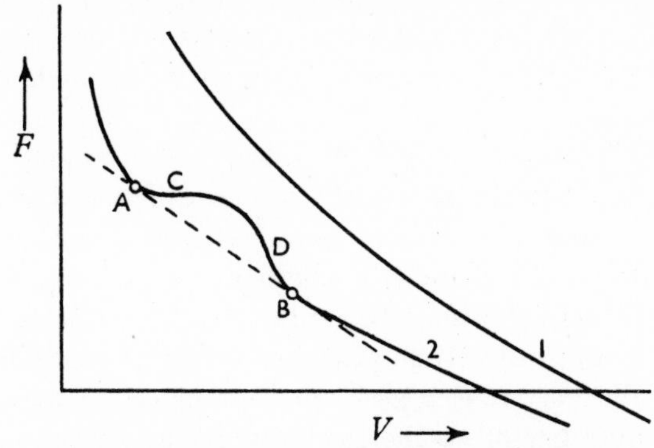

FIG. 16.4. Free energy (F) as function of V at constant T.

which have a common tangent. We now prove that these points represent gas and liquid phases in true equilibrium.

First of all, the fact that A and B have a common tangent means that, from (16.7), the pressures are the same in the two phases. To complete the proof we must show that in addition

$$\mu_A = \mu_B. \tag{16.11}$$

Now in a single component system

$$\mu = \frac{G}{n} = \frac{F}{n} + p\frac{V}{n},$$

whence

$$\mu_A - \mu_B = \frac{1}{n}(F_A - F_B) + \frac{p}{n}(V_A - V_B). \tag{16.12}$$

But since A and B have a common tangent

$$F_A - F_B = (V_A - V_B)\frac{\partial F}{\partial V} = -(V_A - V_B)p. \tag{16.13}$$

Substitution of (16.13) in (16.12) reduces the right hand side to zero so that (16.11) is verified.

3. Statistical problem of Phase Changes.

We have already seen (chap. XI, § 3) that the van der Waals equation of state can be employed to represent, in an approximate way, the isotherms of real gases and of liquids. In the two phase region it leads to isotherms analogous to those shown in figs. 16.2 and 16.3, containing regions both of instability and metastability.

It is important to realize however that the problem of phase changes does not depend upon the existence of an equation of state common to the two phases. No such continuous equation is known, for example, for the solid and liquid. The calculation of the conditions of coexistence by employing a common equation of state and making use of Maxwell's theorem (16.6) must be regarded as an artifice which may lead to correct results, but which cannot be justified by a more fundamental statistical study.*

The problem actually consists of a study of the molar free energy F/n. In the region of coexistence of two phases F/n is a linear function of volume per mole, and the pressure remains constant. Thermodynamics alone can tell us neither whether any such regions exist, nor how many. This problem must be studied by the methods of the statistical mechanics of interacting systems, and these are incompletely worked out. We may notice however that phase changes are closely related to the number of geometrical dimensions of the system. For one dimension, that is for molecules arranged along a line, it may be shown† that, no matter what the intermolecular forces, no phase changes occur. The thermodynamic properties vary *continuously* in the whole range of temperature and " volume " which in this case is the length of the phase.

A general formulation of the conditions which determine the appearance of a new phase remains an important problem in theoretical physics which has not yet been completely solved.

4. Critical Phenomena in the Vaporization of Binary Mixtures.

We shall now give a brief account of critical phenomena in the vaporization of a binary mixture. In this case it is convenient to consider the T, p diagram at constant composition (*cf.* fig. 16.5). For a pure substance we obtain simply the line AC which terminates at the critical point C. For a mixture of constant composition we have to consider two pressures, one corresponding to the liquid, and the other to the vapour at the same composition and temperature. These two pressures correspond to the points in fig. 13.6 where an ordinate at constant composition (*e.g.* $x_B FE$) cuts the vaporization curve (G) and the condensation curve (H). (The vapour and liquid are not of course in equilibrium). As the temperature is raised the shape of the lenticular area of fig. 13.6 varies and finally decreases to zero. We thus obtain the curve $FGKH$ of fig. 16.5 of which the branch from F to K corresponds to liquid and K to H to the vapour. The point K is the critical point at which the two phases are identical. Near to K there will also

* *Cf.* L. van Hove, *Physica*, **15**, 951 (1949).
† L. van Hove, *Physica*, **16**, 137 (1950).

be a point M at the temperature, T_m, at which the lenticular area of fig. 13.6 shrinks to zero, and another point L corresponding to the pressure, p_m, at which the similar area of the boiling point-composition

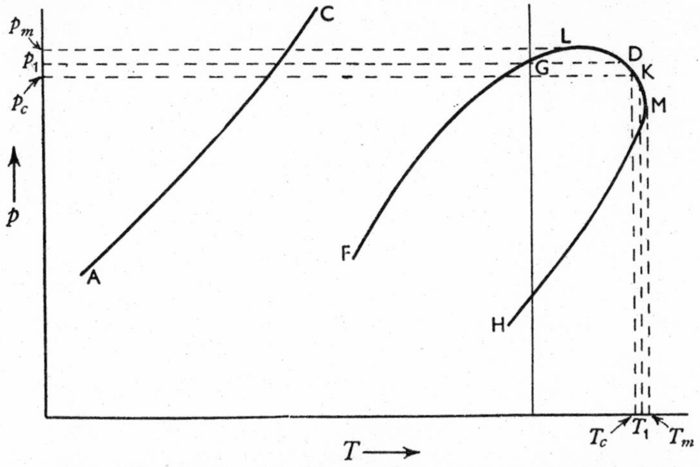

FIG. 16.5. T, p diagram of a binary mixture at constant composition.

diagram (*e.g.* fig. 13.7 or 21.12) becomes zero. It should be pointed out that for some systems the position of K may be different from that shown in fig. 16.5 : it may not lie between L and M, but may be to the left of L, or below M. This can of course only be determined by experiment. The critical pressure and critical temperature have a rather different significance for a binary mixture from that in the case of a pure substance. Thus the point L corresponds to the maximum pressure at which two phases can coexist, while the temperature T_m at M is the maximum temperature at which two phases can exist. In the case shown in fig. 16.5 there is therefore a pressure range $p_c \to p_m$ *above* the critical pressure in which the system can be condensed, while there is also a temperature range $T_c \to T_m$ *above* the critical temperature where condensation can occur. The three points L, K, M coincide for a pure substance but this is not necessarily the case for a binary mixture.

Two further interesting points emerge from a study of fig. 16.5. If the system is maintained at a pressure p_1 and the temperature raised, initially only liquid is present. When the liquid curve is crossed at G, vaporization begins. Now, in general, a horizontal line will cut the curve again at a point on the vapour branch of the curve, and this will correspond to complete vaporization. In this particular case, however, the line cuts the *liquid* curve again at D, between L and K, and at this point the vapour disappears. This phenomenon is known as *retrograde vaporization.* Beyond D the system changes from liquid to vapour without separation into two phases. In the same way if the vapour is compressed at a temperature T_1, it begins to condense when the vapour

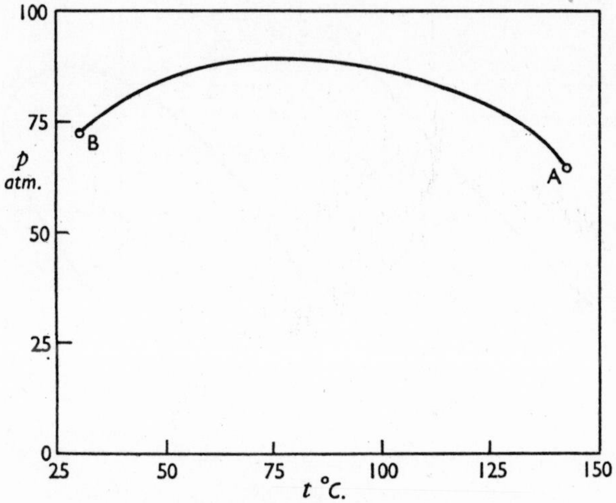

FIG. 16.6. Critical line for the system $CH_3Cl + CO_2$.*
A = critical point of pure CH_3Cl,
B = critical point of pure CO_2.

curve is cut. However, the vapour curve is cut again between M and K and the liquid vaporizes again. This is called *retrograde condensation.*

The locus of the critical points corresponding to a series of mixtures of different composition is the *critical line* shown in fig. 16.6.

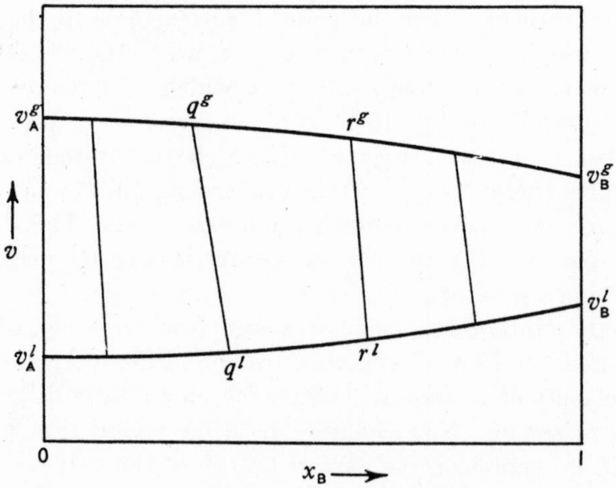

FIG. 16.7. $v-x$ diagram of a binary mixture below the critical region (constant T).

* Timmermans, [45], p. 210.

Besides considering the T, p diagram at constant composition, it is also instructive to examine the molar volumes v of the two phases as a function of composition at constant temperature. If the temperature is lower than any of the critical temperatures along the critical line, then this diagram has the form shown in fig. 16.7.

The line $v_A^g v_B^g$ corresponds to the molar volumes of the vapour phase, while $v_A^l v_B^l$ relates to the liquid phase. The lines such as $v_A^l v_A^g$, $q^l q^g$ ... joining two phases in equilibrium were called *binodals* by van der Waals and his school.

If we consider the v, x diagram at a temperature lying between the critical temperatures of the two pure components, then the behaviour shown in fig. 16.8 will be observed. The binodals become shorter and

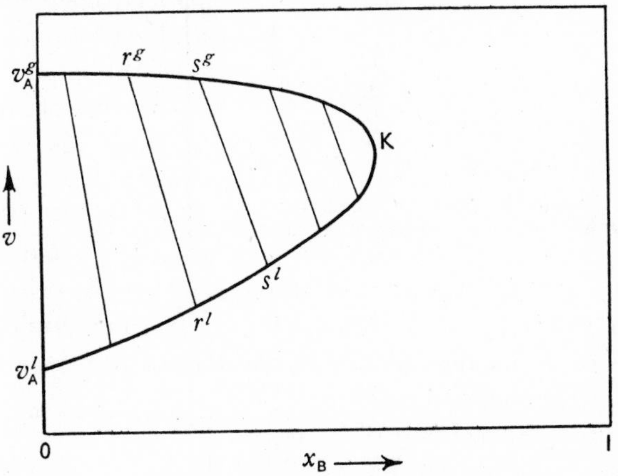

FIG. 16.8. $v - x$ diagram of a binary mixture in the critical region (constant T).

shorter and vanish at a critical point K. The curve $v_A^g r^g K r^l v_A^l$ is called the *saturation curve* and will be discussed later in § 8.

It should be noted that figs. 16.7 and 16.8 only represent typical kinds of behaviour, and that many other forms of curve are possible. A full discussion of these is however outside the scope of the present work.*

5. Critical Solution Phenomena in Binary Mixtures.

In addition to critical phenomena in vaporization where the liquid phase becomes identical with the gas phase, there also exist critical solution phenomena in which two liquid phases, or two solid phases, each of which is a solution, become identical at the critical point.

* *Cf.* van der Waals and Kohnstamm, *loc. cit.*, [47]; J. J. Kuenen, *Theorie der Verdampfung und Verflüssigung von Gemischen*, (Leipzig, 1904); *cf.* also Timmermans [45], chap. VI.

For example *n*-hexane and nitrobenzene are miscible in all proportions at ordinary pressures provided that the temperature is above 19 °C. Below this temperature two phases are formed, one corresponding to a solution more concentrated in hexane and the other more concentrated in nitrobenzene. At 10 °C one of the phases has the composition 0·18 mole fraction nitrobenzene, 0·82 hexane and the other 0·70 nitrobenzene, 0·30 hexane (*cf*. fig. 16.9).

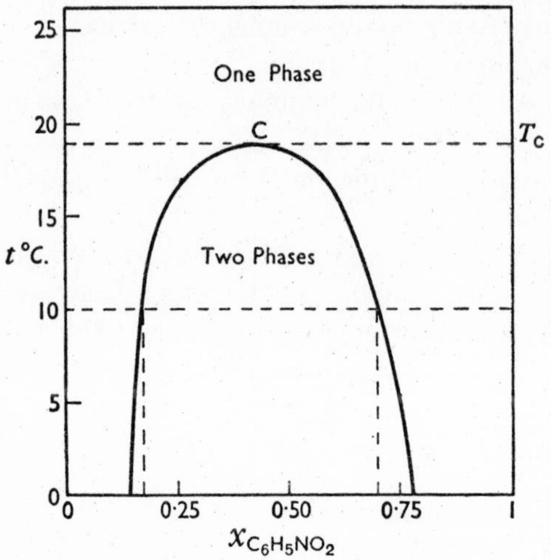

FIG. 16.9. Phase diagram of the system n-hexane + nitrobenzene at atmospheric pressure.*

At the point C the two liquid layers become identical, and this is called the *critical solution point* or *consolute point*. If the total applied pressure is varied, both the critical temperature and composition of the critical mixture alter and we obtain a *critical solution line*. As an example of this we give in table 16.1† the dependence of the critical solution temperature on pressure for the system cyclohexane + aniline. An increase of pressure raises the critical solution temperature, and the mutual solubility of the two substances is decreased. We saw earlier that the applied pressure had only a small effect on the thermodynamic properties of condensed phases, and we notice in this case that an increase of pressure of 250 atm. alters the critical temperature by only 1.6 °C.

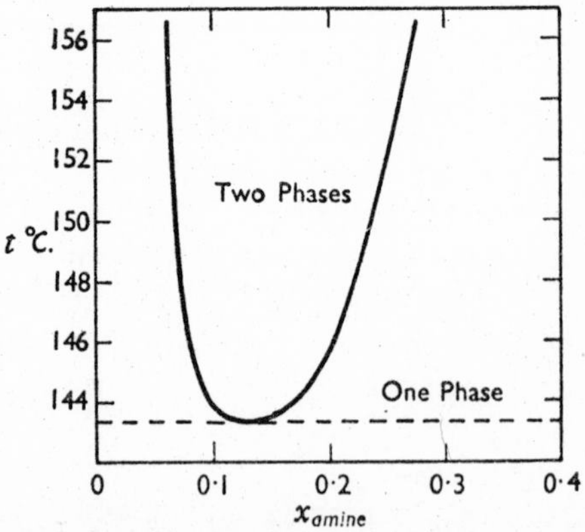

FIG. 16.10. Phase diagram at constant pressure of the system diethylamine + water showing lower consolute temperature.

In the two examples considered so far the critical temperature is the highest at which two phases can coexist: this is called an *upper critical solution temperature*. In

* *Cf*. Timmermans [45], p. 292.
† J. Timmermans, *Thesis* (Brussels, 1911); p. 75.

other cases, however, a different type of behaviour, shown in fig. 16.10 is observed, where there is a *lower critical solution temperature*. Below this temperature the system always forms a single stable phase. Examples of this are the systems liquid carbon dioxide + nitrobenzene,* diethylamine + water, and triethylamine + water.

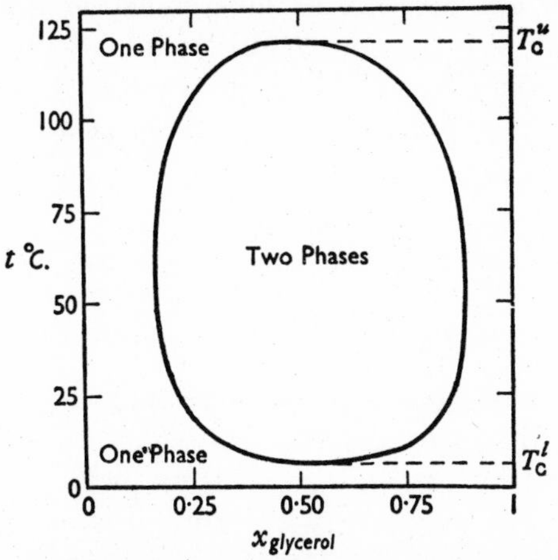

FIG. 16.11. Phase diagram of the mixture *m*-toluidine + glycerol at atmospheric pressure,† showing upper and lower consolute temperatures.

Finally, there are systems which exhibit both an upper and a lower critical solution temperature. An example of this is found in the system *m*-toluidine + glycerol, the data for which are shown in fig. 16.11.

TABLE 16.1

Effect of Pressure on Critical Mixing Temperature in the System Cyclohexane + Aniline

p (*atm.*)	T_c (°C)	*p* (*atm.*)	T_c (°C)
1·80	31·0	148·50	31·9
47·85	31·3	199·25	32·3
98·25	31·6	250·05	32·6

In §§ 9 and 10 of chap. XVIII we shall discuss the thermodynamic conditions that a critical solution temperature shall be an upper or a lower one, and also the influence of pressure on the critical point.

6. Critical Phenomena and Stability with respect to Diffusion.

In our study of critical phenomena in the case of a single component we saw that the condition of mechanical stability played an essential

* *Cf.* Timmermans [45], p. 268.
† *Cf.* Timmermans [45], p. 498.

role. The critical point, in effect, separates those regions which are stable (with respect to the condition of mechanical stability) from those which are metastable and unstable, (*cf.* fig. 16.3).

For binary systems we must in addition take account of the condition of stability with respect to diffusion processes (15.105). It is in fact this condition which here determines the stability of the system. In § 8 we shall show why it is that the condition of mechanical stability plays no part in determining the equilibrium in a binary system.

The condition for equilibrium with respect to diffusion may be written (*cf.* 15.105),

$$\mu_{12} = \mu_{21} < 0,$$

and from (6.44) these equalities are equivalent to

$$\frac{\partial \mu_1}{\partial x_2} < 0 \quad \text{or} \quad \frac{\partial \mu_2}{\partial x_1} < 0. \tag{16.14}$$

As an example these conditions may be applied to the hexane-nitrobenzene system the phase diagram for which was given in fig. 16.9. If we plot at a series of temperatures the chemical potential of hexane as a function of the mole fraction of nitrobenzene at constant pressure we obtain the family of curves shown schematically in fig. 16.12. Above 19 °C (curve 1) we have a single phase, and the conditions (16.14) are always satisfied.

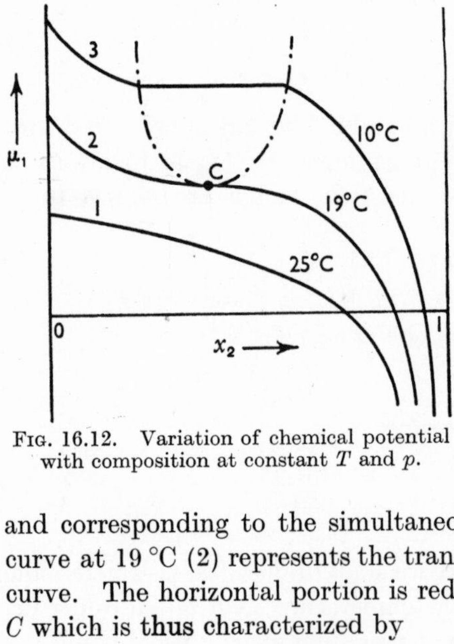

FIG. 16.12. Variation of chemical potential with composition at constant T and p.

On the other hand below 19 °C the curve (*e.g.* 3) consists of three parts, one corresponding to the layer rich in nitrobenzene, one for the hexane-rich layer, and a horizontal line joining these two and corresponding to the simultaneous presence of two phases. The curve at 19 °C (2) represents the transition between these two types of curve. The horizontal portion is reduced to a single point of inflexion C which is thus characterized by

$$\left(\frac{\partial \mu_1}{\partial x_2}\right)_c = 0\,; \quad \left(\frac{\partial^2 \mu_1}{\partial x_2^2}\right)_c = 0\,; \tag{16.15}$$

furthermore, the critical point is stable since

$$\left(\frac{\partial^3 \mu_1}{\partial x_2^3}\right)_c < 0.$$

For if the chemical potential μ_1 is expanded in series in the region of the critical point we have neglecting higher order terms :

$$\mu_1 - \mu_{1,c} = \frac{1}{3!}\left(\frac{\partial^3 \mu_1}{\partial x_2^3}\right)_c (x_2 - x_{2,c})^3. \tag{16.16}$$

We see from fig. 16.12 that the sign of $\mu_1 - \mu_{1,c}$ is opposite to that of $(x_2 - x_{2,c})$ and hence

$$\frac{\partial^3 \mu_1}{\partial x_2^3} < 0. \tag{16.17}$$

7. Geometrical representation of the Condition of Stability with respect to Diffusion.

Just as in the case of a system consisting of a pure substance (*cf.* § 2), the existence of a critical point for a binary system indicates a certain continuity of state between the two phases which become identical at the critical point. Thus, fig. 16.9 shows that, for the hexane + nitrobenzene system, provided we raise the temperature above 19 °C, we can pass from the hexane-rich layer to the nitrobenzene-rich layer without at any stage observing the separation of a new phase.

We may therefore regard the two portions of curve 3 (fig. 16.12) as two segments of the continuous curve *FBMNAE* of fig. 16.13. Just as before (*cf.* fig. 16.3) we can show that the states between *M* and *N* are unstable and are characterized by

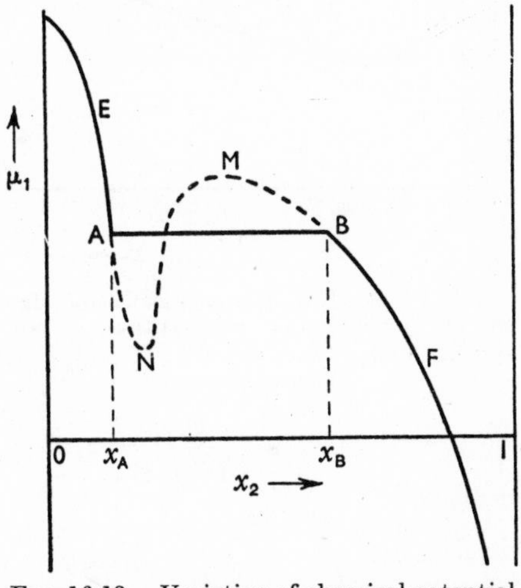

FIG. 16.13. Variation of chemical potential with composition at constant T and p.

$$\frac{\partial \mu_1}{\partial x_2} > 0, \tag{16.18}$$

while *BM* and *AN* correspond to metastable states. The boundary between metastability and instability is determined by

$$\frac{\partial \mu_1}{\partial x_2} = 0. \tag{16.19}$$

The condition of stability (16.14) can be written in another form since we have, (6.50),

$$\left(\frac{\partial \mu_1}{\partial x_2}\right)_{T,p} = -x_2 \left(\frac{\partial^2 g}{\partial x_2^2}\right)_{T,p}.$$

Hence, for stability

$$\frac{\partial^2 g}{\partial x_2^2} > 0. \tag{16.20}$$

This inequality has a simple geometrical interpretation. If, for given values of T and p, g is plotted as a function of x_2, then (16.20) expresses the fact that for the system to be stable *the curve must be convex downwards* (*cf.* fig. 16.14, curve 1). If on the other hand the curve is of type 2 and between certain values of x_2 is convex upwards, then in this range (NM) the system ceases to be in stable equilibrium, and separates into two phases.

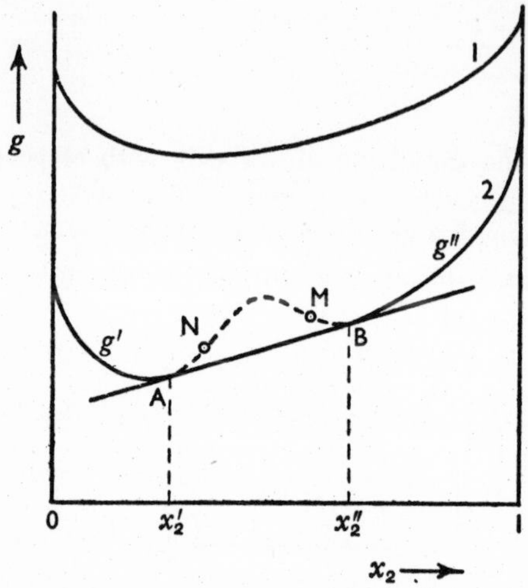

FIG. 16.14. Variation of mean Gibbs free energy ($g = G/n$) with composition, at constant T and p.

The mole fractions x_2' and x_2'' of component 2 in the two phases formed may be calculated in the following manner.

Since μ is a partial molar quantity g is given by, (*cf.* 6.46),

$$g = x_1\mu_1 + x_2\mu_2. \tag{16.21}$$

And using (6.47), namely

$$\left(\frac{\partial g}{\partial x_2}\right)_{T,p} = \mu_2 - \mu_1$$

we have

$$\mu_2 = g - x_1\left(\frac{\partial g}{\partial x_1}\right)_{T,p}. \tag{16.22}$$

Now the condition for true equilibrium of component 2 between the phases is

$$\mathbf{A}_2 = \mu_2' - \mu_2'' = 0,$$

which may be written

$$g' - x_1'\frac{\partial g'}{\partial x_1'} = g'' - x_1''\frac{\partial g''}{\partial x_1''}. \tag{16.23}$$

In the same way, we find from $\mathbf{A}_1 = 0$

$$g' - x_2'\frac{\partial g'}{dx_2'} = g'' - x_2''\frac{\partial g''}{\partial x_2''}. \tag{16.24}$$

Substituting $x_1 = 1 - x_2$ and $\partial g/\partial x_1 = -\partial g/\partial x_2$ in (16.23) we have,

$$g' + \frac{\partial g'}{\partial x_2'} - x_2'\frac{\partial g'}{\partial x_2'} = g'' + \frac{\partial g''}{\partial x_2''} - x_2''\frac{\partial g''}{\partial x_2''}. \tag{16.25}$$

Subtracting (16.24) from (16.25) we see that at true equilibrium

$$\left(\frac{\partial g'}{\partial x_2'}\right)_{T,p}=\left(\frac{\partial g''}{\partial x_2''}\right)_{T,p}, \tag{16.26}$$

which on substitution in (16.25) gives

$$g'-g''=\left(\frac{\partial g'}{\partial x_2'}\right)_{T,p}(x_2'-x_2''). \tag{16.27}$$

Once again the conditions (16.26) and (16.27) have a simple geometrical significance.

The values of x_2, that is to say x_2' and x_2'', relating to the two phases in equilibrium are such that the functions g' and g'' have a common tangent AB (*cf.* fig. 16.14). It is also easily shown that the segments AN and MB correspond to states of metastable equilibrium which will tend to revert to a two phase system $A+B$.

Furthermore at the critical point, (6.50) enables us to write (16.15) and (16.17) in the form

$$\left(\frac{\partial^2 g}{\partial x_2^2}\right)_c=0\ ;\quad \left(\frac{\partial^3 g}{\partial x_2^3}\right)_c=0\ ;\quad \left(\frac{\partial^4 g}{\partial x_2^4}\right)_c>0. \tag{16.28}$$

We shall have occasion to make further use of these formulae in chap. XVIII.

8. Relation between the Conditions of Mechanical and Diffusion Stability in Binary Systems.

Let us now investigate the part played by the condition of mechanical stability in binary systems. This condition can be written

$$-\left(\frac{\partial p}{\partial V}\right)_{T,x_2}>0. \tag{16.29}$$

Introducing the molar free energy, $f=F/n$, and molar volume, $v=V/n$, this inequality can also be written (*cf.* 4.29)

$$\left(\frac{\partial^2 f}{\partial v^2}\right)_{T,x_2}>0. \tag{16.30}$$

At the same time the condition of diffusion stability is (16.20) :

$$\left(\frac{\partial^2 g}{\partial x_2^2}\right)_{T,p}>0. \tag{16.31}$$

We now proceed to express these two last inequalities in a more explicit equivalent form.

For this we first prove that

$$\left(\frac{\partial f}{\partial x_2}\right)_{T,v}=\left(\frac{\partial g}{\partial x_2}\right)_{T,p}. \tag{16.32}$$

We have, from (3.15) and (3.16)

$$\left(\frac{\partial f}{\partial x_2}\right)_{T,v} = \left(\frac{\partial g}{\partial x_2}\right)_{T,v} - v\left(\frac{\partial p}{\partial x_2}\right)_{T,v}. \tag{16.33}$$

But

$$\left(\frac{\partial g}{\partial x_2}\right)_{T,v} = \left(\frac{\partial g}{\partial x_2}\right)_{T,p} + \left(\frac{\partial g}{\partial p}\right)_{T,x_2}\left(\frac{\partial p}{\partial x_2}\right)_{T,v}, \tag{16.33'}$$

while (*cf.* 4.29)

$$\left(\frac{\partial g}{\partial p}\right)_{T,x_2} = v. \tag{16.34}$$

Equation (16.32) follows directly by comparing (16.33) and (16.33′).

We now differentiate (16.32) with respect to x_2 at constant T and p :

$$\left(\frac{\partial^2 g}{\partial x_2^2}\right)_{T,p} = \left(\frac{\partial^2 f}{\partial x_2^2}\right)_{T,v} + \frac{\partial^2 f}{\partial x_2\, \partial v}\left(\frac{\partial v}{\partial x_2}\right)_{T,p}. \tag{16.35}$$

Furthermore

$$\left(\frac{\partial v}{\partial x_2}\right)_{T,p} = -\left(\frac{\partial p}{\partial x_2}\right)_{T,v} \Big/ \left(\frac{\partial p}{\partial v}\right)_{T,x_2} = -\frac{\partial^2 f}{\partial x_2\, \partial v} \Big/ \left(\frac{\partial^2 f}{\partial v^2}\right)_{T,x_2}. \tag{16.36}$$

Substituting back into (16.35) we may now restate (16.31) in the form :

$$\left(\frac{\partial^2 g}{\partial x_2^2}\right)_{T,p} = \left(\frac{\partial^2 f}{\partial x_2^2}\right)_{T,v} - \left(\frac{\partial^2 f}{\partial x_2\, \partial v}\right)_T^2 \Big/ \left(\frac{\partial^2 f}{\partial v^2}\right)_{T,x_2} > 0. \tag{16.37}$$

The condition for stability with respect to diffusion must be satisfied simultaneously with that for mechanical stability (16.30). These two conditions cannot possibly be satisfied simultaneously unless in the first place

$$\left(\frac{\partial^2 f}{\partial x_2^2}\right)_{T,v} > 0. \tag{16.38}$$

We now proceed to find the boundary separating stable states from metastable states, and to show that if we pass from a region where both inequalities (16.30) and (16.37) are satisfied, into another where only one is satisfied, then it is (16.37) which breaks down first.

Now in (16.37) there is no reason why we should not have simultaneously

$$\left(\frac{\partial^2 f}{\partial v^2}\right)_{T,x_2} > 0\,; \quad \left(\frac{\partial^2 f}{\partial x_2^2}\right)_{T,v} > 0\,; \quad \left(\frac{\partial^2 g}{\partial x_2^2}\right)_{T,p} = 0. \tag{16.39}$$

The equation of the boundary could then be

$$\left(\frac{\partial^2 g}{\partial x_2^2}\right)_{T,p} = 0. \tag{16.40}$$

On the other hand if we suppose for the moment that the inequality (16.30) reaches zero first, that is if

$$\left(\frac{\partial^2 f}{\partial v^2}\right)_{T, x_2} = 0 \tag{16.41}$$

is the equation of the boundary, then, as we can readily verify, on passing from the region where (16.30) and (16.37) are satisfied up to the boundary defined by (16.41), we must necessarily pass through a region where (16.37) ceases to be satisfied, since the negative term must exceed the first as $\partial^2 f/\partial v^2$ tends to zero.

The boundary between stable and unstable states must therefore be defined by (16.40) and on that boundary we have in general

$$\left(\frac{\partial^2 f}{\partial v^2}\right)_{T, x_2} > 0. \tag{16.42}$$

The required boundary surface thus has the equation

$$\left(\frac{\partial^2 f}{\partial x_2^2}\right)_{T, v} \left(\frac{\partial^2 f}{\partial v^2}\right)_{T, x_2} - \left(\frac{\partial^2 f}{\partial x_2 \, \partial v}\right)_T^2 = 0. \tag{16.43}$$

The condition of mechanical stability hence plays no part in determining the boundary which is fixed by the fact that at this surface the condition of stability of diffusion ceases to be satisfied. This justifies the method which we have employed in §§ 6 and 7, in which we have made use of only the condition for stability with respect to diffusion.

Now let us see how the condition of mechanical stability arises in the case of a pure substance. For this purpose we write (16.43) in the equivalent form :

$$\frac{\partial^2 f}{\partial x_2^2}\left(-\frac{\partial p}{\partial v}\right) - \left(\frac{\partial p}{\partial x_2}\right)^2 = 0. \tag{16.44}$$

Now when x_2 tends to zero,

$$\frac{\partial^2 f}{\partial x_2^2} \to \infty, \tag{16.45}$$

as we can easily verify from (16.32) and (6.49). On the other hand $(\partial p/\partial x_2)$ in general remains finite. Hence for a pure substance the condition (16.44), leads back again to the boundary condition for mechanical stability

$$-\frac{\partial p}{\partial v} = 0 \tag{16.46}$$

in conformity with equation (16.3).

The v, x diagram, such as we have already used, enables us to visualize these different results (*cf.* figs. 16.8 and 16.15). In fig. 16.15 the curve $v_A^g\,kv_A^l$ is the saturation curve already shown in fig. 16.8. The line AkB is defined by equation (16.40) and inside this curve we have states which are unstable with respect to diffusion. In the language of the van der Waals school this curve is called the *spinodal curve.* We see that the critical point lies both on the saturation curve and on the spinodal curve.

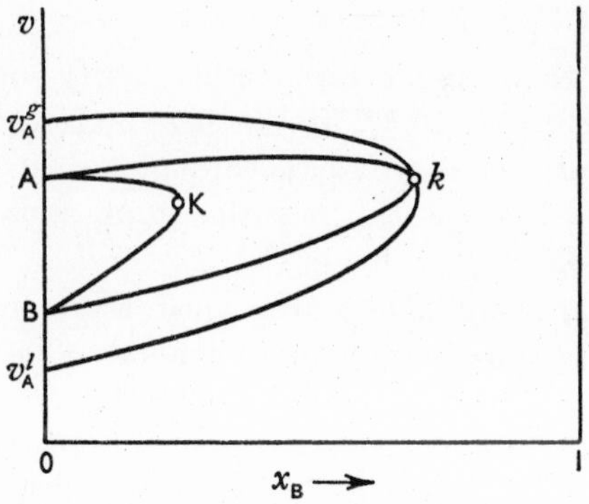

FIG. 16.15. $v-x$ diagram for a binary mixture near the critical point.

The curve AKB is defined by

$$\left(\frac{\partial p}{\partial v}\right)_{T,x_2}=0 \qquad (16.47)$$

and inside this curve neither the diffusion stability condition nor the condition of mechanical stability is satisfied. This curve does not play any part in determining the critical point for the mixture. Finally we notice that the spinodal curve and that defined by (16.47) tend to become identical as we proceed towards pure substance A, in conformity with equations (16.44) to (16.46).

9. Phase Separation in Regular Solutions.

In the preceding paragraphs we have given the general equations relating to critical solution phenomena. To obtain more specific conclusions we must know how the activity coefficients depend upon the independent variables T, p and x_2.

We shall consider the special case in which the activity coefficients γ_1 and γ_2 are given by

$$\left.\begin{aligned} RT\ln\gamma_1 &= \alpha x_2^2 \\ RT\ln\gamma_2 &= \alpha(1-x_2)^2 \end{aligned}\right\}, \qquad (16.48)$$

where α is a constant. As we shall see later this activity coefficient law is characteristic of a class of solutions called *strictly regular solutions* which have been studied in particular by Hildebrand and by Fowler and Guggenheim.*

The physical significance of this law will be examined later but for the moment we may use it to study the general behaviour of the conditions of stability when the activity coefficients are of this particular form. Similar calculations may be made starting from any other

* *Cf.* Hildebrand, [28]; Fowler and Guggenheim [20], chap. VIII.

equations for activity coefficients either obtained experimentally or derived theoretically.

The chemical potentials follow directly from (16.48) in the form (*cf.* 7.63)

$$\mu_1 = \mu_1^0(T, p) + \boldsymbol{R}T \ln (1 - x_2) + \alpha x_2^2, \tag{16.49}$$

$$\mu_2 = \mu_2^0(T, p) + \boldsymbol{R}T \ln x_2 + \alpha(1 - x_2)^2, \tag{16.50}$$

where, by definition, the functions $\mu_1^0(T, p)$ and $\mu_2^0(T, p)$ are equal respectively to the chemical potentials of the pure components 1 and 2 in the same physical state as the solution, and so have the same values, at a given T and p, for all values of x_2. Thus, if the system splits into two phases, μ_1^0 will have the same value in the two layers, and so also will μ_2^0.

Differentiating (16.49) we have

$$\frac{\partial \mu_1}{\partial x_2} = -\frac{\boldsymbol{R}T}{1 - x_2} + 2x_2\alpha. \tag{16.51}$$

If the system is to be in stable equilibrium with respect to phase separation, it is necessary and sufficient that, in accordance with (16.14),

$$\frac{2\alpha}{\boldsymbol{R}T} < \frac{1}{x_2(1 - x_2)}. \tag{16.52}$$

If $\alpha/\boldsymbol{R}T$ is positive and sufficiently large then this inequality cannot be satisfied at all concentrations. For $x_2(1 - x_2)$ has a maximum value of 0·25, and hence $1/\{x_2(1 - x_2)\}$ has a minimum value of 4. Hence for all values of $2\alpha/\boldsymbol{R}T$ greater than four, there must be a range of concentrations for which (16.52) breaks down. In this region the system will no longer be in a state of stable equilibrium, but it will split into two phases.

First we may calculate the position of the critical point at a definite pressure p by employing equations (16.15). If T_c and $(x_2)_c$ are respectively the critical temperature and critical composition ,then

$$\left(\frac{\partial \mu_1}{\partial x_2}\right)_c = -\frac{\boldsymbol{R}T_c}{1 - (x_2)_c} + 2\alpha(x_2)_c = 0, \tag{16.53}$$

$$\left(\frac{\partial^2 \mu_1}{\partial x_2^2}\right)_c = -\frac{\boldsymbol{R}T_c}{\{1 - (x_2)_c\}^2} + 2\alpha = 0, \tag{16.54}$$

whence

$$\boxed{\begin{aligned} (x_2)_c &= 0{\cdot}5, \\ T_c &= \frac{\alpha}{2\boldsymbol{R}} \end{aligned}}. \tag{16.55}$$

Hence the activity coefficient law (16.48) leads to a critical point which corresponds to an equimolecular mixture of the two components. Furthermore the critical temperature is always an upper critical solution temperature, as is readily seen since for $T > T_c$ the inequality (16.52) is always satisfied and the phase is stable whatever the composition.

We now find the boundary separating the metastable states from the unstable states. From (16.19) and (16.51), the equation of this boundary is

$$T = \frac{2\alpha}{R} x_2(1 - x_2); \tag{16.56}$$

or, substituting from (16.55),

$$T = 4T_c x_2(1 - x_2). \tag{16.57}$$

Finally we need to know the *curve of coexistence of* the two layers in true equilibrium. On this curve we must have

$$\mu_1' = \mu_1'' \quad \text{and} \quad \mu_2' = \mu_2'', \tag{16.58}$$

so that, from (16.49) and (16.50)

$$\left.\begin{aligned} \mu_1^0 + RT \ln x_1'' + \alpha(1 - x_1'')^2 &= \mu_1^0 + RT \ln x_1' + \alpha(1 - x_1')^2, \\ \mu_2^0 + RT \ln(1 - x_1'') + \alpha(x_1'')^2 &= \mu_2^0 + RT \ln(1 - x_1') + \alpha(x_1')^2 \end{aligned}\right\}. \tag{16.59}$$

The μ^0 functions can be eliminated from these equations and if

$$x_1'' = 1 - x_1', \tag{16.60}$$

i.e. if the curve is symmetrical, the two equations (16.59) become identical. Hence the two equations (16.59) are really only equivalent

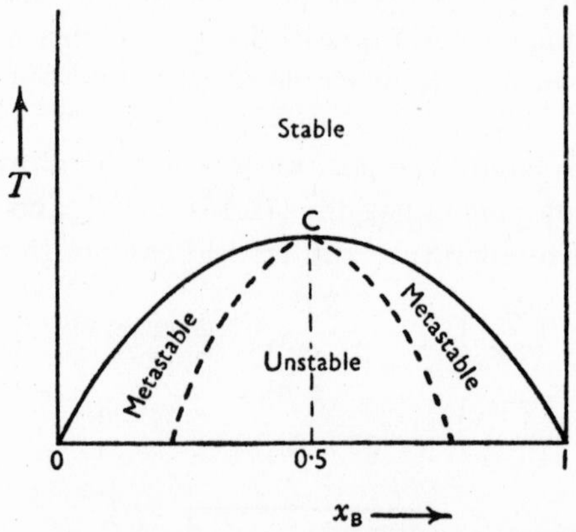

FIG. 16.16. Phase separation in a regular solution at constant p.

to a single independent equation. Taking the first of these equations and eliminating x_1'' we find

$$RT \ln(1 - x_1') + \alpha(x_1')^2 = RT \ln x_1' + \alpha(1 - x_1')^2, \tag{16.61}$$

whence, (*cf.* 16.55),

$$T = 2T_c \frac{1 - 2x_1'}{\ln\{(1 - x_1')/x_1'\}}. \tag{16.62}$$

The disposition of the critical point and the curves (16.57) and (16.62) is shown schematically in fig. 16.16.

10. Mutual Solubility of Crystals.

The phenomenon of critical mixing occurs not only in liquid solutions but also in solid solutions (*mixed crystals*). The conditions of stability for a solid solution are identical with those discussed above for liquid solutions. In particular, a system is always stable with respect to phase separation if it is ideal (*cf.* chap. XV, § 14), and it can only become unstable if the activity coefficients depart sufficiently from unity.*

Substances which have similar compositions and chemical structure are generally capable of forming stable mixed crystals. In other systems the miscibility is often limited, or almost zero, and in these cases we may have two kinds of crystal in equilibrium. Occasionally we may have several zones of immiscibility; thus in fig. 16.17 is shown the case of a system in which there are two zones of immiscibility, x_2^1 to x_2^2 and x_2^3 to x_2^4, in which the system forms two crystalline phases. This behaviour is not unusual, and there may be an even larger number of zones of immiscibility. The zones separating two regions of immiscibility may be extremely narrow and situated close to certain values of the mole fraction (for example $x_2 = 0{\cdot}5$). In this case we speak of *stoichiometric addition compounds*. Thus for the magnesium + nickel alloys the zones of miscibility are very narrow and are in the immediate neighbourhood of $x_2 = 0$ (pure nickel), $x_2 = 1/3$, $x_2 = 2/3$, $x_2 = 1$ (pure magnesium). All systems for which the composition does not correspond to one of these mole fractions consist of two phases.

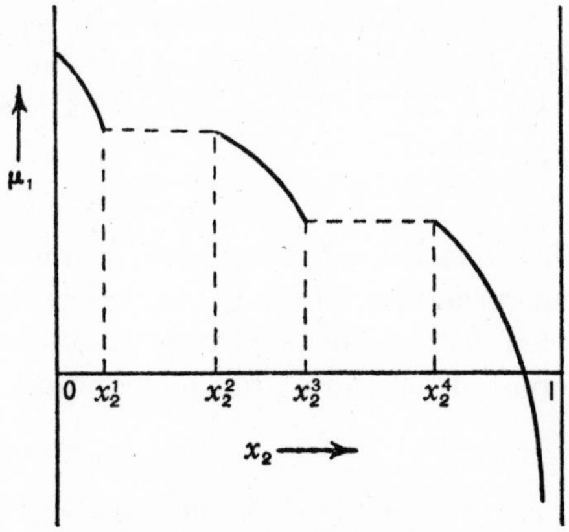

FIG. 16.17. Mixed crystals with two regions of immiscibility.

* *Cf.* Timmermans, [45], p. 81 ; Dehlinger, [14], p. 16.

11. Critical Phenomena in Ternary Systems.

We now consider in more detail the conditions for stability in a ternary system. It was shown in chap. XV that the following conditions ensured stability, *cf.* (15.116),

$$\mu_{11}>0\,;\quad \mu_{22}>0\,;\quad \mu_{11}\mu_{22}-\mu_{12}^2\geqslant 0. \tag{16.63}$$

For *unstable phases* at least one of these inequalities is not satisfied. To find the equation for the boundary separating unstable from stable (and metastable) states we must examine the inequalities of (16.63) and find which of them breaks down first on passing from a stable to an unstable phase.

We notice first that we can have simultaneously

$$\mu_{11}\mu_{22}-\mu_{12}^2=0 \quad \text{with} \quad \mu_{11}>0 \quad \text{and} \quad \mu_{22}>0.$$

On the other hand if

$$\mu_{11}=0 \quad \text{or} \quad \mu_{22}=0,$$

then we must have

$$\mu_{11}\mu_{22}-\mu_{12}^2\leqslant 0,$$

so that the boundary defined by $\mu_{11}=0$ and that defined by $\mu_{22}=0$ must lie inside the region of instability.

Hence the boundary separating the stable from the unstable states is given by

$$\mu_{11}\mu_{22}-\mu_{12}^2=0. \tag{16.64}$$

This equation is due to Gibbs, and may be transformed into an equivalent form, also due to Gibbs, in the following way.

Let us consider a change at constant T, p and n_3. The chemical potentials μ_1 and μ_2 will be functions only of n_1 and n_2, whence

$$\delta\mu_1=\mu_{11}\delta n_1+\mu_{12}\,\delta n_2, \tag{16.65}$$

$$\delta\mu_2=\mu_{21}\,\delta n_1+\mu_{22}\,\delta n_2. \tag{16.66}$$

For a particular change at constant μ_1, equation (16.65) gives

$$\delta n_1=-\frac{\mu_{12}}{\mu_{11}}\,\delta n_2,$$

and (16.66) becomes

$$\delta\mu_2=\left(-\frac{\mu_{12}^2}{\mu_{11}}+\mu_{22}\right)\delta n_2$$

whence

$$\left(\frac{\partial\mu_2}{\partial n_2}\right)_{T,p,\mu_1,n_3}=\frac{\mu_{11}\mu_{22}-\mu_{12}^2}{\mu_{11}}. \tag{16.67}$$

We see therefore that since for stable phases the right hand side must be positive, we must also have

$$\left(\frac{\partial \mu_2}{\partial n_2}\right)_{T,p,\mu_1,n_3} > 0, \quad (16.68)$$

while the boundary between stable and unstable phases is given by

$$\left(\frac{\partial \mu_2}{\partial n_2}\right)_{T,p,\mu_1,n_3} = 0. \quad (16.69)$$

Suppose we know μ_2 for all states, stable and unstable, of a system so that we can plot μ_2 as a function of n_2 at constant values of T, p, μ_1, n_3. Then if the curve increases steadily (fig. 16.18, curve 1), the system is always stable; if, on the other hand, the curve is like 2, then there will be unstable states. The transition will be through the curve 3 which has a point of inflexion. This point is the critical point of the system and is thus characterized by the equations:

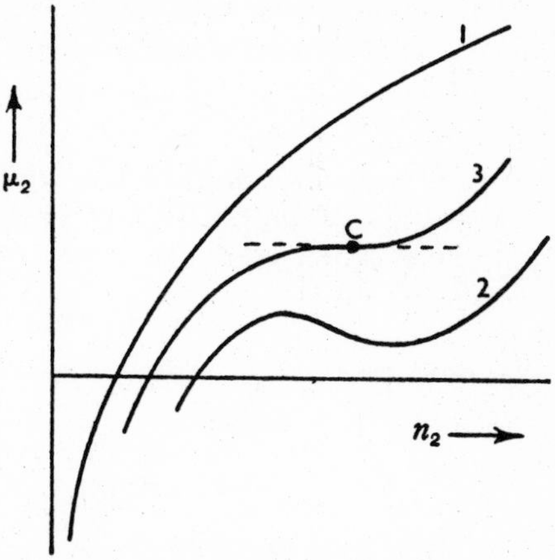

FIG. 16.18. Ternary system: chemical potential μ_2 as a function of n_2, at constant T, p, μ_1, n_3.

$$\left.\begin{aligned}\left(\frac{\partial \mu_2}{\partial n_2}\right)_{T,p,\mu_1,n_3} &= 0,\\ \left(\frac{\partial^2 \mu_2}{\partial n_2^2}\right)_{T,p,\mu_1,n_3} &= 0,\\ \left(\frac{\partial^3 \mu_2}{\partial n_2^3}\right)_{T,p,\mu_1,n_3} &\neq 0\end{aligned}\right\}. \quad (16.70)$$

These are the general equations defining the critical phases in a ternary system: they were first derived by Gibbs.*

The meaning of these equations can best be understood with reference to a geometrical representation of the mean molar Gibbs free energy g. For a system at constant temperature and pressure, we construct the surface $g(x_2, x_3)$ using triangular co-ordinates

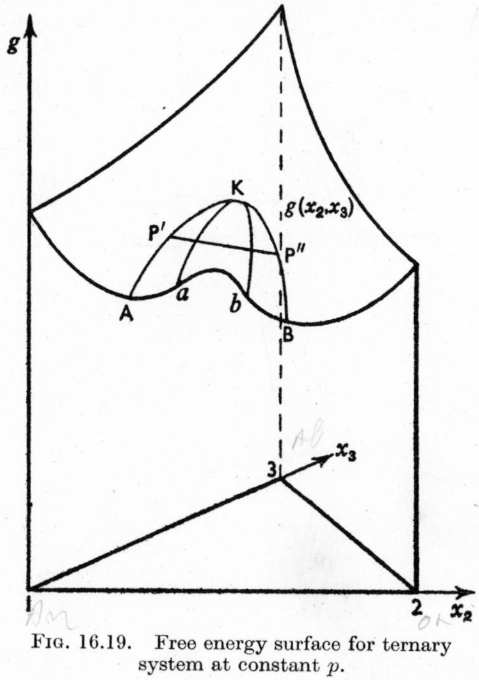

FIG. 16.19. Free energy surface for ternary system at constant p.

* Gibbs, [23], p. 129.

$n\mu_{12} = (1-x_2)\frac{\partial \mu_1}{\partial x_2} - x_3\frac{\partial \mu_2}{\partial x_3}$

for the mole fractions; a surface of this kind is shown in fig. 16.19.

The boundary condition (16.64) is in effect a relation between x_2 and x_3 when T and p are given. This line separates unstable states from metastable states and must lie on the surface $g(x_2, x_3)$; it is the *spinodal* curve in the sense of § 8. The projection of this curve on the base is also termed the spinodal.

As we have seen (*cf.* 15.115), equation (16.64) can be replaced by the equivalent equation

$$\mu_{22}\mu_{33} - \mu_{23}^2 = 0. \tag{16.71}$$

We now proceed to prove that this equation is equivalent to the equation

$$\frac{\partial^2 g}{\partial x_2^2}\frac{\partial^2 g}{\partial x_3^2} - \left(\frac{\partial^2 g}{\partial x_2 \partial x_3}\right)^2 = 0. \tag{16.72}$$

Starting from (*cf.* 6.46),

$$g = x_1\mu_1 + x_2\mu_2 + x_3\mu_3, \tag{16.73}$$

and differentiating with respect to x_2, remembering that

$$x_1 = 1 - x_2 - x_3,$$

we obtain

$$\frac{\partial g}{\partial x_2} = -\mu_1 + \mu_2 + \sum_{i=1}^{i=3} x_i \frac{\partial \mu_i}{\partial x_2}.$$

However the summation term must be zero from the Gibbs-Duhem equation (6.41), so that (*cf.* 6.47),

$$\frac{\partial g}{\partial x_2} = \mu_2 - \mu_1, \text{ and similarly, } \frac{\partial g}{\partial x_3} = \mu_3 - \mu_1. \tag{16.74}$$

Making use of (16.73) and (16.74) we can verify simply that

$$\mu_2 = g + (1 - x_2)\frac{\partial g}{\partial x_2} - x_3 \frac{\partial g}{\partial x_3}, \tag{16.75}$$

together with an analogous equation for μ_3.

We now differentiate to get μ_{22}:

$$\mu_{22} = \left(\frac{\partial \mu_2}{\partial n_2}\right)_{T, p, n_1, n_3} = \frac{\partial \mu_2}{\partial x_2}\left(\frac{1}{n} - \frac{n_2}{n^2}\right) - \frac{\partial \mu_2}{\partial x_3} \cdot \frac{n_3}{n^2}$$

$$= \frac{1}{n}\left[\frac{\partial \mu_2}{\partial x_2}(1 - x_2) - \frac{\partial \mu_2}{\partial x_3} x_3\right],$$

which on inserting the partial derivatives calculated from (16.75) becomes

$$n\mu_{22} = (1 - x_2)^2 \frac{\partial^2 g}{\partial x_2^2} - 2(1 - x_2)x_3 \frac{\partial^2 g}{\partial x_2 \partial x_3} + x_3^2 \frac{\partial^2 g}{\partial x_3^2}. \tag{16.76}$$

$n\mu_{23} = (1-x_3)\frac{\partial \mu_2}{\partial x_3} - x_2 \frac{\partial \mu_2}{\partial x_2}$

Similar equations are obtained for μ_{33} and μ_{23} :

$$n\mu_{33} = (1-x_3)^2 \frac{\partial^2 g}{\partial x_3^2} - 2(1-x_3)x_2 \frac{\partial^2 g}{\partial x_3\, \partial x_2} + x_2^2 \frac{\partial^2 g}{\partial x_2^2}, \tag{16.77}$$

$$n\mu_{23} = -x_2(1-x_2)\frac{\partial^2 g}{\partial x_2^2} + (1-x_2-x_3+2x_2x_3)\frac{\partial^2 g}{\partial x_2\, \partial x_3} - x_3(1-x_3)\frac{\partial^2 g}{\partial x_3^2}. \tag{16.77'}$$

Using these equations we can show readily that

$$\mu_{22}\mu_{33} - \mu_{23}^2 = \left(\frac{1-x_2-x_3}{n}\right)^2 \left[\frac{\partial^2 g}{\partial x_2^2}\frac{\partial^2 g}{\partial x_3^2} - \left(\frac{\partial^2 g}{\partial x_2\, \partial x_3}\right)^2\right] \tag{16.78}$$

which shows that we can use equation (16.72) to define the spinodal.

Consider now a point on the surface $g(x_2, x_3)$ at which

$$\frac{\partial^2 g}{\partial x_2^2} > 0\,; \quad \frac{\partial^2 g}{\partial x_3^2} > 0\,; \quad \frac{\partial^2 g}{\partial x_2^2}\frac{\partial^2 g}{\partial x_3^2} - \left(\frac{\partial^2 g}{\partial x_2\, \partial x_3}\right)^2 > 0. \tag{16.79}$$

At this point we must also have, from (16.77), (16.78) and (16.79),

$$\mu_{22} > 0\,; \quad \mu_{33} > 0\,; \quad \mu_{22}\mu_{33} - \mu_{23}^2 > 0,$$

so that the system is stable. Equations (16.79) may also be shown to imply that at this point the surface g is convex downwards. It is said to be *convex-convex* since all sections made by planes normal to the surface at this point have their radii of curvature on the same side.*

On the other hand, at all points on the surface where

$$\frac{\partial^2 g}{\partial x_2^2}\frac{\partial^2 g}{\partial x_3^2} - \left(\frac{\partial^2 g}{\partial x_2\, \partial x_3}\right)^2 < 0 \tag{16.80}$$

the system is unstable and the surface is *convex-concave* ; that is to say certain normal sections are convex downwards while others are concave downwards.

Thus on the surface $g(x_2, x_3)$, the spinodal is the boundary which separates that part of the surface which is convex-convex from that which is convex-concave.

In fig. 16.19 the line aKb represents the spinodal curve whose presence indicates the existence of a fold in the surface g. Any system whose representative point is situated on the convex-concave surface is unstable and breaks into two stable phases, each of which will be represented by a point on the convex-convex surface. It can be shown

* See *e.g.*, R. J. T. Bell, *Co-ordinate Geometry of Three-dimensions*, (London, 1937), p. 270.

that at the two points representing co-existing phases the tangent planes are coincident. This follows by considering the conditions of coexistence of the two phases, namely

$$\mu_1' = \mu_1'' \; ; \; \mu_2' = \mu_2'' \; ; \; \mu_3' = \mu_3'' ,$$

and by expressing these chemical potentials in each phase in the form of (16.73). It is then found that the conditions of coexistence take the form

$$\frac{\partial g'}{\partial x_2'} = \frac{\partial g''}{\partial x_2''} \; ; \; \frac{\partial g'}{\partial x_3'} = \frac{\partial g''}{\partial x_3''} \; ;$$

$$g' - x_2' \frac{\partial g'}{\partial x_2'} - x_3' \frac{\partial g'}{\partial x_3'} = g'' - x_2'' \frac{\partial g''}{\partial x_2''} - x_3'' \frac{\partial g''}{\partial x_3''} , \qquad (16.81)$$

which shows* that the points g', x_2', x_3' and g'', x_2'', x_3'' have a common tangent plane.

The points P' and P'' in fig. 16.19 represent two coexisting phases; the line joining them is called a *tie-line*. The *coexistence curve*, AKB, is also known as the *binodal curve*.

The two branches of the coexistence curve meet in the point K, and the tangent at this point is the limit to which the tie lines tend as K is approached. Beyond K there are no tie lines and the system exists as a single stable phase. K is the critical solution point at the temperature and pressure under consideration. It also lies on the spinodal curve since it must of necessity lie on the boundary between stable and unstable states.

12. Examples of Critical Solution Phenomena in Ternary Systems.†

Let us consider a ternary system characterized by the independent variables T, p, x_2 and x_3. The critical states of this system will obey the relations (16.70). At constant temperature and pressure there will be a *critical point*, while at constant pressure but variable temperature we find a *critical line*.

Fig. 16.20 represents schematically the phase diagram of the ternary system acetic acid + water + chloroform. The pairs water + acetic acid and acetic acid + chloroform, are completely miscible in all proportions, but water and chloroform are only partially miscible. The composition

* The tangent plane at P' is

$$g - g' = \frac{\partial g'}{\partial x_2'} (x_2 - x_2') + \frac{\partial g'}{\partial x_3'} (x_3 - x_3') \; ;$$

that at P'' is given by a similar equation. The conditions that these planes coincide are obtained by equating coefficients in the two equations and are immediately seen to be (16.81).

† *Cf.* Vogel, [50], p. 327.

of the two phases in equilibrium is given by the ends of the lines $f\phi$, $f_1\phi_1$, $f_2\phi_2$ .... The line $ff_1f_2 \ldots k \ldots \phi$ is the saturation curve. At the point k, the two phases in equilibrium become identical so that k is the critical point under the conditions considered.

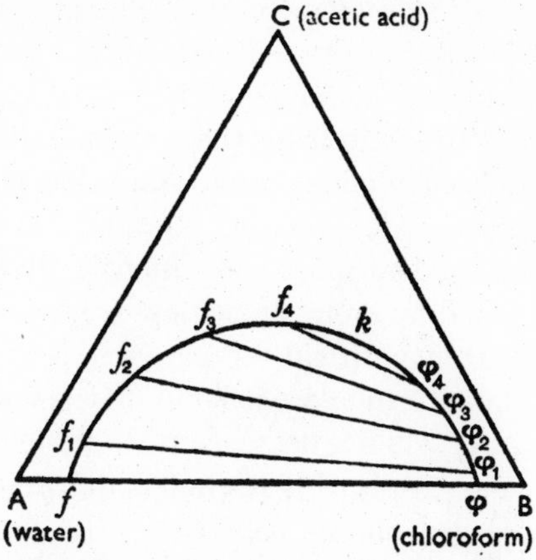

FIG. 16.20. Phase diagram for the ternary system : water + chloroform + acetic acid (schematic).

If we now vary the temperature, the phase diagram is of the form indicated in fig. 16.21. Each section at constant temperature gives a curve of the form shown in fig. 16.20, and the locus of critical points is the line $k_1k_2k_3k_4$.

We cannot in this book examine in detail the numerous other forms which the phase diagram can take. An excellent review of the possible types of behaviour is given by Vogel.

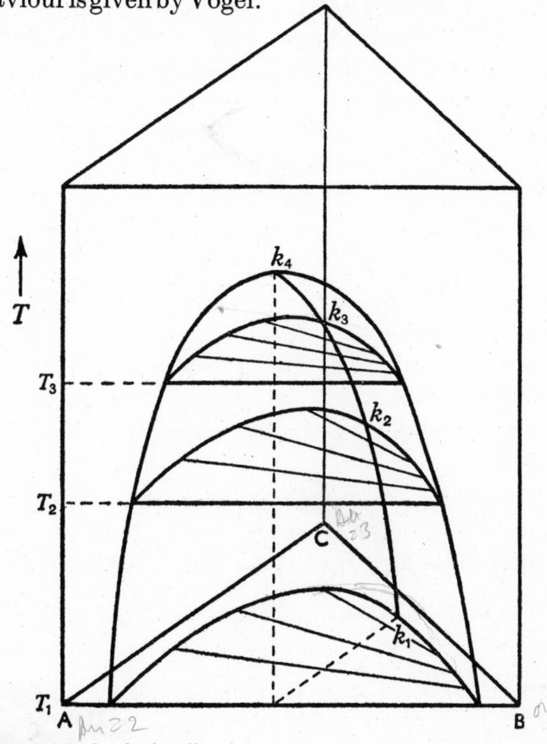

FIG. 16.21. Critical solution line in a ternary system at constant pressure.*

* The projection of the curve k_1k_4 on the horizontal plane is, in general, not linear as shown in this figure.

13. Influence of a Third Component on the Mutual Solubility of Two Liquids.

The problem of the influence of a third component on the mutual solubility of two liquids may be treated as an application of the critical solution phenomena of ternary systems.

We know from the experimental work of Duclaux,* of Pfeiffer,† of Schreinemakers‡ and above all of Timmermans§ that this influence is often very striking, and has many practical applications.|| It may be studied most conveniently by determinations of the effect of added substances on the critical solution temperature of a binary mixture.

If the critical temperature is an upper critical solution temperature, then an increase in solubility leads to a decrease in the critical temperature, while a decrease in solubility will raise the critical temperature.

To study this phenomenon quantitatively¶ we observe first that the critical line at constant p lies, because of the first relation of (16.70) and (16.67), in the surface $\mathfrak{S}_1$ whose equation is

$$\mathfrak{S}_1 \equiv \mu_{11}\mu_{22} - \mu_{12}^2 = 0. \tag{16.82}$$

This equation is in effect a relation between the three variables T, x_2, x_3.

In order to put this equation into a more symmetrical form, we notice that it is identical (*cf.* 15.115) with each of the two equations

$$\mu_{22}\mu_{33} - \mu_{23}^2 = 0, \quad \mu_{33}\mu_{11} - \mu_{13}^2 = 0. \tag{16.83}$$

$\mathfrak{S}_1$ can therefore be written in the form,

$$\mathfrak{S}_1 \equiv \mu_{11}\mu_{22} + \mu_{22}\mu_{33} + \mu_{33}\mu_{11} - \mu_{12}^2 - \mu_{23}^2 - \mu_{31}^2 = 0. \tag{16.84}$$

Now equations (15.112) enable us to write μ_{11}, μ_{22}, μ_{33} in terms of μ_{12}, μ_{23} and μ_{31} :

$$\left.\begin{aligned} \mu_{11} &= -\frac{1}{n_1}(n_2\mu_{12} + n_3\mu_{13}), \\ \mu_{22} &= -\frac{1}{n_2}(n_1\mu_{12} + n_3\mu_{23}), \\ \mu_{33} &= -\frac{1}{n_3}(n_2\mu_{32} + n_1\mu_{31}) \end{aligned}\right\} . \tag{16.85}$$

On substituting these into (16.84) we obtain the symmetrical equation

$$\mathfrak{S}_1 \equiv x_1\mu_{12}\mu_{31} + x_2\mu_{21}\mu_{23} + x_3\mu_{31}\mu_{23} = 0. \tag{16.86}$$

* E. Duclaux, *Ann. Chim. Phys.*, 5th series, **7**, 264 (1876).

† H. Pfeiffer, *Zeit. physik. Chem.*, **9**, 444 (1892).

‡ F. A. H. Schreinemakers, *Zeit. physik. Chem.*, 1897–1900; see Cumulative Index to vols. **1-24**, and to vols. **25-50** for full references.

§ Timmermans, [45].

|| *Cf.* Vogel, *loc. cit.*, [50], p. 341.

¶ C. Wagner, *Zeit. physik. Chem.*, **132**, 273 (1928); I. Prigogine, *Bull. Soc. Chim. Belg.*, **52**, 115 (1943).

The critical line is the intersection of this surface with the surface $\mathfrak{S}_2$ defined by the second equation of (16.70).

To obtain the differential equation of this line, we differentiate the two equations $\mathfrak{S}_1=0$ and $\mathfrak{S}_2=0$, whence at constant pressure,

$$\left.\begin{aligned}\frac{\partial \mathfrak{S}_1}{\partial T}\,\delta T+\frac{\partial \mathfrak{S}_1}{\partial x_2}\,\delta x_2+\frac{\partial \mathfrak{S}_1}{\partial x_3}\,\delta x_3=0,\\ \frac{\partial \mathfrak{S}_2}{\partial T}\,\delta T+\frac{\partial \mathfrak{S}_2}{\partial x_2}\,\delta x_2+\frac{\partial \mathfrak{S}_2}{\partial x_3}\,\delta x_3=0\end{aligned}\right\}. \tag{16.87}$$

These relations then enable us to calculate $\delta T/\delta x_3$, that is to say the influence of the third component on the critical temperature.

We note that in the particular case where

$$\frac{\partial \mathfrak{S}_1}{\partial x_2}=0, \tag{16.88}$$

the first relation of (16.87) gives simply

$$\frac{\delta T}{\delta x_3}=-\frac{\partial \mathfrak{S}_1/\partial x_3}{\partial \mathfrak{S}_1/\partial T}. \tag{16.89}$$

To proceed further we need to know the behaviour of the activity coefficients of the various components.

As an example of the application of the above formulae let us examine the behaviour of a *strictly regular solution*. In a ternary regular solution we have

$$\left.\begin{aligned}\boldsymbol{R}T\ln\gamma_1&=(x_2)^2\alpha_{12}+(x_3)^2\alpha_{13}+x_2x_3(\alpha_{12}-\alpha_{23}+\alpha_{13}),\\ \boldsymbol{R}T\ln\gamma_2&=(x_3)^2\alpha_{23}+(x_1)^2\alpha_{12}+x_3x_1(\alpha_{23}-\alpha_{13}+\alpha_{12}),\\ \boldsymbol{R}T\ln\gamma_3&=(x_1)^2\alpha_{13}+(x_2)^2\alpha_{23}+x_1x_2(\alpha_{13}-\alpha_{12}+\alpha_{23})\end{aligned}\right\}. \tag{16.90}$$

These equations are an extension of the equations (16.48) to which they reduce when $x_3=0$. The quantities α_{12}, α_{23} and α_{13} are constants. Remembering that (*cf.* 7. 63, 21.29)

$$\mu_1=\mu_1^0(T,p)+\boldsymbol{R}T\ln x_1+\boldsymbol{R}T\ln\gamma_1,\ \text{etc.},$$

we can evaluate μ_1, μ_2 and μ_3. On differentiation of these we then obtain

$$\begin{aligned}\mu_{12}=\left(\frac{\partial\mu_1}{\partial n_2}\right)_{T,p,n_1,n_3}&=\frac{1}{n}\{-\boldsymbol{R}T+2x_2\alpha_{12}-2x_2^2\alpha_{12}-2x_3^2\alpha_{13}\\ &\qquad+(\alpha_{12}-\alpha_{23}+\alpha_{13})x_3-2(\alpha_{12}-\alpha_{23}+\alpha_{13})x_2x_3\},\\ \mu_{13}&=\frac{1}{n}\{-\boldsymbol{R}T+2x_3\alpha_{13}-2x_3^2\alpha_{13}-2x_2^2\alpha_{12}\\ &\qquad+(\alpha_{13}-\alpha_{23}+\alpha_{12})x_2-2(\alpha_{13}-\alpha_{23}+\alpha_{12})x_3x_2\},\\ \mu_{23}&=\frac{1}{n}\{-\boldsymbol{R}T+2x_3\alpha_{23}-2x_3^2\alpha_{23}-2x_1^2\alpha_{21}\\ &\qquad+(\alpha_{23}-\alpha_{13}+\alpha_{12})x_1-2(\alpha_{23}-\alpha_{13}+\alpha_{12})x_1x_3\}.\end{aligned} \tag{16.91}$$

The critical point of the binary system 1 +2 is, as we have already seen (*cf.* 16.55), characterized by

$$(x_1)_c=(x_2)_c=0{\cdot}5\;;\; T_c=\frac{\alpha_{12}}{2\mathbf{R}}, \tag{16.92}$$

and, of course,

$$x_3=0. \tag{16.93}$$

At the critical point therefore the expressions (16.91) have the values

$$\left.\begin{aligned}(\mu_{12})_c&=0,\\ (\mu_{13})_c&=-\frac{1}{2n}(\alpha_{12}-\alpha_{13}+\alpha_{23}),\\ (\mu_{23})_c&=-\frac{1}{2n}(\alpha_{12}-\alpha_{23}+\alpha_{13})\end{aligned}\right\}. \tag{16.94}$$

We now proceed to evaluate the partial derivative of $\mathfrak{S}_1$. From (16.86) we have :

$$\begin{aligned}\frac{\partial\mathfrak{S}_1}{\partial T}=x_1\mu_{12}\frac{\partial\mu_{13}}{\partial T}+x_1\mu_{13}\frac{\partial\mu_{12}}{\partial T}+x_2\mu_{12}\frac{\partial\mu_{23}}{\partial T}\\ +x_2\mu_{23}\frac{\partial\mu_{12}}{\partial T}+x_3\mu_{13}\frac{\partial\mu_{23}}{\partial T}+x_3\mu_{23}\frac{\partial\mu_{13}}{\partial T}.\end{aligned} \tag{16.95}$$

We see immediately from (16.91) that

$$n\frac{\partial\mu_{12}}{\partial T}=n\frac{\partial\mu_{13}}{\partial T}=n\frac{\partial\mu_{23}}{\partial T}=-\mathbf{R}. \tag{16.96}$$

Hence substituting into (16.95) the values of the various terms given by (16.92), (16.93), (16.94) and (16.96) we find near the binary critical point

$$\begin{aligned}n^2\left(\frac{\partial\mathfrak{S}_1}{\partial T}\right)_c&=\tfrac{1}{4}\mathbf{R}(\alpha_{12}-\alpha_{13}+\alpha_{23})+\tfrac{1}{4}R(\alpha_{12}-\alpha_{23}+\alpha_{13})\\ &=\frac{\mathbf{R}\alpha_{12}}{2}.\end{aligned} \tag{16.97}$$

To evaluate the partial derivatives of $\mathfrak{S}_1$ with respect to the various mole fractions we need the following equations which follow from (16.91), (16.92) and (16.93) :

$$\left.\begin{aligned}&n\left(\frac{\partial\mu_{12}}{\partial x_3}\right)_c=0\;;\; n\left(\frac{\partial\mu_{12}}{\partial x_2}\right)_c=0\;;\\ &n\left(\frac{\partial\mu_{13}}{\partial x_3}\right)_c=\alpha_{13}-\alpha_{12}+\alpha_{23}=n\left(\frac{\partial\mu_{23}}{\partial x_3}\right)_c\end{aligned}\right\}. \tag{16.98}$$

We are now able to differentiate (16.86) with respect to x_2 and x_3, and employing (16.94) we obtain

$$n^2\left(\frac{\partial \mathfrak{S}_1}{\partial x_2}\right)_c = 0, \tag{16.99}$$

and

$$n^2\left(\frac{\partial \mathfrak{S}_1}{\partial x_3}\right)_c = \tfrac{1}{4}(\alpha_{12}-\alpha_{13}+\alpha_{23})(\alpha_{12}-\alpha_{23}+\alpha_{13}). \tag{16.100}$$

We see that for a regular solution (16.88) is thus valid and hence substituting (16.97) and (16.100) into (16.89) we have*

$$\boxed{\left(\frac{\delta T}{\delta x_3}\right)_c = -\frac{1}{2R}\frac{(\alpha_{12}-\alpha_{13}+\alpha_{23})(\alpha_{12}-\alpha_{23}+\alpha_{13})}{\alpha_{12}}}\,. \tag{16.101}$$

This equation gives the variation of the critical solution temperature of the binary system 1 + 2 caused by the addition of a small amount of a third component, in the case where the activity coefficients follow the law (16.90).

The last equation leads to two important generalizations, which are verified by experiment.†

(*a*) If the third component is about equally soluble in both 1 and 2, then

$$\alpha_{13} \simeq \alpha_{23}, \tag{16.102}$$

and (16.101) may be written approximately as

$$\left(\frac{\delta T}{\delta x_3}\right)_c = -\frac{\alpha_{12}}{2R}. \tag{16.103}$$

But according to (16.55) $T_c = \alpha_{12}/2R$, so that

$$\left(\frac{\delta T}{\delta x_3}\right)_c = -T_c < 0, \tag{16.104}$$

where T_c is the critical temperature of the system 1 + 2. Hence *the introduction of a third component which is equally soluble in the first two components will lower the critical solution temperature, that is to say it will increase the solubility.*‡

(*b*) If the third component is very much less soluble in one of the components than the other, for example if

$$\left.\begin{aligned}\alpha_{23} &\gg \alpha_{13}\\ \alpha_{23} &\gg \alpha_{12}\end{aligned}\right\}, \tag{16.105}$$

* I. Prigogine, *loc. cit.*

† *Cf.* Timmermans [45], p. 280; *Thesis*, (Brussels, 1911) p. 99; *cf.* also F. A. H. Schreinemakers, *Heterogene Gleichgewichte*, II, 3, (Brunswick, 1913).

‡ In this case we are, of course, dealing with an upper consolute temperature *cf.* § 9

so that components 2 and 3 are much less soluble in one another than they are in substance 1, then in this case we have approximately

$$\left(\frac{\delta T}{\delta x_3}\right)_c = \frac{1}{2}\frac{\alpha_{23}^2}{\boldsymbol{R}\alpha_{12}} > 0. \tag{16.106}$$

Similarly if

$$\left.\begin{array}{l}\alpha_{13} \gg \alpha_{23}\\ \alpha_{13} \gg \alpha_{12}\end{array}\right\}, \tag{16.107}$$

we find

$$\left(\frac{\delta T}{\delta x_3}\right)_c = \frac{1}{2}\frac{\alpha_{13}^2}{\boldsymbol{R}\alpha_{12}} > 0. \tag{16.108}$$

Hence *the addition of a third component which is much less soluble in one of the first two components than in the other, will always raise the critical solution temperature, that is to say it decreases the mutual solubility.*

As examples of these generalizations we may mention the following cases quoted by Timmermans.*

The critical solution temperature of the water + phenol system is 65 °C. Addition of 1% of naphthalene raises the critical temperature to 82 °C: naphthalene is soluble in phenol, insoluble in water.

On the other hand addition of 1% of sodium oleate reduces the critical temperature to 43 °C: sodium oleate is very soluble in both substances.

The following substances, which are weak electrolytes with approximately the same solubility in the two components, either lower the critical temperature or raise it only a very little: succinnic acid, mercuric cyanide, salicylic acid, tartaric acid, boric acid. In contrast, electrolytes such as NaCl, KCl, KBr, KNO_2, K_2SO_4, $MgSO_4$ and $Ba(NO_3)_2$ which are soluble in water but not in phenol cause a rapid rise in critical temperature; so do the following organic substances which are insoluble in water: camphor, benzil, benzophenone, azobenzene, anthraquinone, and the hexamethyl ester of mellitic acid.

These examples show the generality of these qualitative rules which were in fact only derived above for strictly regular solutions.†

14. Spinodal Lines in Regular Ternary Solutions.

Although it is very difficult to calculate the coexistence curve in a ternary system, the spinodal curve can be calculated quite simply.‡ If we know this curve we can then obtain a general idea of the nature of the phase diagram. We consider a system at constant T and p, but instead of employing equation (16.86) we make use of (16.72). In a

* *Loc. cit.*

† *Cf.* C. Wagner, *loc. cit.*

‡ J. L. Meijering, *Philips Research Reports*, 5, 333 (1950); 6, 183 (1951).

ternary regular solution it can be readily shown that the free energy is given by (*cf.* 6.46, 16.90)

$$g(x_2, x_3) = \sum_i x_i \mu_i = \sum_i x_i \mu_i^0(T, p) + \sum_i x_i \boldsymbol{RT} \ln x_i$$
$$+ \alpha_{12} x_1 x_2 + \alpha_{13} x_1 x_3 + \alpha_{23} x_2 x_3. \qquad (16.109)$$

If we regard x_1 as a function of x_2 and x_3, we find quite easily that

$$\left.\begin{aligned} \frac{\partial^2 g}{\partial x_2^2} &= -2\alpha_{12} + \boldsymbol{RT}\left(\frac{1}{x_2} - \frac{1}{x_1}\right), \\ \frac{\partial^2 g}{\partial x_3^2} &= -2\alpha_{13} + \boldsymbol{RT}\left(\frac{1}{x_3} + \frac{1}{x_1}\right), \\ \frac{\partial^2 g}{\partial x_2\, \partial x_3} &= \alpha_{23} - \alpha_{12} - \alpha_{13} + \frac{\boldsymbol{RT}}{x_1} \end{aligned}\right\}. \qquad (16.110)$$

Substituting into (16.72) we then obtain the following equation for the spinodal*

$$Lx_1x_2x_3 + \boldsymbol{RT}(2\alpha_{12}x_1x_2 + 2\alpha_{13}x_1x_3 + 2\alpha_{23}x_2x_3) = (\boldsymbol{RT})^2, \quad (16.111)$$

where we have put

$$L = \alpha_{12}^2 + \alpha_{13}^2 + \alpha_{23}^2 - 2\alpha_{12}\alpha_{13} - 2\alpha_{12}\alpha_{23} - 2\alpha_{13}\alpha_{23}. \qquad (16.112)$$

It is convenient to introduce the dimensionless parameters

$$\alpha = \frac{\alpha_{12}}{\boldsymbol{RT}}; \quad \beta = \frac{\alpha_{13}}{\boldsymbol{RT}}; \quad \gamma = \frac{\alpha_{23}}{\boldsymbol{RT}}; \quad \lambda = \frac{L}{(\boldsymbol{RT})^2}; \qquad (16.113)$$

when the equation for the spinodal takes the form :

$$\lambda x_1 x_2 x_3 + 2\alpha x_1 x_2 + 2\beta x_1 x_3 + 2\gamma x_2 x_3 = 1. \qquad (16.114)$$

For example, if $\alpha = -10$, $\beta = 0$, $\gamma = 0$, this equation is that of a closed curve inside the composition triangle. For these values of the coefficients, the immiscibility curve will therefore also consist of a closed ring inside the triangle. The existence of such closed miscibility gaps, which are observed for example with the Cu + Au + Ni system,† can therefore be interpreted in terms of regular solution theory without introducing any specifically " ternary " factor.

* R. Haase, *Zeit. Naturforschung*, **5a**, 109 (1950) ; R. P. Scott, *J. Chem. Phys.*, **17**, 268, 279 (1949).

† Meijering, *loc. cit.*

CHAPTER XVII

THEOREMS OF MODERATION

1. General Formulae.

In this chapter we shall discuss the consequences of perturbing a system, which is initially in stable equilibrium, to a neighbouring non-equilibrium state. Since the initial equilibrium is supposed to be stable then the system will tend to return to an equilibrium state. For the moment we shall only concern ourselves with the way in which the thermodynamic variables change as the perturbed system moves back to equilibrium. The characteristics of the final equilibrium state, which is in general different from the initial state, will be discussed in the next chapter.

Theorems governing the behaviour of perturbed systems are known as *theorems of restraint* or *theorems of moderation.*

The best known thermodynamic theorem of moderation is that of Le Chatelier-Braun,* which in the form stated by Le Chatelier is :

> Any system in chemical equilibrium undergoes, as a result of a variation in one of the factors governing the equilibrium, a compensating change in a direction such that, had this change occurred alone it would have produced a variation of the factor considered in the *opposite* direction.

When a system undergoes an internal compensation of this kind it is said to exhibit moderation of the factor perturbed.

In this chapter we shall study the validity of this principle by making use of De Donder's fundamental inequality (3.29).†

Let us consider a *system* I defined by the physical variables x and y (*e.g.* T and p), and by the chemical variables $n_1, \ldots n_c$, which at an instant t is in a state of true chemical equilibrium ; then

$$\mathbf{A}^{\mathrm{I}}(x, y, n_1 \ldots n_c) = 0, \tag{17.1}$$

and the reaction velocity $\mathbf{v}^{\mathrm{I}}$ in the system is zero.

Let us consider *another system* II called a *perturbed system* whose state differs only infinitesimally from the first and is defined by

$$x + \delta x \; ; \; y + \delta y \; ; \; n_1 + \delta n_1 \; ; \; \ldots \; n_c + \delta n_c. \tag{17.2}$$

* H. Le Chatelier, *Recherches sur les équilibres chimique*, (Paris, 1888) ; *Annales des mines*, 13, 200 (1888) ; F. Braun, *Zeit. physik. Chem.*, 1, 259 (1887).

† Th. De Donder, *Bull. Ac. Roy. Belg.* (*Cl. Sc.*) 19, 881 (1933) ; *Affinity* [9], p. 96; P. Van Rysselberghe, *Bull. Ac. Roy. Belg.* (*Cl. Sc.*), 21, 1042 (1935).

The affinity $\mathbf{A}^{\mathrm{II}}$ of this system must then be

$$\mathbf{A}^{\mathrm{II}} = \delta \mathbf{A} = \frac{\partial \mathbf{A}}{\partial x} \delta x + \frac{\partial \mathbf{A}}{\partial y} \delta y + \sum_{i=1}^{c} \frac{\partial \mathbf{A}}{\partial n_i} \delta n_i. \qquad (17.3)$$

If $\mathbf{v}^{\mathrm{II}}$ is the reaction velocity in the second system, then De Donder's fundamental inequality can be written

$$\delta \mathbf{A} \mathbf{v}^{\mathrm{II}} > 0. \qquad (17.4)$$

This inequality enables us to determine easily the domain of validity of Le Chatelier's principle. We begin by considering two characteristic examples.

2. Mechanical Restraint.

In this paragraph we shall examine restraint in the mechanical variables p and V. For this we consider a state II which is identical with I as regards the temperature and composition, but differs in pressure and volume.

Then if the pressure and volume in I are p and V, they will be $p+\delta p$ and $V+\delta V$ in II.

Equations (4.64) and (4.60) give immediately

$$\delta \mathbf{A} = \left(\frac{\partial p}{\partial \xi}\right)_{T,V} (\delta V)_{T,n} = -\left(\frac{\partial V}{\partial \xi}\right)_{T,p} (\delta p)_{T,n}. \qquad (17.5)$$

Whence, from (17.4),

$$\left(\frac{\partial p}{\partial \xi}\right)_{T,V} (\delta V)_{T,n} \mathbf{v}^{\mathrm{II}} > 0 \qquad (17.6)$$

or

$$\left(\frac{\partial V}{\partial \xi}\right)_{T,p} (\delta p)_{T,n} \mathbf{v}^{\mathrm{II}} < 0. \qquad (17.7)$$

Hence whatever the reaction occurring in II, the reaction velocity at the time t has the same sign as the product $\left(\frac{\partial p}{\partial \xi}\right)_{T,V} (\delta V)_{T,n}$, and is of opposite sign to $\left(\frac{\partial V}{\partial \xi}\right)_{T,p} (\delta p)_{T,n}$.

We note that the increments $(\delta V)_{T,n}$ and $(\delta p)_{T,n}$ are always of opposite sign in a stable phase, since the condition of mechanical stability (15.41) may be written

$$(\delta p)_{T,n} / (\delta V)_{T,n} < 0. \qquad (17.8)$$

Hence (17.6) and (17.7) can be rewritten

$$\left(\frac{\partial p}{\partial \xi}\right)_{T,V} \left(\frac{d\xi}{dt}\right)^{\mathrm{II}} (\delta p)_{T,n} < 0, \qquad (17.9)$$

$$\left(\frac{\partial V}{\partial \xi}\right)_{T,p} \left(\frac{d\xi}{dt}\right)^{\mathrm{II}} (\delta V)_{T,n} > 0. \qquad (17.10)$$

If we now suppose that subsequent to the perturbation the system is maintained at constant T and V,

$$\left(\frac{\partial p}{\partial \xi}\right)_{T,V} \cdot \left(\frac{d\xi}{dt}\right)^{\mathrm{II}}_{T,V} = \left(\frac{dp}{dt}\right)_{T,V} . \tag{17.11}$$

So that

$$\boxed{(\delta p)_{T,n}\left(\frac{dp}{dt}\right)_{T,V} < 0} . \tag{17.12}$$

Hence if the initial perturbation of pressure δp is positive, the reaction occurs in such a way that $(dp/dt)_{T,V}$ is negative.

If, therefore, we have a perturbed reaction system at constant T, V which is not in chemical equilibrium the reaction proceeds in a direction such that the pressure approaches its original equilibrium value. *The system is said to exhibit pressure moderation.*

On the other hand, if the reaction occurs at constant T and p we see immediately from (17.10), that

$$\boxed{(\delta V)_{T,n}\left(\frac{dV}{dt}\right)_{T,p} > 0} . \tag{17.13}$$

This means that the change in volume caused by the reaction is of the same sign as the initial perturbation; thus *there is no volume moderation at constant T and p.* In other words, if the pressure and volume of a system are perturbed and the pressure is then maintained constant at the perturbed value, the reaction will proceed in a direction such that the volume will continue to change in the same direction as the initial perturbation. If the initial perturbation is an increase in pressure and decrease in volume, then if the pressure is maintained at the new value, the reaction will proceed in the direction which leads to a continued decrease in volume until a new equilibrium position is reached. This result may be inferred from the fact that pressure moderation is observed. For following the initial increase in pressure the reaction will tend to proceed in the direction leading to a decrease in the pressure; but if the pressure is maintained at the higher value the reaction continues in the same direction, and there must be a further decrease in volume before equilibrium is reached.

Finally we suppose that, after the perturbation, the system is isolated (*i.e.* adiabatic) and yet remains at constant temperature.

By reference to equation (2.13) we see that if no heat enters or leaves the system $dQ=0$; and if also $dT=0$,

$$\mathbf{v}^{\mathrm{II}}=\left(\frac{d\xi}{dt}\right)^{\mathrm{II}}=-\frac{h_{T,\xi}}{h_{T,p}}\left(\frac{dp}{dt}\right)_{T,U}. \tag{17.14}$$

Substitution in (17.7) give us the condition

$$h_{T,\xi}\frac{v_{T,p}}{h_{T,p}}(\delta p)_{T,n}\left(\frac{dp}{dt}\right)_{T,U}>0. \tag{17.15}$$

However the latent heat of compression $h_{T,\xi}$ is given by (4.42) as equal to $-T(\partial V/\partial T)_{p,\xi}$, and from (4.69), $v_{T,p}$ and $p_{T,V}$ are of the same sign, so that:

$$\frac{p_{T,V}}{h_{T,p}}\left(\frac{\partial V}{\partial T}\right)_{p,\xi}(\delta p)_{T,n}\left(\frac{dp}{dt}\right)_{T,U}<0. \tag{17.16}$$

Hence the system will exhibit pressure moderation only if

$$\frac{p_{T,V}}{h_{T,p}}\left(\frac{\partial V}{\partial T}\right)_{p,\xi} \quad \text{or, written in full,} \quad \frac{(\partial p/\partial \xi)_{T,V}}{(\partial H/\partial \xi)_{T,p}}\left(\frac{\partial V}{\partial T}\right)_{p,\xi} \quad \text{is positive.}$$

In practice $(\partial V/\partial T)_{p,\xi}$ is usually positive so that the heat content change at constant T, p, and the pressure change of reaction at constant T, V must both have the same sign.

This means that if the system is to maintain a constant temperature, the heat of reaction must be taken up by the heat of compression (or decompression). If the initial perturbation is an increase in pressure, then moderation will be observed only if the reaction induced in the system is such that the latent heat of decompression is supplied by the exothermicity of the reaction. The reaction must therefore be exothermal ($h_{T,p}$ negative), and at the same time be one in which the pressure decreases at constant volume ($p_{T,V}$ negative). If the reaction were endothermal, then isothermal conditions could only be maintained by a further increase in pressure.

A similar theorem can be derived for the condition of volume moderation, by using equations (2.7), (17.6) and (4.41). An adiabatic isothermal system only exhibits volume moderation if

$$\frac{v_{T,p}}{u_{T,V}}\left(\frac{\partial p}{\partial T}\right)_{V,\xi} \tag{17.17}$$

is positive. Since $(\partial p/\partial T)_{V,\xi}$ is usually positive, this usually means that $(\partial V/\partial \xi)_{T,p}$ and $(\partial U/\partial \xi)_{T,V}$ must have the same sign.

It is clear from these considerations that the problem of whether or not a system will exhibit moderation, depends upon the exact conditions under which the reaction takes place in the perturbed system.

3. Moderation of Composition.

We already know that if a closed system is in a state of stable chemical equilibrium, then a perturbation of the mole fraction of a component i (accompanied by a simultaneous change in all other mole fractions) leads to a reaction tending to restore the equilibrium composition. The situation is not quite so simple in the case of an open system when the composition is altered by the addition or removal of one of the components. In this case the perturbation may consist of a change in the number of moles n_i of component i, at constant T and p. The affinity of the perturbed system is now

$$\delta \mathbf{A} = \left(\frac{\partial \mathbf{A}}{\partial n_i}\right)_{T, p, n_j} \delta n_i. \tag{17.18}$$

On the other hand, from (1.40′), we have for the perturbed system

$$\left(\frac{d\xi}{dt}\right)^{\text{II}} = \frac{1}{\nu_i}\left(\frac{dn_i}{dt}\right)^{\text{II}},$$

and the inequality (17.4) becomes

$$\frac{1}{\nu_i}\left(\frac{dn_i}{dt}\right)(\delta n_i)_{T,p}\left(\frac{\partial \mathbf{A}}{\partial n_i}\right)_{T,p} > 0. \tag{17.19}$$

The sign of $(\delta n_i)_{T,p}$ and (dn_i/dt) will only be opposite *i.e.* the system will only exhibit moderation with respect to addition or removal of component i provided that

$$\frac{1}{\nu_i}\left(\frac{\partial \mathbf{A}}{\partial n_i}\right)_{T,p} \quad \text{is negative.}$$

We shall now examine this condition in more detail. This is readily done since

$$\left(\frac{\partial \mathbf{A}}{\partial n_i}\right)_{T,p} = -\sum_j \nu_j \left(\frac{\partial \mu_j}{\partial n_i}\right)_{T,p} \tag{17.20}$$
$$= -\sum_j \nu_j \mu_{ij}.$$

However, from (6.55),

$$\mu_{ii} = -\frac{1}{n_i} \sum_j{}' \mu_{ij} n_j \tag{17.21}$$

where the symbol Σ' means that the summation is taken over all values of j *except* $j = i$. Equation (17.20) can, however, be written

$$\left(\frac{\partial \mathbf{A}}{\partial n_i}\right)_{T,p} = -\sum_j{}' \nu_j \mu_{ij} - \nu_i \mu_{ii},$$

so that using (17.21) we have

$$\left(\frac{\partial \mathbf{A}}{\partial n_i}\right)_{T,p} = -\sum_j{}' \left(\nu_j \mu_{ij} - \frac{\nu_i n_j}{n_i} \mu_{ij}\right) = -\sum_j{}' \mu_{ij} n_j \left(\frac{\nu_j}{n_j} - \frac{\nu_i}{n_i}\right). \tag{17.22}$$

Since in fact if we were to put $i=j$, this term in the summation would vanish we need no longer distinguish between Σ' and Σ, so that

$$\left(\frac{\partial \mathbf{A}}{\partial n_i}\right)_{T,p} = -\sum_j \mu_{ij}\, n_j \left(\frac{\nu_j}{n_j} - \frac{\nu_i}{n_i}\right). \tag{17.23}$$

It is therefore not sufficient that the initial state of equilibrium shall be one of stable chemical equilibrium. For the condition that the unperturbed state is stable is that all μ_{ij}, $i \neq j$ must be negative. But the condition (17.19) is not satisfied by (17.23) since this expression can be positive or negative depending upon the relative values of the stoichiometric coefficients ν_j and the numbers of moles n_j.

We shall only examine in detail the case of an *ideal system* for which (*cf.* 7.7)

$$\frac{1}{\nu_i}\left(\frac{\partial \mathbf{A}}{\partial n_i}\right)_{T,p} = \frac{RT}{\nu_i}\left(\frac{\nu}{n} - \frac{\nu_i}{n_i}\right) \tag{17.24}$$

where as before $\nu = \sum_i \nu_i$.

Moderation will be exhibited only when the sign of

$$\frac{1}{\nu_i}\left(\frac{\nu}{n} - \frac{\nu_i}{n_i}\right) \quad \text{is negative.}$$

That is if

$$\frac{1}{n_i} > \frac{\nu}{\nu_i} \cdot \frac{1}{n} \tag{17.25}$$

or

$$\frac{1}{x_i} > \frac{\nu}{\nu_i}.$$

Whether or not this condition is satisfied will depend not only upon the reaction considered (*i.e.* ν, ν_i) but also on the mole fraction of i in the mixture, (x_i).

We notice in particular that if $\nu=0$ this inequality is always satisfied. *Hence moderation of composition with respect to the addition of a component at constant T and p is exhibited by all reactions which take place in an ideal system without a change in the number of moles present* (*i.e.* $\nu=0$).

Two other particular cases for which moderation is exhibited in an ideal system are when ν_i and ν are (*a*) of opposite sign or (*b*) of the same sign but $\nu/\nu_i < 1$.

The behaviour in other cases may be illustrated by means of an example, *e.g.* the synthesis of ammonia :

$$N_2 + 3H_2 \rightarrow 2NH_3,$$

for which

$$\nu_{N_2} = -1\,;\quad \nu_{H_2} = -3\,;\quad \nu_{NH_3} = +2$$

and

$$\nu = -2.$$

Considering the moderation with respect to addition of nitrogen, we see that the condition for moderation is

$$x_{N_2} < +\tfrac{1}{2}.$$

Hence provided that the mole fraction of N_2 in the system is less than 0·5, the addition of a small amount of N_2 to the system at constant T and p, results in a small amount of reaction with the formation of ammonia. However, if the mixture is rich in nitrogen ($x_{N_2} > 0{\cdot}5$) then the addition of a little more nitrogen is followed by a further dissociation of ammonia to form more nitrogen and hydrogen. Conversely, if a little nitrogen is removed the reaction will proceed in the other direction and remove even more nitrogen before equilibrium is set up.*

On the other hand if we consider the possibility of moderation with respect to addition of ammonia we find that the condition for moderation is

$$\frac{1}{x_{NH_3}} > -1,$$

and this is always satisfied. Perturbation of the equilibrium by adding a little ammonia always leads to the production of more nitrogen and hydrogen.

The case of reactions in solution can be treated in a similar manner. Thus it can be shown that moderation is always observed if one adds (or removes) a small quantity of one of the reacting solutes of an ideal dilute solution. This follows since in a very dilute solution n_i is small in comparison with n so that ν/n is negligible in comparison with ν_i/n_i since ν_i is not zero.

Analogous considerations apply to the moderation of mole fractions† as well as to moderation of composition under conditions of constant T and V.‡

4. Domain of validity of the Le Chatelier-Braun Principle.

The two examples discussed above show that the principle of Le Chatelier and Braun suffers from a number of important exceptions. Many workers have attempted to restate this principle in a completely general form ; but this form, if it exists at all, is necessarily very complex.§ It seems therefore more logical to discuss problems arising in

* *Cf.* K. Posthumus, *Rec. trav. chim.*, **52**, 25 (1933) ; J. E. Verschaffelt, *Nat. Tijd.*, **15**, 146 (1933) ; J. M. Bijvoet, *Chem. Weekbl.*, **30**, 742 (1933) ; A. Sloof, *Rec. trav. chim.*, **60**, 349 (1941).

† H. Le Chatelier, *C. R.*, **196**, 1756 (1933) ; R. Etienne, *C. R.*, **196**, 1887 (1933) ; I. Prigogine, *Bull. Ac. Roy. Belg.* (*Cl. Sc.*), **29**, 695 (1943).

‡ J. E. Verschaffelt, *Bull. Ac. Roy. Belg.* (*Cl. Sc.*), **31**, 201 (1945).

§ *Cf. e.g.* Schottky [42], p. 486 ; J. E. Verschaffelt, *Wis-en Natuurkundige Tijdschrift*, **7**, 190 (1935).

this connection by means of the appropriate " moderation theorem " which can be deduced from the fundamental inequality

$$\mathbf{Av} > 0$$

and which gives an unambiguous answer.

To this extent we may regard this inequality as the most general form of the Le Chatelier-Braun principle.

It is interesting to observe that systems involving irreversible changes may also under certain circumstances obey the moderation theorems.*

* I. Prigogine, [37].

CHAPTER XVIII

DISPLACEMENTS ALONG AN EQUILIBRIUM LINE

1. Equilibrium Displacements in Closed Systems : the Theorems of van't Hoff and Le Chatelier.

Let us consider two systems both in internal equilibrium, but differing from one another in the values of the external variables x, y (*e.g.* T and p) as well as in the variables $n_1 \ldots n_c$. These two systems may be regarded as initial and final equilibrium states, passage from one to the other having been achieved by a perturbation of the kind discussed in the previous chapter.

We shall now study the modification, or the displacement of thermodynamic equilibrium, as we pass from one system to the other. First we shall compare two *closed* systems composed of the same initial quantities of the various components, but differing in the final equilibrium values of T, p, ξ.

The independent variables describing the two systems are

system I :	p	T	ξ
system II :	$p+\delta p$	$T+\delta T$	$\xi+\delta\xi$.

The numbers of moles of each component will be n_i in the first system, and $n_i+\delta n_i$ in the second, with

$$\delta n_i = \nu_i \, \delta\xi. \tag{18.1}$$

Since the affinity is zero both for system I and for system II, the variation on passing from I to II must also be zero : $\delta \mathbf{A} = 0$.

Hence from (4.60)*

$$-\frac{h_{T,p}}{T}\,\delta T + v_{T,p}\,\delta p - a_{T,p}\,\delta\xi = 0. \tag{18.2}$$

At constant pressure, therefore,

$$\left(\frac{\delta\xi}{\delta T}\right)_p = -\frac{h_{T,p}}{T a_{T,p}}, \tag{18.3}$$

while at constant temperature,

$$\left(\frac{\delta\xi}{\delta p}\right)_T = \frac{v_{T,p}}{a_{T,p}}, \tag{18.4}$$

* In this chapter we shall make extensive use of the abbreviations

$$(\partial H/\partial\xi)_{T,p} = h_{T,p}\,; \quad (\partial V/\partial\xi)_{T,p} = v_{T,p}\,; \quad (\partial/\mathbf{A}\partial\xi)_{T,p} = a_{T,p}.$$

and finally at constant extent of change,

$$\left(\frac{\delta p}{\delta T}\right)_{\xi}=\frac{h_{T,\,p}}{T\,v_{T,\,p}}\,. \tag{18.5}$$

Equation (18.5) is analogous to the Clausius-Clapeyron equation (14.4).

If the equilibria considered are stable, then

$$a_{T,\,p}<0 \tag{18.6}$$

and equation (18.3) expresses the fact that if a reaction is exothermic ($h_{T,\,p}<0$), an increase in temperature ($\delta T>0$) moves the equilibrium position of the reaction back ($\delta\xi<0$). On the other hand if the reaction is endothermic ($h_{T,\,p}>0$), a rise in temperature advances the equilibrium position ($\delta\xi>0$), (*van't Hoff's theorem*). This general formula is due to De Donder* but was rediscovered later by Schottky, Ulich and Wagner.†

In the same way (18.4) expresses the fact that if a reaction is accompanied by an increase in volume ($v_{T,\,p}>0$), an increase in pressure ($\delta p>0$) leads to reduction of the extent of change ($\delta\xi<0$); correspondingly if $v_{T,p}$ is negative an increase in pressure advances the equilibrium value of the extent of reaction (*Le Chatelier's theorem*).

2. Equilibrium Displacements in Open Systems.

Here we consider two single phase open systems, the independent variables now being

system I :	T	p	$n_1, \ldots n_c$
system II :	$T+\delta T$	$p+\delta p$	$n_1+\delta n_1, \ldots n_c+\delta n_c$.

Equation (18.2) must now be replaced by

$$-\frac{h_{T,\,p}}{T}\,\delta T+v_{T,\,p}\,\delta p-\sum_i\left(\frac{\partial \mathbf{A}}{\partial n_i}\right)_{T,\,p}\delta n_i=0. \tag{18.7}$$

We have already obtained an equation (*cf.* 17.24) for $(\partial\mathbf{A}/\partial n_i)_{T,\,p}$ in an ideal system, so that for this particular case, (18.7) becomes :

$$-\frac{h_{T,\,p}}{T}\,\delta T+v_{T,\,p}\,\delta p+\boldsymbol{R}T\sum_i\left(\frac{\nu_i}{n_i}-\frac{\nu}{n}\right)\delta n_i=0. \tag{18.8}$$

If we suppose that the only difference between the two systems lies in p and n_j, then

$$\frac{\delta n_j}{\delta p}=-\frac{v_{T,\,p}}{\boldsymbol{R}T}\,\frac{1}{\dfrac{\nu_j}{n_j}-\dfrac{\nu}{n}}\,. \tag{18.9}$$

* Th. De Donder, *C. R.*, **180**, 1334 (1925) ; [6], p. 47.
† Schottky, Ulich and Wagner, [42], p. 492.

In the same way one can write a series of other equations by supposing that only two of the $c+2$ increments δp, δT, $\delta n_1 \dots \delta n_c$ are different from zero.

First of all we shall examine (18.9) in more detail, and to fix our ideas we suppose that the system is an ideal solution and that $v_{T,p}>0$. The sign of the term $\left(\frac{\nu_j}{n_j}-\frac{\nu}{n}\right)$ must be examined.

In the case of the simple reaction

$$A+B \rightarrow C+D,$$

we have for component A

$$\nu_A = -1\,; \quad \nu = 0,$$

and so

$$\frac{\nu_A}{n_A}-\frac{\nu}{n} = -\frac{1}{n_A}<0.$$

Thus

$$\frac{\delta n_A}{\delta p}>0. \tag{18.10}$$

That is to say, if equilibrium is to be maintained without alteration of the number of moles of the components other than A, an increase in pressure ($\delta p>0$) at constant T must be accompanied by an increase in the number of moles of component A.

However, if the stoichiometric equation for the reaction is more complicated, for example if we have

$$C \rightarrow A+2B \tag{18.11}$$

the sign of $\delta n_A/\delta p$ will depend not only on the stoichiometric coefficients, but also on the relative concentrations of the components. Thus

$$\nu_A = +1\,; \quad \nu = +2.$$

$$\frac{\nu_A}{n_A}-\frac{\nu}{n} = \frac{1}{n_A}-\frac{2}{n_A+n_B+n_C} = \frac{1}{n_A}(1-2x_A).$$

The sign of $\delta n_A/\delta p$ will thus depend upon whether the mole fraction of A is greater or less than 0·5.

We may notice that in an open system the change in the number of moles of component i may be attributed to two causes: on the one hand to the increment $\delta\xi$ in the extent of reaction which causes a change in n_i of $\nu_i\,\delta\xi$, and on the other to an additional increment $\delta_e n_i$ caused by a transfer of matter to or from the surroundings.

We thus have

$$\delta n_i = \nu_i\,\delta\xi + \delta_e n_i. \tag{18.12}$$

Now, from (1.40′)

$$\sum_i \frac{\partial \mathbf{A}}{\partial n_i} \delta n_i = \frac{\partial \mathbf{A}}{\partial \xi} \sum_i \frac{\delta n_i}{\nu_i} = \frac{\partial \mathbf{A}}{\partial \xi} \delta \xi ,$$

so that equation (18.7) may be written :

$$-\frac{h_{T,p}}{T} \delta T + v_{T,p}\, \delta p - \sum_i \left(\frac{\partial \mathbf{A}}{\partial n_i}\right)_{T,p} \delta_e n_i - \left(\frac{\partial \mathbf{A}}{\partial \xi}\right)_{T,p} \delta \xi = 0, \qquad (18.13)$$

which in the case of an ideal system, by virtue of (18.8) becomes

$$-\frac{h_{T,p}}{T} \delta T + v_{T,p}\, \delta p + \mathbf{R}T \sum_i \left(\frac{\nu_i}{n_i} - \frac{\nu}{n}\right) \delta_e n_i - a_{T,p}\, \delta \xi = 0. \qquad (18.14)$$

If the only increments are in $\delta_e n_j$ and $\delta \xi$ we have

$$\frac{\delta \xi}{\delta_e n_j} = \frac{\mathbf{R}T}{a_{T,p}} \left(\frac{\nu_j}{n_j} - \frac{\nu}{n}\right). \qquad (18.15)$$

This equation allows us to calculate for an ideal system the effect upon the position of equilibrium of the introduction of a certain amount $\delta_e n_j$ of one component. The discussion of the sign of the right-hand side follows the same lines as above.

3. Equilibrium Displacements in Heterogeneous Systems : Passage of a Component from one Phase to another.

Let us consider a two phase system containing c components. We denote the two phases by a single prime and double prime respectively. The affinity of transfer of component i from one phase to the other is, (*cf.* 6.73 and 7.63),

$$\mathbf{A}_i = \mu_i' - \mu_i'' = \mu_i^{\ominus\prime} - \mu_i^{\ominus\prime\prime} + \mathbf{R}T \ln \frac{x_i' \gamma_i'}{x_i'' \gamma_i''}$$

$$= \mathbf{R}T \ln K_i(T, p) + \mathbf{R}T \ln \frac{x_i' \gamma_i'}{x_i'' \gamma_i''}, \qquad (18.16)$$

where we have put

$$\mu_i^{\ominus\prime} - \mu_i^{\ominus\prime\prime} = \mathbf{R}T \ln K_i. \qquad (18.17)$$

If we set the affinity equal to zero we obtain the general form of the Nernst distribution law (7.42):

$$\frac{x_i'' \gamma_i''}{x_i' \gamma_i'} = K_i(T, p). \qquad (18.18)$$

The constant K_i possesses the properties of an ordinary equilibrium constant such as (7.36) and (7.37). Hence starting from (18.16),

$$\delta \frac{\mathbf{A}_i}{T} = \mathbf{R} \frac{\partial \ln K_i}{\partial T} \delta T + \mathbf{R} \frac{\partial \ln K_i}{\partial p} \delta p + \mathbf{R}\, \delta \ln \frac{x_i' \gamma_i'}{x_i'' \gamma_i''}$$

$$= \frac{(h_{T,p}^{\ominus})_i}{T^2} \delta T - \frac{(v_{T,p}^{\ominus})_i}{T} \delta p + \mathbf{R}\, \delta \ln \frac{x_i' \gamma_i'}{x_i'' \gamma_i''}. \qquad (18.19)$$

This expression must be zero along the path of an equilibrium displacement. The importance of this formula lies in the fact that the standard heat content change $h^{\ominus}_{T,p}$ of transfer from the first phase to the second, and the standard volume change $v^{\ominus}_{T,p}$ are functions of T and p only, and are *independent of the composition of the phases.*

As a particular case we may consider a binary system in which component 2 can exist in only one of the phases (say the second). The first phase must then be pure component 1 and we have $x_1'=1$, $\gamma_1'=1$, and the only affinity of transfer to be considered is that of component 1. We may now compare two equilibrium states. The initial state will be denoted by $T^0, p^0, (x_1'')^0$, and the final state by T, p, x_1''.

Integrating (18.19) between these two states, remembering that $\mathbf{A}_1$ is zero in both states, gives

$$\ln \frac{x_1''\,\gamma_1''}{(x_1'')^0(\gamma_1'')^0} = \int_{T^0}^{T} \frac{(h^{\ominus}_{T,p})_1}{RT^2}\,dT - \frac{1}{RT}\int_{p^0}^{p} (v^{\ominus}_{T,p})_1\,dp. \qquad (18.19')$$

In general we shall choose as initial state pure component 1 so that

$$(x_1'')^0 = (\gamma_1'')^0 = 1, \qquad (18.20)$$

and (18.19′) reduces to

$$\ln x_1''\,\gamma_1'' = \int_{T^0}^{T} \frac{(h^{0}_{T,p})_1}{RT^2}\,dT - \frac{1}{RT}\int_{p^0}^{p} (v^{0}_{T,p})_1\,dp, \qquad (18.20')$$

where $^{\ominus}$ has been replaced by ^{0} since we choose pure component 1 as standard reference system (*cf.* chap. XXI).

In particular, for an equilibrium displacement *at constant pressure* ($p=p^0$) we have

$$\ln x_1''\,\gamma_1'' = \int_{T^0}^{T} \frac{(h^{0}_{T,p})_1}{RT^2}\,dT\,; \qquad (18.21)$$

and for an equilibrium displacement *at constant temperature* ($T=T^0$)

$$\ln x_1''\,\gamma_1'' = -\frac{1}{RT}\int_{p^0}^{p} (v^{0}_{T,p})_1\,dp. \qquad (18.22)$$

4. Sublimation.

Let us consider a system composed of a solid phase consisting of crystals of component 1, and a vapour phase consisting of a mixture of components 1 and 2. The initial state is taken as pure component 1 at a pressure p^0; T_1^0 will be the temperature at which crystals of 1 are in true equilibrium with its vapour at a pressure p^0.

We now apply equation (18.21) for a displacement at constant pressure. In this example $(h^0_{T,p})_1$ is the heat content change corresponding to the passage of 1 from the crystalline state to the ideal gas state, or more correctly to a perfect gas mixture of 1 and 2. It is thus (apart from a small correction for gas imperfection) the latent heat of sublimation $\Delta_s h_1$.

If $\Delta_s h_1$ is assumed independent of T in the temperature range considered, (18.21) can be integrated to obtain the simple formula :

$$\ln x_1^g = -\frac{\Delta_s h_1}{R}\left(\frac{1}{T}-\frac{1}{T_1^0}\right). \tag{18.23}$$

This equation gives the curve of co-existence at constant pressure of crystals of 1 and a vapour phase consisting of a mixture of components 1 and 2.

The coexistence curve between crystals of 2 and the mixed vapour can be obtained in just the same way :

$$\ln x_2^g = -\frac{\Delta_s h_2}{R}\left(\frac{1}{T}-\frac{1}{T_2^0}\right), \tag{18.23'}$$

where $\Delta_s h_2$ is the heat of sublimation of 2 and T_2^0 is the temperature at which it possesses a sublimation pressure of p^0.

Fig. 18.1 represents schematically the coexistence curves given by (18.23), (curve AB), and (18.23′), (curve DC). At the point of intersection (E) of these curves we have, coexisting in true equilibrium, crystals of 1 and 2 and the vapour. The point E thus has properties analogous to those of a eutectic point in solution-crystal equilibria (*cf.* fig. 13.4), and is therefore called *the eutectic point of the vapour*.

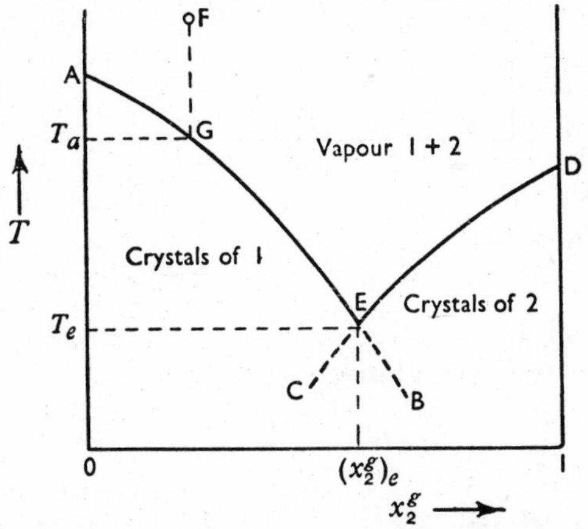

FIG. 18.1. Sublimation temperatures and eutectic point of a mixture of vapours at constant p.

If we consider a gaseous system under conditions represented by F in fig. 18.1, then on lowering the temperature, crystals of 1 will condense at T_a. The vapour becomes richer in 2, and as the temperature falls the system follows the line GE. At E both crystals of 1 and 2 condense. The co-ordinates of E, T_e and $(x_2^g)_e$, are found by solving the two simultaneous equations (18.23) and (18.23′), remembering of course that $x_1^g = 1 - x_2^g$.

We now consider equilibrium displacements at constant temperature for the same system. The initial system will be chosen as pure component 1 at T^0. The pressure p_1^0 will be the pressure of coexistence of crystals of 1 and pure vapour 1 at temperature T^0; *i.e.* the vapour pressure of pure 1 at T^0. In applying equation (18.22) to an equilibrium displacement at constant temperature, we may neglect initially the volume of the solid phase so that

$$(v_{T,p}^0)_1 = v_1^{g,\,\mathrm{id}} - v_1^s \approx \boldsymbol{R}T/p. \tag{18.24}$$

and (18.22) gives

$$p = \frac{p_1^0}{x_1^g\,\gamma_1^g}. \tag{18.25}$$

If we assume the gas phase to be perfect this simplifies to

$$p = \frac{p_1^0}{x_1^g}. \tag{18.26}$$

This approximate equation is that of the line of coexistence, at the given temperature, between crystals of 1 and a vapour phase consisting of a perfect gas mixture of 1 and 2.

In the same way the line of coexistence of crystals of 2 with the perfect gas mixture is

$$p = \frac{p_2^0}{x_2^g}. \tag{18.26'}$$

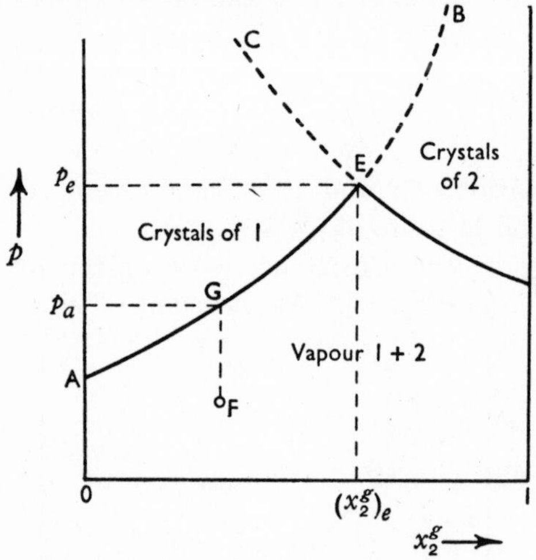

FIG. 18.2. Sublimation pressure and eutectic point of a mixture of vapours at constant T.

These two coexistence curves are shown schematically in fig 18.2. At the eutectic point E, both equations must be satisfied simultaneously, and hence

$$p_e = p_1^0 + p_2^0,$$
$$(x_2^g)_e = \frac{p_2^0}{p_1^0 + p_2^0}. \tag{18.27}$$

5. Transfer of Two Components from one Phase to another.

The discussion of the previous paragraph may now be extended to a binary system in which both components can pass from one phase to another.

Equation (18.19) may now be applied successively to the two components. First we integrate $\delta(\mathbf{A}_1/T)$ from an initial state T_1^0, p_1^0, $(x_1')^0 = 1$, $(x_1'')^0 = 1$, corresponding to equilibrium between the phases when they both consist of pure 1, to a final equilibrium state T, p, x_1', x_1''. In the initial state $(\gamma_1')^0 = 1$, $(\gamma_1'')^0 = 1$ and also $\mathbf{A}_1 = \mathbf{A}_1^0 = 0$, so that

$$\ln \frac{x_1'' \gamma_1''}{x_1' \gamma_1'} = \int_{T_1^0}^{T} \frac{(h_{T,p}^0)_1}{RT^2} dT - \frac{1}{RT} \int_{p_1^0}^{p} (v_{T,p}^0)_1 \, dp. \tag{18.28}$$

Similarly by integrating (18.19) from an initial state consisting of pure component 2, we obtain

$$\ln \frac{x_2'' \gamma_2''}{x_2' \gamma_2'} = \int_{T_2^0}^{T} \frac{(h_{T,p}^0)_2}{RT^2} dT - \frac{1}{RT} \int_{p_2^0}^{p} (v_{T,p}^0)_2 \, dp. \tag{18.29}$$

In each case $h_{T,p}$ and $v_{T,p}$ refer to the transfer of the component from the first to the second phase and can therefore be written

$$\left. \begin{aligned} (h_{T,p}^0)_1 &= \Delta_{\prime}^{\prime\prime} h_1^0 \\ (h_{T,p}^0)_2 &= \Delta_{\prime}^{\prime\prime} h_2^0 \end{aligned} \right\}, \tag{18.30}$$

where $\Delta_{\prime}^{\prime\prime} h^0$ is the latent heat of transfer of the *pure component* from the first to the second phase.

We may choose $p_1^0 = p_2^0 = p^0$, where p^0 is an arbitrary pressure (*e.g.* 1 atm.); then T_1^0 will be the temperature of coexistence, at pressure p^0, of the two phases in equilibrium when they both consist of pure component 1. In the same way T_2^0 is the temperature of coexistence of pure 2 in the two phases at pressure p^0. Remembering that $x_1 = 1 - x_2$ in each phase, we can then calculate x_2'' and x_2' as a function of T and p.

If we assume that both phases are ideal and that the latent heats are independent of temperature, then introducing the abbreviations :

$$\lambda_1 = \frac{\Delta_{\prime}^{\prime\prime} h_1^0}{R} \left(\frac{1}{T} - \frac{1}{T_1^0} \right), \tag{18.31}$$

$$-\lambda_2 = \frac{\Delta_{\prime}^{\prime\prime} h_2^0}{R} \left(\frac{1}{T} - \frac{1}{T_2^0} \right), \tag{18.32}$$

and applying (18.28) and (18.29) to a series of equilibrium states at constant pressure we obtain

$$1 - x_2'' = (1 - x_2') \mathrm{e}^{-\lambda_1},$$

$$x_2'' = x_2' \mathrm{e}^{\lambda_2},$$

or

$$x_2'' = \frac{\mathrm{e}^{\lambda_1} - 1}{\mathrm{e}^{\lambda_1} - \mathrm{e}^{-\lambda_2}}, \tag{18.33}$$

$$x_2' = \frac{\mathrm{e}^{\lambda_1} - 1}{\mathrm{e}^{\lambda_1 + \lambda_2} - 1}. \tag{18.34}$$

These relations are due to van Laar, and may be applied to the following cases, among others :

(*a*) calculation of the evaporation and condensation curves of a binary solution ;

(*b*) calculation of the liquidus and solidus curves for a system which forms a continuous series of mixed crystals.

Examples of the application of these formulae will be given in chapters XXI and XXIII. For the extension of these formulae to ternary systems the reader is referred to the work of Seltz.*

6. The Gibbs-Konovalow Theorems.

In this paragraph we shall study the differential relations which must be satisfied by two phase binary systems of the kind discussed in the previous paragraph.

The affinities of transport of components 1 and 2 from the first phase to the second are of the form :

$$\left.\begin{aligned}\mathbf{A}_1&=\mu_1'(T,p,x_2')-\mu_1''(T,p,x_2''),\\ \mathbf{A}_2&=\mu_2'(T,p,x_2')-\mu_2''(T,p,x_2'')\end{aligned}\right\}. \tag{18.35}$$

The differentials of the chemical potentials are obtained from (6.32) and (6.28) and are all of the form

$$\delta\frac{\mu}{T}=-\frac{h}{T^2}\,\delta T+\frac{v}{T}\,\delta p+\frac{1}{T}\left(\frac{\partial\mu}{\partial x}\right)\delta x\,; \tag{18.36}$$

while the differentials of the affinity may be expressed as

$$\delta\,\frac{\mathbf{A}_1}{T}=\delta\,\frac{\mu_1'}{T}-\delta\,\frac{\mu_1''}{T}\,;\quad \delta\,\frac{\mathbf{A}_2}{T}=\delta\,\frac{\mu_2'}{T}-\delta\,\frac{\mu_2''}{T}\,. \tag{18.37}$$

We have therefore

$$\left.\begin{aligned}\delta\,\frac{\mathbf{A}_1}{T}&=\frac{\Delta_{\prime}^{\prime\prime}h_1}{T^2}\,\delta T-\frac{\Delta_{\prime}^{\prime\prime}v_1}{T}\,\delta p+\frac{1}{T}\left(\frac{\partial\mu_1'}{\partial x_2'}\right)\delta x_2'-\frac{1}{T}\left(\frac{\partial\mu_1''}{\partial x_2''}\right)\delta x_2''\\ \delta\,\frac{\mathbf{A}_2}{T}&=\frac{\Delta_{\prime}^{\prime\prime}h_2}{T^2}\,\delta T-\frac{\Delta_{\prime}^{\prime\prime}v_2}{T}\,\delta p+\frac{1}{T}\left(\frac{\partial\mu_2'}{\partial x_2'}\right)\delta x_2'-\frac{1}{T}\left(\frac{\partial\mu_2''}{\partial x_2''}\right)\delta x_2''\end{aligned}\right\}, \tag{18.38}$$

where we have written

$$\Delta_{\prime}^{\prime\prime}h_1=h_1''-h_1'\,;\quad \Delta_{\prime}^{\prime\prime}v_1=v_1''-v_1'. \tag{18.39}$$

and similarly for component 2. It must be remembered that in this case $\Delta_{\prime}^{\prime\prime}h$ and $\Delta_{\prime}^{\prime\prime}v$ will in general be functions of the composition of the phases.

Along the curves of coexistence of the two phases in equilibrium the affinity is zero, so that these curves must satisfy (18.38) with the right hand sides equated to zero.

* H. Seltz, *J. Chem. Phys.*, 3, 503 (1935).

These relations may be simplified by use of the molar Gibbs free energy of each phase defined by :

$$g' = G'/n' \; ; \; g'' = G''/n''. \tag{18.40}$$

We have already seen (6.47) that

$$\left(\frac{\partial g'}{\partial x_2'}\right)_{T,p} = \mu_2' - \mu_1' \; ; \; \left(\frac{\partial g''}{\partial x_2''}\right)_{T,p} = \mu_2'' - \mu_1'' \; ; \tag{18.41}$$

while in each phase, from (6.50) and (6.49) :

$$\left.\begin{aligned} \left(\frac{\partial \mu_1}{\partial x_2}\right)_{T,p} &= -x_2 \left(\frac{\partial^2 g}{\partial x_2^2}\right)_{T,p}, \\ \left(\frac{\partial \mu_2}{\partial x_2}\right)_{T,p} &= (1-x_2)\left(\frac{\partial^2 g}{\partial x_2^2}\right)_{T,p} \end{aligned}\right\} . \tag{18.42}$$

We recall also that for all *stable* phases of two components (*cf.* 16.20)

$$\left(\frac{\partial^2 g}{\partial x_2^2}\right)_{T,p} > 0. \tag{18.43}$$

Substituting in (18.38) and equating to zero, we now obtain

$$\left.\begin{aligned} &-\frac{\Delta_\prime'' h_1}{T}\,\delta T + \Delta_\prime'' v_1\,\delta p \\ &\qquad - x_2''\left(\frac{\partial^2 g''}{\partial x_2''^2}\right)_{T,p}\delta x_2'' + x_2'\left(\frac{\partial^2 g'}{\partial x_2'^2}\right)_{T,p}\delta x_2' = 0, \\ &-\frac{\Delta_\prime'' h_2}{T}\,\delta T + \Delta_\prime'' v_2\,\delta p \\ &\qquad + (1-x_2'')\left(\frac{\partial^2 g''}{\partial x_2''^2}\right)_{T,p}\delta x_2'' - (1-x_2')\left(\frac{\partial^2 g'}{\partial x_2'^2}\right)_{T,p}\delta x_2' = 0 \end{aligned}\right\} \tag{18.44}$$

It is of particular interest to consider the four sets of equilibrium states obtained when the four increments δp, δT, $\delta x_2'$, $\delta x_2''$ are successively zero.

(*a*) *constant pressure :* $\delta p = 0.$ (18.45)

Equations (18.44) then reduce to two linear relations between the three increments δT, $\delta x_2'$, $\delta x_2''$, so that along the equilibrium line at constant p :

$$\left(\frac{\partial x_2'}{\partial T}\right)_p = \frac{x_2''\,\Delta_\prime'' h_2 + (1-x_2'')\Delta_\prime'' h_1}{T(x_2' - x_2'')(\partial^2 g'/\partial x_2'^2)}, \tag{18.46}$$

and

$$\left(\frac{\partial x_2''}{\partial T}\right)_p = \frac{x_2'\,\Delta_\prime'' h_2 + (1-x_2')\Delta_\prime'' h_1}{T(x_2' - x_2'')(\partial^2 g''/\partial x_2''^2)} . \tag{18.47}$$

If we consider only stable phases the quantities $(\partial^2 g/\partial x^2)$ in the denominator are positive, so that the signs of the differentials $(\partial x/\partial T)_p$ are determined partly by the heats of transfer $\Delta_{\prime}^{\prime\prime} h_1$ and $\Delta_{\prime}^{\prime\prime} h_2$, and partly by the difference $(x_2^{\prime} - x_2^{\prime\prime})$.

(*b*) *constant temperature :* $\delta T = 0.$ (18.48)

When $\delta T = 0$, equations (18.44) enable us to evaluate the differential coefficients $(\partial x_2^{\prime}/\partial p)_T$ and $(\partial x_2^{\prime\prime}/\partial p)_T$ along the equilibrium line at constant T.

They are

$$\left(\frac{\partial x_2^{\prime}}{\partial p}\right)_T = \frac{x_2^{\prime\prime}\,\Delta_{\prime}^{\prime\prime} v_2 + (1 - x_2^{\prime\prime})\,\Delta_{\prime}^{\prime\prime} v_1}{(x_2^{\prime\prime} - x_2^{\prime})(\partial^2 g^{\prime}/\partial x_2^{\prime 2})}, \tag{18.49}$$

$$\left(\frac{\partial x_2^{\prime\prime}}{\partial p}\right)_T = \frac{x_2^{\prime}\,\Delta_{\prime}^{\prime\prime} v_2 + (1 - x_2^{\prime})\,\Delta_{\prime}^{\prime\prime} v_1}{(x_2^{\prime\prime} - x_2^{\prime})(\partial^2 g^{\prime\prime}/\partial x_2^{\prime\prime 2})}. \tag{18.50}$$

Again, for stable phases, the sign of these coefficients depends on $\Delta_{\prime}^{\prime\prime} v_1$, $\Delta_{\prime}^{\prime\prime} v_2$ and $(x_2^{\prime\prime} - x_2^{\prime})$.

(*c*) *constant composition in first phase :* $\delta x_2^{\prime} = 0.$ (18.51)

The differential coefficients $(\partial p/\partial T)_{x_2^{\prime}}$ and $(\partial x_2^{\prime\prime}/\partial T)_{x_2^{\prime}}$ may now be obtained in the form :

$$\left(\frac{\partial p}{\partial T}\right)_{x_2^{\prime}} = \frac{x_2^{\prime\prime}\,\Delta_{\prime}^{\prime\prime} h_2 + (1 - x_2^{\prime\prime})\,\Delta_{\prime}^{\prime\prime} h_1}{T\,[x_2^{\prime\prime}\,\Delta_{\prime}^{\prime\prime} v_2 + (1 - x_2^{\prime\prime})\,\Delta_{\prime}^{\prime\prime} v_1]}, \tag{18.52}$$

$$\left(\frac{\partial x_2^{\prime\prime}}{\partial T}\right)_{x_2^{\prime}} = \frac{\Delta_{\prime}^{\prime\prime} v_1\,\Delta_{\prime}^{\prime\prime} h_2 - \Delta_{\prime}^{\prime\prime} v_2\,\Delta_{\prime}^{\prime\prime} h_1}{T\,(\partial^2 g^{\prime\prime}/\partial x_2^{\prime\prime 2})[x_2^{\prime\prime}\,\Delta_{\prime}^{\prime\prime} v_2 + (1 - x_2^{\prime\prime})\,\Delta_{\prime}^{\prime\prime} v_1]}. \tag{18.53}$$

Equation (18.52) is the extension of the Clausius-Clapeyron equation to a phase change involving two substances. It gives the influence of temperature on the total vapour pressure of a phase whose composition remains constant.

Equation (18.53) can be expressed in a much simpler form in the case of equilibrium between a liquid and vapour. In this case

$$\left.\begin{aligned} \Delta_e v_1 &= v_1^g - v_1^l \approx v_1^g \\ \Delta_e v_2 &= v_2^g - v_2^l \approx v_2^g \end{aligned}\right\}, \tag{18.54}$$

since the molar volume of the liquid can usually be neglected in comparison with that of the vapour. Furthermore if the vapour may be considered as a perfect gas

$$v_1^g = v_2^g = \boldsymbol{R}T/p. \tag{18.55}$$

Hence (18.53) can be written in the approximate form

$$\left(\frac{\partial x_2^g}{\partial T}\right)_{x_2^l} = \frac{\Delta_e h_2 - \Delta_e h_1}{T\,(\partial^2 g^g/\partial x_2^{g2})}. \tag{18.56}$$

Again since $(\partial^2 g^g/\partial x_2^{g2})$ is positive for stable phases, the sign of $(\partial x_2^g/\partial T)_{x_2^l}$ is the same as that of $\Delta_e h_2 - \Delta_e h_1$, or

$$(\Delta_e h_2 - \Delta_e h_1)(\partial x_2^g/\partial T)_{x_2^l} > 0. \tag{18.57}$$

Thus if the composition of the liquid phase is kept constant, the mole fraction of component 2 in the vapour increases with temperature if $\Delta_e h_2 - \Delta_e h_1$ is positive. In other words an increase in temperature of a liquid phase of given composition will lead to an enrichment of the vapour phase in the component with the higher latent heat of evaporation from the solution.

(*d*) *constant composition in second phase* : $\delta x_2'' = 0.$ (18.58)

The equations for this case follow exactly as before and need not be written out in full.

The general methods used above may be extended without difficulty to more general problems than have been treated here. We shall use them for example in the study of indifferent states and azeotropy in chapters XXVIII and XXIX.

The above equations enable us to derive two important theorems first enunciated by Gibbs, and later rediscovered by Konovalow and Duhem.

First we consider equations (18.46) and (18.47) relating to states at constant pressure. If in these equations we put $x_2' = x_2''$ we obtain

$$\frac{\partial T}{\partial x_2'} = 0 \quad \text{and} \quad \frac{\partial T}{\partial x_2''} = 0, \tag{18.59}$$

or simply

$$\delta T = 0. \tag{18.60}$$

Hence in an equilibrium displacement at constant pressure of a binary system, the temperature of coexistence passes through an extreme value (maximum, minimum or inflexion with a horizontal tangent) if the composition of the two phases is the same.

This is the first Gibbs-Konovalow theorem for equilibria at constant pressure.

The reciprocal of this theorem is also true : namely, if the temperature of coexistence passes, at constant pressure, through an extremum, then the two phases must have the same composition. This follows immediately for from (18.46) and (18.47), $(\partial T/\partial x_2')_p$ and $(\partial T/\partial x_2'')_p$ can only be zero if the phases are of the same composition.

This theorem may be applied for example to the equilibrium at constant pressure between a binary solution and vapour. The reciprocals of the differential coefficients in (18.46) and (18.47) are the slopes of the tangents to the condensation and boiling point curves. It follows therefore that if the boiling point curve passes through a maximum, then the point is common to both boiling point and condensation curves, and the two curves have a common tangent at this point.

Similarly, in the case of equilibrium between a binary solid solution (mixed crystals) and liquid, if the liquidus and solidus curves meet, then this point must be at an extreme value of the temperature of coexistence. Conversely, if the two curves pass through an extreme value, this point must be common to the two curves and the two phases have the same composition.

We shall consider examples of this type of behaviour when discussing solutions in chapters XXI and XXIII.

The theorem derived above refers to equilibrium states at constant pressure ; an exactly similar discussion of isothermal states leads to the *second theorem* which may be stated in the form :

If in a series of isothermal equilibrium states of a two phase binary system, the composition of the phases becomes the same, then the pressure must pass through an extreme value ; and conversely, at a point at which the pressure passes through an extreme value, the phases must be of the same composition.

In chapter XXIX we shall give a formulation of the Gibbs-Konovalow theorems applicable to systems of a more general type.

7. Sign of the Slopes of Coexistence Curves.

In this paragraph we shall first consider equilibrium between liquid and vapour. The slopes of the boiling point and condensation curves at constant pressure and temperature are given by equations (18.46), (18.47) and (18.49), (18.50). In these the latent heats of evaporation will always be positive

$$\Delta_e h_1 > 0 \; ; \;\; \Delta_e h_2 > 0 \; ; \qquad (18.61)$$

as also will be the change in volume accompanying the transfer from liquid to gas :

$$\Delta_e v_1 > 0 \; ; \;\; \Delta_e v_2 > 0. \qquad (18.62)$$

It then follows that for stable phases the slopes at corresponding points of the boiling point and condensation curves at constant pressure are both of the same sign. Similarly, for the slopes of the two coexistence curves at constant temperature.

For solid-liquid equilibrium also the latent heats are usually positive, and it follows that the slopes at corresponding points on the solidus and liquidus curves at constant pressure also have the same sign. If the latent heats were not positive, then the slopes could be the same or different.

It should be noted that if both (18.61) and (18.62) are satisfied as in the case of liquid-vapour equilibrium, the slopes of the coexistence curves at *constant pressure*, (18.46) and (18.47), are always of the *opposite* sign to the curves of coexistence *at constant temperature*, (18.49) and (18.50). Thus if the isobaric curves are increasing at a given composition, the isothermal curves are decreasing, and furthermore if the isobaric curves pass through a maximum, the isothermal curves must pass through a minimum, and conversely.

8. Analytical Conditions for a Maximum or Minimum.

In the case of a set of isothermal equilibrium states we have already seen that if the pressure passes through an extreme value, then a sufficient condition for this is that the two phases shall have identical compositions. (Gibbs-Konovalow theorem). We now require to find the condition that this extreme value is a maximum or minimum, and to do this it is necessary to investigate the second differentials of the coexistence curves.

We take the reciprocal of equation (18.49) and differentiate with respect to x_2' and obtain

$$\frac{\partial^2 p}{\partial x_2'^2} = \left(\frac{\partial x_2''}{\partial x_2'} - 1\right) \frac{\partial^2 g'/\partial x_2'^2}{x_2'' \Delta_r'' v_2 + (1 - x_2'')\Delta_r'' v_1} + (x_2'' - x_2') \frac{\partial}{\partial x_2'}\left[\frac{\partial^2 g'/\partial x_2'^2}{x_2'' \Delta_r'' v_2 + (1 - x_2'')\Delta_r'' v_1}\right]. \tag{18.63}$$

If the composition of the two phases is the same then the second term vanishes. Furthermore to evaluate $\partial x_2''/\partial x_2'$ we may divide (18.50) by (18.49), and put the composition of the two phases the same. This gives simply

$$\frac{\partial x_2''}{\partial x_2'} = \frac{(\partial^2 g'/\partial x_2'^2)}{(\partial^2 g''/\partial x_2''^2)}. \tag{18.64}$$

Equation (18.63) then becomes:

$$\frac{\partial^2 p}{\partial x_2'^2} = \frac{-1}{x_2'' \Delta_r'' v_2 + (1 - x_2'')\Delta_r'' v_1} \left(\frac{\partial^2 g''}{\partial x_2''^2} - \frac{\partial^2 g'}{\partial x_2'^2}\right) \frac{(\partial^2 g'/\partial x_2'^2)}{(\partial^2 g''/\partial x_2''^2)} \tag{18.65}$$

If both phases are stable then the sign of this second derivative is given by the sign of

$$\frac{-1}{x_2'' \Delta_r'' v_2 + (1 - x_2'')\Delta_r'' v_1} \left(\frac{\partial^2 g''}{\partial x_2''^2} - \frac{\partial^2 g'}{\partial x_2'^2}\right). \tag{18.66}$$

In the particular case of liquid-vapour equilibrium, for which $\Delta_e v_2$ and $\Delta_e v_1$ are positive, the second derivative will have the same sign as

$$-\left(\frac{\partial^2 g^g}{\partial (x_2^g)^2} - \frac{\partial^2 g^l}{\partial (x_2^l)^2}\right). \tag{18.67}$$

We conclude therefore that if the two phases have the same composition, the pressure of the system is a *maximum* if

$$\frac{\partial^2 g^g}{\partial (x_2^g)^2} - \frac{\partial^2 g^l}{\partial (x_2^l)^2} > 0, \tag{18.68}$$

but is a minimum if

$$\frac{\partial^2 g^g}{\partial (x_2^g)^2} - \frac{\partial^2 g^l}{\partial (x_2^l)^2} < 0. \tag{18.69}$$

We shall not consider the exceptional case where (18.67) is zero.*

These important inequalities will be employed in the discussion of azeotropy in chapter XXVIII. Analogous considerations may be applied to the problem of coexistence curves at constant pressure.

9. Identification of Upper and Lower Critical Solution Temperatures.

The relations which have been derived above apply to equilibrium between any pair of phases and can be used to discuss the two phase equilibria between immiscible liquids, and to calculate the coexistence curves such as those shown in chapter XVI (figs. 16.9, 16.10 and 16.11).

At the critical point C the two phases are identical. We shall assume† that the coexistence curves AC, BC meet continuously at the point C.

Two coexistent phases such as P' and P'' (figs. 18.3 and 18.4) are represented by two points on the same horizontal line (same T). At the point C where the phases are the same, the tangent to the curve ACB must then be horizontal. That is

$$\left(\frac{dT}{dx_2'}\right)_c = \left(\frac{dT}{dx_2''}\right)_c = 0, \tag{18.70}$$

where the derivatives are taken along the coexistence curves AC and CB. Since the phases are identical at the critical point

$$\left.\begin{aligned} (x_2')_c &= (x_2'')_c, \\ \text{and} \qquad (\Delta_\prime^{\prime\prime} h_1)_c &= (\Delta_\prime^{\prime\prime} h_2)_c = 0 \end{aligned}\right\}. \tag{18.71}$$

In addition the conditions (16.28) must also be satisfied at the critical point.

We now have to find the conditions which determine whether the critical point shall be a maximum of the coexistence curve *i.e.* an upper

* *Cf.* Duhem, [15], Vol. IV and Schouls [41].

† There is no theoretical reason to doubt that the two coexistence curves form a continuous curve. J. E. Mayer's theory of condensation (*cf.* Mayer and Mayer [34]) cannot be applied with certainty near the critical point because of the arbitrary nature of its hypotheses. For a recent experimental study of the shape of the coexistence curves of liquid and vapour near the critical point see D. Atack and W. G. Schneider, *J. Phys. Coll. Chem.*, 55, 532 (1951).

consolute point, fig. 18.3, or a minimum, or lower consolute point fig. 18.4. The slope of the curve CA is given by (*cf.* 18.46)

$$\frac{dT}{dx_2'} = -\frac{T(x_2'' - x_2')(\partial^2 g'/\partial x_2'^2)}{x_2''\Delta_{\prime}'' h_2 + (1 - x_2'')\Delta_{\prime}'' h_1}. \tag{18.72}$$

We shall adopt the convention of calling the first phase that which is the more dilute in component 2 ; this means that

$$x_2'' > x_2' \quad \text{or} \quad (x_2'' - x_2') > 0. \tag{18.73}$$

If (18.72) is positive in the neighbourhood of C on the curve AC, then C is an upper consolute temperature ; while if the slope is negative on AC, C is a lower consolute temperature.

Now the numerator is always positive for stable phases because of (18.73), and the fact that (*cf.* 18.43)

$$\partial^2 g'/\partial x_2'^2 > 0 \tag{18.74}$$

except at C where it is zero (*cf.* 16.28).

Hence the sign of (18.72) is determined by the sign of the denominator.

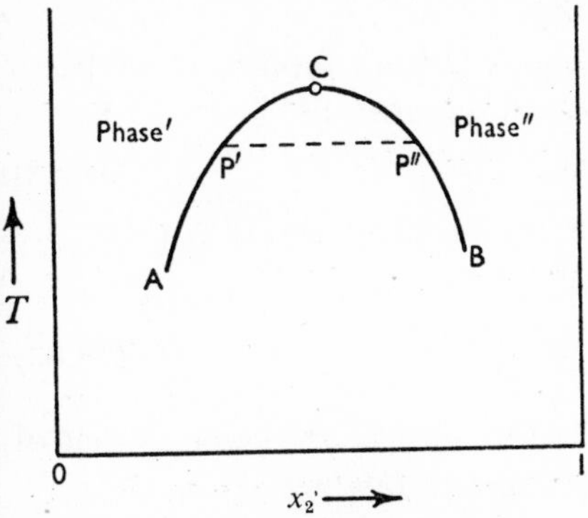

FIG. 18.3. Phase diagram with upper consolute temperature.

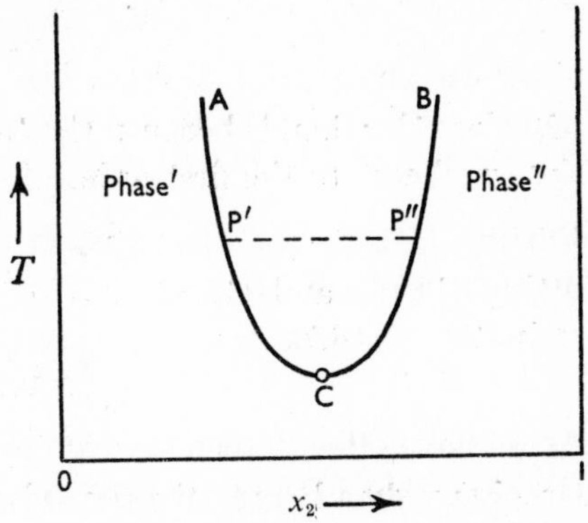

FIG. 18.4. Phase diagram with lower consolute temperature.

Now consider two co-existing phases close to the critical point, let their co-ordinates be $T_c + \delta T, (x_2)_c + \delta x_2'$ and $T_c + \delta T, (x_2)_c + \delta x_2''$. The partial molar heat of component 1 in these solutions can be obtained by developing h_1' and h_1'' in series in the neighbourhood of the critical point :

$$h_1' = (h_1)_c + \left(\frac{\partial h_1}{\partial x_2}\right)_c \delta x_2' + \left(\frac{\partial h_1}{\partial T}\right)_c \delta T, \tag{18.75}$$

$$h_1'' = (h_1)_c + \left(\frac{\partial h_1}{\partial x_2}\right)_c \delta x_2'' + \left(\frac{\partial h_1}{\partial T}\right)_c \delta T. \tag{18.76}$$

The heat of transfer of component 1 from the first to the second phase is therefore :

$$\Delta_{\prime}^{\prime\prime} h_1 = h_1^{\prime\prime} - h_1^{\prime} = \left(\frac{\partial h_1}{\partial x_2}\right)_c (\delta x_2^{\prime\prime} - \delta x_2^{\prime}). \tag{18.77}$$

However, the partial molar heats, like all partial molar quantities, must satisfy the equation (*cf.* 1.34) :

$$x_1 \left(\frac{\partial h_1}{\partial x_2}\right)_{T,p} + x_2 \left(\frac{\partial h_2}{\partial x_2}\right)_{T,p} = 0. \tag{18.78}$$

The denominator of (18.72) can therefore be written

$$-\delta x_2^{\prime\prime} \left[\left(\frac{\partial h_2}{\partial x_2}\right)_c - \left(\frac{\partial h_1}{\partial x_2}\right)_c \right] (\delta x_2^{\prime\prime} - \delta x_2^{\prime}). \tag{18.79}$$

This expression simplifies if we introduce the mean molar heat content $h = H/n$, whose derivative in a binary system is (*cf.* 1.36)

$$\frac{\partial h}{\partial x_2} = h_2 - h_1, \tag{18.80}$$

so that

$$\frac{\partial^2 h}{\partial x_2^2} = \frac{\partial h_2}{\partial x_2} - \frac{\partial h_1}{\partial x_2}. \tag{18.81}$$

On the other hand, because the tangent is horizontal at the critical point, we have, to the first order of small quantities.*

$$\delta x_2^{\prime} = -\delta x_2^{\prime\prime}. \tag{18.82}$$

Putting (18.81) and (18.82) into (18.79) we then obtain for the denominator of (18.72) :

$$-2 \left(\frac{\partial^2 h}{\partial x_2^2}\right)_c (\delta x_2^{\prime})^2. \tag{18.83}$$

As we have already seen the sign of (18.72) must be the same as that of (18.83) ; that is to say it is of opposite sign to $(\partial^2 h/\partial x_2^2)_c$.

Therefore, at an upper consolute temperature,

$$\left(\frac{\partial^2 h}{\partial x_2^2}\right)_c < 0, \tag{18.84}$$

* Because of (18.70) the development of the function $T(x_2)$ in series on either side of the critical point is of the form

$$T = T_c + a(\delta x_2^{\prime})^2 + b(\delta x_2^{\prime})^3 + \ldots$$

$$T = T_c + a(\delta x_2^{\prime\prime})^2 + b(\delta x_2^{\prime\prime})^3 + \ldots$$

So that for points at the same T on either side of C we have

$$a[(\delta x_2^{\prime})^2 - (\delta x_2^{\prime\prime})^2] + b[(\delta x_2^{\prime})^3 - (\delta x_2^{\prime\prime})^3] + \ldots = 0.$$

Neglecting powers greater than the second, we have therefore

$$(\delta x_2^{\prime})^2 = (\delta x_2^{\prime\prime})^2 ;$$

and hence (18.82).

and at a lower consolute temperature

$$\left(\frac{\partial^2 h}{\partial x_2^2}\right)_c > 0. \qquad (18.85)$$

These conditions relate the nature of the consolute temperature to the curvature of the line $h(x_2)$. In the case of an upper consolute temperature (fig. 18.3) we have a curve such as (1) in fig. 18.5 which is convex upwards; while for a lower consolute temperature (fig. 18.4) we have a curve such as (2) convex downwards. In principle of course the curves can have more complicated shapes such as (3) in which the curvature changes sign with concentration. In any case, whether a critical point corresponds to an upper or a lower consolute temperature is determined by the curvature at the critical concentration.

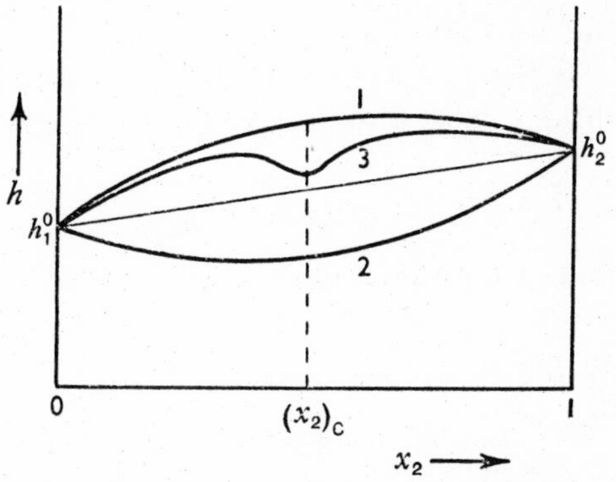

Fig. 18.5. Mean molar enthalpy ($h = H/n$) as function of composition at constant T and p.

In fact it is uncommon for the curvature of the relation between heat content and composition to change sign, and we shall limit the present discussion to curves such as (1) and (2). In the first case the heat content of the mixture is greater than that of the same quantities of the pure substances taken separately, given by the straight line joining h_1^0 and h_2^0. The mixture will therefore be formed from the pure components with an *absorption of heat* (endothermic mixture). On the other hand, in the case of curve (2) the mixture is formed with *evolution of heat* (exothermic mixture).

We conclude therefore that an upper consolute temperature can occur only with endothermic mixtures while lower consolute temperatures are limited to exothermic mixtures. These predictions have been verified in all cases which have been studied.*

We shall make a systematic study of heats of mixing later but we may mention now that the great majority of liquid mixtures are endothermic (*cf.* chapter XXIV, § 4).

The above conditions can be expressed in a different form by employing the relation

$$g = h - Ts, \qquad (18.86)$$

* *Cf.* Timmermans [45]; see also J. Timmermans, *J. Chim. Phys.*, 20, 491 (1923).

together with the fact that at the critical point $(\partial^2 g/\partial x_2^2)$ is zero (*cf.* 16.28). It follows then that

$$\left(\frac{\partial^2 h}{\partial x_2^2}\right)_c = T\left(\frac{\partial^2 s}{\partial x_2^2}\right)_c. \tag{18.87}$$

The curvature of the heat content and entropy have the same sign at the critical point ; the same is also true, from (16.28), of the third differentials of h and s.

Instead of (18.84) and (18.85) we now have the alternative conditions :* at an upper consolute temperature

$$\frac{\partial^2 s}{\partial x_2^2} < 0, \tag{18.88}$$

and at a lower consolute temperature

$$\frac{\partial^2 s}{\partial x_2^2} > 0. \tag{18.89}$$

In the case of an ideal system we have from (7.22) (*cf.* also chapter XX, § 3)

$$\frac{\partial^2 s}{\partial x_2^2} = \frac{\partial^2}{\partial x_2^2}(x_1 s_1 + x_2 s_2) = -\frac{\boldsymbol{R}}{x_1 x_2}. \tag{18.90}$$

If a solution possesses an ideal entropy of mixing, the second derivative is always negative and the system can only exhibit an upper consolute temperature. For a non-ideal solution to exhibit a lower consolute temperature, the deviations from ideality must be such that both the sign and the curvature of $s(x_2)$ is changed (*cf.* chapter XXIV, § 6 ; chapter XXVI, § 7).

10. Effect of Pressure on the Consolute Temperature.

At all points along the line joining the critical points at varying pressure equations (16.28) must still be satisfied. Differentiating (16.28) we have

$$\delta\left(\frac{\partial^2 g}{\partial x_2^2}\right) = \left(\frac{\partial^3 g}{\partial x_2^2\,\partial p}\right)_c \delta p + \left(\frac{\partial^3 g}{\partial x_2^2\,\partial T}\right)_c \delta T = 0\,; \tag{18.91}$$

$$\delta\left(\frac{\partial^3 g}{\partial x_2^3}\right) = \left(\frac{\partial^4 g}{\partial x_2^3\,\partial p}\right)_c \delta p + \left(\frac{\partial^4 g}{\partial x_2^3\,\partial T}\right)_c \delta T + \left(\frac{\partial^4 g}{\partial x_2^4}\right)_c \delta x_2 = 0. \tag{18.92}$$

From the first of these the effect of pressure on the critical temperature is seen to be

$$\frac{dT_c}{dp} = -\left(\frac{\partial^3 g}{\partial x_2^2\,\partial p}\right)_c \Big/ \left(\frac{\partial^3 g}{\partial x_2^2\,\partial T}\right)_c = \left(\frac{\partial^2 v}{\partial x_2^2}\right)_c \Big/ \left(\frac{\partial^2 s}{\partial x_2^2}\right)_c. \tag{18.93}$$

* These conditions are equivalent to those given by O. K. Rice, *Chem. Reviews*, **44**, 65 (1949).

while the effect on the critical composition is

$$\frac{d(x_2)_c}{dp} = \frac{\left(\frac{\partial^3 s}{\partial x_2^3}\right)_c \left(\frac{\partial^2 v}{\partial x_2^2}\right)_c - \left(\frac{\partial^3 v}{\partial x_2^3}\right)_c \left(\frac{\partial^2 s}{\partial x_2^2}\right)_c}{\left(\frac{\partial^2 s}{\partial x_2^2}\right)_c \left(\frac{\partial^4 g}{\partial x_2^4}\right)_c} . \tag{18.94}$$

We shall not discuss this last equation in any detail because so far no systematic experimental study has been made of the influence of pressure on the critical composition. We may notice in passing that this is one of the rare formulae in thermodynamics which correlates a readily measureable phenomenon with the fourth derivative of the free energy. It might be very useful if one wished to verify to a high degree of precision an analytical form assumed for the thermodynamic functions of a system.

The effect of pressure on the critical temperature has been studied by Timmermans.* We see from (18.93) and (18.89) that the sign of dT_c/dp depends both upon $(\partial^2 v/\partial x_2^2)_c$ and on whether the consolute temperature is an upper or a lower point.

Thus for an *upper consolute temperature*

$$\frac{dT_c}{dp} \text{ has the opposite sign to } \left(\frac{\partial^2 v}{\partial x_2^2}\right)_c , \tag{18.95}$$

while for a *lower consolute temperature*

$$\frac{dT_c}{dp} \text{ has the same sign as } \left(\frac{\partial^2 v}{\partial x_2^2}\right)_c . \tag{18.96}$$

The effect of pressure on the consolute temperature is thus determined by the curvature of the mean molar volume $v(x_2)$ at the critical point. We may represent the two simple cases by the curves (1) and (2) in fig. 18.6, and ignore for the moment any more complicated behaviour. For curve (1) $\partial^2 v/\partial x_2^2$ is negative and the molar volume of the solution is greater than the sum of the corresponding amounts of pure substance taken separately: the process of mixing is accompanied by an expansion. On the other hand for curve (2) $\partial^2 v/\partial x_2^2$ is positive and the mixing is accompanied by a contraction.

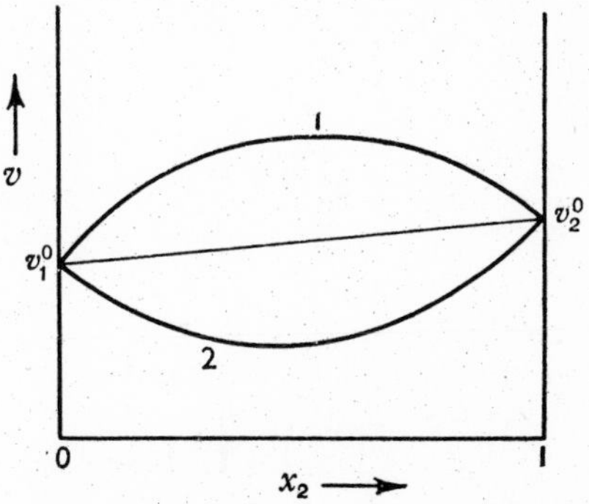

FIG. 18.6. Mean molar volume as function of composition at constant T and p.

The conclusions of the above discussion of critical mixing may be summarized in the following way:

* *Cf.* Timmermans, *loc. cit.*

1. endothermic solutions may have an upper consolute point, and

(*a*) if formed with an expansion, $\frac{dT_c}{dp} > 0$ *e.g.* water + phenol;

(*b*) if formed with a contraction, $\frac{dT_c}{dp} < 0$, *e.g.* hexane + nitrobenzene,

2. exothermic solutions may have a lower consolute point, and

(*a*) if formed with an expansion, $\frac{dT_c}{dp} < 0$,

(*b*) if formed with a contraction, $\frac{dT_c}{dp} > 0$ *e.g.* CO_2 + *o*-nitrophenol.

Compression thus increases the solubility in cases 1(*b*) and 2(*b*); but decreases it in 1(*a*) and 2(*a*).

It may be noted that the cases most frequently observed in practice are 1(*a*) and 2(*b*). In the case of endothermic mixtures with expansion, part of the energy added to the system corresponds in a general way to the work needed to separate the molecules a little more against the attractive intermolecular forces. The inverse is true of exothermic mixing accompanied by a contraction.

A number of examples of type 1(*b*) exist, but no example of type 2 (*a*) is known.

CHAPTER XIX

EQUILIBRIUM PROCESSES RELAXATION PHENOMENA AND TRANSFORMATIONS OF SECOND ORDER

1. Definition of Equilibrium Processes.

Consider a process during the course of which the affinity remains less than a given value $\mathbf{A}_0$. Now let $\mathbf{A}_0$ tend to zero. The limiting case defined in this way is called an *equilibrium process* or *equilibrium transformation.* The uncompensated heat of this transformation is zero because of (3.21), and so equation (3.5) reduces to

$$dS=\frac{dQ}{T}. \qquad (19.1)$$

2. Conditions for an Equilibrium Process : Time of relaxation of the Affinity.

Suppose we have a process during the course of which T and p vary with time in accordance with some given law. The corresponding change in the affinity may be calculated as follows.

Equation (4.60) gives us

$$\frac{d\mathbf{A}}{dt}=\frac{\mathbf{A}+h_{T,\,p}}{T}\frac{dT}{dt}-v_{T,\,p}\frac{dp}{dt}+a_{T,\,p}\frac{d\xi}{dt}. \qquad (19.2)$$

The term $d\xi/dt$ is of course the reaction velocity $\mathbf{v}$. The reaction velocity is zero if $\mathbf{A}=0$, since the system is then in equilibrium. In close proximity to equilibrium we may assume that the velocity is proportional to the affinity

$$\mathbf{v}=k\mathbf{A}, \qquad (19.3)$$

where k is a proportionality constant which is independent of T and p. This assumption will be discussed in greater detail in the part of this treatise dealing with irreversible phenomena.

Combining (19.2) and (19.3) we have

$$\frac{d\mathbf{A}}{dt}-a_{T,\,p}k\mathbf{A}=\frac{\mathbf{A}+h_{T,\,p}}{T}\frac{dT}{dt}-v_{T,\,p}\frac{dp}{dt}. \qquad (19.4)$$

Near equilibrium we may usually neglect $\mathbf{A}$ in comparison with the heat of reaction. Furthermore, to a first approximation, we may take for $v_{T,\,p}$ and $h_{T,\,p}$ the values of these functions on the equilibrium surface;

they will be functions of T and p only since ξ_e is a function of T and p. On the other hand $a_{T,p}$ is directly related to the time of relaxation of the affinity. For suppose that T and p are constant, then (19.4) reduces to

$$\frac{d\mathbf{A}}{dt} - a_{T,p} k \mathbf{A} = 0, \tag{19.5}$$

that is to say the affinity disappears in accordance with the exponential law

$$\mathbf{A} = \mathbf{A}_0 \, e^{-t/\tau} \tag{19.6}$$

with a relaxation time

$$\tau = -\frac{1}{k a_{T,p}}. \tag{19.7}$$

Equation (19.4) can therefore be written

$$\frac{d\mathbf{A}}{dt} + \frac{\mathbf{A}}{\tau} = \frac{h_{T,p}}{T}\frac{dT}{dt} - v_{T,p}\frac{dp}{dt}, \tag{19.8}$$

where the right hand side is a given function of time. This equation then enables $\mathbf{A}$ to be calculated as a function of time.

Several special cases will now be considered. First we suppose that both T and p are made to vary linearly with time and we start from the equilibrium state; that is $\mathbf{A} = 0$ when $t = 0$. As a first approximation we may, in (19.8) replace $v_{T,p}$, $h_{T,p}$ and τ, which are functions of T and p, by constants which represent their mean values in the range of temperature and pressure considered. The right hand side of (19.8) can then be replaced by a constant independent of time which we shall designate by α. We now have to consider the equation

$$\frac{d\mathbf{A}}{dt} + \frac{\mathbf{A}}{\tau} = \alpha, \tag{19.9}$$

whose solution is

$$\mathbf{A} = \alpha\tau[1 - e^{-t/\tau}]. \tag{19.10}$$

At the end of a time interval τ, the affinity will thus have reached a value of the order of $\alpha\tau$.

We may consider, for example, a reaction consisting of the recombination of the ions of a weak electrolyte. Conductivity data indicate that the time of relaxation in this case is about 10^{-4} sec.* The volume change $v_{T,p} = (\partial v/\partial\xi)_{T,p}$ is of the order of the partial molar volumes of the components, say several cm.^{3}/mole. If then the system is subjected to a compression of one atmosphere a second, the quantity α in (19.10) will be of the order of 10^6 c.g.s. units, and $\mathbf{A} \sim \alpha\tau \sim 10^2$ ergs/mole $\sim 10^{-5}$ cal./mole. The value of the affinity is therefore very small indeed. To obtain larger effects it is necessary to consider systems in which the

* *Cf.* Harned and Owen, [27], p. 222.

relaxation time is very much larger or processes which are very much faster. Some examples of systems in which the relaxation time is of the order of a second or more are provided by substances which can pass into a vitreous state *; while the very rapid pressure and temperature changes in the region of an explosion wave must lead to appreciable departures from equilibrium.

We now consider *quasi-instantaneous* changes in T and p. The affinity takes on abruptly a value $\mathbf{A}_0$ which then falls progressively to zero according to (19.6). The value of $\mathbf{A}_0$ is given directly by (4.60) in which we can set $d\xi$ equal to zero as the initial change is supposed to be so rapid that ξ has no time to change. Thus if we have a sudden change in pressure Δp, this corresponds to

$$\mathbf{A}_0 = -v_{T,p}\,\Delta p. \tag{19.11}$$

For $\Delta_p = 10^4$ atm., and $v_{T,p} \sim 1$ cm.³/mole,

$$|\,\mathbf{A}_0\,| \approx 200 \text{ cal./mole.} \tag{19.12}$$

These calculations enable us to define the conditions under which a given transformation can be regarded as an equilibrium transformation. It is seen that these conditions are dependent upon the time of relaxation of the affinity and the way in which the external variables change with time.

3. Configurational Heat Capacity.

Consider the heat capacity at constant p of a system in which a transformation defined by a parameter ξ may occur. By virtue of (2.13) we have

$$C_p = \left(\frac{dQ}{dT}\right)_p = C_{p,\xi} + h_{T,p}\left(\frac{d\xi}{dT}\right)_p. \tag{19.13}$$

The second term on the right hand side refers to the effect of the temperature on the reaction co-ordinate ξ.

In particular, if we consider an equilibrium transformation, equation (4.60) leads to the relations

$$\left.\begin{aligned}
\left(\frac{\partial \xi}{\partial T}\right)_{p,\mathbf{A}=0} &= -\frac{h_{T,p}}{T a_{T,p}}, \\
\left(\frac{\partial \xi}{\partial p}\right)_{T,\mathbf{A}=0} &= \frac{v_{T,p}}{a_{T,p}}, \\
\left(\frac{\partial p}{\partial T}\right)_{\xi,\mathbf{A}=0} &= \frac{h_{T,p}}{T v_{T,p}}
\end{aligned}\right\}. \tag{19.14}$$

* Frenkel [21], chaps. II and IV.

Substituting into (19.13) we obtain

$$C_{p,\mathbf{A}=0} = C_{p,\xi} - \frac{h^2_{T,p}}{T a_{T,p}}, \tag{19.15}$$

or

$$C_{p,\mathbf{A}=0} = C_{p,\xi} - T a_{T,p} \left(\frac{\partial \xi}{\partial T}\right)^2_{p,\mathbf{A}=0}. \tag{19.16}$$

Remembering that in a system in stable equilibrium $a_{T,p}$ is negative, we see that *the heat capacity at constant composition is always less than that for an equilibrium transformation.*

These two heat capacities correspond to two limiting cases. $C_{p,\mathbf{A}=0}$ corresponds to a transformation carried out sufficiently slowly. On the other hand, if the transformation is rapid enough, ξ does not have time to maintain its equilibrium value and the heat capacity approximates to $C_{p,\xi}$. An increase in the rate of temperature change leads to C_p approaching $C_{p,\xi}$ while a slower change leads more closely to $C_{p,\mathbf{A}=0}$.

The above considerations may be applied directly to the configurational heat capacity of the vitreous state. Following Simon* we may say that the vitreous state is distinguished from the liquid state by the fact that internal chemical equilibrium is not established; we thus have $\mathbf{A} \neq 0$ for the vitreous state, and $\mathbf{A} = 0$ for the liquid state. As an example we may take the case of glycerol, whose molecules are dipolar and interact strongly with one another. In the crystalline state the molecules vibrate relative to one another, without rotating completely; this restricted rotation is often called a *libration*. In the liquid state however an ever increasing number of molecules undergo complete rotation as the temperature is raised. The transformation *libration→rotation* can be described in terms of reaction co-ördinate ξ, which gives at any instant the number of molecules which can rotate freely. Let us suppose that $\mathbf{A}$ is the affinity of this transformation. In the crystalline state ξ remains practically constant: all the molecules librate in the lattice. The heat capacity of the crystalline state at constant pressure is thus $C_{p,\xi}$. On the other hand, if the temperature of liquid glycerine is changed, ξ has a value at each instant given by the equation,

$$\mathbf{A}(T, p, \xi) = 0$$

corresponding to equilibrium between the molecules which are librating and those which are rotating. The heat capacity of liquid glycerine is thus $C_{p,\mathbf{A}=0}$. Finally in the vitreous state, ξ varies more slowly with T than in the liquid state. The general disposition of the heat capacity curves for glycerine is shown in fig. 19.1.

In this example ξ is in effect a parameter which characterizes the

* F. E. Simon, *Zeit. anorg. Chem.*. 203, 219 (1931).

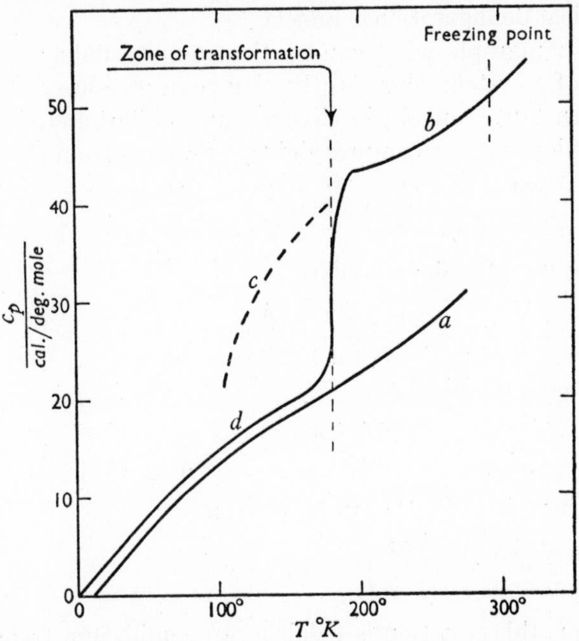

FIG. 19.1. Heat capacity of glycerol*, (*a*) crystal; (*b*→*d*) liquid—super-cooled liquid—glass; (*c*) super-cooled liquid, extrapolation assuming very slow transformation to glass.

structure or internal configuration of the system. Hence we may call the second term on the right hand side of (19.13) the *configurational heat capacity*:

$$C_p^{\text{config}} = h_{T,p}\left(\frac{\partial \xi}{\partial T}\right)_p . \tag{19.17}$$

Finally we may consider the relaxation phenomena associated with the heat capacity. For a transformation at constant p, (19.13) can be written in the form:

$$C_p = C_{p,\xi} + h_{T,p}\frac{(d\xi/dt)}{(dT/dt)}, \tag{19.18}$$

or replacing $d\xi/dt$ by the value given by (19.3) we have

$$C_p = C_{p,\xi} + \frac{h_{T,p}k\mathbf{A}}{dT/dt} . \tag{19.19}$$

If we know the relaxation time τ of the affinity we can calculate $\mathbf{A}$ by the method outlined in the previous paragraph. Equation (19.19) then gives the heat capacity as a function of time in a system approaching equilibrium.

* A. G. Oblad, and R. F. Newton, *J. Amer. Chem. Soc.*, 59, 2495 (1937); *cf.* also G. O. Jones and F. E. Simon, *Endeavour*, 8, 175 (1949).

4. Mechanical Configurational Effects.

In this paragraph we compare the compressibility and thermal expansion of a system when (*a*) the change in pressure or temperature occurs at constant ξ and (*b*) the change is an equilibrium transformation.

We consider first the compressibility. Starting from the identity

$$\left(\frac{\partial V}{\partial p}\right)_{\mathbf{A},T} = \left(\frac{\partial V}{\partial p}\right)_{T,\xi} + \left(\frac{\partial V}{\partial \xi}\right)_{T,p} \left(\frac{\partial \xi}{\partial p}\right)_{\mathbf{A},T}, \tag{19.20}$$

and making use of (4.39) we have

$$\left(\frac{\partial V}{\partial p}\right)_{\mathbf{A},T} = \left(\frac{\partial V}{\partial p}\right)_{T,\xi} - \left(\frac{\partial \mathbf{A}}{\partial p}\right)_{T,\xi} \left(\frac{\partial \xi}{\partial p}\right)_{\mathbf{A},T}. \tag{19.21}$$

We also have the identity,

$$\left(\frac{\partial p}{\partial \xi}\right)_{\mathbf{A},T} = -\frac{(\partial \mathbf{A}/\partial \xi)_{T,p}}{(\partial \mathbf{A}/\partial p)_{T,\xi}} = -\frac{a_{T,p}}{(\partial \mathbf{A}/\partial p)_{T,\xi}}. \tag{19.22}$$

It follows then that (19.21) can be written

$$\left(\frac{\partial V}{\partial p}\right)_{\mathbf{A},T} = \left(\frac{\partial V}{\partial p}\right)_{T,\xi} + a_{T,p} \left(\frac{\partial \xi}{\partial p}\right)^2_{\mathbf{A},T}. \tag{19.23}$$

In particular, this equation is valid for an equilibrium transformation for which $\mathbf{A} = 0$, and we can thus obtain a relation between the coefficient of compressibility

$$\kappa_{\mathbf{A}=0} = -\frac{1}{V}\left(\frac{\partial V}{\partial p}\right)_{\mathbf{A}=0,T},$$

for an isothermal equilibrium compression and the coefficient κ_ξ for an isothermal compression at constant ξ:

$$\kappa_{\mathbf{A}=0} = \kappa_\xi - \frac{a_{T,p}}{V}\left(\frac{\partial \xi}{\partial p}\right)^2_{\mathbf{A}=0,T}. \tag{19.24}$$

We see that the coefficient $\kappa_{\mathbf{A}=0}$ *is always greater than* κ_ξ since $a_{T,p}$ is always negative for a stable phase. In other words if the pressure change is applied so rapidly that the composition of the system does not have time to change, then the resulting volume change is *smaller* than that which occurs when the pressure is applied sufficiently slowly.*

An analogous calculation can be made for the coefficient of thermal expansion, giving the result,

$$\alpha_{\mathbf{A}=0} = \alpha_\xi + \frac{a_{T,p}}{V}\left(\frac{\partial \xi}{\partial p}\right)_{\mathbf{A}=\ ,T}\left(\frac{\partial \xi}{\partial T}\right)_{\mathbf{A}=0,p}. \tag{19.25}$$

The differential coefficients $(\partial \xi/\partial p)_{\mathbf{A}=0,T}$ and $(\partial \xi/\partial T)_{\mathbf{A}=0,p}$ which appear in (19.24) and (19.25) are given by (19.14).

* *Cf.* J. E. Verschaffelt, *Wis- en Naturkundig Tijdschrift*, **6**, 243, (1933); **7**, 140 (1935); Frenkel, [21], p. 76.

If ξ is a parameter determining the configuration of the system (*e.g.* the degree of long range order), the second terms on the right hand side of (19.24) and (19.25) may be called the *configurational compressibility* and the *configurational expansion*, respectively.

Thus

$$\kappa^{\text{config}} = -\frac{1}{V}\left(\frac{\partial V}{\partial \xi}\right)_{T,p}\left(\frac{\partial \xi}{\partial p}\right)_{\mathbf{A}=0,T} = -\frac{1}{V}a_{T,p}\left(\frac{\partial \xi}{\partial p}\right)^2_{\mathbf{A}=0,T}. \quad (19.26)$$

$$\alpha^{\text{config}} = \frac{1}{V}\left(\frac{\partial V}{\partial \xi}\right)_{T,p}\left(\frac{\partial \xi}{\partial T}\right)_{\mathbf{A}=0,p} = \frac{1}{V}a_{T,p}\left(\frac{\partial \xi}{\partial p}\right)_{\mathbf{A}=0,T}\left(\frac{\partial \xi}{\partial T}\right)_{\mathbf{A}=0,p}. \quad (19.27)$$

On comparison of (19.16), (19.24) and (19.25) it is seen that there is a simple relationship between the configurational heat capacity, the configurational compressibility and the configurational thermal expansion:

$$C_p^{\text{config}}\,\kappa^{\text{config}} = VT\,(\alpha^{\text{config}})^2,$$

or

$$C_p^{\text{config}} = VT\,\frac{(\alpha^{\text{config}})^2}{\kappa^{\text{config}}}. \quad (19.28)$$

If two of these coefficients can be measured experimentally the third can be calculated.

5. An Example of the Calculation of Configurational Heat Capacity.

Let us calculate the configurational heat capacity in a simple case, such as an isomerization reaction of the type

$$M_1 \to M_2. \quad (19.29)$$

Suppose that this transformation occurs in an ideal system (perfect gas or perfect solution). Then the free energy G of the system will be of the form (*cf.* 6.24 and 7.1)

$$G = n_1(\mu_1^0 + \boldsymbol{R}T \ln x_1) + n_2(\mu_2^0 + \boldsymbol{R}T \ln x_2), \quad (19.30)$$

or per mole,

$$g = \mu_1^0 + x_2(\mu_2^0 - \mu_1^0) + x_2\boldsymbol{R}T \ln x_2 + (1 - x_2)\boldsymbol{R}T \ln(1 - x_2). \quad (19.31)$$

The affinity can then be written (*cf.* 7.26)

$$\mathbf{A} = -\omega - \boldsymbol{R}T \ln x_2 + \boldsymbol{R}T \ln(1 - x_2), \quad (19.32)$$

where we have put

$$\omega = \mu_2^0 - \mu_1^0. \quad (19.33)$$

The significance of ω is easily seen, for from table 7.1, we see that:

$$h_{T,p} = \left(\frac{\partial H}{\partial \xi}\right)_{T,p} = -T^2\frac{\partial}{\partial T}\left(\frac{\omega}{T}\right). \quad (19.34)$$

If it is assumed that in the temperature range considered ω is constant, then

$$h_{T,p} = \omega. \tag{19.35}$$

This approximation is equivalent to neglecting the difference between the heat capacities of M_1 and M_2.

At equilibrium $\mathbf{A} = 0$ and (19.32) gives for the mole fraction of 2

$$x_2 = \frac{1}{1 + e^{\omega/RT}}. \tag{19.36}$$

If $\omega > 0$ (endothermic reaction) $x_2 \to 0$ when $T \to 0$ and $x_2 \to 1/2$ for $T \to \infty$; it is readily shown that $x_2(T)$ increases monotonically with T. Furthermore the system is in stable equilibrium since, as proved in chap. XV, §§ 12 and 13, chemical equilibria in ideal systems are always stable.

If in the initial state $n_1^0 = 1$ and $n_2^0 = 0$, then the extent of change can be defined simply by

$$x_2 = \xi. \tag{19.37}$$

Substituting into (19.17) we find for the configurational heat capacity :

$$\frac{c_p^{\text{config}}}{R} = \left(\frac{\omega}{RT}\right)^2 \frac{e^{\omega/RT}}{(1 + e^{\omega/RT})^2}. \tag{19.38}$$

The configurational heat capacity is positive as deduced from the general case, and passes through a maximum at a temperature (T_m) given by the equation :

$$\frac{\omega}{2RT_m} = \frac{1 + e^{-\omega/RT_m}}{1 - e^{-\omega/RT_m}}. \tag{19.39}$$

This may be written*

$$\frac{\omega}{2RT_m} \tanh \frac{\omega}{2RT_m} = 1. \tag{19.40}$$

The solution of this equation is well known :†

$$\frac{\omega}{2RT_m} = 1{\cdot}199678 \ldots$$
$$\simeq 1{\cdot}20. \tag{19.41}$$

The configurational heat capacity as a function of temperature is shown schematically in fig. 19.2. At the maximum c_p^{config}/R has a

* By definition

$$\tanh x = \frac{1 - e^{-2x}}{1 + e^{-2x}},$$

† *Cf.* F. Emde, *Tafeln elementarer Functionen*, (Leipzig, 1940), p. 131.

value of about 0·40 which shows that the configurational heat capacity is only a fraction of the ordinary heat capacity.

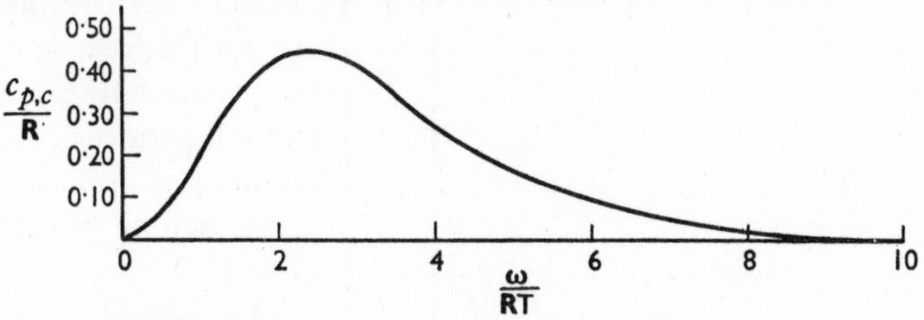

FIG. 19.2. Configurational heat capacity of isomerization.

We notice also, that when ξ has the simple form (19.37), equation (19.31) can be written

$$g = \mu_1^0 + \omega\xi + \xi \boldsymbol{R}T \ln \xi + (1-\xi)\boldsymbol{R}T \ln (1-\xi). \tag{19.42}$$

The molar entropy and heat content are easily seen, from (19.30), to be

$$\begin{aligned} s &= x_1 s_1^0 + x_2 s_2^0 - \boldsymbol{R}x_1 \ln x_1 - \boldsymbol{R}x_2 \ln x_2, \\ h &= x_1 h_1^0 + x_2 h_2^0, \end{aligned} \tag{19.43}$$

so that with the simple form of ξ,

$$\left.\begin{aligned} s &= s_1^0 + \xi(s_2^0 - s_1^0) - \boldsymbol{R}[\xi \ln \xi + (1-\xi)\ln(1-\xi)], \\ h &= h_1^0 + \xi(h_2^0 - h_1^0). \end{aligned}\right\} \tag{19.43'}$$

Equation (19.38) is due to Schottky.*

The configurational heat capacities of certain polymorphic transformations are in close agreement with this formula. As examples may be quoted the transformation of grey tin at 29 °K, of Si at 103° and of diamond at 450°.† In these instances the above model seems to describe the behaviour adequately ; other phenomena of a similar kind require a different treatment and these are considered in the next paragraph.

6. Curie Points : Co-operative Phenomena.

If we consider the properties of an equimolecular alloy of copper and gold, we find that in the neighbourhood of a certain temperature T ($\sim$710 °K), the heat capacity and the coefficient of thermal expansion exhibit anomalies. The heat capacity curve has the shape shown in fig. 19.3.

The temperature at which this anomaly occurs is called the *Curie temperature* by analogy with the temperature, studied by Pierre Curie,

* W. Schottky, *Phys. Zeit.*, 22, 1 (1921) ; 23, 9 (1922) ; *cf.* also F. E. Simon, *Erg. Naturw.*, 9, 222 (1930).

† For further details see Simon, *loc. cit.*

at which ferromagnetism disappears. It is sometimes called a *lambda point*, because of the resemblance of the shape of the heat capacity curve to the capital Greek Λ; for this reason we shall adopt the notation T_λ for this temperature. A similar anomaly is also shown by liquid helium in the region of 2 °K.*

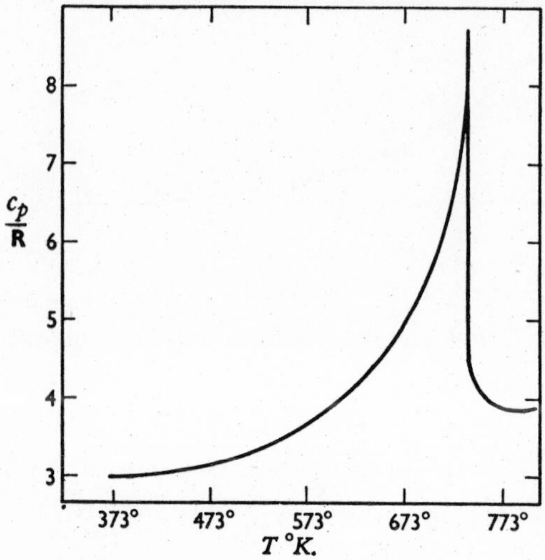

FIG. 19.3. Heat capacity of an equimolar mixture of Au + Cu in the neighbourhood of the Curie point.

The discussion in the preceding paragraphs suggests that we may be able to interpret these phenomena by supposing that the state of the system is determined by the three variables T, p, ξ, and that in the region of the Curie point ξ undergoes a very rapid change. The anomaly in the heat capacity would thus be interpreted in terms of a configurational heat capacity.

In the case of gold-copper alloys the nature of this third variable ξ is well known.† At low temperatures the crystal structure is such that each copper atom is surrounded by gold atoms as nearest neighbours, and *vice versa*. There are in effect two interpenetrating sub-lattices a and b, one occupied entirely by gold atoms and the other by copper atoms. In a crystal of this kind there is perfect *long range order*. This means that if we choose two lattice points, then however far apart they may be we can always specify the mode of occupation of one when we know what kind of atom occupies the other. When the temperature is raised, a certain number of gold atoms move from the sub-lattice a to b; and the same number of copper atoms occupy sites in the a lattice. The long distance order decreases steadily, and at the Curie point it disappears completely. Above this point the idea of two sub-lattices ceases to have any meaning, and each lattice point has an equal chance of being occupied by a copper or a gold atom.

It is important not to confuse the idea of long-range order with that of *local order*.‡ Even above the Curie point, there is a slightly greater

* *Cf.* W. H. Keesom, *Helium*, (Amsterdam, London, New York, 1942).
† *Cf.* especially F. C. Nix and W. Shockley, *Rev. Mod. Phys.*, **10**, 1, (1938).
‡ Nix and Shockley, *loc. cit.*, Fowler and Guggenheim, [20], chap. XIII.

chance of finding a gold atom as nearest neighbour of a copper atom and *vice versa*.

Let us denote by N_+ the number of lattice points which are "correctly" occupied *i.e.* lattice points on the a sub-lattice which are occupied by Au, and on the b lattice occupied by Cu. Then we shall write N_- as the number of lattice sites "incorrectly" occupied, *i.e.* a lattice points occupied by Cu, and b lattice points by Au.

The long-range order can then be defined by

$$\xi = N_+ - N_-. \tag{19.44}$$

In this case it is more convenient to employ the parameter ϵ defined by :

$$\epsilon = \frac{\xi}{N} = \frac{N_+ - N_-}{N}, \tag{19.45}$$

$$N = N_+ + N_-, \tag{19.46}$$

and which has the advantage of being an *intensive* variable. It may be called the *degree of order*. (*cf.* p. 13). We see immediately that in a state of perfect order $N_- = 0$ and $\epsilon = 1$, while in the complete absence of long-range order $N_+ = N_-$ and $\epsilon = 0$.

These relations can be written

$$\left.\begin{aligned} N_+ &= \tfrac{1}{2}N(1+\epsilon), \\ N_- &= \tfrac{1}{2}N(1-\epsilon) \end{aligned}\right\}. \tag{19.47}$$

We can now calculate the configurational heat capacity corresponding to a variation of ξ or ϵ with temperature. The problem consists essentially in understanding the reason for the difference between the curve in fig. 19.2 and that in fig. 19.3. In the previous paragraph we assumed, because of the ideality of the solution that the heat of reaction was independent of the composition of the system, and therefore of the number of molecules which had reacted. In the present case, on the other hand, the energy needed to exchange a pair of atoms depends upon the nature of the neighbouring atoms. At first, when we have perfect order ($\epsilon = 1$), exchange of the Au and Cu atoms which occupy sites 1 and 2 (fig. 19.4), requires a certain energy since the surroundings of each atom which takes part in the change are profoundly altered by this exchange. Thus the Cu atom which is initially surrounded by z

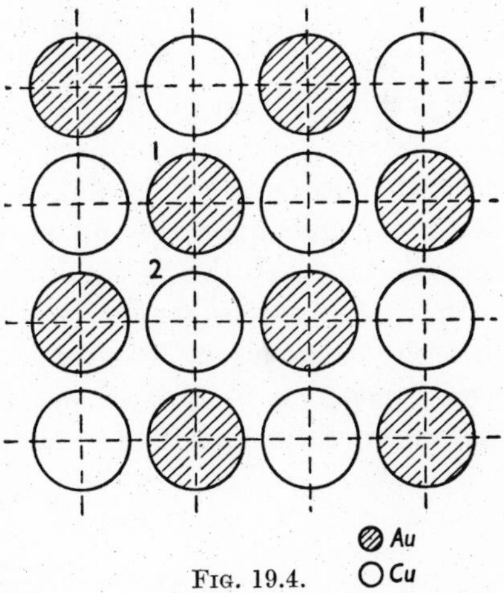

FIG. 19.4.

(=number of nearest neighbours) atoms of Au, finds itself surrounded by $(z-1)$ atoms of Cu and only one atom of Au. On the other hand, in the case of complete disorder ($\epsilon=0$) all sites are, on the average, equivalent so that the energy needed for the exchange is zero.

This is an example of a *co-operative phenomenon* in which the energy needed to carry out an elementary process depends upon the state of the whole system. To take account of this co-operative effect, let us make the simple assumption that the energy needed to exchange a pair of unlike atoms is given by

$$U=\omega\epsilon, \tag{19.48}$$

where ω is an energy per atom (and not per mole as in the previous paragraph). The energy is thus a maximum for $\epsilon=1$ and is zero for $\epsilon=0$. If we consider the destruction of order by the successive exchange of pairs of unlike atoms between the sub-lattices, then the first exchange, when $\epsilon=1$, will require an energy ω, while the $(N_-+1)^{\text{th}}$ exchange will need

$$\omega\epsilon=\omega\frac{N-2N_-}{N}. \tag{19.49}$$

The total variation of the energy caused by N_- exchanges will therefore be given by

$$U-U_{N_-=0}=\omega\int_0^{N_-}\frac{N-2N_-}{N}\,dN_-=\omega\frac{N_+N_-}{N}. \tag{19.50}$$

In terms of the parameter ϵ this becomes

$$U(\epsilon)=U(1)+\frac{\omega N}{4}(1-\epsilon^2). \tag{19.51}$$

It is this equation which determines the difference in behaviour of the two systems. For on comparing (19.51) with (19.43′), and neglecting the difference between U and H, we see that in the present case the energy depends upon the square of ϵ or ξ, while in the first example it depended only on the first power. The entropy, on the other hand, is given by an expression analogous to (19.43′). In effect, we may assume that the existence of long-range order contributes to the entropy a term analogous to that of an ideal binary solution of N_+ and N_- molecules of different kinds; that is*

$$-\boldsymbol{k}N_+\ln\frac{N_+}{N}-\boldsymbol{k}N_-\ln\frac{N_-}{N}, \tag{19.52}$$

* The statistical justification of this rests on the assumption that the contribution to the entropy is given by

$$\boldsymbol{k}\ln\Omega=\boldsymbol{k}\ln\frac{N!}{N_+!\,N_-!};$$

that is it depends on the number of ways of arranging N_+ objects of one kind and N_- objects of another among N places, *cf.* chap. III, § 9.

where k is the Boltzmann constant. This may be expressed in terms of ϵ, in the form :

$$\frac{S(\epsilon)}{kN}=\frac{S(1)}{kN}-\tfrac{1}{2}(1+\epsilon)\ln(1+\epsilon)-\tfrac{1}{2}(1-\epsilon)\ln(1-\epsilon)+\ln 2. \quad (19.53)$$

From (19.51) and (19.53), neglecting the pV term, we have for the free energy :

$$G(\epsilon)=G(1)+\frac{\omega N}{4}(1-\epsilon^2)+\tfrac{1}{2}NkT(1+\epsilon)\ln(1+\epsilon)$$
$$+\tfrac{1}{2}NkT(1-\epsilon)\ln(1-\epsilon)-NkT\ln 2. \quad (19.54)$$

This equation for the free energy is due to Gorsky* and to Bragg and Williams.† The affinity, corresponding to the parameter ξ, is thus

$$\mathbf{A}=-\frac{\partial G}{\partial \xi}=-\frac{\partial G}{\partial \epsilon}\cdot\frac{1}{N}=\tfrac{1}{2}\omega\epsilon-\tfrac{1}{2}kT\ln\frac{1+\epsilon}{1-\epsilon}. \quad (19.55)$$

Equilibrium is therefore attained when

$$\ln\frac{1+\epsilon}{1-\epsilon}=\frac{\omega\epsilon}{kT}, \quad (19.56)$$

or (*cf.* footnote p. 298).

$$\tanh u=\frac{2kT}{\omega}u, \quad (19.57)$$

where we have put

$$u=\frac{\omega\epsilon}{2kT}. \quad (19.58)$$

Equation (19.57) may be solved graphically in the following simple fashion. If we plot on the same graph

(i) $y=\tanh u$

and (ii) $y=\frac{2kT}{\omega}u$

the solution of (19.57) is given by the point of intersection of these two lines.

The straight line (ii) will depend upon the temperature while (i) is always the same. At a series of temperatures we shall obtain lines such as (1), (2) and (3), fig. 19.5.

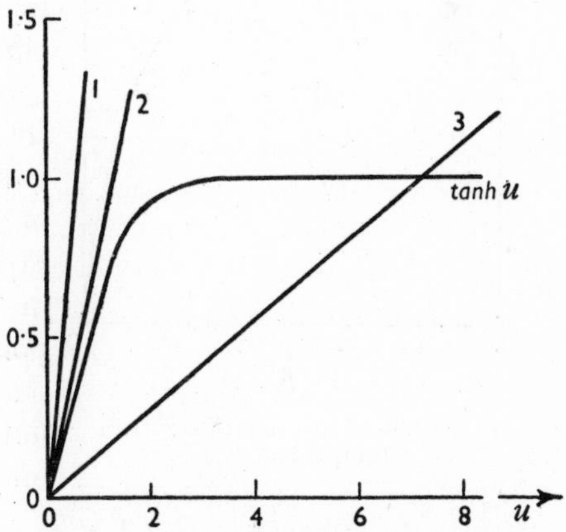

FIG. 19.5. Graphical method for solution of equation. (19.57).

For very high temperatures, therefore, the lines intersect only

* W. Gorsky, *Zeit. Phys.*, **50**, 64 (1928).
† W. L. Bragg and E. J. Williams, *Proc. Roy. Soc.*, **A145**, 699 (1934).

at the origin, and the only solution of (19.57) is $u=0$, that is $\epsilon=0$: at high temperatures the system possesses no long-range order.

At sufficiently low temperatures, we have a line such as (3) for which there are two points of intersection; one at $\epsilon=0$, the other at $\epsilon\neq 0$. To decide which will be observed in practice the stability of the system at these two points must be examined. For this we consider the sign of $\partial \mathbf{A}/\partial\epsilon$, which is given by

$$\frac{\partial \mathbf{A}}{\partial \epsilon}=\frac{\omega}{2}-\frac{kT}{(1+\epsilon)(1-\epsilon)}. \tag{19.59}$$

When $\epsilon=0$

$$\frac{\partial \mathbf{A}}{\partial \epsilon}=\frac{\omega}{2}-kT, \tag{19.60}$$

so that for

$$\left.\begin{array}{ll} T>\omega/2k \text{ we have } \left(\dfrac{\partial \mathbf{A}}{\partial\epsilon}\right)_{\epsilon=0}<0: & \text{the state is stable,} \\ \text{while for} & \\ T<\omega/2k, \quad \left(\dfrac{\partial \mathbf{A}}{\partial\epsilon}\right)_{\epsilon=0}>0: & \text{the state is unstable} \end{array}\right\}. \tag{19.61}$$

Hence the solution $\epsilon=0$, which corresponds to complete absence of long-range order is only stable above the temperature

$$T_\lambda=\omega/2k, \tag{19.62}$$

which we identify with the Curie temperature. At this point $\epsilon=0$ is the solution not only of the equation $\mathbf{A}=0$, but also $\partial\mathbf{A}/\partial\epsilon=0$; it corresponds to the case in which equation (19.56) has two coincident roots. This is shown in fig. 19.5 by line (2) which is a tangent to the curve (1) at the origin.

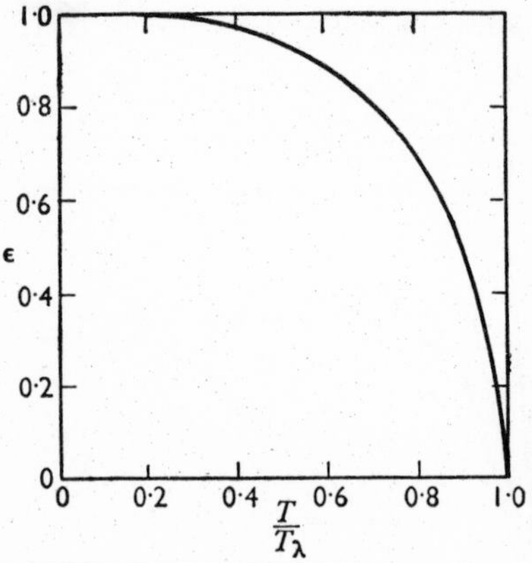

FIG. 19.6. Variation of ϵ with temperature.

Application of this method of solution leads to the equilibrium values of ϵ as a function of T shown in fig. 19.6. We notice especially the rapid variation of ϵ with temperature in the neighbourhood of the Curie point. In the proximity of T_λ we may solve (19.57) by developing the left hand side in a series and retaining only the first two terms*; we obtain

$$\epsilon^2\simeq 3\left(\frac{T}{T_\lambda}\right)^2\frac{T_\lambda-T}{T_\lambda}\simeq 3\,\frac{T_\lambda-T}{T_\lambda}. \tag{19.63}$$

* $\tanh x=x\left(1-\dfrac{x^2}{3}\right)+\ldots$

This formula explains the parabolic shape of the curve near T_λ. To obtain the configurational heat capacity, using (19.17) we require $(\partial H/\partial \epsilon)$ which is obtained by differentiating (19.51) :

$$(\partial H/\partial \epsilon)_{T,p} = -\tfrac{1}{2}\omega \epsilon N. \tag{19.64}$$

Hence

$$C_p^{\text{config}} = -\tfrac{1}{2}\omega \epsilon N \frac{d\epsilon}{dT} = -\tfrac{1}{4}\omega N \frac{d(\epsilon^2)}{dT}. \tag{19.65}$$

In particular, at the lambda point we have, using (19.63) and (19.62)

$$C_p^{\text{config}} = \frac{3}{4}\frac{\omega N}{T_\lambda} = \frac{3}{2} Nk, \tag{19.66}$$

which per mole is

$$c_p^{\text{config}} = \tfrac{3}{2} R. \tag{19.67}$$

The configurational heat capacity calculated on the basis of this model is shown in fig. 19.7 ; it rises steadily up to T_λ and then falls abruptly to zero.

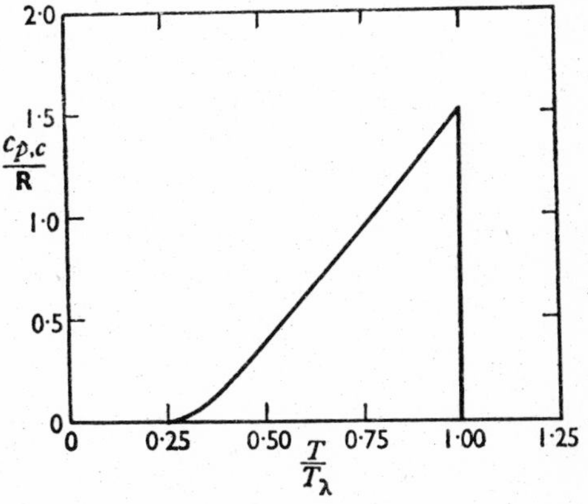

FIG. 19.7. Configurational heat capacity according to the Bragg-Williams model.

The introduction of the co-operative effect into equation (19.17) changes the magnitude of the configurational heat capacity and alters radically the way in which it varies with temperature.

The model which we have discussed represents only the first approximation to a theory of the Curie point, but we cannot deal here with the subject in greater detail.*

7. Influence of Pressure on the Curie Point : Ehrenfest's Formulae.

The Clausius-Clapeyron equation is not limited to ordinary phase changes, but is applicable to any system whose state can be described in terms of the variables T, p, ξ. When applied to the present problem we obtain a formula due to Ehrenfest.†

We have, (19.14), along the equilibrium line at constant ξ,

$$\left(\frac{\partial p}{\partial T}\right)_\xi = \frac{h_{T,p}}{T v_{T,p}}. \tag{19.68}$$

* For a more detailed statistical treatment see especially H. A. Kramers and G. Wannier, *Phys. Rev.*, **60**, 252, 263 (1941) ; L. Onsager, *Phys. Rev.*, **65**, 117 (1944).

† P. Ehrenfest, *Proc. K. Akad. Wetensch*, **36**, 153 (1933).

This may be transformed, using (19.17) and (19.27), into the form :

$$\left(\frac{\partial p}{\partial T}\right)_\xi = \frac{h_{T,p}(\partial\xi/\partial T)_p}{Tv_{T,p}(\partial\xi/\partial T)_p} = \frac{C_p^{\text{config}}}{TV\alpha^{\text{config}}}. \tag{19.69}$$

The ratio $(\partial p/\partial T)_\xi$ is thus determined essentially by the ratio of the configurational heat capacity to the configurational thermal expansion coefficient. This equation may be applied in particular to the case where there is a discontinuity in the heat capacity at the Curie point $\xi=0$, $\epsilon=0$ (*cf.* fig. 19.7). If this discontinuity is written $C_p' - C_p''$, and the corresponding discontinuity in the coefficient of expansion is $\alpha' - \alpha''$, then at the Curie point

$$C_p^{\text{config}} = C_p' - C_p'' \text{ and } \alpha^{\text{config}} = \alpha' - \alpha''. \tag{19.70}$$

Equation (19.69) then takes on the form due to Ehrenfest :

$$\left(\frac{\partial p}{\partial T}\right)_{\xi=0} = \frac{C_p' - C_p''}{T_\lambda V_\lambda(\alpha' - \alpha'')}. \tag{19.71}$$

A second formula, also derived by Ehrenfest, is obtained by considering the identity, valid for all systems in equilibrium described by the variables T, p, ξ :

$$\left(\frac{\partial p}{\partial T}\right)_\xi = \frac{(\partial\xi/\partial T)_p}{(\partial\xi/\partial p)_T}. \tag{19.72}$$

Multiplying top and bottom by $(\partial V/\partial\xi)_{T,p}$, and making use of (19.26) and (19.27) we find

$$\left(\frac{\partial p}{\partial T}\right)_\xi = \frac{\alpha^{\text{config}}}{\kappa^{\text{config}}}. \tag{19.73}$$

In particular at the Curie point

$$\left(\frac{\partial p}{\partial T}\right)_{\xi=0} = \frac{\alpha' - \alpha''}{\kappa' - \kappa''}. \tag{19.74}$$

This is the second of Ehrenfest's formulae.

To obtain (19.73) we have assumed only that the derivatives $\partial\xi/\partial p$ and $\partial\xi/\partial T$ exist ; these derivatives are given by equations (19.14) and have well-determined values provided that $a_{T,p} \neq 0$. The above form derived from the Clausius-Clapeyron equation cannot be applied to the case of an ordinary phase change since we then have

$$\left(\frac{\partial G}{\partial\xi}\right)_{T,p} = -\mathbf{A} = \mu''(T,p) - \mu'(T,p)$$

whence $a_{T,p} = 0$.

In all other cases, however, (19.73) is valid. We may note finally that instead of multiplying (19.72) by $(\partial V/\partial\xi)_{T,p}$, we could have multiplied by any expression of the form $(\partial X/\partial \xi)_{T,p}$ where X is an arbitrary function of T, p, ξ. For example, if we multiply by $(\partial H/\partial \xi)_{T,p}$ we have, using (2.17) and (19.17)

$$\left(\frac{\partial p}{\partial T}\right)_\xi = -\frac{h_{T,p}(\partial \xi/\partial T)_p}{h_{T,p}(\partial \xi/\partial p)_T} = \frac{C_p^{\text{config}}}{h_T^{\text{config}}}, \tag{19.75}$$

where h_T^{config} is the excess of the heat required to change the pressure at constant temperature, over the heat required at constant T and ξ (*cf.* 2.13). Other analogous equations can be derived in a similar fashion.

8. Transformations of higher order.

Let us now consider a *closed* system which is at least bivariant. Then, apart from the case of indifferent states, we can, from Duhem's theorem (*cf.* chap. XIII, §§ 6 and 7), describe all *equilibrium* states of the system in terms of two variables, T and p. We have

$$\left(\frac{\partial G}{\partial T}\right)_p = -S\,; \quad \left(\frac{\partial G}{\partial p}\right)_T = V. \tag{19.76}$$

If we consider an equilibrium transformation of the system, then if this is an ordinary phase change, at least one of these first order derivatives of G must exhibit a discontinuity. For this reason ordinary phase changes are called *transformations of the first order* (Ehrenfest).

In the Bragg-Williams model studied in § 6, not only G (given by 19.54) but also S and V change continuously on passage through the Curie point. On the other hand the second derivatives

$$\frac{\partial^2 G}{\partial T^2} = -\frac{\partial S}{\partial T} = -\frac{C_p}{T}\,; \quad \frac{\partial^2 G}{\partial p\,\partial T} = \frac{\partial V}{\partial T} = V\alpha, \tag{19.77}$$

exhibit discontinuities. For this reason the lambda point phenomenon is said to be associated with a *transformation of second order*.

In the same way it is possible to define transformations of the third, fourth or higher orders.

9. Equilibrium Changes at Constant Mass.

If we have a two-phase one-component system and we carry out an equilibrium change during the course of which the masses of the two phases remain unchanged, then the change is called a constant-mass equilibrium change.

We have from (19.14)

$$\left(\frac{\partial p}{\partial T}\right)_{A=0,\xi} = \frac{\Delta_{\prime}^{\prime\prime} h}{T\Delta_{\prime}^{\prime\prime} v}, \tag{19.78}$$

where we now imply by constant ξ, that the relative amounts of substance in the two phases remain constant. However in the system considered the index ξ can be deleted on the left-hand side since at equilibrium p depends only on T; in other words the condition $\mathbf{A}(T, p, \xi) = 0$ reduces to

$$\mu'(T, p) = \mu''(T, p), \tag{19.79}$$

and is independent of ξ.

For each of the phases there is an equation of the form

$$dV' = \left(\frac{\partial V'}{\partial T}\right)_{p,\xi} dT + \left(\frac{\partial V'}{\partial p}\right)_{T,\xi} dp + \left(\frac{\partial V'}{\partial \xi}\right)_{T,p} d\xi, \tag{19.80}$$

so that for an equilibrium change ($\mathbf{A} = 0$) at constant ξ:

$$\begin{aligned}\left(\frac{\partial V'}{\partial T}\right)_{\xi,\mathbf{A}=0} &= \left(\frac{\partial V'}{\partial T}\right)_{p,\xi} + \left(\frac{\partial V'}{\partial p}\right)_{T,\xi} \left(\frac{\partial p}{\partial T}\right)_{\mathbf{A}=0} \\ &= \left(\frac{\partial V'}{\partial T}\right)_{p,\xi} + \left(\frac{\partial V'}{\partial p}\right)_{T,\xi} \frac{\Delta_{\prime}^{\prime\prime} h}{T \Delta_{\prime}^{\prime\prime} v}.\end{aligned} \tag{19.81}$$

On dividing this expression by n', the number of moles in the first phase, we have:

$$\left(\frac{\partial v'}{\partial T}\right)_{\xi,\mathbf{A}=0} = \left(\frac{\partial v'}{\partial T}\right)_{p,\xi} + \frac{\Delta_{\prime}^{\prime\prime} h}{T \Delta_{\prime}^{\prime\prime} v} \left(\frac{\partial v'}{\partial p}\right)_{T,\xi}; \tag{19.82}$$

while for the second phase similarly:

$$\left(\frac{\partial v''}{\partial T}\right)_{\xi,\mathbf{A}=0} = \left(\frac{\partial v''}{\partial T}\right)_{p,\xi} + \frac{\Delta_{\prime}^{\prime\prime} h}{T \Delta_{\prime}^{\prime\prime} v} \left(\frac{\partial v''}{\partial p}\right)_{T,\xi}. \tag{19.83}$$

These equations may be applied for example to the case of liquid-vapour equilibrium. If we assume that the vapour behaves as a perfect gas, and that we can neglect the molar volume of the liquid in comparison with the gas, then (19.83) simplifies. For then

$$\left(\frac{\partial v^g}{\partial T}\right)_{\xi,p} = \frac{\mathbf{R}}{p} = \frac{v^g}{T},$$

$$\left(\frac{\partial v^g}{\partial p}\right)_{T,\xi} = -\frac{\mathbf{R}T}{p^2} = -\frac{(v^g)^2}{\mathbf{R}T},$$

and also

$$\Delta_{\prime}^{\prime\prime} v = \Delta_e v = v^g - v^l \simeq v^g \simeq \frac{\mathbf{R}T}{p}.$$

We have therefore:

$$\left(\frac{\partial v^g}{\partial T}\right)_{\xi,\mathbf{A}=0} = \frac{v^g}{T}\left(1 - \frac{\Delta_e h}{\mathbf{R}T}\right). \tag{19.84}$$

For all temperatures sufficiently far from the critical temperature, we have in general

$$\Delta_e h \gg \mathbf{R} T, \tag{19.85}$$

so that from (19.84)

$$\left(\frac{\partial v^g}{\partial T}\right)_{\xi, \mathbf{A}=0} < 0. \tag{19.86}$$

Hence the molar volume of the vapour phase decreases with increase of temperature ; that is to say that *the density of the saturated vapour increases with temperature.* On the other hand, the molar volume of the liquid increases with temperature, or its density diminishes.

Finally we consider the heat capacity in the course of an equilibrium transformation at constant mass. By virtue of (2.13), (19.78) and (4.42) we have for such a transformation

$$C_{\xi, \mathbf{A}=0} = \left(\frac{\partial Q}{\partial T}\right)_{\xi, \mathbf{A}=0} = h_{T,\xi} \left(\frac{\partial p}{\partial T}\right)_{\xi, \mathbf{A}=0} + C_{p,\xi}$$

$$= -\left(\frac{\partial V}{\partial T}\right)_{p,\xi} \frac{\Delta_l^{\prime\prime} h}{\Delta_l^{\prime\prime} v} + C_{p,\xi}, \tag{19.87}$$

This equation may be applied to the calculation of the heat capacity of each of the two phases in a liquid-vapour system. These heat capacities are called the *heat capacities at saturation.*

We have (*cf.* 19.82)

$$c^l_{\xi, \mathbf{A}=0} = c^l_{p,\xi} - \frac{\Delta_l^{\prime\prime} h}{\Delta_l^{\prime\prime} v} \left(\frac{\partial v^l}{\partial T}\right)_{p,\xi}. \tag{19.88}$$

$$c^g_{\xi, \mathbf{A}=0} = c^g_{p,\xi} - \frac{\Delta_l^{\prime\prime} h}{\Delta_l^{\prime\prime} v} \left(\frac{\partial v^g}{\partial T}\right)_{p,\xi}. \tag{19.89}$$

For the condensed phase $\partial v^l/\partial T$ is small (*cf.* chap. XII, § 1) so that

$$c^l_{\xi, \mathbf{A}=0} \simeq c^l_{p,\xi}. \tag{19.90}$$

On the other hand, for the vapour phase, the second term may become the more important. Thus for water vapour at 100 °C,* we have (using the gram as unit of mass)

$$\underline{c}^g_{p,\xi} = 0{\cdot}47 \text{ cal./deg. g.}$$

$$\Delta_e \underline{h} = 538{\cdot}7 \text{ cal./g.}$$

$$\underline{v}^g = 1674{\cdot}0 \text{ cm.}^3\text{/g.}$$

$$\underline{v}^l = 1 \text{ cm.}^3\text{/g.}$$

$$(\partial \underline{v}^g/\partial T)_{p,\xi} = 4{\cdot}81 \text{ cm.}^3\text{/g. deg.,}$$

* After M. Planck, *Thermodynamik*, 6th Edn., p. 154 (Berlin, 1921). *Treatise on Thermodynamics* 3rd Ed. (London, 1927). *Cf.* also Schottky, Ulich and Wagner, [42], p. 505.

so that

$$\underline{c}^{g}_{\xi, \mathbf{A}=0} = \quad 0{\cdot}47 - 1{\cdot}55 = -1{\cdot}08 \text{ cal./g. deg.}$$

To raise the temperature at constant ξ, that is to say without allowing further evaporation to take place, the system must be compressed. The negative value of the specific heat simply means that the heat evolved by the gas on compression at constant temperature is greater than that which must be absorbed to raise its temperature.

CHAPTER XX

SOLUTIONS

1. General.

A solution is, by definition, a condensed phase (liquid or solid) composed of several components. We must stress at the outset that, even in very dilute solutions, it is incorrect to compare the state of the dissolved components with that of molecules in the gas state.* Each dissolved molecule is subject to strong forces exerted on it by solvent molecules. This point is clearly illustrated by the fact that the heat of solution of a solid is usually very close to the heat of fusion, and differs considerably from the heat of vaporization. For example, for naphthalene the heat of solution in a series of solvents varies from 4,180 to 5,110 cal./mole. The heat of fusion is 4,570 cal./mole while the heat of vaporization is 9,700 cal./mole.

The fundamental difference between the dissolved state and the gaseous state is also apparent if we compare the solubility of a substance with its vapour pressure at the same temperature. Thus, for example, it is possible to dissolve 75 g. of hydroquinone in a litre of water at 20 °C ; that is a nearly 0·59 molar solution. At the same temperature the vapour pressure of hydroquinone is of the order of 10^{-6} mm. Hg., which corresponds to a gaseous concentration of about $0{\cdot}59 \times 10^{-10}$ mole/litre.

2. Thermodynamic Classification of Solutions.

In view of the wide variety of behaviour exhibited by solutions it is important to classify them according to their thermodynamic properties. On this basis we distinguish between *ideal solutions* and *non-ideal solutions*.

An ideal solution is a special case of an ideal system as defined in chapter VII. The chemical potentials are thus of the form given by (7.1), namely

$$\mu_i = \mu_i^{\ominus}(T, p) + \boldsymbol{R}T \ln x_i. \tag{20.1}$$

If the various substances composing the solution are present in concentrations which are of the same order of magnitude, there is no distinction between solvent and solute. On the other hand, if one of them

* *Cf.* the work of K. L. Wolf and his school ; *cf.* H. G. Trieschmann, *Z. physik. Chem.*, *B*39, 109 (1938).

is at a concentration much larger than the others, then it is called the solvent. We then employ the index 1 to refer to the solvent and 2, 3 ... to refer to the various solutes.

It is found experimentally that all sufficiently dilute solutions, when the mole fractions of all solutes are sufficiently near to zero, behave ideally. Statistical mechanics leads to the same conclusion, (*cf.* § 5).

The concentration at which a particular solution begins to exhibit appreciable deviations from ideality depends very largely upon the nature of the substances involved.

Thus in the case of strong electrolytes the deviations are important even in very dilute solutions, and this is evidently related to the long range of action of electrostatic forces. On the other hand in some solutions, such as chlorobenzene + bromobenzene, where the two molecules are of closely similar chemical structure, the solutions deviate very little from ideality over the whole concentration range. Solutions which remain ideal at all concentrations are called *perfect solutions.* We shall return in the next paragraph to a consideration of the conditions which must be satisfied for a solution to be perfect.

We now examine the way in which $\mu_i^{\ominus}(T, p)$ depends upon the pressure. Let us define for each component a compressibility coefficient κ_i^{id} :

$$\kappa_i^{\text{id}} = -\frac{1}{v_i^{\text{id}}}\left(\frac{\partial v_i^{\text{id}}}{\partial p}\right)_T, \qquad (20.2)$$

where v_i^{id} is the partial molar volume of i in an ideal solution. To a first approximation we can consider κ_i^{id} as independent of pressure, as we did when dealing with a one-component condensed phase (*cf.* 12.10). Hence

$$v_i^{\text{id}} = v_i^{\text{id}}(T, 0)(1 - \kappa_i^{\text{id}} p),$$

where $v_i^{\text{id}}(T, 0)$ is the partial molar volume at temperature T, of i in the ideal solution extrapolated to zero pressure.

Equation (7.21) then gives us

$$\left(\frac{\partial \mu_i^{\ominus}(T, p)}{\partial p}\right)_T = v_i^{\text{id}}(T, 0)(1 - \kappa_i^{\text{id}} p)$$

whence on integration

$$\mu_i^{\ominus}(T, p) = \mu_i^{\dagger}(T) + p v_i^{\text{id}}(T, 0)(1 - \tfrac{1}{2}\kappa_i^{\text{id}} p). \qquad (20.3)$$

If we now compare equations (10.35), (10.36), (20.1) and (20.3) we see that the chemical potentials in a mixture of perfect gases, and in an ideal solution, depend in the same way on the mole fractions, but in very different ways upon the applied pressure. Both systems are ideal, but the functional dependence of $\mu_i^{\ominus}(T, p)$ on p is very different in the two cases.

In the case of non-ideal solutions, we write, in accordance with (7.63), the chemical potentials in the form

$$\mu_i = \mu_i^{\ominus}(T, p) + \boldsymbol{R}T \ln x_i \gamma_i \tag{20.4}$$

where γ_i is the activity coefficient of component i. We must bear in mind that the values of $\mu_i^{\ominus}(T, p)$ and γ_i depend upon the choice of ideal reference system (*cf.* chap. XXI, § 3).

Since all solutions become ideal when sufficiently dilute, we often choose as ideal reference state the state of infinite dilution of the solution. We then have

$$\gamma_i \to 1 \tag{20.5}$$

as

$$x_1 \to 1 \tag{20.6}$$

and

$$x_2, x_3 \ldots x_c \to 0.$$

As we shall see, however, in paragraph 3 of chapter XXI it is sometimes convenient to choose other ideal reference states. Activity coefficients are of particular interest because they enable us when dealing with non-ideal solutions to retain a simple formal similarity with the equations valid for ideal or perfect systems.

The general condition for ideality is easily seen by comparing (20.1) and (20.4):

$$\gamma_i(T, p, x_2 \ldots x_c) = 1, \quad i = 1, 2 \ldots c. \tag{20.7}$$

Instead of characterizing deviations from ideality of the solvent by its activity coefficient γ_1, it is often advantageous to introduce the *osmotic coefficient* (ϕ) of Bjerrum and Guggenheim, and to write the chemical potential in the form

$$\mu_1 = \mu_1^0(T, p) + \phi \boldsymbol{R}T \ln x_1. \tag{20.8}$$

Comparing this with (20.4) we see that

$$\phi \ln x_1 = \ln x_1 \gamma_1 \tag{20.9}$$

or

$$\phi - 1 = \ln \gamma_1 / \ln x_1. \tag{20.9'}$$

By employing the osmotic coefficient (which incidentally could also be called the *boiling point* or *freezing point coefficient*) we lose some of the formal resemblance to the equations of ideal solutions, but on the other hand ϕ is much more sensitive to deviations from ideality. Thus in dilute solutions x_1 is close to unity; and under these conditions γ_1 approaches unity (*cf.* 20.5, 20.6) and $\ln \gamma_1$ is almost zero. On the other hand division of $\ln \gamma_1$ by $\ln x_1$, which is also very small may lead to quite large values of $\phi - 1$.

3. Fundamental Properties of Perfect Solutions.

A solution is described as *perfect* if equation (20.1) is valid for all values of the mole fractions. If in (20.1) we put $x_i = 1$, we see that $\mu_i^{\ominus}(T, p)$ is simply the chemical potential of pure component i at the same temperature and pressure *i.e.* $\mu_i^0(T, p)$. The term $\boldsymbol{R}T \ln x_i$ thus corresponds to the change in chemical potential accompanying mixing of the perfect solution.

The Gibbs free energy per mole of a binary mixture is given by

$$g = x_1\mu_1 + x_2\mu_2 = g^0 + \boldsymbol{R}Tx_1 \ln x_1 + \boldsymbol{R}Tx_2 \ln x_2, \tag{20.10}$$

where g^0 is the mean molar free energy of n_1 moles of component 1 and n_2 moles of component 2, taken separately at temperature T, and pressure p :

$$g^0 = \frac{n_1 g_1^0 + n_2 g_2^0}{n_1 + n_2}. \tag{20.10'}$$

Thus g^M the increase of g which results from mixing the components 1 and 2, or the Gibbs *free energy of mixing* is

$$g^M = \boldsymbol{R}Tx_1 \ln x_1 + \boldsymbol{R}Tx_2 \ln x_2. \tag{20.11}$$

This simple form for the free energy of mixing is a characteristic of perfect solutions. The *enthalpy of mixing* corresponding to (20.11) is zero since (*cf.* 4.32)

$$-\frac{h^M}{T^2} = \frac{\partial\left(\frac{g^M}{T}\right)}{\partial T} = 0. \tag{20.12}$$

Thus the mixing of two components to form a perfect solution takes place at constant enthalpy. This means that if the components are mixed at constant T and p, no absorption or evolution of heat occurs. For since p is constant, the first law gives, *cf.* (2.15),

$$dQ = dH\,; \tag{20.13}$$

and if dH is zero, so is dQ. Alternatively if we carry out the mixing at constant pressure, but *adiabatically*, then no temperature change occurs.

Furthermore, if we consider the variation of volume of the system consequent upon mixing we find that this change v^M, the *volume of mixing* is zero for perfect solutions. This follows from

$$v^M = \frac{\partial g^M}{\partial p} = 0. \tag{20.14}$$

The volume of a perfect solution is thus equal to the volume occupied by n_1 moles of component 1 and n_2 moles of component 2 taken separately at temperature T and pressure p. That is, the process of *mixing is accompanied by neither an expansion nor contraction.* If we write $v_1^0(T, p)$ and $v_2^0(T, p)$ as the molar volumes of the pure components 1 and 2, then the mean molar volume of the solution is

$$v = x_1 v_1^0 + x_2 v_2^0. \quad (20.15)$$

The molar volume is thus a linear function of mole fraction. Fig. 20.1 shows that this is so, for example, in mixtures of *n*-propyl acetate and ethyl propionate at 20 °C.*

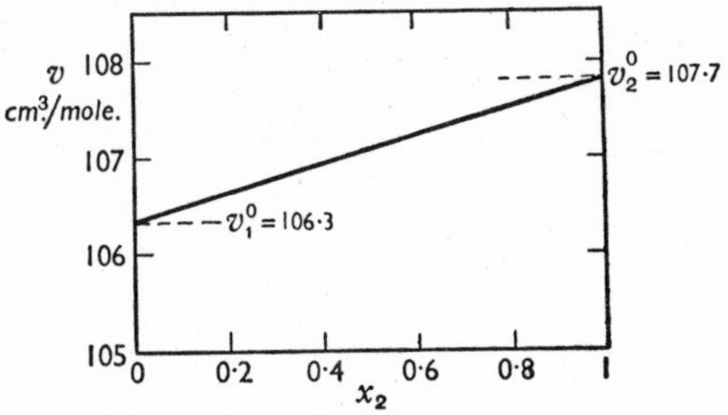

FIG. 20.1. Molar volume as function of composition for the system ethyl propionate (1) + propyl acetate (2) at 20 °C.*

From equations (20.12) and (20.14) it follows that the *energy of mixing*, which is equal to (*cf.* 3.12)

$$u^M = h^M - pv^M \quad (20.16)$$

must also be zero.

Finally we consider the *entropy of mixing*, which is obtained by differentiating (20.11) with respect to temperature (*cf.* 4.29),

$$s^M = -\frac{\partial g^M}{\partial T} = -x_1 \mathbf{R} \ln x_1 - x_2 \mathbf{R} \ln x_2. \quad (20.17)$$

The entropy of mixing for perfect solutions thus has a simple form identical with that for perfect gases (*cf.* 10.32).

The above properties enable us to form some idea as to the conditions which given molecules must satisfy in order that they shall form perfect solutions.

The internal energy of a solution is very closely related to the interactions between the molecules. The fact that the energy of mixing is zero, that is to say that the internal energy is unaffected by the mixing process, means that the interactions between the different molecules in the solution must be equal to the arithmetic mean of those between the molecules in the two pure liquids (*cf.* chap. XXIV § 4).

Next we consider the entropy of mixing (20.17). To interpret this equation, we must make use of the Boltzmann formula relating the number of configurations accessible to the system to the entropy (*cf.* chap. III, § 9). If the number of accessible configurations increases by a factor Ω as a result of the mixing, then the entropy of mixing is given by

$$S^M = \mathbf{k} \ln \Omega. \quad (20.18)$$

* *Cf.* Timmermans [45], p. 121.

To evaluate Ω for a binary solution, let us consider a particular model in which we imagine the molecules in the solution to occupy lattice points in a three-dimensional lattice. Suppose there are N sites and that each molecule occupies one site. Ω is then the number of ways of arranging the N_1 molecules of 1 and the N_2 molecules of 2 on the $N = N_1 + N_2$ sites. This number is equal to the number of distinct combinations

$$\Omega = \frac{(N_1 + N_2)!}{N_1!\, N_2!} \cdot \tag{20.19}$$

Division by $N_1!$ and $N_2!$ is necessary because it is impossible to distinguish the N_1 molecules 1 among themselves, and the N_2 molecules 2 among themselves. If we make use of Stirling's approximation that when x is large

$$x! = \left(\frac{x}{\mathrm{e}}\right)^x \tag{20.20}$$

where e is the base of natural logarithms, the entropy of mixing deduced from (20.18) is

$$\begin{aligned} S^M &= -\boldsymbol{k} N_1 \ln \frac{N_1}{N} - \boldsymbol{k} N_2 \ln \frac{N_2}{N} \\ &= -\boldsymbol{R} n_1 \ln x_1 - \boldsymbol{R} n_2 \ln x_2. \end{aligned} \tag{20.21}$$

The entropy of mixing per mole is thus

$$s^M = S^M/(n_1 + n_2) = -\boldsymbol{R} x_1 \ln x_1 - \boldsymbol{R} x_2 \ln x_2. \tag{20.22}$$

which is precisely the expression for the entropy of mixing derived above for a perfect solution.

The above reasoning is instructive from two points of view. In the first place, to obtain (20.19) we have to assume that molecules 1 and 2 are of approximately the same size, otherwise they would not each occupy a single lattice point in the liquid. If, for example, the molecules of kind 1 occupy three places, while molecules 2 occupy one place, then the combinatory factor (20.19) must be replaced by an expression of a different form which leads to a different entropy of mixing (*cf.* chap. XXV).

A solution can only be perfect if the molecules of the various components are sufficiently alike from the point of view of the molecular interactions which they exert on one another, and from the point of view of their shapes and sizes. These general considerations are confirmed in practice, for we find that the solutions most nearly perfect are those consisting of mixtures of isotopes or of optically active isomers * The laws of perfect solutions are thus limiting laws which

* *Cf.* Timmermans [45], chaps. I to IV.

are obeyed more closely, the greater the similarity with regard to size, shape and energy, between the components.

The statistical reasoning given above is also interesting from a second standpoint. We may ask ourselves why the gas constant $\boldsymbol{R}$ appears both in the equation for the chemical potentials of perfect gases, and in that for a perfect solution. The fact that there exist also perfect solid solutions (*e.g.* Cu + Ni alloys) dismisses any hypothesis that this constant has any fundamental connection with the gaseous or liquid states. The statistical approach shows that the constant $\boldsymbol{R}$ comes from the Boltzmann constant in equation (20.18). This is a perfectly general statistical formula quite independent of any hypothesis regarding the physical state of the system, and it is through this that $\boldsymbol{R}$ appears not only in the formulae for perfect gases, but for liquid and solid solutions also.

Finally we may observe that we have defined perfect solutions through equation (20.1) for the chemical potentials, and from this we have established the properties discussed in this paragraph. Conversely, for a solution to be perfect, all these properties must be satisfied *simultaneously*. Thus it is not sufficient that the mixture can be made without heat effect, and without change in volume. The entropy of mixing must also have the form (20.17). Indeed later on we shall discuss solutions (*athermal solutions*) for which the deviations from ideality arise entirely from the entropy term.

4. Perfect Solutions and Ideal Solutions.

Just as for all ideal systems (*cf.* 7.20 and 7.21), the partial molar enthalpies h_i^{id} and the partial molar volumes v_i^{id} of perfect or ideal solutions are dependent only on T and p. We then have for the mean molar enthalpy and volume

$$h = \sum_i x_i h_i^{\mathrm{id}} \quad \text{and} \quad v = \sum_i x_i v_i^{\mathrm{id}}. \tag{20.23}$$

For *perfect solutions* these formulae are valid for all values of the mole fractions, and in particular for $x_i = 1$, $x_j = 0$ $(i \neq j)$. It follows then that h_i^{id} and v_i^{id} are equal to the molar enthalpy, h_i^0, and molar volume, v_i^0, respectively of the pure component.

On the other hand for a solution which is only ideal when it is sufficiently dilute, (20.23) is only exact when x_1 is close to unity. For the solvent in a very dilute solution

$$h_1^{\mathrm{id}} = h_1^0\,; \quad v_1^{\mathrm{id}} = v_1^0 \tag{20.24}$$

while for the substances in solution we have in general

$$h_s^{\mathrm{id}} \neq h_s^0\,; \quad v_s^{\mathrm{id}} \neq v_s^0, \quad s = 2, 3 \ldots c. \tag{20.25}$$

This difference between perfect solutions and ideal dilute solutions is a consequence of the fact that the enthalpy and volume of mixing, which are both zero for perfect solutions, are not necessarily zero for ideal solutions. For example, if we consider for simplicity a dilute binary solution, the enthalpy before mixing is

$$H^0 = n_1 h_1^0 + n_2 h_2^0, \tag{20.26}$$

while that of the same number of molecules in solution is

$$H = n_1 h_1^0 + n_2 h_2^{\mathrm{id}}. \tag{20.27}$$

It follows that

$$h^M = \frac{H - H^0}{n_1 + n_2} = x_2 (h_2^{\mathrm{id}} - h_2^0). \tag{20.28}$$

Equation (20.13) then shows that the formation of the solution from the pure components at constant temperature and pressure is accompanied by a thermal effect given by (20.28) (*cf.* also chap. XXIV, § 2). In the same way the volume of mixing is given by

$$v^M = x_2 (v_2^{\mathrm{id}} - v_2^0). \tag{20.29}$$

Thus the formation of an ideal dilute solution is in general accompanied by a contraction or expansion. But despite this volume change, and despite the thermal effects, the mean molar enthalpy and volume both vary linearly with mole fraction, in accordance with (20.23), within the range of ideal behaviour.

In fig. 20.2 we show the molar volume of the system ethyl acetate + aniline at −9 °C. A solution of aniline in ethyl acetate up to a mole fraction of 0·05 can be regarded, as far as the behaviour of the density is concerned, as an ideal solution. The same is also true for a dilute solution of ethyl acetate in aniline up to a mole fraction of ethyl acetate of 0·075.

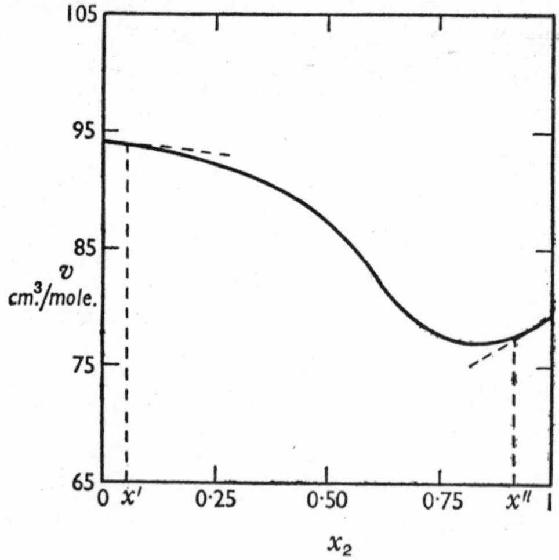

Fig. 20.2. Molar volume as function of composition for the system ethyl acetate (1) + aniline (2) at −9 °C.

Since the partial molar volumes and enthalpies of the components of an ideal solution are independent of mole fraction, it follows that the mixing of two ideal solutions (of the same solutes in the same solvent) takes place without any thermal effect and without volume change.

It is also worth stressing that since the entropy of an ideal dilute solution has the form

$$s = [x_1 s_1^0 + x_2 s_2^{\ominus}] - \boldsymbol{R}[x_1 \ln x_1 + x_2 \ln x_2], \tag{20.30}$$

the entropy of mixing of the two pure components to form an ideal dilute solution is not equal to the so-called " ideal entropy of mixing ", (20.17), but includes an extra term $x_2(s_2^{\ominus} - s_2^0)$. The " ideal entropy of mixing " refers to the mixing of pure component 1 with a hypothetical substance whose molar entropy $s_2^{\ominus}$ is equal to the partial molar entropy of 2 in the real solution extrapolated to infinite dilution.

The conclusions arrived at in this paragraph are all of course a direct consequence of the definition of ideal systems in which $\mu^{\ominus}$, $h^{\ominus}$, $s^{\ominus}$, $v^{\ominus}$, etc. are not necessarily identified with the corresponding quantities for the pure components.

5. Statistical Interpretation of the Limiting Laws of Very Dilute Solutions.

We have already remarked that all solutions when sufficiently dilute become ideal. This limiting behaviour can be interpreted by statistical considerations analogous to those employed in § 3 in the interpretation of the properties of perfect solutions.*

If we consider a sufficiently dilute solution, we can neglect the interactions between the solute molecules, so that each solute molecule 2 will contribute the same quantity to the energy of the system which will be of the form :

$$U = N_1 \epsilon_1(T, p) + N_2 \epsilon_2(T, p). \tag{20.31}$$

Let us now consider the number of configurations Ω. In a sufficiently dilute solution this number will be equal to the number of ways of arranging the N_2 molecules in the solution. If $\Phi(N_1, N_2)$ is the number of arrangements assuming the individual N_2 molecules to be distinguishable, then

$$\Omega = \frac{\Phi(N_1, N_2)}{N_2!}, \tag{20.32}$$

where the division by $N_2!$ is necessary since by considering the molecules 2 to be distinguishable we count $N_2!$ times too many configurations.

Let us suppose that there are $B(N_1)$ possible configurations for any one molecule of kind 2. Now since there are very few molecules 2 compared with the number of kind 1, the number of arrangements of the N_2 molecules of kind 2 will be

$$\Phi(N_1, N_2) = [B(N_1)]^{N_2}. \tag{20.33}$$

* A. J. Staverman, *Rec. trav. chim.*, **60**, 76 (1941) ; J. J. Hermans, *Colloid Science*, vol. II, (New York, Amsterdam, London, 1949), chap. III.

We may now substitute this value of Φ in (20.32) and use (20.18) and (20.20) to obtain the entropy of mixing

$$\frac{S^M}{k}=N_2 \ln B - N_2(\ln N_2 - 1). \tag{20.34}$$

The total entropy is therefore

$$S=N_1 s_1^0 + N_2 s_2^0 + kN_2 \ln B - kN_2(\ln N_2 - 1). \tag{20.35}$$

To obtain the free energy we neglect the pV term, which is small for condensed phases, and obtain

$$G=N_1(\epsilon_1 - Ts_1^0)+N_2(\epsilon_2 - Ts_2^0) - kTN_2 \ln B + kTN_2(\ln N_2 - 1), \tag{20.36}$$

and for the chemical potentials per molecule

$$\left.\begin{aligned} \frac{\mu_1}{\mathbf{N}}&=\frac{\partial G}{\partial N_1}=\epsilon_1 - Ts_1^0 - kTN_2\frac{\partial \ln B}{\partial N_1}, \\ \frac{\mu_2}{\mathbf{N}}&=\frac{\partial G}{\partial N_2}=\epsilon_2 - Ts_2^0 + kT \ln \frac{N_2}{B}. \end{aligned}\right\} \tag{20.37}$$

We notice that, since B represents the number of sites which can be occupied by a single molecule of 2 among the N_1 molecules of solvent, this number must be proportional to the extent of the phase, and therefore to N_1.

Hence

$$B(N_1)=N_1\beta(T, p), \tag{20.38}$$

which on substitution in (20.37) gives, for one mole,

$$\left.\begin{aligned} \mu_1&=\mu_1^0(T, p) - \boldsymbol{R}T\frac{N_2}{N_1}, \\ \mu_2&=\mu_2^{\ominus}(T, p)+\boldsymbol{R}T \ln \frac{N_2}{N_1}, \end{aligned}\right\} \tag{20.39}$$

where

$$\mu_2^{\ominus}=\mu_2^0 - \boldsymbol{R}T \ln \beta. \tag{20.40}$$

Now since the solution is very dilute we have

$$\frac{N_2}{N_1}\approx x_2 \approx -\ln(1-x_2)= -\ln x_1$$

so that to this approximation, in a sufficiently dilute solution, the chemical potentials are of the form

$$\begin{aligned} \mu_1&=\mu_1^0(T, p)+\boldsymbol{R}T \ln x_1 \\ \mu_2&=\mu_2^{\ominus}(T, p)+\boldsymbol{R}T \ln x_2. \end{aligned} \tag{20.41}$$

We thus obtain on this model the laws of ideal solutions, and conclude that all solutions, when sufficiently dilute behave as ideal solutions.

6. Concentration Scales.

As an alternative to the use of mole fractions, we may express concentrations in terms of the *weight fractions* :

$$w_i = \frac{m_i}{m}, \tag{20.42}$$

which must, of course, satisfy :

$$\sum_i w_i = 1. \tag{20.42'}$$

The transformation from mole fractions to weight fractions or conversely, is made using the equations

$$w_i = \frac{m_i}{m} = \frac{n_i M_i}{\sum_i n_i M_i} = \frac{x_i M_i}{\Sigma x_i M_i}; \tag{20.43}$$

$$x_i = \frac{n_i}{n} = \frac{m_i / M_i}{\sum_i (m_i / M_i)} = \frac{w_i}{M_i \sum_i (w_i / M_i)}. \tag{20.44}$$

In particular for a binary mixture

$$w_2 = \frac{x_2}{\frac{M_1}{M_2} + x_2\left(1 - \frac{M_1}{M_2}\right)}; \quad x_2 = \frac{w_2}{\frac{M_2}{M_1} + w_2\left(1 - \frac{M_2}{M_1}\right)}. \tag{20.45}$$

An interesting property relating to mole fractions and weight fractions appears if we apply (20.43) and (20.44) to a two-phase system. It follows that *if the mole fractions of i are the same in the two phases, then the weight fractions are also equal.* In other words, for each of the components

if $\quad x_i' = x_i'' \quad (i = 1, \dots c)$

then $\quad w_i' = w_i'' \quad (i = 1, \dots c),$

and conversely.

Other concentration scales, which are of particular application to dilute solutions are the molar concentration and the molality.

The *molar concentration* of a solute s is defined as

$$c_s = \frac{n_s}{V} = \frac{n_s}{\sum_i n_i v_i} = \frac{x_s}{x_1 v_1 + \sum_s x_s v_s}. \tag{20.46}$$

In a very dilute solution x_1 is close to 1 while v_1 is close to $v_1^0(T, p)$ while all the x_s are small. We thus have approximately

$$c_s \simeq \frac{x_s}{v_1^0}. \tag{20.47}$$

Inserting x_s from this equation into (20.4) we have

$$\mu_s = \mu_s^c(T, p) + \boldsymbol{R}T \ln c_s \gamma_s, \tag{20.48}$$

where we have substituted

$$\mu_s^c(T, p) = \mu_s^{\ominus}(T, p) + \boldsymbol{R}T \ln v_1^0(T, p). \tag{20.49}$$

The *molality* m_s of a solute s is defined as the number of moles of s dissolved in 1000 g. of solvent. If a solution contains n_s moles of solute and n_1 of solvent, then the mass of solvent is $n_1 M_1$ g. There are therefore $n_s/n_1 M_1 \times 1000$ moles of s per kilogramme of solvent.

$$\mathrm{m}_s = \frac{1000\, n_s}{n_1 M_1} = \frac{1000\, x_s}{x_1 M_1}. \tag{20.50}$$

In very dilute solutions $x_1 \approx 1$, whence

$$\mathrm{m}_s \simeq 1000 \frac{x_s}{M_1}. \tag{20.51}$$

The chemical potential of a solute can be expressed in terms of molality

$$\mu_s = \mu_s^m(T, p) + \boldsymbol{R}T \ln \mathrm{m}_s \gamma_s, \tag{20.52}$$

where we have written

$$\mu_s^m(T, p) = \mu_s^{\ominus}(T, p) + \boldsymbol{R}T \ln \frac{M_1}{1000}. \tag{20.53}$$

It should be stressed that *the same activity coefficient is employed in all three formulae* (20.4), (20.48) and (20.52); the identity of these three activity coefficients depends on the assumption that the solution is very dilute. In more concentrated solutions the activity coefficients differ from one another.

The chemical potential of the solvent can also be expressed in terms of the osmotic coefficient ϕ. An approximate form of (20.8) for dilute solutions is

$$\mu_1 = \mu_1^0(T, p) - \phi \boldsymbol{R}T \sum_s x_s \tag{20.54}$$

since

$$\ln x_1 = \ln (1 - \sum_s x_s) \approx -\sum_s x_s. \tag{20.55}$$

Expressed in terms of the alternative concentration scales (20.54) becomes

$$\mu_1 = \mu_1^0(T, p) - \phi \boldsymbol{R}T v_1^0 \sum_s c_s \tag{20.56}$$

$$\mu_1 = \mu_1^0(T, p) - \phi \boldsymbol{R}T \frac{M_1}{1000} \sum_s \mathrm{m}_s. \tag{20.57}$$

7. Activity Coefficients and the Osmotic Coefficient.

At constant T and p the Gibbs-Duhem equation (6.38) reduces to

$$\sum_i n_i \, \delta\mu_i = 0,$$

and with chemical potentials of the form (20.4) we find, also at constant T and p,

$$\sum_i x_i \, \delta \ln \gamma_i = 0. \tag{20.58}$$

Alternatively, introducing the osmotic coefficient of the solvent by means of (20.9′),

$$x_1 \, \delta \left\{ (1-\phi) \ln \frac{1}{x_1} \right\} + \sum_2^c x_i \, \delta \ln \gamma_i = 0, \tag{20.58′}$$

or

$$-x_1 \ln \frac{1}{x_1} \, \delta\phi - (1-\phi) \, \delta x_1 + \sum_2^c x_i \, \delta \ln \gamma_i = 0 \, ; \tag{20.59}$$

or again

$$x_1 \ln x_1 \, \delta\phi + (1-\phi) \sum_2^c \delta x_i + \sum_2^c x_i \, \delta \ln \gamma_i = 0. \tag{20.60}$$

In particular for a binary solution, (20.60) can be written

$$(1-x_2) \ln (1-x_2) \, \delta\phi + (1-\phi) \, \delta x_2 + x_2 \, \delta \ln \gamma_2 = 0, \tag{20.61}$$

or in the integral form :

$$-\ln \gamma_2 = \int_0^{x_2} \frac{1-x_2}{x_2} \ln (1-x_2) \, d\phi + \int_0^{x_2} (1-\phi) \, d \ln x_2. \tag{20.62}$$

This last equation enables the activity coefficient of the solute to be evaluated if the osmotic coefficient of the solvent is known for all solutions more dilute than the solution under consideration.

Let us consider the particular case of a very dilute solution. Then, (*cf*. 20.55),

$$\left(1 - \sum_2^c x_i\right) \ln \left(1 - \sum_2^c x_i\right) \simeq -\left(1 - \sum_2^c x_i\right) \sum_2^c x_i \simeq \sum_2^c x_i, \tag{20.63}$$

so that (20.60) becomes

$$-\sum_2^c x_i \, \delta\phi + (1-\phi) \sum_2^c \delta x_i + \sum_2^c x_i \, \delta \ln \gamma_i = 0. \tag{20.64}$$

For a binary solution

$$-\delta\phi + \frac{(1-\phi)}{x_2} \, \delta x_2 + \delta \ln \gamma_2 = 0,$$

or expressed in terms of molar concentration

$$\delta \ln \gamma_2 = \delta\phi - (1-\phi) \, \delta \ln c_2. \tag{20.65}$$

On integration, we obtain in place of (20.62), remembering that $\phi \to 1$ as $c_2 \to 0$,

$$-\ln \gamma_2 = (1-\phi) + \int_0^{c_2} (1-\phi)\, d \ln c_2. \tag{20.66}$$

In particular if $(1-\phi)$ varies with concentration according to

$$1-\phi = \alpha c_2^r, \tag{20.67}$$

where α and r are independent of concentration, then

$$-\ln \gamma_2 = \frac{r+1}{r} \alpha c_2^r = \frac{r+1}{r}(1-\phi). \tag{20.68}$$

This last formula is due to Bjerrum.

8. Affinity and Chemical Equilibrium in Solutions.

The affinity of a reaction taking place in a non-reactive solvent is given by (7.74) and the law of mass action by (7.75). If the reaction occurs between dissolved molecules in very dilute solution, the affinity is readily expressed as a function of the molar concentrations (20.47) or the molalities (20.51). Instead of (7.27) we now have to define two new equilibrium constants K_c and K_m :

$$\boldsymbol{R}T \ln K_c(T, p) = -\sum_2^c \nu_i \mu_i^c(T, p), \tag{20.69}$$

$$\boldsymbol{R}T \ln K_m(T, p) = -\sum_2^c \nu_i \mu_i^m(T, p). \tag{20.69'}$$

The affinity can then be expressed in two forms :

$$\mathbf{A} = \boldsymbol{R}T \ln \frac{K_c(T, p)}{(c_2\gamma_2)^{\nu_2} \dots (c_c\gamma_c)^{\nu_c}}, \tag{20.70}$$

$$\mathbf{A} = \boldsymbol{R}T \ln \frac{K_m(T, p)}{(\mathrm{m}_2\gamma_2)^{\nu_2} \dots (\mathrm{m}_c\gamma_c)^{\nu_c}}. \tag{20.70'}$$

The quantities K_c and K_m are related to the equilibrium constant K_x by the following relations which follow from (20.49) and (20.53),

$$K_c(T, p) = K_x(T, p)(v_1^0)^{-\nu} \tag{20.71}$$

$$K_m(T, p) = K_x(T, p)\left(\frac{M_1}{1000}\right)^{-\nu}, \tag{20.72}$$

The derivatives of K_x with respect to T or p in an ideal system are given by (7.37) and (7.36). In a non-ideal solution these equations become

$$\frac{\partial \ln K_x(T, p)}{\partial T} = \frac{h_{T,p}^{\ominus}}{\boldsymbol{R}T^2}; \quad \frac{\partial \ln K_x(T, p)}{\partial p} = -\frac{v_{T,p}^{\ominus}}{\boldsymbol{R}T}, \tag{20.73}$$

where $h^{\ominus}_{T,p}$ and $v^{\ominus}_{T,p}$ are the standard heats and expansions given in table 7.2. Since K_m only differs from K_x by a constant factor, the derivatives of $\ln K_m$ and $\ln K_x$ are identical. On the other hand the relation between K_c and K_x involves the molar volume v^0_1 which is a function of T and p, so that *

$$\frac{\partial \ln K_c(T,p)}{\partial T} = \frac{\partial \ln K_x(T,p)}{\partial T} - \nu \frac{\partial \ln v^0_1}{\partial T} = \frac{h^{\ominus}_{T,p}}{RT^2} - \nu\alpha_1 \quad (20.73')$$

where α_1 is the coefficient of thermal expansion of the pure solvent defined by (12.1),

$$\alpha_1 = \frac{1}{v^0_1}\frac{\partial v^0_1}{\partial T} = \frac{\partial \ln v^0_1}{\partial T}. \quad (20.74)$$

In the same way

$$\frac{\partial \ln K_c(T,p)}{\partial p} = -\frac{v^{\ominus}_{T,p}}{RT} + \nu\kappa_1, \quad (20.75)$$

where κ_1 is the coefficient of compressibility of the pure solvent defined by

$$\kappa_1 = -\frac{1}{v^0_1}\frac{\partial v^0_1}{\partial p} = -\frac{\partial \ln v^0_1}{\partial p}. \quad (20.76)$$

From equation (20.70′) for the affinity, we can define a standard affinity just as in (7.79), and calling this $\mathbf{A}^m$ we have

$$\mathbf{A}^m = RT \ln K_m(T,p). \quad (20.77)$$

This standard affinity is related to the standard affinity $\mathbf{A}^{\ominus}$ by the relation

$$\mathbf{A}^m = \mathbf{A}^{\ominus} - \nu RT \ln \frac{M_1}{1000}. \quad (20.77')$$

The standard affinity defined in this way may be regarded as the affinity of the reaction in a hypothetical ideal solution in which the reactants and products are at unit molality ; or in an actual solution in which the products $(m_i\gamma_i)$ are unity for all substances partaking in the reaction.

This standard affinity was introduced and employed systematically by Lewis, and it is this affinity which is tabulated in affinity tables based on Lewis' conventions. The affinities tabulated in chap. VIII, table 8.1 corresponding to aqueous solutions are expressed as $\mathbf{A}^m$ not $\mathbf{A}^{\ominus}$. Corresponding to the standard affinity $\mathbf{A}^m$ we have a standard heat of reaction $h^m_{T,p}$ and a standard entropy change $s^m_{T,p}$; these are

* *Cf.* R. P. Bell and O. Gatty, *Phil. Mag.* **19**, 75 (1935) ; E. A. Guggenheim, *Trans. Faraday Soc.*, **33**, 607 (1937).

related by an equation similar to (8.3). As noted above, $h^m_{T,p}$ is identical with $h^{\ominus}_{T,p}$ while

$$s^m_{T,p} = s^{\ominus}_{T,p} + \nu \boldsymbol{R} \ln \frac{M_1}{1000} \,. \qquad (20.77'')$$

9. The Nernst Distribution Law.

We conclude this chapter with some applications of the above formulae. Let us consider two phases both of which we will suppose, to fix our ideas, to be solutions. Introducing activity coefficients into the condition for equilibrium with respect to transport of matter between the two phases $\mu_i' = \mu_i''$, we see that the equilibrium is governed by the relation (*cf.* 7.42 ; 18.18)

$$\frac{x_i'' \gamma_i''}{x_i' \gamma_i'} = K_i(T, p). \qquad (20.78)$$

The equilibrium constant $K_i(T, p)$, which is independent of mole fraction is called the *distribution or partition coefficient* of the substance i between the solutions 1 and 2. This equation is the generalized form of the Nernst distribution law.

If one of the phases is ideal, and the other not, then (20.78) enables us to calculate the activity coefficient in the non-ideal phase.

One of the most interesting applications of the partition law is in the technique of *partition chromatography.** Let us consider a system consisting of two non-miscible solutions, containing a number of dissolved substances. Then the partition coefficients K_s for these solutes will, in general, be different, such that in equilibrium some of the solutes will be concentrated in the first solvent and others in the second solvent. By allowing a solution containing several substances in solution to come into contact with constantly renewed amounts of a second solvent, it is possible to achieve a separation of the dissolved substances. The success of this method depends upon the magnitude of the differences between the partition coefficients.

10. Osmotic Pressure.

Let us consider a solution (denoted by a single prime) separated from the pure solvent (denoted by a double prime) by a membrane which is permeable only to the solvent. A membrane of this kind is called a *semi-permeable membrane.* The chemical equilibrium eventually established between the phases is called osmotic equilibrium.

The affinity corresponding to passage of solvent molecules (component 1) from the pure solvent to the solution is

$$\mathbf{A} = \mu_1'' - \mu_1'. \qquad (20.79)$$

* A. J. P. Martin and R. L. M. Synge, *Biochem. J.*, 37, 79 (1943).

Let us suppose that the pressures applied to the two phases are p' and p'', then the chemical potential of *solvent in the solution* will be given, according to (20.8), by

$$\mu_1' = \mu_1^0(T, p') + \phi RT \ln x_1, \tag{20.80}$$

while for the second phase, which is *pure solvent*,

$$\mu_1'' = \mu_1^0(T, p''). \tag{20.81}$$

The affinity of the transfer of solvent is therefore

$$\mathbf{A} = \mu_1^0(T, p'') - \mu_1^0(T, p') - \phi RT \ln x_1. \tag{20.82}$$

Now if $p' = p''$, we must have

$$\mathbf{A} = -\phi RT \ln x_1. \tag{20.83}$$

This cannot be equal to zero unless $x_1 = 1$. Hence osmotic equilibrium cannot be established unless

$$p'' \neq p'$$

so that (20.82) can be satisfied with $\mathbf{A} = 0$.

At osmotic equilibrium, therefore, the pressures applied to the phases must be different, and this difference

$$\pi = p' - p'' \tag{20.84}$$

is defined as the *osmotic pressure*.

To find the condition of equilibrium we require to know the effect of pressure on $\mu_1^0(T, p)$. This is given by (20.3), so that :

$$\left.\begin{aligned} \mu_1' &= \mu_1^\dagger(T) + p' v_1^0(T, 0)(1 - \tfrac{1}{2}\kappa_1 p') + \phi RT \ln x_1, \\ \mu_1'' &= \mu_1^\dagger(T) + p'' v_1^0(T, 0)(1 - \tfrac{1}{2}\kappa_1 p'') \end{aligned}\right\}, \tag{20.85}$$

where $v_1^0(T, 0)$ is the molar volume of the solvent extrapolated to zero pressure, and κ_1 is its compressibility.

Now $v_1^0(T, 0)[1 - \frac{1}{2}\kappa_1(p'' + p')]$ is the molar volume of the pure solvent at the average pressure $(p'' + p')/2$; let us call this $\overline{v_1^0}$.

We may now equate μ_1' and μ_1'' given by (20.85), and obtain

$$\boxed{\pi = -\frac{\phi RT \ln x_1}{\overline{v_1^0}}}. \tag{20.86}$$

This equation due to Donnan and Guggenheim* enables the osmotic pressure to be calculated from ϕ, x_1, $\overline{v_1^0}$ and T.

In the case of ideal solutions

$$\pi^{\text{id}} = -\frac{RT \ln x_1}{\overline{v_1^0}}, \tag{20.87}$$

* F. G. Donnan and E. A. Guggenheim, *Z. physik. Chem.*, **A162**, 346 (1932).

which shows that the osmotic pressure of an ideal solution at a given mole fraction is *independent of the nature of the dissolved substance.*

Equations (20.86) and (20.87) show immediately that the osmotic coefficient is equal to the ratio of the osmotic pressure of the given solution, to that of an ideal solution at the same mole fraction, that is

$$\phi = \frac{\pi}{\pi^{\text{id}}}. \tag{20.88}$$

This explains the use of the term osmotic for this coefficient.

If we neglect the compressibility of the pure solvent, equations (20.86) and (20.87) reduce to

$$\pi = -\frac{\phi \boldsymbol{R}T \ln x_1}{v_1^0}, \tag{20.89}$$

$$\pi^{\text{id}} = -\frac{\boldsymbol{R}T \ln x_1}{v_1^0}. \tag{20.90}$$

This last formula is due to van Laar.*

For very dilute solutions, since $\ln x_1 = \ln (1 - \sum_s x_s) \simeq -\sum_s x_s$, and $c_s \simeq x_s/v_1^0$, (20.89) can be written

$$\pi = \phi \boldsymbol{R}T \sum_s c_s, \tag{20.91}$$

so that for solutions which are both very dilute and ideal

$$\boxed{\pi = \boldsymbol{R}T \sum_s c_s.} \tag{20.92}$$

This is *van't Hoff's equation* for the osmotic pressure and shows that, in the limit, the osmotic pressure is *independent of the nature of the solvent.*

Example : The Osmotic Pressure of Sucrose Solutions†

Let us consider the application of (20.92) to very dilute ideal solutions of sucrose in water. For a single solute this equation becomes

$$\pi = \boldsymbol{R}Tc_2$$

or inserting the numerical value of $\boldsymbol{R}$ in litre atmospheres we have

$$\pi = 0{\cdot}0821\ c_2 T \text{ atm.} \tag{20.92'}$$

In table 20.1 are given the experimentally observed osmotic pressures at two temperatures compared with those calculated from (20.92′).

* J. J. van Laar, *Z. physik. Chem.*, **15**, 64 (1894).
† *Cf.* Eucken [17], p. 28.

TABLE 20.1

Osmotic Pressure of Aqueous Sucrose Solutions

$T=273$ °K			$T=333$ °K		
c (mole/litre)	π (obs) (atm.)	π (calc) (atm.)	c (mole/litre)	π (obs) (atm.)	π (calc) (atm.)
0·02922	0·65	0·655	0·098	2·72	2·68
0·05843	1·27	1·330	0·1923	5·44	5·25
0·1315	2·91	2·95	0·3701	10·87	10·11
0·2739	6·23	6·14	0·533	16·54	14·65
0·5328	14·21	11·95	0·6855	22·33	18·8
0·8766	26·80	19·70	0·8273	28·37	22·7

The van't Hoff formula is in close agreement with experiment for solutions more dilute than 0·2 mole/litre, but above this concentration the calculated values deviate more and more from those observed. Van't Hoff's formula, as we have seen above, is only valid for solutions which are very dilute and ideal.

It is important to stress that there is a fundamental difference between the van't Hoff formula and the perfect gas equation

$$p=\boldsymbol{R}Tc.$$

In the first place the latter equation is satisfied for any gaseous phase which behaves as a mixture of perfect gases, whereas the van't Hoff equation is obeyed if the solution is not only ideal but also at the same time very dilute. The existence of deviations from van't Hoff's equation does not in any way prove that the solution is non-ideal.

We now examine the application of the phase rule and Duhem's theorem to an osmotic system. The phase rule was deduced in chap. XIII by assuming that all phases of the system were subject to the same applied pressure p. The introduction of a semi-permeable membrane increases the variance of the system by one, and renders possible the existence of two different pressures p' and p''. Instead of the $2+c\phi$ variables T, p, $x_1^1 \ldots x_c^\phi$, we have now $3+c\phi$ variables T, p', p'', $x_1^1 \ldots x_c^\phi$.

Similarly, instead of the two independent variables which characterize the equilibrium state of a closed system (Duhem's theorem, chap. XIII), we now have three variables.

Finally we notice that by comparing (20.83) and (20.86)

$$\pi=\frac{\mathbf{A}_{(p'=p'')}}{\overline{v}_1^0}\,, \tag{20.93}$$

where $\mathbf{A}_{(p'=p'')}$ is the affinity of diffusion of the solvent into the solution when both compartments are at the same pressure. This affinity is thus measured directly by the osmotic pressure. This formula demonstrates clearly that the osmotic pressure may be regarded as the pressure difference which must be established between solution and solvent to balance the affinity of diffusion of solvent molecules from the pure solvent into the solution.

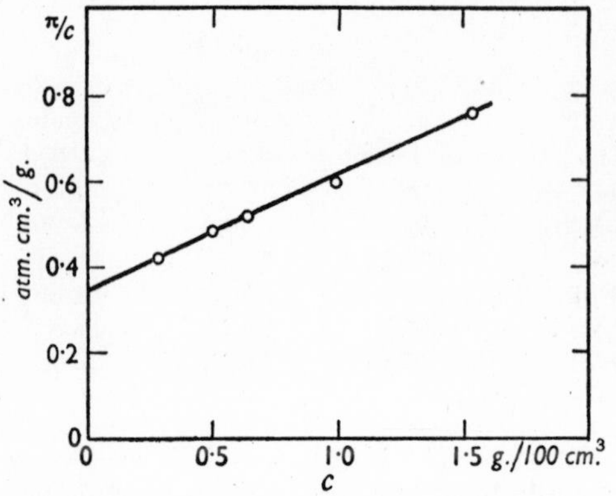

FIG. 20.3. Osmotic pressure of a vinyl chain polymer in cyclohexanone at 27 °C.*

Osmotic pressure measurements are of value in determining osmotic coefficients and hence activity coefficients of solutions. We shall defer consideration of the application of these methods to electrolytes until later (*cf.* chap. XXVII), but we may mention here their use in studying high polymer solutions. Because of the large difference between the masses and dimensions of the solvent and the solute molecules it is relatively simple to make semi-permeable membranes for solutions of this kind. In general the osmotic method is useful for polymers having molecular weights in the range 20,000 to 400,000. For smaller molecules it is difficult to obtain suitable membranes, while above 400,000 the osmotic pressures become too small to measure accurately in the range of concentration which is most interesting.

In fig. 20.3 are shown data for the osmotic pressure of a polyvinyl chloride polymer in cyclohexanone solution at 27 °C.

We see that in the concentration range examined π/c_2 is a linear function of c_2. This behaviour can be interpreted on the basis of a consideration of the activity coefficients of non-electrolytes which we shall examine later. For the moment we may note that in sufficiently dilute solutions, the activity coefficients of non-electrolytes can often be represented by the equation

$$\ln \gamma_1 = \beta x_2^2. \tag{20.94}$$

It follows then, from (20.86) and (20.9) that the osmotic pressure will be

$$\pi = -\frac{RT \ln x_1}{\overline{v}_1^0} - \frac{RT\beta x_2^2}{\overline{v}_1^0} \simeq \frac{RTx_2}{v_1^0} - \frac{RT\beta x_2^2}{v_1^0}. \tag{20.95}$$

* L. de Brouckère (unpublished).

Transforming from mole fractions to concentrations (*cf.* 20.47), we obtain

$$\frac{\pi}{c_2} = RT + \alpha c_2, \tag{20.96}$$

where α is a quantity independent of c_2. This is the relation shown by the data in fig. 20.3.

If the concentrations are expressed in terms of gm./cm.^{3}, this equation becomes

$$\frac{\pi}{c_2} = \frac{RT}{M_2} + \frac{\alpha}{M_2^2} c_2. \tag{20.97}$$

Hence by extrapolating the line in fig. 20.3 back to its intercept with the π/c axis we can evaluate M_2, the molecular weight of the polymer. This calculation is easily extended to the case of a mixture of polymer molecules of different weights; we see that the molecular weight calculated on the basis of (20.97) is the *arithmetic mean molecular weight* of the polymer.

CHAPTER XXI

SOLUTION-VAPOUR EQUILIBRIUM

1. Vapour Pressure of Perfect Solutions.

Let us consider a perfect solution (denoted by l) in equilibrium with vapour (denoted by g); then

$$\mu_i^l = \mu_i^g. \tag{21.1}$$

We may now replace the chemical potential of the solution by the value given in (20.1), and assume the gas phase to behave as a mixture of perfect gases* so that equation (10.34) can be used for the chemical potential of the vapour. Hence

$$\mu_i^0(T, p) + \boldsymbol{R}T \ln x_i = \mu_i^\dagger(T) + \boldsymbol{R}T \ln p_i, \tag{21.2}$$

where x_i is the mole fraction of i in the solution and p_i is the partial pressure of its vapour; μ_i^0 refers to the pure liquid, and $\mu_i^\dagger$ to the pure gas at unit pressure.

We see immediately that (21.2) can be written very simply as

$$p_i = k_i x_i, \tag{21.3}$$

with

$$k_i \equiv \exp\left[\frac{\mu_i^0(T, p) - \mu_i^\dagger(T)}{\boldsymbol{R}T}\right]. \tag{21.4}$$

Now k_i is in principle a function of T and p, but we can show that, at ordinary pressures, it is practically independent of pressure. For, on differentiating (21.4), we obtain (*cf.* 7.21)

$$\frac{\partial \ln k_i}{\partial p} = \frac{1}{\boldsymbol{R}T}\frac{\partial \mu_i^0(T, p)}{\partial p} = \frac{v_i^0}{\boldsymbol{R}T}. \tag{21.5}$$

Thus at constant T,

$$\frac{dk_i}{k_i} = \frac{v_i^0}{\boldsymbol{R}T}\, dp.$$

If, for example, $v_i^0 = 20$ cm.$^3 = 0{\cdot}02$ litre; $\boldsymbol{R} = 0{\cdot}08$ litre. atm.; $T = 300$ °K; then $\frac{v_i}{\boldsymbol{R}T} \simeq 10^{-3}$, and for a change in pressure of one atmosphere

$$\frac{dk_i}{k_i} \simeq 10^{-3}.$$

We can, therefore, consider k_i as a function of T only.

* If the vapour does not behave as a perfect gas mixture, then we must employ the fugacity p^* instead of the partial pressure p; *cf.* for example, J. N. Brønsted and J. G. Koefoed, *Det. Kgl. Danske Vid. Selsk.* (*Mat-fys*) 22, part 17 (1946).

If we now put $x_i = 1$ in (21.3) we see that

$$k_i = p_i^0, \tag{21.6}$$

where p_i^0 is the vapour pressure of pure i. We can therefore write (21.3) in the form

$$\boxed{p_i = p_i^0 x_i} \; . \tag{21.7}$$

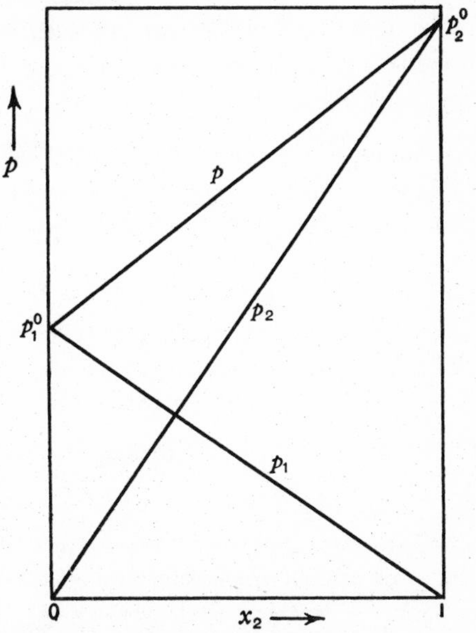

FIG. 21.1. Total and partial vapour pressure of a perfect solution at constant T.

The vapour pressure of each component in a perfect solution is thus proportional to its mole fraction. This is *Raoult's law*. The total vapour pressure, p, will be given by, (*cf.* 10.25),

$$p = \Sigma p_i = \Sigma p_i^0 x_i. \tag{21.8}$$

Fig. 21.1 shows the partial vapour pressures and the total pressure of a perfect solution as a function of composition. In the case of a binary solution (21.8) may be written

$$p = p_1^0(1 - x_2) + p_2^0 x_2 = p_1^0 + (p_2^0 - p_1^0) x_2, \tag{21.9}$$

so that the total pressure is a linear function of x_2.

There are relatively few examples of perfect solutions. A perfect solid solution is formed by mixtures of p-dibromo- and p-dichloro-benzene. The total pressure curves are linear functions of mole fraction as shown in fig. 21.2 where data are given at several temperatures.

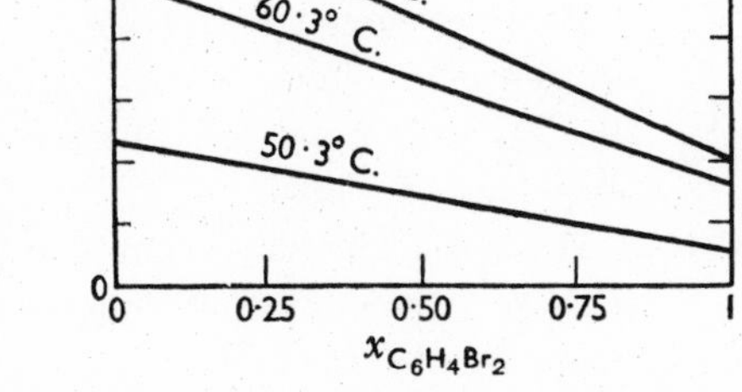

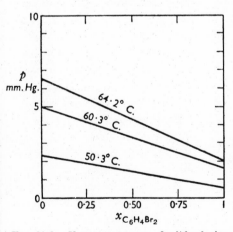

FIG. 21.2. Vapour pressures of solid solutions of p-bromo-chlorobenzene + p-dibromobenzene.

We note finally that if equation (21.7) is satisfied at a series of different temperatures, then the chemical potentials are necessarily of the form (20.1) and the solution is perfect. Vapour pressure studies thus provide a criterion for deciding whether or not a solution is perfect.

2. Vapour Pressure of Ideal Solutions.

Let us now consider a solution which is not perfect, but which is ideal when sufficiently dilute. Equation (21.3) will now only be valid if the mole fraction of solvent x_1, is sufficiently close to unity and the other mole fractions x_i are small. By considering the behaviour as $x_1 \rightarrow 1$ we can, as before, write

$$p_1 = p_1^0 x_1 \tag{21.10}$$

within the range of ideality. On the other hand we must preserve the form (21.3) for all the other components of the solution :

$$p_s = k_s x_s \quad (s = 2, 3 \ldots c). \tag{21.11}$$

This shows that the vapour pressure of the dissolved substances are proportional to their mole fractions in an ideal solution. (*Henry's law*). Equation (21.10) can be rewritten

$$\frac{p_1^0 - p_1}{p_1^0} = 1 - x_1 = \sum_s x_s. \tag{21.12}$$

The relative lowering of vapour pressure of the solvent is thus equal to the sum of the mole fractions of the solutes. This is another form of *Raoult's law*. The lowering of vapour pressure is thus independent of the nature of the dissolved substances. The significance of Raoult's and Henry's laws in a non-perfect solution is shown in fig. 21.3. If we consider very dilute solutions, $x_1 \rightarrow 1$, then p_1 and p_2 are linear with respect to x_2. The first of these lines, relating to the solvent corresponds to Raoult's law, the other to Henry's law. In a perfect solution the two laws are synonymous.

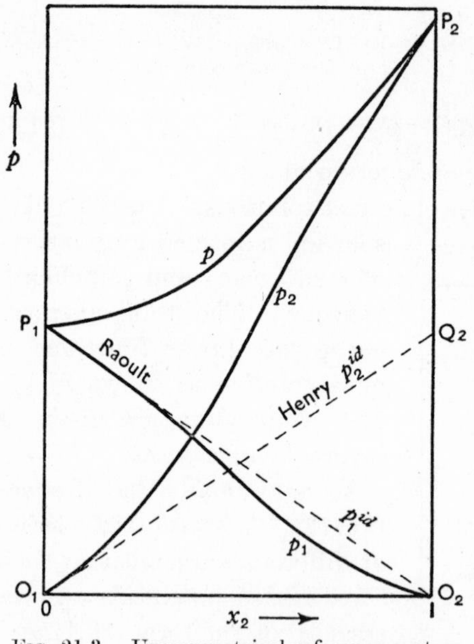

FIG. 21.3. Unsymmetrical reference system (T constant).

We now prove that if the $(c-1)$ solutes obey Henry's law, then the solvent must of necessity obey Raoult's law.

We must first show that if in a certain concentration range, a solution is ideal with respect to $(c-1)$ components, that is if

$$\mu_s = \mu_s^\ominus (T, p) + \boldsymbol{R}T \ln x_s, \quad (s = 2, 3 \ldots c), \tag{21.13}$$

then the solution is ideal for all components, that is to say that in addition

$$\mu_1 = \mu_1^0(T, p) + \boldsymbol{R}T \ln x_1. \tag{21.14}$$

For this we employ the Gibbs-Duhem equation (6.39), which at constant T and p is

$$\sum_i x_i \, \delta\mu_i = 0. \tag{21.15}$$

For the $(c-1)$ dissolved substances we have, from (21.13)

$$\delta\mu_s = \boldsymbol{R}T \, \delta \ln x_s, \quad (s = 2, 3 \ldots c), \tag{21.16}$$

so that (21.15) may be written

$$x_1 \, \delta\mu_1 + \boldsymbol{R}T \sum_{s=2}^{c} x_s \, \delta \ln x_s = 0. \tag{21.17}$$

But since $\sum_i x_i = 1$, or $\sum_i \delta x_i = 0$, it follows that

$$\sum_{i=1}^{c} x_i \, \delta \ln x_i = 0 \quad \text{or} \quad x_1 \, \delta \ln x_1 = \sum_{s=2}^{c} x_s \, \delta \ln x_s. \tag{21.18}$$

Comparing (21.18) and (21.17) we see that

$$\delta\mu_1 = \boldsymbol{R}T \, \delta \ln x_1, \tag{21.19}$$

which on integration gives

$$\mu_1 = \mu_1^0(T, p) + \boldsymbol{R}T \ln x_1. \tag{21.20}$$

The solution is therefore ideal with respect to component 1. But equation (21.13) implies that the dissolved species obey Henry's law, and equation (21.20) ensures that the solvent obeys Raoult's law.

3. Vapour Pressure of Non-Ideal Solutions : Choice of Reference System.

Starting from equations (20.4) for the chemical potentials of a non-ideal solution, we have instead of (21.3)

$$p_i = k_i x_i \gamma_i, \tag{21.21}$$

and in these equations the numerical values of k_i and γ_i depend upon the choice of reference system (*cf.* chap. VII, § 8). On the other hand the product $k_i\gamma_i$ is equal to p_i/x_i and is independent of this choice.

There are two reference systems which are commonly employed, one unsymmetrical and the other symmetrical. In discussing them we shall, for convenience, deal with binary solutions.

We first take as reference system a sufficiently dilute solution of 2 in 1. If the solution is dilute enough to be ideal, the chemical potentials will be of the form (*cf.* 20.41)

$$\left.\begin{aligned} \mu_1 &= \mu_1^0 + \boldsymbol{R}T \ln x_1, \\ \mu_2 &= \mu_2^{\ominus} + \boldsymbol{R}T \ln x_2 \end{aligned}\right\}. \tag{21.22}$$

While if the solution is not dilute enough to be regarded as ideal, we write the chemical potentials in the form

$$\left.\begin{aligned}\mu_1 &= \mu_1^0 + RT \ln x_1 \gamma_1^*,\\ \mu_2 &= \mu_2^{\ominus} + RT \ln x_2 \gamma_2^*,\end{aligned}\right\}. \tag{21.23}$$

where μ_1^0 and $\mu_2^{\ominus}$ *are the same functions as in* (21.22). We then say that the ideal dilute solution is taken as reference system for a study of less dilute solutions. As the solution becomes more dilute (21.23) approaches (21.22), that is to say as

$$\left.\begin{aligned}x_2 &\to 0,\\ x_1 &\to 1,\end{aligned}\right\} \quad \left.\begin{aligned}\gamma_1^* &\to 1\ ;\\ \gamma_2^* &\to 1.\end{aligned}\right\} \tag{21.24}$$

We see that these properties are unsymmetrical since the two components have not been treated in the same fashion. If we put $x_1 = 1$ in (21.21) we have, since $\gamma_1^* = 1$,

$$k_1 = p_1^0$$

where p_1^0 is the vapour pressure of pure solvent at the same temperature. Thus for a binary system

$$\begin{aligned}p_1 &= p_1^0 x_1 \gamma_1^*,\\ p_2 &= k_2 x_2 \gamma_2^*.\end{aligned} \tag{21.25}$$

If, in fig. 21.3, we put

$$\begin{aligned}p_1^{\text{id}} &= p_1^0 x_1,\\ p_2^{\text{id}} &= k_2 x_2,\end{aligned} \tag{21.26}$$

then p_1^{id} is represented by the line P_1O_2, and p_2^{id} by the line Q_2O_1. We shall verify in § 5 that the line P_1O_2 which represents Raoult's law is tangential to the actual vapour pressure curve p_1 at P_1.

On comparing (21.25) with (21.26) we see that

$$\gamma_1^* = \frac{p_1}{p_1^{\text{id}}}, \quad \gamma_2^* = \frac{p_2}{p_2^{\text{id}}}; \tag{21.27}$$

which enables us to calculate the activity coefficients if the experimental curves p_1 and p_2, and the two straight lines corresponding to Raoult's and Henry's laws are known. The Raoult law line can be drawn immediately if we know the vapour pressure of the pure solvent, but on the other hand the Henry law line, which is the tangent to the curve p_2 at O_1, cannot be drawn with the same precision and in practice we usually employ other methods of finding γ_2^*. We may, for example, use the relation between γ_1^* and γ_2^* derived from the Gibbs-Duhem equation (*cf.* 7.72, chap. XX, § 7, and § 6 below).

Instead of choosing an unsymmetrical reference system, we may employ a symmetrical reference system in the following manner.

This time we define each function $\mu^{\ominus}(T, p)$ as equal to the chemical potential μ_i of the pure component i, at temperature T, and pressure p, that is

$$\mu_i^{\ominus}(T, p) = \mu_i^0(T, p), \textit{ for all } i, \tag{21.28}$$

so that

$$\mu_i = \mu_i^0(T, p) + \boldsymbol{R}T \ln x_i \gamma_i. \tag{21.29}$$

This equation shows that with this convention

$$\text{when} \quad \left. \begin{array}{l} \gamma_i \to 1 \\ x_i \to 1 \end{array} \right\}. \tag{21.30}$$

That is to say, the activity coefficient becomes unity for each pure component.

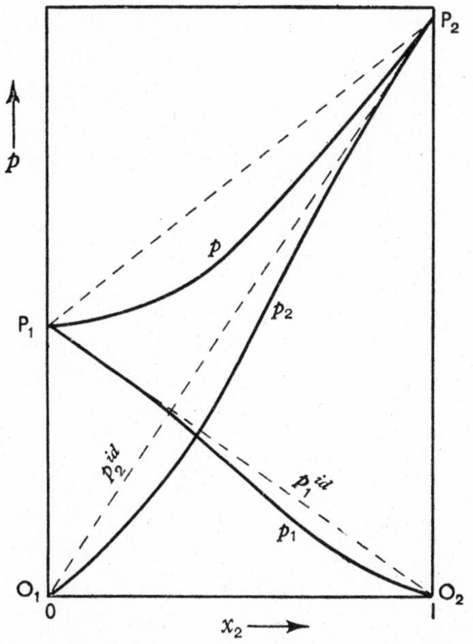

FIG. 21.4. Symmetrical reference system (T constant).

The vapour pressure equations (21.21) show that in the present case for

$$\left. \begin{array}{ll} x_1 = 1, & p_1^0 = k_1 \\ x_2 = 1, & p_2^0 = k_2 \end{array} \right\}; \tag{21.31}$$

so that

$$p_1 = p_1^0 x_1 \gamma_1 \,; \; p_2 = p_2^0 x_2 \gamma_2. \tag{21.32}$$

If we write now,

$$p_1^{\text{id}} = p_1^0 x_1 \quad \text{and} \quad p_2^{\text{id}} = p_2^0 x_2 \qquad (21.33$$

where p_1^{id} and p_2^{id} are the ideal vapour pressures represented by the lines P_1O_2 and O_1P_2 (*cf.* fig. 21.4), then

$$\gamma_1 = \frac{p_1}{p_1^{id}}, \; \gamma_2 = \frac{p_2}{p_2^{id}}. \tag{21.34}$$

This symmetrical system of reference has the advantage of treating all the components in the same way, and is particularly valuable in the study of concentrated solutions.

The activity coefficients (21.34) have a simple interpretation. They are equal to the ratio of the observed partial pressure to that which would have been observed if the solution were perfect. Thus the activity coefficients using the symmetrical system measure directly the deviations of the solution from perfection.

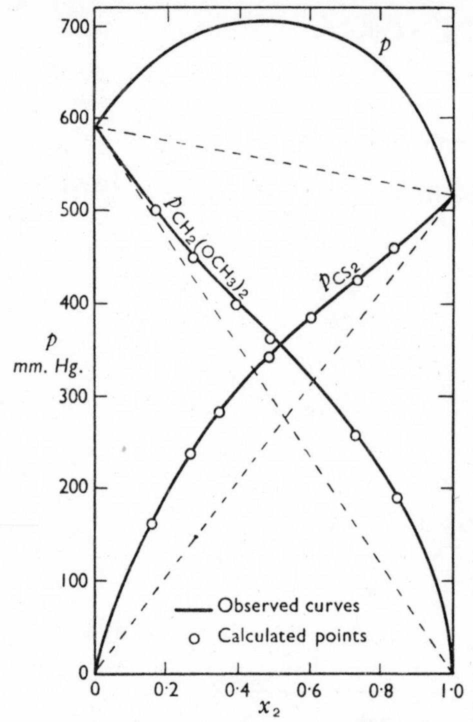

FIG. 21.5. Total and partial vapour pressure of the system methylal + carbon disulphide.*

In fig. 21.4 all the activity coefficients are less than unity, and the total pressure p is less than the perfect pressure represented by the line P_1P_2. In this case we describe the deviations from ideality as negative. An example of this behaviour is to be found in chloroform + ethyl ether solutions. Alternatively the deviations from ideality may be positive as in methylal + carbon disulphide solutions (fig. 21.5).

If deviations from ideality are large enough the total vapour pressure p passes through a maximum or a minimum. We have already seen (*cf.* chap. XIII, § 8 and chap. XVIII, § 6) that an extreme value of p corresponds to the formation of azeotropes. Thus azeotropes can only occur as a result of non-ideal behaviour of the solution.

We shall return later, in chaps. XXIV–XXVII, to discuss the relation between deviations from ideality and molecular structure.

* J. v. Zawidski, *Z. physik. chem.* 35, 129 (1900). The points are those calculated by Joukowsky following the method described in § 8 below.

4. Change from one Reference System to the other.

We denote the activity coefficients in the unsymmetrical reference system γ_1^* and γ_2^*, and in the symmetrical system γ_1 and γ_2. Then, from equations (21.26), (21.27), (21.33), (21.34) we have :

$$\gamma_1 = \gamma_1^* = \frac{p_1}{p_1^0 x_1}, \tag{21.35}$$

and

$$\frac{\gamma_2}{\gamma_2^*} = \frac{k_2}{p_2^0}. \tag{21.36}$$

If we note that when $x_2 \to 0$, $\gamma_2^* \to 1$ this equation gives

$$\lim_{x_2 \to 0} \gamma_2 = k_2/p_2^0, \tag{21.37}$$

so that (21.36) can be re-written

$$\frac{\gamma_2}{\gamma_2^*} = \lim_{x_2 \to 0} \gamma_2. \tag{21.38}$$

Similarly we find that

$$\frac{\gamma_2^*}{\gamma_2} = \lim_{x_2 \to 0} \gamma_2^*. \tag{21.39}$$

These equations enable us to change easily from one system of reference to another. Suppose, for example, that we have determined γ_2 as a function of composition, then equation (21.38) enables us to calculate γ_2^*.

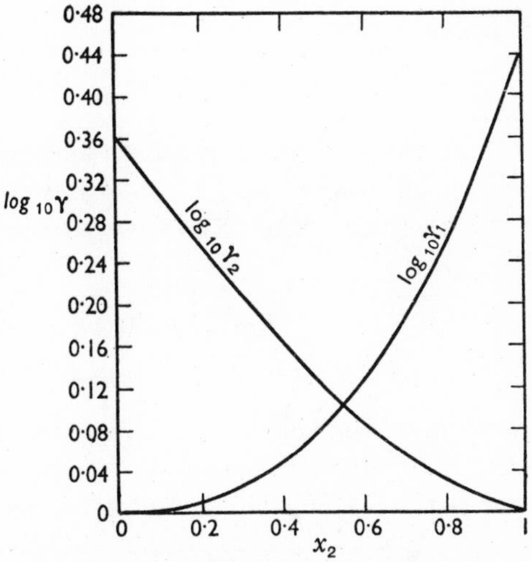

Fig. 21.6. Logarithms of activity coefficients as function of composition in the system methylal (1) + carbon disulphide (2) (*cf.* fig. 21.5).*

For the rest of this chapter we shall employ the symmetrical reference system.

5. Analytical Form of Activity Coefficients.

As we have already seen, activity coefficients in liquid solutions may be derived from partial vapour pressure curves. As an example we give in fig. 21.6 the activity coefficients of methylal and carbon disulphide in mixtures of these substances, calculated from the data in fig. 21.5.

The curves obtained for the logarithm of the activity coefficient against mole fraction are usually of a fairly simple shape and may be developed in series in the form :

$$\ln \gamma_1 = \sum_k \alpha_k x_2^{\lambda_k}, \tag{21.40}$$

* *Cf.* Hildebrand [28], p. 40.

where the exponents λ_k may or may not be whole numbers. If we consider sufficiently dilute solutions ($x_2 \to 0$) we can limit the terms in (21.40) to the first term only; in this region the activity coefficient of the solvent is given by :

$$\ln \gamma_1 = \alpha x_2^{\lambda}. \tag{21.41}$$

The thermodynamic behaviour of the solution has different characteristics depending upon whether λ is greater than, equal to, or less than two. For, from (20.9′), on replacing $\ln x_1$ by $\ln(1-x_2) \simeq -x_2$ we have, for the osmotic coefficient

$$1-\phi = -\frac{\ln \gamma_1}{\ln x_1} \simeq \frac{\alpha x_2^{\lambda}}{x_2} = \alpha x_2^{\lambda-1}. \tag{21.42}$$

Whence

$$\frac{\partial(1-\phi)}{\partial x_2} = \alpha(\lambda-1)x_2^{\lambda-2}. \tag{21.43}$$

Now the osmotic coefficient, and the osmotic pressure itself must remain finite when $x_2 \to 0$. It is therefore necessary that $\lambda > 1$.

Furthermore, from (21.43) we see that

$$\lim_{x_2\to 0} \frac{\partial(1-\phi)}{\partial x_2} = \begin{cases} 0 & \text{if } \lambda > 2 \quad (a) \\ \text{non-zero} & \text{if } \lambda = 2 \quad (b) \\ \infty & \text{if } \lambda < 2 \quad (c). \end{cases} \tag{21.44}$$

As examples of this, fig. 21.7 contains data on the osmotic coefficient of various aqueous solutions : strong electrolytes such as NaCl, KCl, and H_2SO_4 exhibit behaviour (*c*), while non-electrolytes behave as (*b*).

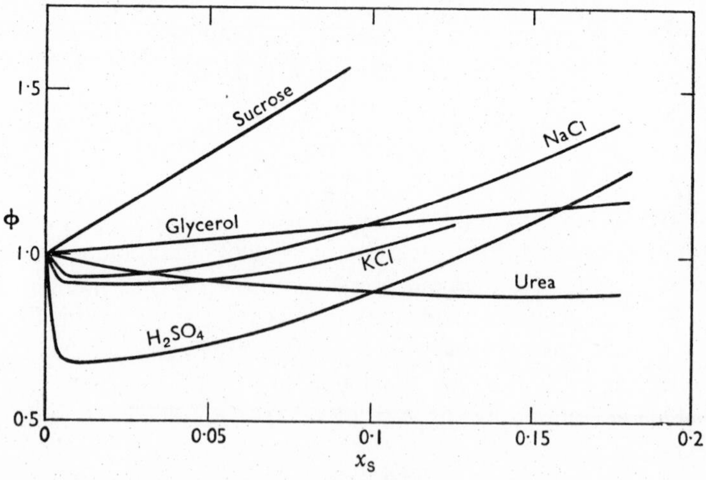

FIG. 21.7. Osmotic coefficient of aqueous solutions of sucrose, glycerol, urea, NaCl, KCl and H_2SO_4 at high dilutions ; x_s = mole fraction of dissolved substance assuming that it is completely dissociated, *i.e.* $x_s = x_+ + x_-$.

Behaviour (*c*) is in fact only observed in strong electrolyte solutions ; as we shall see in chap. XXVII $\lambda = 1{\cdot}5$, and this behaviour is to be attributed to the long range of electrostatic forces between ions. Cases (*a*) and (*b*) arise in other solutions so that, apart from electrolytes, the lowest power of x_2 appearing in (21.40) is the second.

We note that the derivative of the activity coefficient is

$$\frac{\partial \ln \gamma_1}{\partial x_2} = \alpha \lambda x_2^{\lambda - 1},$$

and this tends to zero with x_2 provided that $\lambda > 1$.

It follows therefore that

$$\frac{\partial \gamma_1}{\partial x_2} \to 0 \text{ as } x_2 \to 0,$$

which demonstrates immediately the tangency at P_1 in fig. 21.3 of the experimental vapour pressure curve to the Raoult law line.

6. Relation between the Activity Coefficients of a Binary Solution.

Just as in § 7 of chapter XX we can show that it is sufficient to know the activity coefficient of one component of a binary solution in order to calculate the activity coefficient of the other. This fact is of importance when only one of the two components has a measurable vapour pressure.

The state of a binary solution may be determined by the variables T, p, x_2, so that equation (20.58) can be written in the form

$$(1 - x_2) \frac{\partial \ln \gamma_1}{\partial x_2} + x_2 \frac{\partial \ln \gamma_2}{\partial x_2} = 0. \tag{21.45}$$

Let us assume that $\ln \gamma_1$ can be represented by the power series (21.40) with $\lambda_k \geqslant 2$; then the above equation can be written

$$\frac{\partial \ln \gamma_1/\gamma_2}{\partial x_2} = \frac{1}{x_2} \frac{\partial \ln \gamma_1}{\partial x_2} = \sum_k \alpha_k \lambda_k x_2^{\lambda_k - 2}. \tag{21.46}$$

On integration of this equation we obtain

$$\ln \gamma_2 = \ln \gamma_1 - \sum_k \frac{\alpha_k \lambda_k}{\lambda_k - 1} x_2^{\lambda_k - 1} - I,$$

$$= \sum_k \alpha_k x_2^{\lambda_k} - \sum_k \frac{\alpha_k \lambda_k}{\lambda_k - 1} x_2^{\lambda_k - 1} - I. \tag{21.47}$$

The constant of integration I is determined from the fact that when $x_2 = 1$, $\gamma_2 = 1$; hence

$$0 = \sum_k \alpha_k - \sum_k \frac{\alpha_k \lambda_k}{\lambda_k - 1} - I. \tag{21.48}$$

Substituting this value of I into (21.47) we obtain*

$$\ln \gamma_2 = \sum_k \alpha_k x_2^{\lambda_k} - \sum_k \frac{\alpha_k}{\lambda_k - 1} (\lambda_k x_2^{\lambda_k - 1} - 1). \tag{21.49}$$

This equation enables γ_2 to be calculated from γ_1.

In most cases it is possible to represent the logarithm of the activity coefficients in terms of a series in integral powers of the mole fraction.† For example if only the first three terms need be retained, so that

$$\ln \gamma_1 = \alpha_2 x_2^2 + \alpha_3 x_2^3 + \alpha_4 x_2^4 ; \tag{21.50}$$

then, as is easily verified from (21.49) the activity coefficient of the other component is given by

$$\ln \gamma_2 = (\alpha_2 + \tfrac{3}{2}\alpha_3 + 2\alpha_4) x_1^2 - (\alpha_3 + \tfrac{8}{3}\alpha_4) x_1^3 + \alpha_4 x_1^4. \tag{21.51}$$

Thus, if $\ln \gamma_1$ is expressed as a power series in x_2, $\ln \gamma_2$ can also be represented by an analogous series in x_1. It is important to observe, however, that the coefficient of x_1^2 in (21.51) is not the same as that of x_2^2 in (21.50), but depends also upon α_3 and α_4. It follows that it is necessary to know $\ln \gamma_1$ very accurately and to obtain precise values of the higher coefficients α_3 and α_4, before we can calculate $\ln \gamma_2$. For this reason the method just described is only useful when the activity coefficients can be expressed in an expansion containing only one or two terms. This is usually possible when the deviations from ideality are small. Often only the first term is needed, so that

$$\ln \gamma_1 = \alpha_2 x_2^2 \text{ and } \ln \gamma_2 = \alpha_2 x_1^2. \tag{21.52}$$

An alternative method of calculation which is more useful where the deviations from ideality are large, is due to Boissonnas and will be explained in § 8.

In chap. XXV we shall show that for an important class of solutions the logarithms of the activity coefficients are inversely proportional to T (regular solutions). In this case (21.52) may be written

$$RT \ln \gamma_1 = \alpha x_2^2 ; \quad RT \ln \gamma_2 = \alpha x_1^2, \tag{21.52'}$$

where α is independent of temperature and is defined in terms of the coefficient in (21.52) as :

$$\alpha = \alpha_2 RT.$$

* J. N. Brønsted and P. Colmant, *Z. physik. Chem.*, **A168**, 381 (1934).

† H. Margules, *Sitzungber. Wien Akad.*, **104**, 1243 (1895), *cf.* Hildebrand [28]. On the form of this series when the components play a symmetrical role, see Guggenheim [26′], pp. 201–202.

Example :

Brønsted and Colmant studied the vapour pressures, at 18 °C, of solutions in which the two components had widely different molecular dimensions (*e.g.* benzene + *n*-butyl sebacate). In these systems only the solvent has an appreciable vapour pressure. From measurements of this vapour pressure it is possible to determine the activity coefficient of the solvent. For the system benzene + *n*-butyl sebacate, the activity coefficients of the benzene can be expressed very accurately by an equation of the form

$$\ln \gamma_1 = a x_2^2 + b x_2^{5/2} + c x_2^3.$$

The numerical values of a, b and c, in terms of decadic logarithms, are $a = -1{\cdot}816$, $b = 2{\cdot}473$, $c = -0{\cdot}950$.

Equation (21.49) enables us to calculate the activity coefficients of the *n*-butyl sebacate :

$$\ln \gamma_2 = \ln \gamma_1 + (a + \tfrac{2}{3}b + \tfrac{1}{2}c) - 2a x_2 - \tfrac{5}{3}b x_2^{3/2} - \tfrac{3}{2}c x_2^2.$$

The curve calculated in this way is shown in fig. 21.8. Closely similar

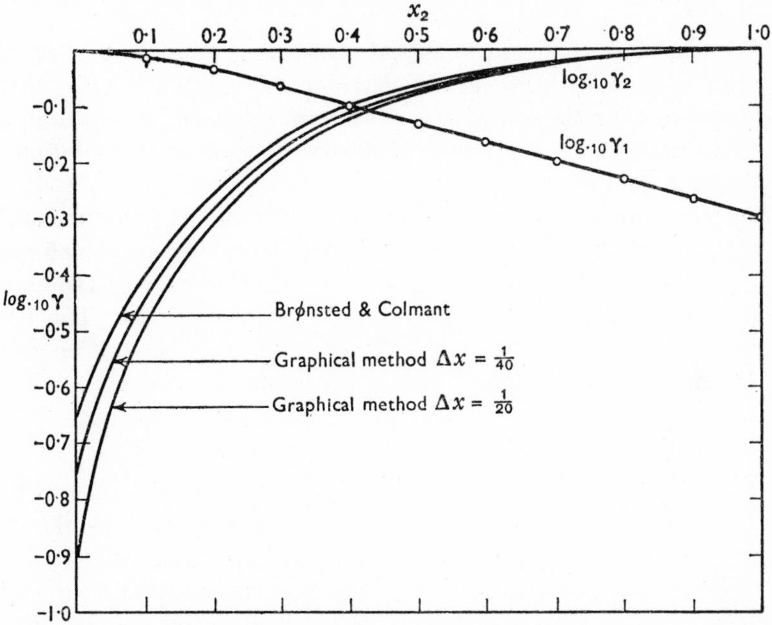

FIG. 21.8. Calculations of the activity coefficient of the solute from that of the solvent by the method of Brønsted and Colmant, and Boissonas' method (*cf.* § 8) for the system benzene (1) + *n*-butyl sebacate (2).

results are obtained using the graphical method of Boissonnas which we shall consider in § 8.

We notice incidentally that these activity coefficients are all less than unity. This is a property which is often found in solutions consisting of molecules of very different size ; we shall consider solutions of this kind in more detail in chap. XXVI.

7. The Duhem-Margules Equation and Beatty and Callingaert's Criterion.

If we insert in equation (21.45) the values for the activity coefficient given in (21.32) we have

$$(1-x_2)\left(\frac{\partial \ln p_1}{\partial x_2}\right)_{T,p}+x_2\left(\frac{\partial \ln p_2}{\partial x_2}\right)_{T,p}=0. \tag{21.53}$$

Strictly speaking the partial pressures depend on the total pressure, but it is readily shown, as in § 1, that the variation is negligible at ordinary pressure because of the small molar volumes of condensed phases.

Equation (21.53) therefore reduces to the Duhem-Margules equation,*

$$\boxed{(1-x_2)\left(\frac{\partial \ln p_1}{\partial x_2}\right)_{T}+x_2\left(\frac{\partial \ln p_2}{\partial x_2}\right)_{T}=0} \tag{21.54}$$

in which the temperature only is maintained constant in the differentiation.

This equation between the partial pressures is valid no matter what are the deviations from ideal behaviour, and depends only on the assumptions that the gas phases consist of a perfect gas mixture, and that the partial molar volumes of the components in the solution are negligible,† (*cf.* § 1).

Suppose that both p_1 and p_2 have been determined experimentally; then equation (21.54) leads to a simple criterion by which we can assess the accuracy of the experimental results. This equation can be written in the form

$$\frac{\partial p_1/\partial x_1}{p_1/x_1}=\frac{\partial p_2/\partial x_2}{p_2/x_2}. \tag{21.55}$$

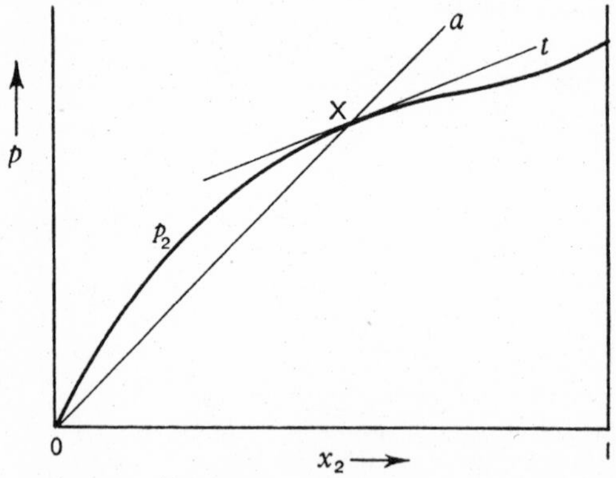

FIG. 21 9. The Beatty-Callingaert Criterion.

Referring to fig. 21.9 we see that $\partial p_2/\partial x_2$ is the slope of the tangent (t) to the curve $p_2(x_2)$ at X, and p_2/x_2 is the slope of the line (a) joining the origin to X. Similarly for the curve of p_1 against x_2.

Thus from (21.55) we can deduce, among others, the following criteria.‡

* Margules, *loc. cit.*, Duhem [15], vol. IV.

† *Cf.* P. Tuomikoski, *Annales acad. Scientiarum Fennicæ* Series A, No. **17**, (Helsinki, 1943).

‡ H. A. Beatty and L. Callingaert, *Ind. Eng. Chem.*, **26**, 904 (1934); *cf.* M. Ewert, *Bull. Soc. Chim. Belge.*, **45**, 493 (1936).

(*a*) The ratio of the slope of the partial pressure curve at a point, to the slope of the line joining the point to the origin is the same for both partial pressure curves.

(*b*) If

$$\partial p_1/\partial x_1 = p_1/x_1$$

then also

$$\partial p_2/\partial x_2 = p_2/x_2.$$

That is to say, if the tangent to one partial vapour pressure curve passes through one origin, then, at the same composition, the tangent to the other curve must pass through the other origin.

As an example of the application of this criterion we may quote the system water + methanol.* The data on the partial pressure of water in the range of concentrations below 0·2 mole fraction of alcohol are very inconsistent. The results of Wrewsky† and of Bredig and Bayer‡ on the one hand, differ considerably from those of Ferguson and Funnel§ (fig. 21.10).

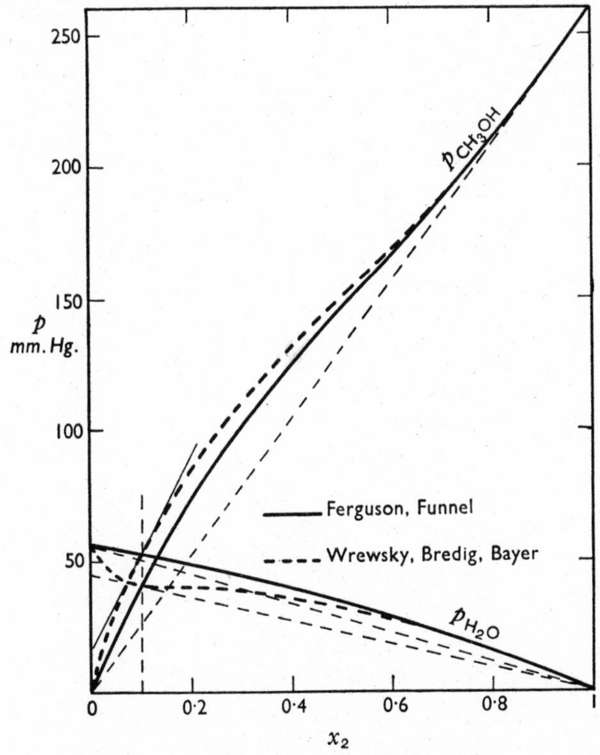

FIG. 21.10. Partial pressures of the system water + methanol at 40 °C. (after Ewart).

* M. Ewert, *loc. cit.*
† M. Wrewsky *Z. physik. Chem.*, **83**, 551 (1913).
‡ G. Bredig and R. Bayer, *Z. physik. Chem.*, **A130**, 141 (1927).
§ J. H. Ferguson and W. Funnel, *J. Phys. Chem.*, **33**, 1 (1927).

The second criterion given above shows immediately that the work of the first named authors is wrong. For we see that at $x_2=0{\cdot}1$ the tangent to the water vapour pressure curve of Wrewsky, Bredig and Bayer, passes through the origin, while at the same concentration the tangent to the alcohol vapour pressure curve does not. On the other hand Ferguson and Funnel's data do not contradict the above criteria.

8. The Total Pressure and the Partial Pressures.

By combining the Duhem-Margules equation (21.54) with the equality

$$p=p_1+p_2, \tag{21.56}$$

and eliminating p_2, we obtain

$$\frac{\partial p_1}{\partial x_2}=\frac{(1-x_1)p_1}{p_1-x_1p}\cdot\frac{\partial p}{\partial x_2}. \tag{21.56'}$$

These equations enable us to calculate the partial pressures p_1 and p_2, and hence also the activity coefficients, when we know the total pressure as a function of mole fraction. This is an extremely interesting possibility since, from the point of view of experimental technique it is much easier to determine total pressures than partial pressures.

Suppose, for example, we consider equation (21.50), but limit the expansion to the x_2^3 term. Then with (21.51), we find

$$\begin{aligned} p&=p_1^0x_1\gamma_1+p_2^0x_2\gamma_2\\ &=p_1^0x_1\exp{(\alpha_2x_2^2+\alpha_3x_2^3)}+p_2^0x_2^3\exp{[(\alpha_2+\tfrac{3}{2}\alpha_3)x_1^2-\alpha_3x_1^3]}. \end{aligned} \tag{21.57}$$

We can then find values of α_2 and α_3 from two points on the total vapour pressure curve, or by finding the tangents to the total pressure curve at $x_2=0$ and $x_2=1$.*

This method is particularly simple when the deviations from ideality are small.† If we neglect α_3 in (21.57), expand the exponentials, and retain only the first two terms we find that

$$\alpha_2=\frac{p-p^{\mathrm{id}}}{x_1x_2\,[p_1^0+(p_2^0-p_1^0)\,x_1]}, \tag{21.58}$$

where p^{id} is the value of p corresponding to a perfect solution, that is to say

$$p^{\mathrm{id}}=p_1^0x_1+p_2^0x_2. \tag{21.58'}$$

In this case determination of the total pressure gives directly the value of α_2, and hence also the activity coefficients and the partial pressures.

When deviations from ideality are large, then it is better to employ

* N. I. Joukowsky, *Bull. Soc. Chim. Belg.*, **43**, 299 (1934); *cf.* also I. Kritschevsky and J. Kasarnowsky, *Zeit. anorg. allg. Chem.* **218**, 49 (1934); V. de Landsberg, *Bull. Soc. Chim. Belg.*, **49**, 21 (1940); P. Tuomikoski, *loc. cit.*

† *Cf.* O. Redlich and A. T. Kister, *J. Amer. Chem. Soc.*, **71**, 505 (1949)

the graphical method suggested by Boissonnas.* To do this we write (21.56′) in the form

$$\frac{\partial p_2}{\partial x_2} = \frac{1}{1 - \dfrac{p_1 x_2}{p_2 x_1}} \cdot \frac{\partial p}{\partial x_2}. \tag{21.58''}$$

If both p and $\partial p/\partial x_2$ are known, and if in addition we know p_2 for the composition x_2 under consideration, then this equation allows us to calculate $(\partial p_2/\partial x_2)$. From this coefficient we can therefore calculate p_2 at an adjacent composition. By proceeding from point to point it is then possible to calculate p_2 over the whole range of composition.

To obtain a starting point for this calculation we note that for a sufficiently dilute solution (*i.e.* x_2 sufficiently small) we have from (21.10):

$$p_1 = p_1^0 x_1$$

or

$$dp_1 = p_1^0\, dx_1 \quad \text{and} \quad dp_2 = dp - dp_1 = dp + p_1^0\, dx_2.$$

In practice, we divide the composition range into a number of equal intervals Δx_2, and use the approximate equations

$$\Delta p_2 = \frac{\Delta p}{1 - \dfrac{p_1 x_2}{p_2 x_1}},$$

$$\Delta p_2 = \Delta p + p_1^0 \Delta x_2 \qquad \text{for } x_2 = 0.$$

The smaller the value chosen for Δx_2, the more precise is the method.† Fig. 21.11 shows the excellent agreement obtained between observed and calculated partial vapour pressures for the system ethanol + chloroform at 45 °C.

Essentially the same method is also applicable to the calculation of the activity coefficients of one component from measured values for the other component. Here again the precision of the method depends on the size of the interval Δx_2. In fig. 21.8 are given the results of calculations taking Δx_2 as 0·050 and 0·025 respectively.

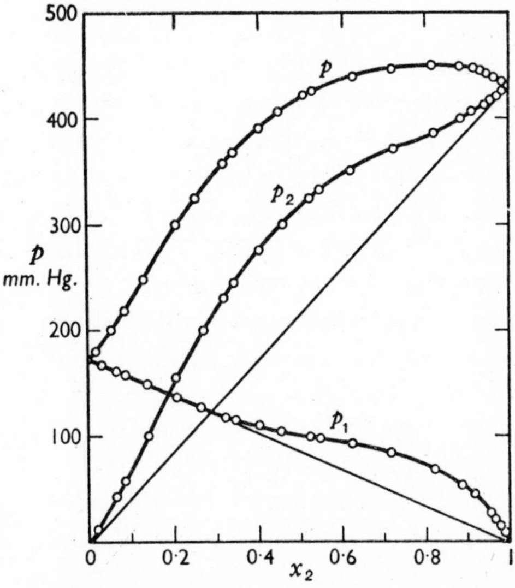

FIG. 21.11. Partial pressures calculated from the total pressure curve by Boissonnas' method (points) compared with observed partial pressures (full lines) for the system ethanol (1) + chloroform (2) at 45 °C.

* C. G. Boissonnas, *Helv. Chim. Acta.*, 22, 541 (1939).

† For further details see Boissonnas *loc. cit.*

9. The Boiling Point Law.

Up till now we have considered the equilibrium curves of liquids under isothermal conditions. We pass on now to examine the curves obtained when the total pressure remains constant.

A particularly simple case arises when all the solute species may be regarded as non-volatile. The solvent is then the only species which is

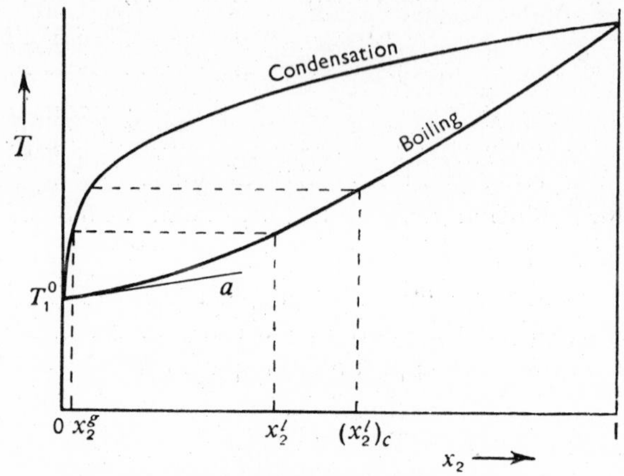

FIG. 21.12. Boiling point and condensation curves for solution of involatile solute, at constant pressure.

present in both the liquid phase (denoted by l) and the vapour phase (denoted by g). This case is approximately realized in a binary mixture for which the boiling and condensation curves have the form shown schematically in fig. 21.12, provided that the solution is fairly dilute (*e.g.* in fig. 21.12 when $x_2^l < (x_2^l)_c$). In this case a mole fraction of x_2^l in the solution corresponds to a mole fraction of x_2^g in the vapour, this concentration being so small that the vapour may be considered as consisting only of the solvent.

In what follows we shall assume that $x_2^g \dots x_c^g$ may be taken as zero. We have already studied in chap. XVIII, §§ 3 and 4, the equilibrium distribution of a component between one phase consisting of a pure compound, and a second phase consisting of a solution.

By employing equation (18.21) directly,* and assuming that the latent heat of vaporization of the pure solvent $\Delta_e h^0$ is independent of T in the temperature interval considered† we have

$$\ln x_1\gamma_1 = \frac{\Delta_e h^0}{\mathbf{R}}\left(\frac{1}{T} - \frac{1}{T^0}\right), \tag{21.59}$$

* Here $(h^0_{T,p})_1 = \Delta'_{\prime\prime} h^0_1 = -\Delta_e h^0$ since we have identified phase $'$ with the gas and phase $''$ with the liquid.

† For the corrections to be made if account is taken of the effect of temperature on the latent heat $\Delta_e h^0$, *cf.* the similar problem treated in § 2 of chap. XXII.

where $x_1\gamma_1$ has been written in place of $x_1^l\gamma_1^l$, the activity of the solvent in the solution, and T^0 is the boiling point of the pure solvent at the pressure concerned. For a dilute solution the difference

$$\theta \equiv T - T^0, \tag{21.60}$$

will be small compared with T^0. If also the solution is ideal, equation (21.59) may be written

$$\theta \frac{\Delta_e h^0}{\mathbf{R}(T^0)^2} = -\ln x_1 = \sum_s x_s. \tag{21.61}$$

This approximation corresponds to identifying the boiling point curve with the tangent a at the origin (*cf.* fig. 21.12).

Written in molalities, (21.61) becomes (*cf.* 20.51)

$$\theta = \frac{\mathbf{R}(T^0)^2}{\Delta_e h^0} \cdot \frac{M_1}{1000} \Sigma \, \mathrm{m}_s = \theta_e \Sigma \, \mathrm{m}_s, \tag{21.62}$$

where θ_e is called the *boiling point*, or *ebullioscopic*, *constant*. Its value depends only on the properties of the solvent.

The following table gives the values of the ebullioscopic constant for some important solvents.

TABLE 21.1*

Solvent	*Ebullioscopic Constant* °C
Water	0·51
Diethyl ether	2·06
Ethanol	1·20
Benzene	2·53
Acetone	1·71

The elevation of boiling point resulting from the addition to the solvent of a known weight of solute, enables the molality of the dissolved substance to be calculated, and hence the molecular weight of the solute if its weight concentration is known. *This is the principle of the ebullioscopic method of determining molecular weights.*

The use of equation (21.62) clearly supposes that the solution is ideal and non-ionized (*cf.* chap. XXVII). For a solution which is dilute, but non-ideal, we see immediately that by replacing $\ln x_1\gamma_1$ in (21.59) by $\phi \ln x_1$ (*cf.* 20.9) we obtain equation (21.62) in the form

$$\theta = \phi \frac{\mathbf{R}(T^0)^2}{\Delta_e h^0} \cdot \frac{M_1}{1000} \Sigma \, \mathrm{m}_s = \phi \theta^{\mathrm{id}}. \tag{21.62'}$$

We notice that the ebullioscopic constants of most solvents are only

* C. S. Hoyt and C. K. Finck, *J. Phys. Chem.*, **41**, 453 (1937).

a few degrees, in contrast to cryoscopic constants (*cf.* chap. XXII, § 2) which are several times larger. This is one of the reasons why the cryoscopic method leads to much more precise results than the ebullioscopic method.*

10. Boiling and Condensation Curves for Completely Miscible Liquids.

We shall now consider the case in which both components of a binary system are present in both the liquid and the vapour phase. We may apply to this problem the equations developed in §§ 5–7 of chapter XVIII.

We shall consider first the constant pressure curves. The tangents to the boiling and condensation curves are given by equations (18.46) and (18.47), while the equations for the complete curves are given by (18.28) and (18.29) which may be written in this case ($dp=0$) :

$$\ln \frac{x_2^g \gamma_2^g}{x_2^l \gamma_2^l} = \int_{T_2^0}^{T} \frac{\Delta_e h_2^0}{RT^2}\, dT, \tag{21.63}$$

$$\ln \frac{(1-x_2^g)\gamma_1^g}{(1-x_2^l)\gamma_1^l} = \int_{T_1^0}^{T} \frac{\Delta_e h_1^0}{RT^2}\, dT, \tag{21.64}$$

where $\Delta_e h^0$ designates the heat of evaporation of the pure liquid component, and T^0 its boiling point.

We now make the substitutions, as in (18.31) and (18.32),

$$\lambda_1 = \frac{\Delta_e h_1^0}{R}\left(\frac{1}{T} - \frac{1}{T_1^0}\right); \quad \lambda_2 = \frac{\Delta_e h_2^0}{R}\left(\frac{1}{T_2^0} - \frac{1}{T}\right). \tag{21.65}$$

With the additional assumptions that the latent heats are independent of temperature, and that the vapour phase is a perfect gas mixture we obtain :

$$x_2^g = \frac{e^{\lambda_1}\gamma_2^l - \gamma_1^l \gamma_2^l}{e^{\lambda_1}\gamma_2^l - e^{-\lambda_2}\gamma_1^l}, \tag{21.66}$$

$$x_2^l = \frac{e^{\lambda_1} - \gamma_1^l}{e^{\lambda_1+\lambda_2}\gamma_2^l - \gamma_1^l}. \tag{21.67}$$

If the phases are both ideal, we have finally (*cf.* 18.33, 18.34)

$$x_2^g = \frac{e^{\lambda_1} - 1}{e^{\lambda_1} - e^{-\lambda_2}}, \tag{21.68}$$

$$x_2^l = \frac{e^{\lambda_1} - 1}{e^{\lambda_1+\lambda_2} - 1}. \tag{21.69}$$

We notice that, in general, equations (21.66) and (21.67) only give *implicit* equations for the condensation and boiling point curves, since the activity coefficients depend upon the compositions.

* For a full account of the experimental methods of the ebullioscopic technique, *cf.* W. Swietoslawski, *Ebulliometry*, (New York, 1937).

Examples : The acetone + ether system.

Let us consider the acetone + ether system and calculate the boiling point curve.

Suppose, to fix our ideas, that the activity coefficients follow the simple law (*cf.* 21.52′).

$$RT \ln \gamma_1 = \alpha (x_2^l)^2, \qquad (21.70)$$
$$RT \ln \gamma_2 = \alpha (x_1^l)^2,$$

where α is a constant. These equations have in fact been verified for this system by Porter* from a study of the vapour pressures of the solutions at 30 °C ; he found $\alpha \sim 450$ cal./mole.

By inserting the values of γ_1 and γ_2 calculated from (21.70) into (21.67) we have

$$x_2^l = \frac{e^{\lambda_1} - e^{\frac{\alpha}{RT}\left(x_2^l\right)^2}}{e^{\left\{\lambda_1 + \lambda_2 + \frac{\alpha}{RT}\left(1 - x_2^l\right)^2\right\}} - e^{\frac{\alpha}{RT}\left(x_2^l\right)^2}}. \qquad (21.71)$$

In principle this equation enables us to calculate x_2 as a function of T, that is to calculate the boiling point curve. In practice of course this can only be done by successive approximations.

In the case of the acetone + ether system we have

for acetone $\Delta_e h_1^0 = 8120$ cal./mole ; $T_1^0 = 329{\cdot}8$ °K ;

for ether $\Delta_e h_2^0 = 6260$ cal./mole ; $T_2^0 = 308{\cdot}0$ °K ;

whence

$$\lambda_1 = 4060 \left(\frac{1}{T} - \frac{1}{329{\cdot}8}\right)$$
$$\lambda_2 = 3130 \left(\frac{1}{308} - \frac{1}{T}\right).$$

Using these values together with $\alpha = 450$ cal./mole the values of x_2 at various temperatures have been calculated. They are given, together with the experimental values, in table 21.2. The agreement is perfect within the accuracy of the calculations.

TABLE 21.2

Calculation of Boiling Point Curve of the System acetone (1) + ether (2)

T °K	λ_1	λ_2	$\lambda_1+\lambda_2$	e^{λ_1}	$e^{\lambda_1+\lambda_2}$	$\frac{\alpha}{RT}$	x_2^l (calc) *ether*	x_2^l(obs) *ether*
308	—	—	—	—	—	—	1	1
313	0·662	0.162	0·824	1·939	2·279	0·72	0.45 ± 0·02	0·45
317	0·499	0·288	0·787	1·647	2·197	0·71	0·28	0·28
321	0·337	0·413	0·750	1·401	2·117	0·70	0·16	0·16
325	0·183	0·532	0·715	1·201	2·045	0·69	0·007	0·007
329·8	—	—	—	—	—	—	0	0

* A. W. Porter, *Trans. Faraday Soc.*, 16, 336 (1920).

The n-hexane + nitrobenzene system.

We now apply equation (21.71) to calculate the boiling point curve of this system, but here there is no direct experimental information as to the value of α. However it is known that this system has an upper consolute temperature T_c of 19 °C. Now we saw in chapter XVI that the upper consolute temperature of a regular solution is related to α by equation (16.55). Assuming the present system to be regular we have then :

$$\alpha = 2\boldsymbol{R}T_c = 4 \times 292 = 1168 \text{ cal./mole.}$$

For the purpose of an approximate calculation we may take this as 1200 cal./mole, and employ the following values of latent heats and boiling points.

For n-hexane : $\Delta_e h_1^0 = 6800$ cal./mole, $T_1^0 = 341$ °K ;
and for nitrobenzene : $\Delta_e h_2^0 = 7940$ cal./mole, $T_2^0 = 484$ °K.

The results of an approximate calculation of the boiling point curve are given in table 21.3 ; again the agreement with the observed curve is entirely satisfactory.

TABLE 21.3

Calculation of Boiling Point Curve for the System n-hexane (1) + nitrobenzene (2)

T °K	λ_1	λ_2	$\lambda_1+\lambda_2$	e^{λ_1}	$e^{\lambda_1+\lambda_2}$	$\dfrac{\alpha}{\boldsymbol{R}T}$	x_2^l (calc)	x_2^l (obs)
341	—	—	—	—	—	—	0	0
343	−0·0578	−3·37	−3·43	0·944	0·0325	1·75	0·08	0·09
348	−0·201	−3·21	−3·41	0·818	0·0332	1·72	0·3	0·3
359	−0·500	−2·86	−3·36	0·607	0·0349	1·67	0·8	0·8
383	−1·09	−2·16	−3·26	0·336	0·0385	1·57	0·9	0·8
484	—	—	—	—	—	—	1	1

We now consider the isothermal curves. The vapour and liquid curves at a given temperature are, from (18.28) and (18.29), given by the simultaneous equations

$$\ln \frac{(1-x_2^g)\gamma_1^g}{(1-x_2^l)\gamma_1^l} = -\frac{1}{\boldsymbol{R}T}\int_{p_1^0}^{p} \Delta_e v_1^0\, dp, \tag{21.72}$$

$$\ln \frac{x_2^g\,\gamma_2^g}{x_2^l\,\gamma_2^l} = -\frac{1}{\boldsymbol{R}T}\int_{p_1^0}^{p} \Delta_e v_2^0\, dp, \tag{21.73}$$

where p_1^0 and p_2^0 are the saturated vapour pressures of pure component 1, and component 2 respectively.

If we neglect the molar volumes of the components in the liquid phase in comparison with those in the vapour phase, we have simply

$$\Delta_e v_1^0 = \Delta_e v_2^0 = \boldsymbol{R}T/p, \tag{21.74}$$

so that equations (21.72) and (21.73) are readily integrated to give

$$\ln \frac{(1-x_2^g)\gamma_1^g}{(1-x_2^l)\gamma_1^l} = \ln \frac{p_1^0}{p}, \tag{21.75}$$

$$\ln \frac{x_2^g\,\gamma_2^g}{x_2^l\,\gamma_2^l} = \ln \frac{p_2^0}{p}. \tag{21.76}$$

Furthermore, if the vapour phase behaves as a perfect gas mixture γ_1^g and γ_2^g are both unity and the equations can be solved for x_2^l and x_2^g to give

$$x_2^l = \frac{p_1^0\gamma_1^l - p}{p_1^0\gamma_1^l - p_2^0\gamma_2^l}, \quad \text{(boiling point curve)}, \tag{21.77}$$

$$x_2^g = \frac{p_1^0 p_2^0 \gamma_1^l \gamma_2^l - p p_2^0 \gamma_2^l}{p p_1^0 \gamma_1^l - p p_2^0 \gamma_2^l}, \quad \text{(condensation curve)}. \tag{21.78}$$

We see immediately that (21.77) can be rewritten in the more familiar form (*cf.* 21.32) :

$$\begin{aligned} p &= p_1^0\gamma_1^l - p_1^0\gamma_1^l x_2 + p_2^0\gamma_2^l x_2^l \\ &= p_1^0\gamma_1^l x_1^l + p_2^0\gamma_2^l x_2^l. \end{aligned} \tag{21.79}$$

Finally, if the system is perfect,

$$x_2^l = \frac{p_1^0 - p}{p_1^0 - p_2^0}, \tag{21.80}$$

$$x_2^g = \frac{p_2^0(p_1^0 - p)}{p(p_1^0 - p_2^0)}; \tag{21.81}$$

or

$$p = p_1^0(1 - x_2^l) + p_2^0 x_2^l \quad \text{(boiling point curve)}, \tag{21.82}$$

$$\frac{1}{p} = \frac{x_2^g}{p_2^0} - \frac{1 - x_2^g}{p_1^0} \quad \text{(condensation curve)}. \tag{21.83}$$

From the latter pair of equations we see that for a perfect system at constant temperature, the boiling point curve is a straight line while, unless $p_1^0 = p_2^0$, the condensation curve is a hyperbola.

If the two pure liquids have the same vapour pressure ($p_1^0 = p_2^0$) then the two curves degenerate into a simple horizontal straight line (fig. 21.13). The greater the difference between the vapour pressures of the components at the temperature considered, the greater the deviation of the condensation curve from a straight line ; this is shown schematically in fig. 21.13.

We note that, because of equations (21.80) and (21.81), the composition of an ideal solution is not equal to the composition of the vapour in equilibrium with it, unless the two pure liquids have the same

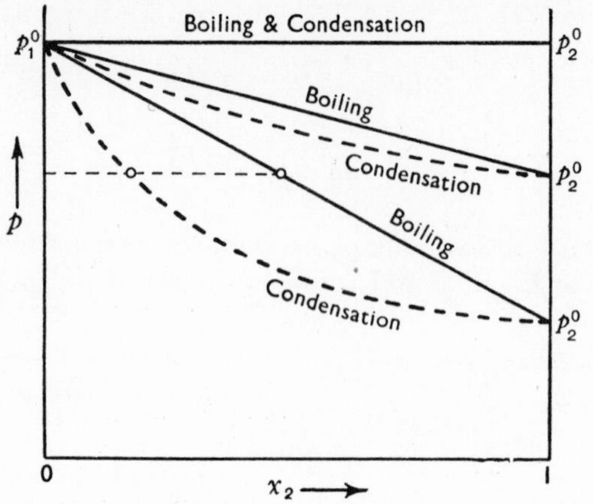

FIG. 21.13. Isothermal equilibrium between solution and vapour for perfect solution.

vapour pressure at the given temperature. The ratio of the compositions of liquid and vapour phases in a perfect solution is seen immediately to be

$$\frac{x_2^g}{x_2^l} = \frac{p_2^0}{p}. \tag{21.84}$$

In other words, for a perfect solution (for which p always lies between p_1^0 and p_2^0) the vapour is always richer than the solution in the more volatile component.

11. Boiling and Condensation Curves for Immiscible Liquids.

We shall now consider two components which are immiscible in the liquid state. The discussion of the co-existence curves in this case is

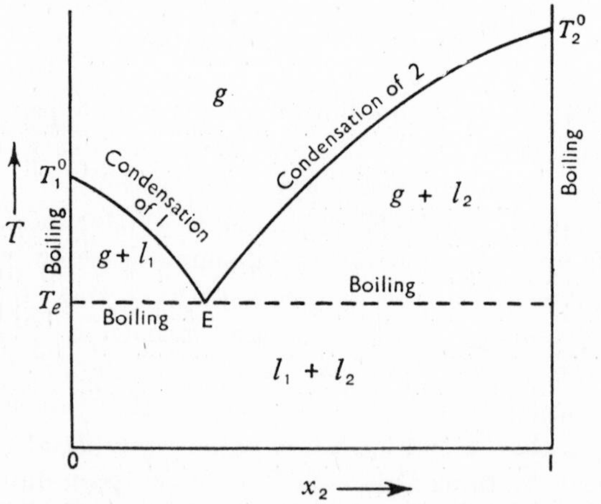

FIG. 21.14. Evaporation of immiscible liquids at constant pressure.

identical with that of chap. XVIII, § 4, when we considered the transfer of a component from the vapour phase to a condensed phase formed of crystals of this component. The only difference is that here the condensed phase is the liquid state.

The constant pressure diagram for this system is shown schematically in fig. 21.14. The boiling point of the mixture is independent of composition as shown by the horizontal dotted line at T_e, except when the second component disappears when, of course, the boiling point rises abruptly to that of the pure component (T_1^0 or T_2^0). The line T_1^0E gives the composition of the vapour in equilibrium with pure liquid 1 as a function of temperature. The equilibrium temperature is lower than the boiling point of 1 as its partial pressure in the vapour phase is lower than total pressure. Similarly T_2^0E gives the composition of mixed vapour in equilibrium with liquid 2. At the eutectic point we have co-existence of the two liquid phases and vapour. The lines T_1^0E and T_2^0E are given by equations like (18.23) and (18.23′).

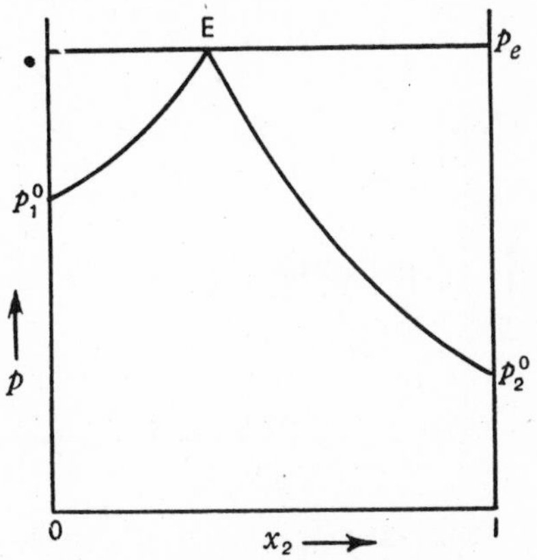

FIG. 21.15. Evaporation of immiscible liquids at constant temperature.

We turn now to isothermal equilibrium, for which the curves of co-existence are given by (18.26) and (18.26′). The phase diagram takes the form shown schematically in fig. 21.15.

At the eutectic point we have

$$p_e = \frac{p_1^0}{1-(x_2^g)_e} = \frac{p_2^0}{(x_2^g)_e}, \tag{21.85}$$

or, in other words,

$$p_e = p_1^0 + p_2^0, \tag{21.86}$$

$$\frac{(x_1^g)_e}{(x_2^g)_e} = \frac{p_1^0}{p_2^0} \tag{21.87}$$

The pressure at which the two liquid phases co-exist with the vapour is equal to the sum of the pressures exerted by the two components in the pure state. This law, which was discovered by Gay-Lussac in 1832, shows that the boiling point of the system is always lower than that of either of the two components alone. Whatever quantities of the two phases are present, the system boils at the eutectic temperature and the vapour has the eutectic composition. It is this property which enables us to call the horizontal line at E in fig. 21.14, the boiling curve.

This phenomenon is employed in the laboratory process of *steam distillation.* If we wish to distil a substance which does not mix with water and which decomposes when heated to its normal boiling point, we may do this by adding water to it. The boiling point of the system will then be much lower than that of the substance alone. It is not in fact necessary to have liquid water present, for the temperature of distillation is lowered simply by passing a stream of steam through the liquid.

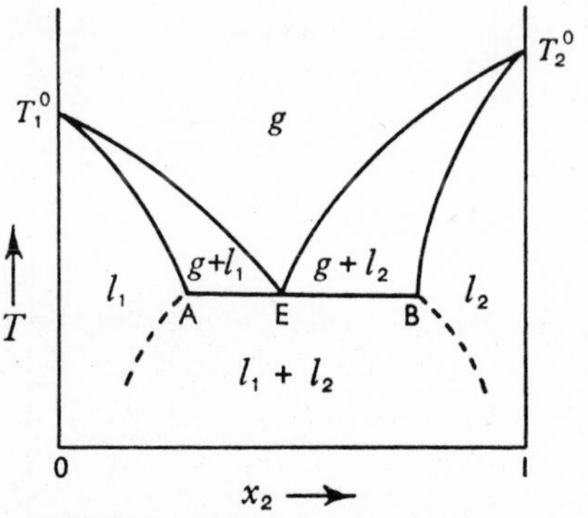

FIG. 21.16. Evaporation of partially miscible liquids at constant pressure.

We have now considered the vapour-liquid equilibria in the two extreme cases of complete miscibility and complete immiscibility. The extension to the case of partial miscibility is straightforward. Fig. 21.16 shows an example of the behaviour of a system of this kind. In this figure l_1 and l_2 are liquid phases of variable composition, l_1 being richer in component 1 than l_2. The dotted curves give the co-existence compositions of the two liquid phases. At the eutectic temperature the liquid phases A and B co-exist with the vapour of composition given by E.

CHAPTER XXII

SOLUTION-CRYSTAL EQUILIBRIUM: EUTECTICS

1. The Crystallization Curve. The Schröder-van Laar Equation.

Let us consider a system of c components and suppose first that these *components are completely miscible in the liquid state, but completely immiscible in the solid state.* On freezing, the solution yields various crystals each variety of which consists of a *single* constituent, since the formation of mixed crystals is excluded. The co-existence curve of the solution with crystals of component 1 is given by (18.21):

$$\boxed{\ln x_1^l \gamma_1^l = \int_{T_1^0}^{T} \frac{\Delta_f h_1^0}{\mathbf{R} T^2}\, dT} \quad , \tag{22.1}$$

where x_1^l and γ_1^l are respectively the mole fraction and activity coefficient of component 1 in the solution, $\Delta_f h_1^0$ the latent heat of fusion at temperature T, and T_1^0 the melting point, of pure component 1.

To integrate this equation accurately we must take account of the variation of $\Delta_f h_1^0$ with temperature, and this may be done by using Kirchhoff's equation (2.32), which in this case gives us

$$\Delta_f h_1^0 = \Delta_f h_1^0(T_1^0) + \int_{T_1^0}^{T} (c_{p,1}^s - c_{p,1}^l)\, dT, \tag{22.2}$$

where $c_{p,1}^l$ is the molar heat capacity at constant pressure of component 1 in the pure liquid state, and $c_{p,1}^s$ that for the same component in the crystalline state, and $\Delta_f h_1^0(T_1^0)$ is the latent heat of fusion at the freezing point T_1^0 of pure component 1.

We may write

$$\Delta_f c_{p,1}^0 = (c_{p,1}^l - c_{p,1}^s). \tag{22.3}$$

For most practical applications it is sufficiently accurate to take $\Delta_f c_{p,1}^0$ as a constant in the range of temperature considered, so that on integrating (22.1) we obtain

$$-\ln x_1^l \gamma_1^l = \frac{\Delta_f h_1^0(T_1^0)}{\mathbf{R}} \left(\frac{1}{T} - \frac{1}{T_1^0} \right) + \frac{\Delta_f c_{p,1}^0}{\mathbf{R}} \left(\ln \frac{T_1^0}{T} + 1 - \frac{T_1^0}{T} \right). \tag{22.4}$$

If this approximation is not sufficiently accurate then we must express $\Delta_f c_p^0$ as a power series in T in the same way as in chap. II, § 5.*

* For further details of these power series *cf.* esp. Harned and Owen [27], pp. 283–285.

In particular, if we neglect $\Delta_f c_p^0$ and so assume the latent heat of fusion to be temperature independent, we have (dropping the specification of temperature attached to $\Delta_f h$),

$$-\ln x_1^l \gamma_1^l = \frac{\Delta_f h_1^0}{R}\left(\frac{1}{T} - \frac{1}{T_1^0}\right), \tag{22.5}$$

and for an ideal solution

$$-\ln x_1^l = \frac{\Delta_f h_1^0}{R}\left(\frac{1}{T} - \frac{1}{T_1^0}\right). \tag{22.5'}$$

This is the equation for the crystallization curve of a solution provided that the solution is ideal, that no mixed crystals are formed, and that the difference between the heat capacities in the liquid and solid states is small enough to justify neglecting the second term in (22.4). This important equation is due to Schröder* and van Laar.†

If we plot the logarithm of the mole fraction of the component which crystallizes out, against the reciprocal of the absolute temperature a straight line will be obtained if equation (22.5′) is satisfied. The slope of this line and its intercept, depend only on the nature of this component and are independent of the other components of the solution.

We observe also that x_1^l is, by definition, the solubility of component 1 in the solution, and that this may be calculated from (22.5) in the form

$$\ln \frac{1}{x_1^l} = \frac{\Delta_f h_1^0 (T_1^0 - T)}{RTT_1^0}, \tag{22.6}$$

and is independent of the nature of the solvent.

It must of course be remembered that this equation is only applicable to ideal solutions and even for them it is an approximate formula. Nevertheless, we can derive from it several general rules concerning the solubility of solids. These were first stated by Hildebrand‡ and are found to be applicable, at least qualitatively, to the majority of cases. They are:

(*a*) The solubility of a solid increases with the temperature.

(*b*) Of two solids having roughly the same latent heats of fusion, that with the lower melting point will be the more soluble in a given solvent at a given temperature.

(*c*) Of two solids having roughly the same melting points, that with the lower heat of fusion will be the more soluble.

The second rule is illustrated by the following figures given by Hildebrand.

* I. Schröder, *Z. physik. Chem.*, **11**, 449 (1893); A. Dahms, *Wied. Ann.* **64**, 507 (1898).
† J. J. van Laar, *Arch. Néerl* II, **8**, 264 (1903).
‡ Hildebrand, [28], p. 35.

TABLE 22.1*

Substance	T_f (°C)	*Solubility in moles per cent* in C_6H_6	in C_6H_{14}	*Temperature* (°C)
Phenanthrene - -	100	18·6	4·2	25
Anthracene - - -	217	0·63	0·18	25
m-dinitrobenzene - -	90	37·6	—	50
o-dinitrobenzene - -	116	17·5	—	50
p-dinitrobenzene - -	170	3·1	—	50

2. The Freezing Point Law.

Let us consider the crystallization curve (or the freezing curve) of a dilute solution. We define the depression of freezing point (θ) of the solvent by

$$\theta \equiv T_1^0 - T. \tag{22.7}$$

Equation (22.4) may now be expressed in the form :

$$-\ln x_1^l \gamma_1^l = \frac{\Delta_f h_1^0}{\mathbf{R}} \frac{\theta}{T_1^0(T_1^0-\theta)} + \frac{\Delta_f c_{p,1}^0}{\mathbf{R}} \left\{ \ln \frac{T_1^0}{T_1^0-\theta} + 1 - \frac{T_1^0}{T_1^0-\theta} \right\} \tag{22.8}$$

where it is understood that $\Delta_f h_1^0$ refers to the temperature T_1^0.

Expanding in powers of θ/T_1^0, and neglecting terms higher than the second order in θ/T_1^0,†

$$-\ln x_1^l \gamma_1^l = \frac{\Delta_f h_1^0}{\mathbf{R}T_1^0} \frac{\theta}{T_1^0} + \left(\frac{\Delta_f h_1^0}{\mathbf{R}} - \frac{\Delta_f c_{p,1}^0}{2\mathbf{R}} \right) \frac{\theta^2}{(T_1^0)^2}. \tag{22.9}$$

For *very dilute solutions* it is sufficient to retain only the term in θ/T_1^0. Then, by employing the osmotic coefficient defined by (20.9) we find that (*cf.* 20.55)

$$\theta = \phi \frac{\mathbf{R}(T_1^0)^2}{\Delta_f h_1^0} \sum_s x_s. \tag{22.10}$$

Analogous formulae are readily derived relating the lowering of freezing point to the molar concentrations c_s and the molalities m_s of the solute species, by substituting (20.47) or (20.51) into (22.10).

If a solution is both very dilute and ideal, we have, in terms of molalities (*cf.* 20.51)

$$\theta = \frac{\mathbf{R}(T_1^0)^2}{\Delta_f h_1^0} \frac{M_1}{1000} \sum_s \mathrm{m}_s. \tag{22.11}$$

The quantity

$$\theta_c \equiv \frac{\mathbf{R}(T_1^0)^2}{\Delta_f h_1^0} \frac{M_1}{1000} \tag{22.12}$$

* Hildebrand, [28], p. 35.

† For the coefficients of higher order *cf.* Harned and Owen, *loc. cit.*, formula (9.2.11).

is called the *cryoscopic or freezing point constant. It depends only on the nature of the solvent.* Numerical values for several solvents are given in table 22.2.

TABLE 22.2

Solvent	*Cryoscopic Constant* °C/*mol in* 1000 g.
Water - - - -	1·86
Benzene - - -	5·08
Phenol - - - -	6·11
Naphthalene - -	6·9
Camphor - - -	37·7
Acetic acid - - -	3·73
Cyclohexanol - -	41·6

We notice that θ_c exhibits wide variations from one solvent to another. This is clearly related to the fact that θ_c contains the term

$$\varDelta_f s_1^0 = \varDelta_f h_1^0 / T_1^0, \tag{22.13}$$

the entropy of fusion of the solvent. We have already seen (*cf.* chap. XIV, § 5) that this varies considerably from substance to substance. In particular spherical molecules, such as camphor and cyclohexanol, whose entropy of fusion is small, have large cryoscopic contants.

We now examine more closely the relationship between entropy of fusion and the freezing point curve of a solution.

3. Entropy of Fusion and the Freezing Curve.

Let us limit ourselves in this discussion to equation (22.5′) which we write in the form :

$$T = \frac{\varDelta_f h_1^0}{R} \frac{1}{\dfrac{\varDelta_f h_1^0}{R T_1^0} - \ln x_1} . \tag{22.14}$$

On differentiation, we have, since $\varDelta_f h_1^0$ has been assumed to be independent of temperature,

$$\left(\frac{\partial^2 T}{\partial x_1^2}\right)_p = \frac{\varDelta_f h_1^0}{R} \frac{1}{\left(\dfrac{\varDelta_f h_1^0}{R T_1^0} - \ln x_1\right)^2} \left\{ \frac{2}{\dfrac{\varDelta_f h_1^0}{R T_1^0} - \ln x_1} - 1 \right\} \frac{1}{x_1^2} . \tag{22.15}$$

The sign of this derivative, which tells us the curvature of the line of co-existence of crystals and solution, depends upon the sign of the term

$$2 - \left(\frac{\varDelta_f h_1^0}{R T_1^0} - \ln x_1\right) . \tag{22.16}$$

In the region of the origin, $x_1 \rightarrow 1$, we see that

$$\text{if} \quad \frac{\Delta_f h_1^0}{\boldsymbol{R}T_1^0} > 2, \quad \left(\frac{\partial^2 T}{\partial x_1^2}\right) < 0\,; \tag{22.17}$$

while,

$$\text{if} \quad \frac{\Delta_f h_1^0}{\boldsymbol{R}T_1^0} < 2, \quad \left(\frac{\partial^2 T}{\partial x_1^2}\right) > 0. \tag{22.18}$$

These two cases are shown diagrammatically in figs. 22.1 and 22.2; they correspond to the entropy of fusion of the solvent at the melting point having a value greater or less than $2\boldsymbol{R}$, respectively.

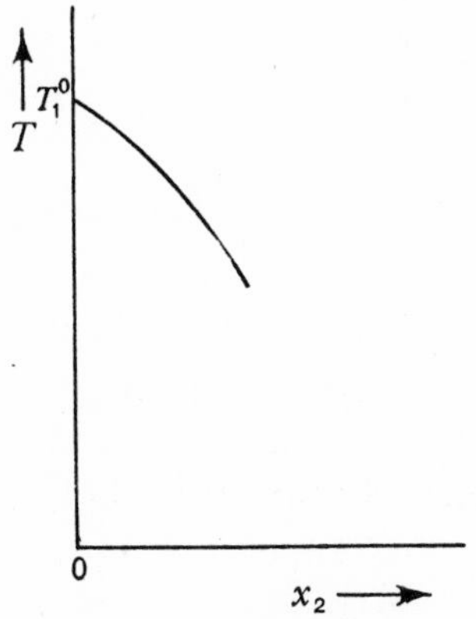

FIG. 22.1. Shape of freezing point curve if $\Delta_f h_1^0/\boldsymbol{R}T_1^0 > 2$.

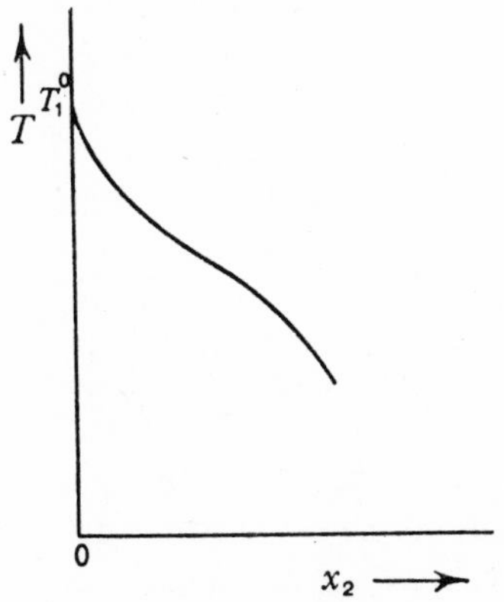

FIG. 22.2. Shape of freezing point curve if $\Delta_f h_1^0/\boldsymbol{R}T_1^0 < 2$.

The dependence of the curvature of the freezing point curve at the origin upon the entropy of fusion of the solvent was first pointed out by van Laar.* The most common case corresponds to (22.17) and fig. 22.1 (*cf.* chap. XIV, § 5, table 14.6). On the other hand, for spherical solvent molecules (*cf.* table 14.5) for which the entropy of fusion is abnormally small, the case (22.18) is realized. The form of the freezing point curve at the origin is thus a useful criterion, in the absence of calorimetric data, for the identification of those compounds which have a low entropy of fusion.†

4. Calculation of the Eutectic Point.

The results obtained in the first paragraph of this chapter may now be applied to binary mixtures. The isobaric phase diagram is then of the form shown diagrammatically in fig. 22.3.

* van Laar, [48], pp. 297–298.
† V. Mathot, *Bull. Soc. Chim. Belg.*, 59, 137 (1950).

The curves T_1^0E and T_2^0E are given, respectively, by the equations

$$\left.\begin{aligned} -\ln(1-x_2^l)\gamma_1^l &= \frac{\Delta_f h_1^0}{R}\left(\frac{1}{T}-\frac{1}{T_1^0}\right) \\ -\ln x_2^l\gamma_2^l &= \frac{\Delta_f h_2^0}{R}\left(\frac{1}{T}-\frac{1}{T_2^0}\right) \end{aligned}\right\}. \tag{22.19}$$

At the eutectic point crystals of both 1 and 2, and the solution coexist in equilibrium and the two equations (22.19) are simultaneously satis-

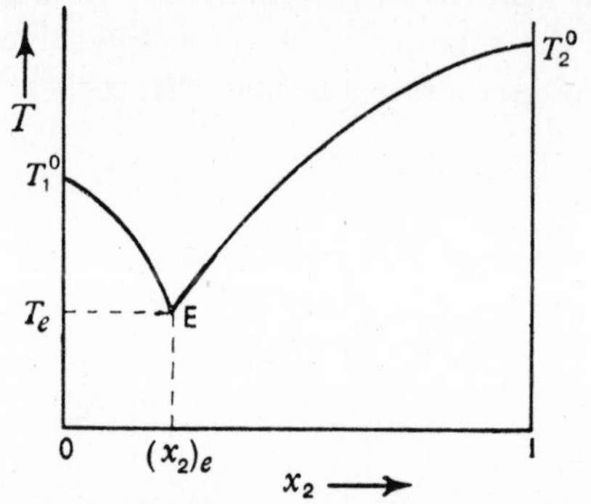

FIG. 22.3. Calculation of eutectic point from crystallization or freezing point curves at constant pressure.

fied. In particular, if the solution is perfect, the eutectic point is obtained by solving the two equations

$$\left.\begin{aligned} -\ln\{1-(x_2)_e\} &= \frac{\Delta_f h_1^0}{R}\left(\frac{1}{T_e}-\frac{1}{T_1^0}\right) \\ -\ln(x_2)_e &= \frac{\Delta_f h_2^0}{R}\left(\frac{1}{T_e}-\frac{1}{T_2^0}\right) \end{aligned}\right\}. \tag{22.19$'$}$$

As an example we show in fig. 22.4 the freezing point diagram of a mixture of *o*- and *p*-chloronitrobenzene.* The curves calculated from equation (22.5′) are shown dotted; they coincide with the observed behaviour over most of their length.

Now we consider the case where the entropies of fusion of the two components are nearly the same. Let us suppose that

$$\frac{\Delta_f h_1^0}{RT_1^0} \simeq \frac{\Delta_f h_2^0}{RT_2^0} = \alpha. \tag{22.20}$$

Then equations (22.19′) take the form

$$\left.\begin{aligned} \ln\{1-(x_2)_e\} &= \alpha\left(\frac{T_e-T_1^0}{T_e}\right) \\ \ln(x_2)_e &= \alpha\left(\frac{T_e-T_2^0}{T_e}\right) \end{aligned}\right\}. \tag{22.21}$$

It is seen immediately that if $T_2^0 = T_1^0$ then $(x_2)_e = 1-(x_2)_e = 0{\cdot}5$.

* A. F. Holleman, *Rec. trav. chim.*, **19**, 101 (1900); G. T. Kohman, *J. Phys Chem.*, **25**, 1048 (1925); *cf.* Timmermans [45], p. 54.

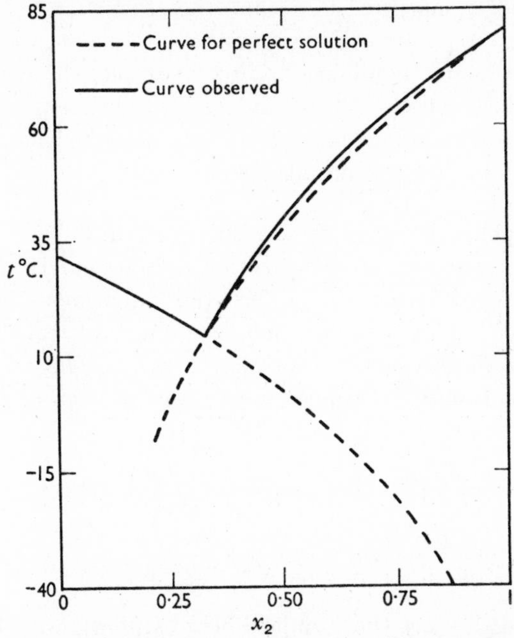

FIG. 22.4. Freezing point curves for *o*- + *p*-chloronitrobenzene.

Thus to obtain the most fusible mixture of two compounds having approximately the same melting point, we should take an approxi-

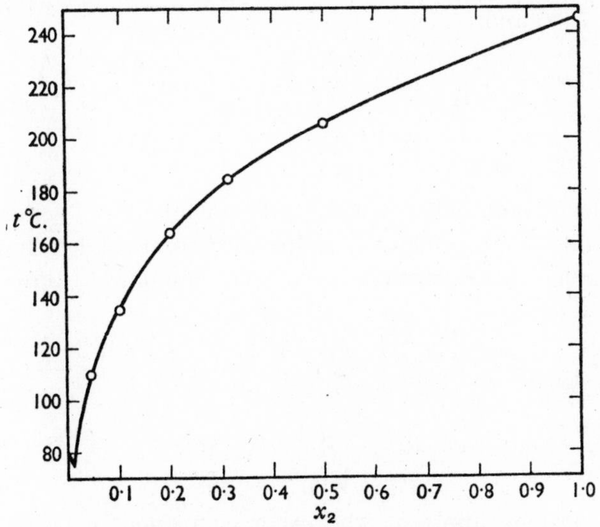

FIG. 22.5. Freezing point curves for naphthalene + 1 . 8 . diphenyl-octatetraene.*

* J. Marechal, *Thesis*, (Brussels, 1951).

mately equimolar mixture. On the other hand if the difference between the freezing points is large then the eutectic may almost coincide with the more fusible component. For example, the results of Marechal's* measurements on the system naphthalene + 1.8-diphenyloctatetraene are given in fig. 22.5; the eutectic mixture contains about 98 moles per cent of naphthalene.

5. Effect of Applied Pressure on the Eutectic Point.

The effect of pressure on the position of the eutectic point may be examined by considering the differential equations obeyed by the *eutectic line*, at all points along which the affinity of transfer of the two components from the solid to solution is zero. The affinity is given by (18.19) which may be applied separately to each of the two components:

$$\left.\begin{aligned} -\frac{\Delta_s^l h_1^0}{T}\,\delta T + \Delta_s^l v_1^0\,\delta p + RT\,\delta \ln x_1^l \gamma_1^l = 0 \\ -\frac{\Delta_s^l h_2^0}{T}\,\delta T + \Delta_s^l v_2^0\,\delta p + RT\,\delta \ln x_2^l \gamma_2^l = 0 \end{aligned}\right\}, \tag{22.22}$$

where $\Delta_s^l h^0$ and $\Delta_s^l v^0$ are the standard heat content and volume changes for transfer of the pure component concerned from solid to liquid; they are the latent heat of fusion and the volume change on fusion, respectively.

If we replace the changes in the activity coefficients by the values given by (7.68) and (7.69) we have

$$\begin{aligned} \delta \ln x_1\gamma_1 &= \left(\frac{\partial \ln \gamma_1}{\partial T}\right)_{p,x_2} \delta T + \left(\frac{\partial \ln \gamma_1}{\partial p}\right)_{T,x_2} \delta p + \left(\frac{\partial \ln x_1\gamma_1}{\partial x_2}\right)_{T,p} \delta x_2 \\ &= -\frac{(h_1 - h_1^0)}{RT^2}\,\delta T + \frac{(v_1 - v_1^0)}{RT}\,\delta p + \left(\frac{\partial \ln x_1\gamma_1}{\partial x_2}\right)_{T,p} \delta x_2. \end{aligned} \tag{22.23}$$

We must be careful to distinguish the heat content and volume changes corresponding to transfer of a component from solid to liquid in the system under consideration from the standard values of these quantities:

$$\left.\begin{aligned} \Delta_s^l h_1 = h_1^l - h_1^s\,;\quad \Delta_s^l h_1^0 = h_1^{0,l} - h_1^s\,; \\ \Delta_s^l v_1 = v_1^l - v_1^s\,;\quad \Delta_s^l v_1^0 = v_1^{0,l} - v_1^s\,; \end{aligned}\right\} \tag{22.23'}$$

so that,

$$\begin{aligned} \Delta_s^l h_1 - \Delta_s^l h_1^0 = h_1^l - h_1^{0,l}, \\ \Delta_s^l v_1 - \Delta_s^l v_1^0 = v_1^l - v_1^{0,l}. \end{aligned}$$

Similar equations apply to the other component, so that equation (22.22) may be replaced by

* J. Marechal, *Thesis* (Brussels, 1951).

$$\left.\begin{aligned} -\frac{\Delta_s^l h_1}{T}\,\delta T+\Delta_s^l v_1\,\delta p+RT\left(\frac{\partial \ln x_1\gamma_1}{\partial x_2}\right)_{T,p}\delta x_2=0 \\ -\frac{\Delta_s^l h_2}{T}\,\delta T+\Delta_s^l v_2\,\delta p+RT\left(\frac{\partial \ln x_2\gamma_2}{\partial x_2}\right)_{T,p}\delta x_2=0 \end{aligned}\right\} \tag{22.24}$$

Furthermore, the Gibbs-Duhem equation at constant T, p, (*cf.* 21.45), is

$$x_1\frac{\partial \ln x_1\gamma_1}{\partial x_2}+x_2\frac{\partial \ln x_2\gamma_2}{\partial x_2}=0. \tag{22.24'}$$

Eliminating first δx_2 and then δT from equations (22.24) we obtain, along the eutectic curve

$$\left(\frac{\delta T}{\delta p}\right)_e=-T\,\frac{x_1\,\Delta_s^l v_1+x_2\,\Delta_s^l v_2}{x_1\,\Delta_s^l h_1+x_2\,\Delta_s^l h_2}; \tag{22.25}$$

$$\left(\frac{\delta x_2}{\delta p}\right)_e=-x_1\,\frac{\Delta_s^l h_1\,\Delta_s^l v_2-\Delta_s^l h_2\,\Delta_s^l v_1}{RT\,\dfrac{\partial \ln x_2\gamma_2}{\partial x_2}(x_1\,\Delta_s^l h_1+x_2\,\Delta_s^l h_2)}. \tag{22.26}$$

These equations were given by van Laar.* The quantities which figure on the right hand side of equations (22.25) and (22.26) refer to the eutectic line. Equation (22.25) is analogous to the Clausius-Clapeyron equation (14.4).

Formula (22.26) enables us to see easily the sign of the derivative $(\delta x_2/\delta p)_e$, for this equation can be expressed in an alternative form :

$$\left(\frac{\delta x_2}{\delta p}\right)_e=\frac{x_1\,\Delta_s^l h_1\,\Delta_s^l h_2}{RT\,\dfrac{\partial \ln x_2\gamma_2}{\partial x_2}(x_1\,\Delta_s^l h_1+x_2\,\Delta_s^l h_2)}\left(\frac{\Delta_s^l v_1}{\Delta_s^l h_1}-\frac{\Delta_s^l v_2}{\Delta_s^l h_2}\right). \tag{22.27}$$

The sign of this expression is that of the term

$$\frac{\Delta_s^l v_1}{\Delta_s^l h_1}-\frac{\Delta_s^l v_2}{\Delta_s^l h_2}, \tag{22.28}$$

since the latent heats are always positive and the condition of stability $(\partial\mu_2/\partial x_2)>0$ ensures that $(\partial \ln x_2\gamma_2/\partial x_2)>0$ (*cf.* 15.83).

In the case of aqueous solutions (water being taken as component 1) we have generally $v_1^s>v_1^l$ so that $\Delta_s^l v_1$ is negative. If the solute is such that $\Delta_s^l v_2$ is positive, which is often the case, we have $(\delta x_2/\delta p)_e<0$. Thus as the pressure is increased the eutectic contains a lower concentration of component 2.

Two typical diagrams for aqueous solutions are shown in figs. 22.6 and 22.7 which show the effect of pressure on the eutectic points of the hydroxylamine hydrochloride + water and ammonium perchlorate +

* J. J. van Laar, *Lehrbuch math. Chemie.* (Leipzig, 1901), p. 179.

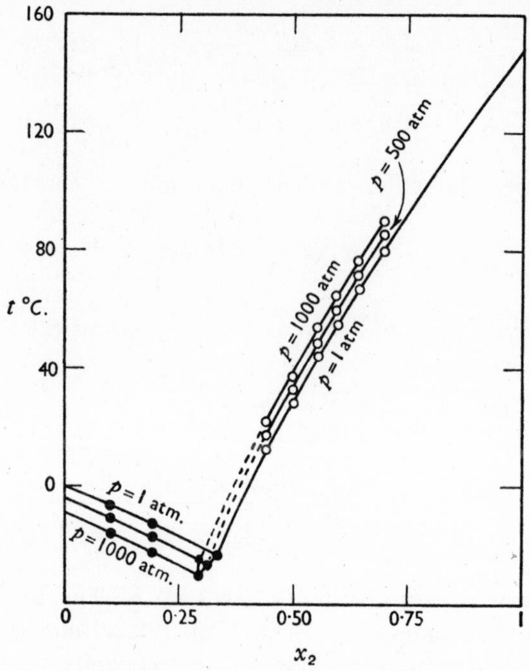

FIG. 22.6. Effect of pressure on the freezing points of aqueous solutions of hydroxylamine hydrochloride.

water systems.* The behaviour exhibited in fig. 22.6 is in fact very much more common than that shown in fig. 22.7.

6. Effect of Applied Pressure on Solubility.

The discussion in the preceding paragraph may now be used to examine the effect of pressure on solubility ; that is to say on conditions away from the eutectic point. We now have crystals of 2 in equilibrium with a solution consisting of 1 and 2. We need now only consider the second equation of (22.24). Under isothermal conditions

$$\left(\frac{\partial x_2}{\partial p}\right)_T = -\frac{\Delta_s^l v_2.}{RT\left(\frac{\partial \ln x_2\gamma_2}{\partial x_2}\right)_{T,p}}. \tag{22.29}$$

As before the denominator must be positive because of the stability condition so that the sign of this expression is that of

$$-\Delta_s^l v_2 = v_2^s - v_2^l. \tag{22.30}$$

This difference can be regarded as the sum of

$$v_2^s - v_2^{0,l}, \tag{22.31}$$

* M. P. Mathieu, *Thesis* (Brussels, 1948–1949) ; *Bull. Soc. Chim. Belge.*, 58, 112, (1949).

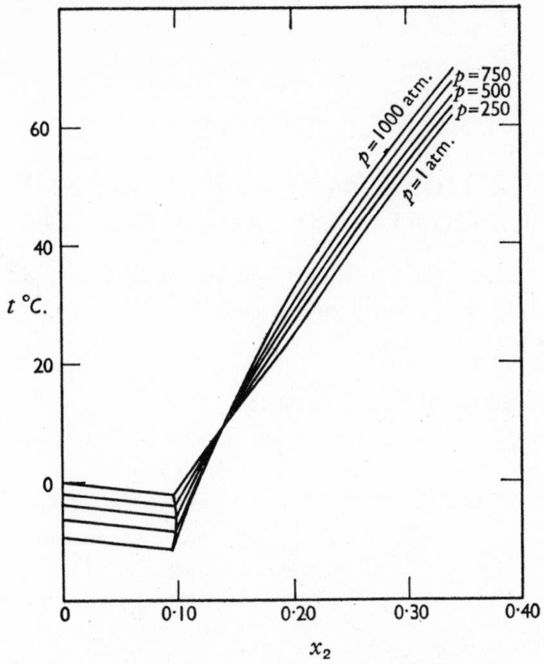

FIG. 22.7. Effect of pressure on the freezing points of aqueous solutions of ammonium perchlorate.

where $v_2^{0,l}$ is the molar volume of the pure liquid 2, and

$$v_2^{0,l} - v_2^l, \tag{22.32}$$

which corresponds to transfer of this component from the pure liquid to the solution. The term (22.31) is usually negative. For an *ideal* solution (22.32) is zero and (22.29) has the same sign as (22.31)—usually negative. For non-ideal solutions (22.32) may be positive or negative, and the behaviour of the system depends upon the relative magnitude of (22.31) and (22.32).

The behaviour of strong electrolyte solutions is of particular interest in this connection.* The expansion on fusion is opposed by the contraction on mixing and under certain circumstances these may cancel exactly so that

$$\left(\frac{\partial x_2}{\partial p}\right)_T = 0. \tag{22.33}$$

An example of this behaviour has been given already in fig. 22.7, where there is a temperature at which the solubility is independent of the pressure.

* For a study of the specific volumes of electrolytes under pressure, see especially the work of L. H. Adams and R. E. Gibson ; *cf.* R. E. Gibson, *J. Amer. Chem. Soc.*, **59**, 1521 (1937) and earlier papers. *Cf.* also Harned and Owen [27], p. 262.

CHAPTER XXIII

SOLUTION-CRYSTAL EQUILIBRIUM: MIXED CRYSTALS AND ADDITION COMPOUNDS

In the last chapter we considered one particular type of freezing point diagram, namely that exhibiting a eutectic. We now study other kinds of freezing point diagram.

1. Continuous Series of Mixed Crystals.

The simplest case is that in which a binary system forms a continuous series of mixed crystals. The discussion of this case follows exactly the same lines as that in chap. XVIII, § 5 and in chap. XXI, § 10 for completely miscible liquids. The vapour curves in the latter case now correspond to the liquidus curves here, and the liquid curves correspond now to the solidus curves.

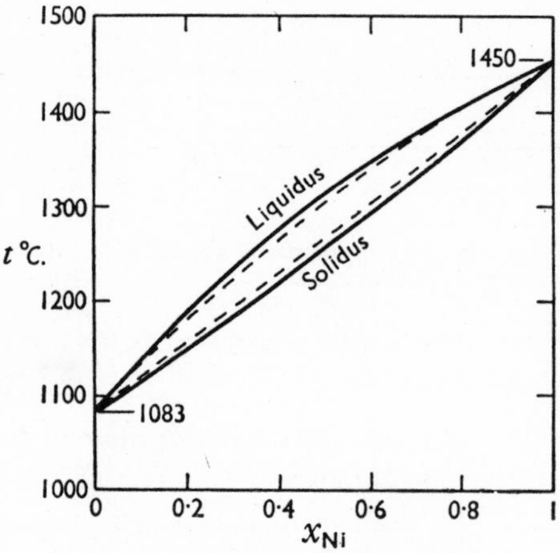

FIG. 23.1. Phase diagram of the system Cu + Ni.
——— observed - - - - - ideal

The equations for liquidus and solidus are therefore given by, (*cf.* 21.66 and 21.67).

$$x_2^l = \frac{e^{\lambda_1}\gamma_1^l\gamma_2^s - \gamma_2^s\gamma_1^s}{e^{\lambda_1}\gamma_1^l\gamma_2^s - e^{-\lambda_2}\gamma_2^l\gamma_1^s}, \tag{23.1}$$

$$x_2^s = \frac{e^{\lambda_1}\gamma_1^l\gamma_2^l - \gamma_2^l\gamma_1^s}{e^{\lambda_1+\lambda_2}\gamma_1^l\gamma_2^s - \gamma_2^l\gamma_1^s}. \tag{23.2}$$

For ideal systems these equations reduce to the van Laar equations (18.33) and (18.34).

$$x_2^l = \frac{e^{\lambda_1} - 1}{e^{\lambda_1} - e^{-\lambda_2}}; \quad x_2^s = \frac{e^{\lambda_1} - 1}{e^{\lambda_1+\lambda_2} - 1}. \tag{23.3}$$

There are only a few systems, where the two components are closely similar in nature, in which the liquidus and solidus curves are given by the simple equations (23.3). As examples we may mention the systems chlorobenzene + bromobenzene, silver + gold, copper + nickel, and certain pairs of optical isomers. The data for the system copper + nickel*

* H. Seltz, *J. Amer. Chem. Soc.*, 56, 307 (1934).

are shown in fig. 23.1; the theoretical and experimental curves are in good agreement showing that this system is nearly ideal.

A particularly simple case arises when both the melting points and latent heats of fusion of the two components are equal. Writing T_0 and $\Delta_f h$ as the common values of the melting point and latent heat we have (*cf.* 18.31 and 18.32)

$$\lambda_1 = -\lambda_2 = \frac{\Delta_f h}{\mathbf{R}}\left(\frac{1}{T} - \frac{1}{T_0}\right). \tag{23.4}$$

Under these conditions the solution of (23.3) must be

$$x_2^l = x_2^s \quad \text{and} \quad \lambda_1 = -\lambda_2 = 0. \tag{23.5}$$

Hence also

$$T = T_0. \tag{23.6}$$

The solidus and liquidus curves coincide and reduce to a single horizontal line. Two examples of this behaviour may be mentioned: first, the *d*-camphroxime + *l*-camphroxime system studied by Adriani* and secondly the dichloro- + chlorobromo ethyl acetamide system.†

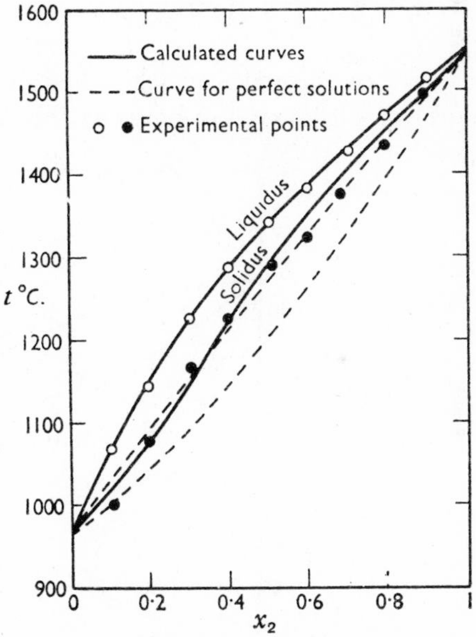

FIG. 23.2. Freezing point diagram for the system Ag (1) + Pd. (2)

In the case of a system where, although the phases are not ideal, they can be treated as regular solutions, the liquidus and solidus curves can be calculated from (23.1) and (23.2), using (21.52′) for the activity coefficients. This has been done by Scatchard and Hamer‡ for a number of systems; the results for the silver + palladium and gold + platinum systems are shown in figs. 23.2 and 23.3. The agreement between the calculated and observed freezing point curves is entirely satisfactory.

Finally we give an example of a system (fig. 23.4) in which a series of mixed crystals is formed, but where the deviations from ideality are such that the solidus and liquidus curves pass through a minimum

* J. H. Adriani, *Z. physik. Chem.*, 33, 453 (1899); *cf.* Timmermans, [45], p. 28.
† Timmermans, [45], p. 82.
‡ G. Scatchard and W. J. Hamer, *J. Amer. Chem. Soc.*, 57, 1810 (1935).

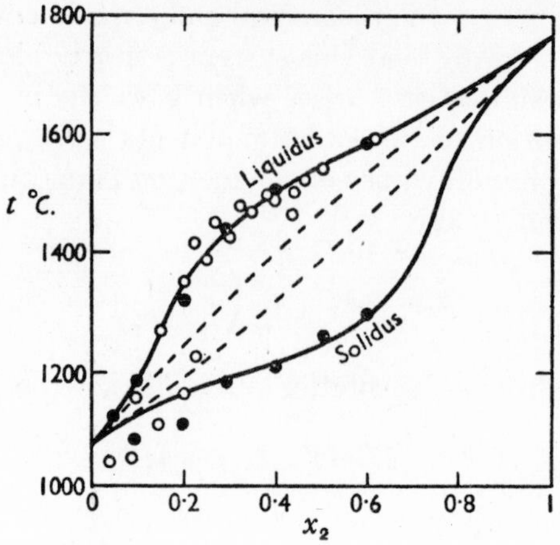

FIG. 23.3. Freezing point diagram for the system Au (1) + Pt (2).
● exptl. points (Doerinckel*) ——— calculated curves
○ exptl. points (Grigorjew†) - - - - - ideal curves

value. In accordance with the Gibbs-Konovalow theorems the solidus and liquidus curves coincide at this point (*cf.* chap. XVIII, § 6).

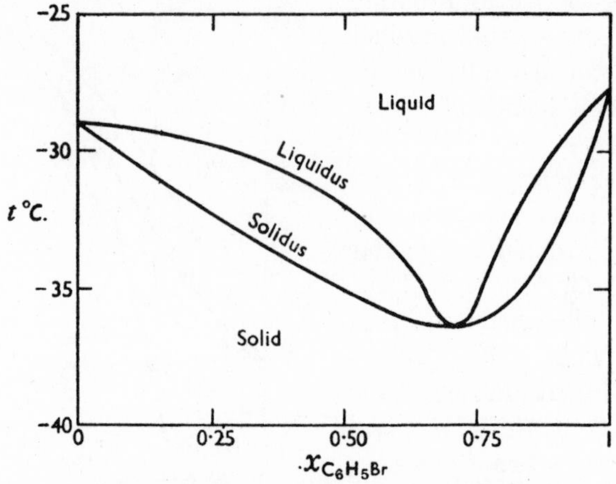

FIG. 23.4. Phase diagram for the system iodo- + bromo-benzene at atmospheric pressure.‡

2. Transition from Mixed Crystals to Addition Compounds and Eutectics.

If the deviations from ideality of the solid solution become very large, then it may be unstable for certain ranges of composition (*cf.* chap. XVI, § 10). We then have the phenomenon of *miscibility gaps*

* F. Doerinckel, *Z. anorg. Chem.*, **54**, 345 (1907).
† A. T. Grigorjew, *Z. anorg. Chem.*, **178**, 97 (1929).
‡ Timmermans [45], p. 88.

in the series of mixed crystals. Thus at the point E in fig. 23.5 there are two solid phases and one liquid phase in equilibrium (*cf.* fig. 21.16).

We consider first the case in which there is only one region of immiscibility. As this zone extends over a wider and wider range of concentration its limits may reach close to $x_2=0$ and $x_2=1$, and in the limit we may consider the two components as completely immiscible in the solid state. The solidus curves T_1^0A and T_2^0B in fig. 23.5 will then coincide with the vertical axes at $x_2=0$ and $x_2=1$, and we have the conditions already discussed in the previous chapter (*cf.* fig. 22.3).

We may now examine the case of more than one miscibility gap, when the phase diagram has the form shown in fig. 23.6. As the zones of immiscibility increase, T_1^0A approaches the axis T_1^0O, while T_cF and T_cG move toward one another and tend to coincide with T_cx_c, while T_2^0B approaches T_2^0O. In the limit the zones of miscibility are reduced to the immediate neighbourhood of $x_2=0$, $x_2=1$ and $x_2=x_c$: we say that the two components form an *addition compound* of composition x_c (*cf.* chap. XVI, § 10). Once again we find, as for eutectic mixtures, that we need consider only the liquidus curves, since the various curves which make up the solidus reduce to vertical lines.

As an example of this behaviour we give in fig. 23.7, the liquidus

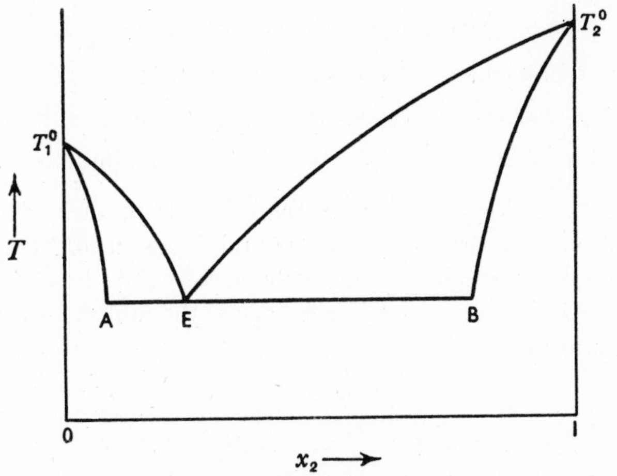

FIG. 23.5. Freezing point diagram for system with zone of immiscible crystals.

curve for the system water + sulphur trioxide. This system forms addition compounds having the compositions SO_3+5H_2O; SO_3+3H_2O; SO_3+2H_2O; SO_3+H_2O ($=H_2SO_4$); $SO_3+\frac{1}{2}H_2O$; these are represented in the diagram by the points C, E, H, K and M.

A further interesting example occurs in the so-called *racemoids* investigated by Timmermans.* In general it is found that mixtures of a mono-substituted and a poly-substituted hydrocarbon are nearly

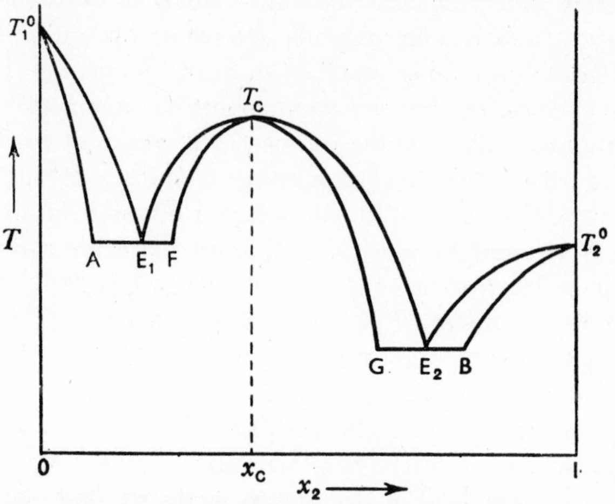

FIG. 23.6. Freezing point diagram for system with two zones of immiscible crystals.

perfect and form eutectics. For example, this behaviour is shown by the following mixtures :

chloroethane + 1, 2-dichloroethane,
1, 1, 2-trichloroethane + 1, 2-dichloroethane,
1, 1, 2-trichloroethane + 1, 1, 2, 2-tetrachloroethane,
pentachloroethane + 1, 1, 2, 2-tetrachloroethane.

In contrast to this, a mixture of the symmetrical dichloro-compound and the symmetrical tetrachloro-compound, forms an addition compound containing one molecule of each substance. This behaviour can be understood if we assume that in the crystal the molecules are arranged in the *trans* form :

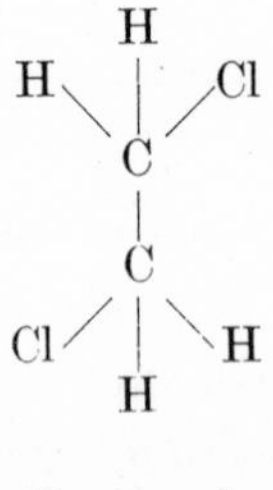

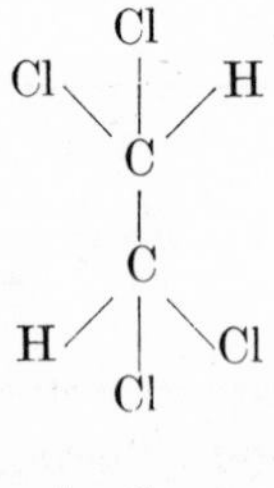

In these formulae the two hydrogen atoms in the tetrachlor-compound occupy the same positions as the chlorine atoms in the dichlor-com-

* *Cf.* Timmermans, [45], p. 76.

pound. Timmermans has shown that many pairs of compounds possessing this complementary structure tend to form equimolecular complexes, in the same way as optical isomers tend to form racemic compounds. From this analogy Timmermans derived the name *racemoids* for complexes of this type.

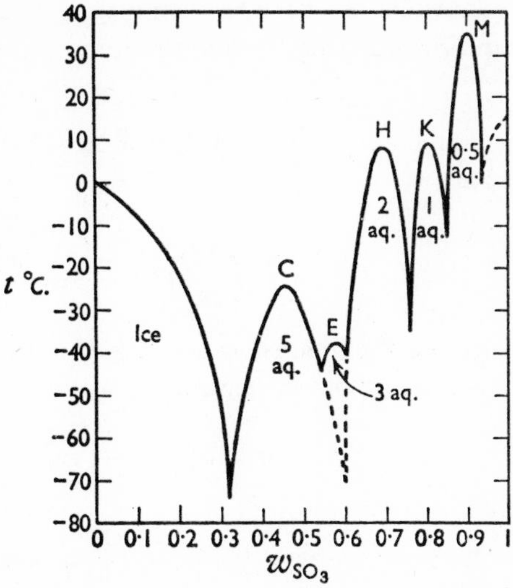

FIG. 23.7. Freezing point diagram for the system $SO_3 + H_2O$.*

3. Dystectic or Indifferent Points.

Let us consider an addition compound formed by ν_1 molecules of component 1 and ν_2 molecules of component 2. The affinity of dissociation of this solid compound (c) into the two components 1 and 2 in the liquid phase is given by

$$\mathbf{A} = \mu_c^s - \nu_1 \mu_1^l - \nu_2 \mu_2^l. \tag{23.7}$$

Suppose we take T, p and x_2^l as the independent variables defining the state of the system, and compare two states of the system in which the variables have the following values :

State I	T	p	x_2^l,
State II	$T+\delta T$	p	$x_2^l + \delta x_2^l$.

The affinity of dissociation will be $\mathbf{A}$ in the first state and $\mathbf{A}+\delta\mathbf{A}$ in the second, and $\delta\mathbf{A}$ will be given by (*cf.* 4.60)

$$\delta\mathbf{A} = \frac{\mathbf{A} + h_{T,p}}{T}\,\delta T + \left(\frac{\partial \mathbf{A}}{\partial x_2^l}\right)_{T,\,p} \delta x_2^l, \tag{23.8}$$

where $h_{T,p}$ is the heat of dissociation of the addition compound.

Employing the Gibbs-Duhem equation in the form (6.45) with (23.7), we obtain

$$\frac{\partial \mathbf{A}}{\partial x_2^l} = -\nu_1 \frac{\partial \mu_1^l}{\partial x_2^l} - \nu_2 \frac{\partial \mu_2^l}{\partial x_2^l} = \nu_1 \left(\frac{x_2^l}{x_1^l} - \frac{\nu_2}{\nu_1}\right) \frac{\partial \mu_2^l}{\partial x_2^l}. \tag{23.9}$$

The ratio ν_2/ν_1 can be regarded as the ratio of mole fractions when the liquid has the same composition as the addition compound.

* *Cf.* Eucken [17], p. 246; *cf.* also C. K. Ingold, *et. al.*, *J. Chem. Soc.*, 1950, 2473.

Now let us find the conditions that the states I and II are both equilibrium states; the fundamental conditions are of course

$$\mathbf{A} = \delta \mathbf{A} = 0.$$

Equation (23.8) together with (23.9), thus gives the condition in the form

$$\left(\frac{\partial T}{\partial x_2^l}\right)_p = -\frac{\nu_1 T \left(\frac{x_2^l}{x_1^l} - \frac{\nu_2}{\nu_1}\right) \frac{\partial \mu_2^l}{\partial x_2^l}}{h_{T,p}}. \tag{23.10}$$

In the first place, when the liquid phase has the same composition as the addition compound in equilibrium with it, *i.e.*

$$\frac{x_2^l}{x_1^l} = \frac{\nu_2}{\nu_1} \tag{23.11}$$

then

$$\left(\frac{\partial T}{\partial x_2^l}\right)_p = 0. \tag{23.12}$$

That is to say along the freezing point curve the temperature passes through an extremum.

If we now limit ourselves to stable states, for which (*cf.* 15.83)

$$\frac{\partial \mu_2^l}{\partial x_2^l} > 0, \tag{23.13}$$

it is easily shown that the extreme value is a maximum. In all known cases it is found that

$$h_{T,p} > 0,$$

so that from (23.10),

$$\frac{\partial T}{\partial x_2^l} > 0 \quad \text{for} \quad \frac{x_2^l}{x_1^l} < \frac{\nu_2}{\nu_1}, \tag{23.14}$$

and

$$\frac{\partial T}{\partial x_2^l} < 0 \quad \text{for} \quad \frac{x_2^l}{x_1^l} > \frac{\nu_2}{\nu_1}. \tag{23.15}$$

This maximum is called a *dystectic* or *indifferent* point. The justification for the latter name, introduced by Duhem, will appear in chap. XXIX.

This behaviour is illustrated by fig. 23.7 (p. 373) which shows the maxima in the coexistence curve of the $SO_3 + H_2O$ system.

4. Solubility Curve of an Addition Compound in a Perfect Solution.

Let us return to equation (23.10) and apply it to a perfect solution. For this case we know that (*cf.* 20.1)

$$\left(\frac{\partial \mu_2^l}{\partial x_2^l}\right)_{T,p} = \frac{RT}{x_2^l}, \tag{23.16}$$

so that substituting into (23.10) and employing the latent heat of fusion (*i.e.* dissociation) of the addition compound $\Delta_f h^0$ we have :

$$\frac{\Delta_f h^0}{RT^2}\,\delta T = \left(\frac{\nu_2}{x_2} - \frac{\nu_1}{1-x_2}\right)\delta x_2. \tag{23.17}$$

This equation may now be integrated from the indifferent point, where x_2 and T have the values x_c^l and T_c, to the point x_2^l and T. Assuming that the latent heat is constant in this range of temperature we obtain

$$\frac{\Delta_f h^0}{R}\left(\frac{1}{T} - \frac{1}{T_c}\right) = -\ln (x_2^l)^{\nu_2}(1-x_2^l)^{\nu_1} + \ln (x_c)^{\nu_2}(1-x_c)^{\nu_1}. \tag{23.18}$$

When the addition compound contains one molecule of each component we have

$$\frac{\Delta_f h^0}{R}\left(\frac{1}{T} - \frac{1}{T_c}\right) = -\ln x_2^l(1-x_2^l) + \ln 0{\cdot}25. \tag{23.19}$$

The freezing point curve then has the simple form

$$\frac{1}{T} = -\frac{R}{\Delta_f h^0}\ln x_2^l(1-x_2^l) + \text{const.} \tag{23.20}$$

Example : Crystallization of Mixtures of Optical Isomers : Formation of Racemic Compounds.

Fig. 23.8 gives the freezing point curve of the system d- + l-dimethyl tartrate, which has a maximum at the melting point of the racemic compound. To test equation (23.20), $\log_{10} x_2(1-x_2)$ is plotted against $1/T$ in fig. 23.9. A straight line is obtained, whose slope gives for the latent heat a value of about 10500 cal./mole.

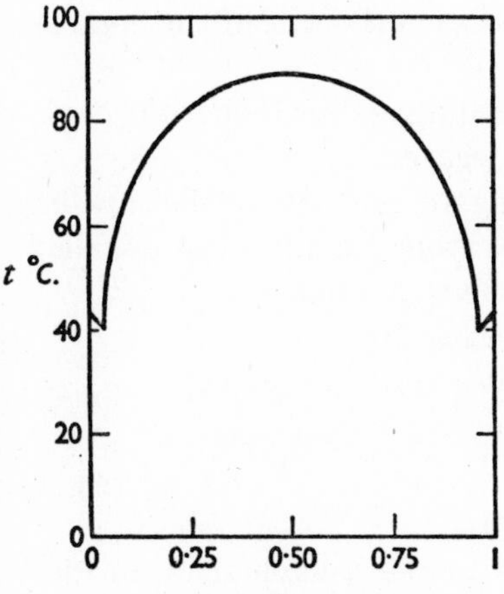

FIG. 23.8. Freezing point diagram for the system d- + l-dimethyl tartrate.*

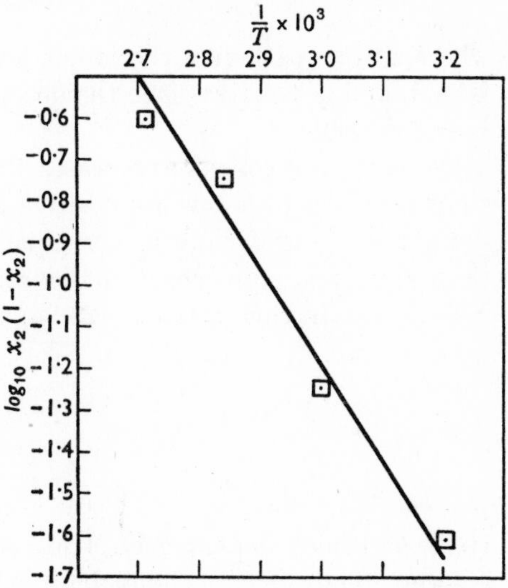

FIG. 23.9. Test of equation (23.20).

* *Cf.* Timmermans [45], p. 29.

5. Solubility Curve of an Addition Compound in a Non-Ideal Solution.

For a non-ideal solution we have in place of (23.16):

$$\left(\frac{\partial \mu_2^l}{\partial x_2^l}\right)_{T,p} = \frac{RT}{x_2} + RT\left(\frac{\partial \ln \gamma_2}{\partial x_2}\right)_{T,p}, \tag{23.21}$$

and, from (7.76)

$$h_{T,p} = h_{T,p}^0 + RT^2\left(\nu_1 \frac{\partial \ln \gamma_1}{\partial T} + \nu_2 \frac{\partial \ln \gamma_2}{\partial T}\right). \tag{23.22}$$

To fix our ideas, let us consider a regular solution for which

$$RT \ln \gamma_1 = \alpha x_2^2,$$
$$RT \ln \gamma_2 = \alpha x_1^2.$$

Then equations (23.21) and (23.22) become

$$\left(\frac{\partial \mu_2^l}{\partial x_2^l}\right)_{T,p} = \frac{RT}{x_2} - 2\alpha(1-x_2), \tag{23.23}$$

$$h_{T,p} = h_{T,p}^0 - \alpha(\nu_1 x_2^2 + \nu_2 x_1^2). \tag{23.24}$$

In general, we can neglect the second term of the right hand side of (23.24), but in (23.23) both terms are of the same order of magnitude.

An approximate form of (23.10) is, for this case,

$$\frac{\delta T}{\delta x_2} = -\frac{\nu_1 T\left(\frac{x_2}{x_1} - \frac{\nu_2}{\nu_1}\right)\left[\frac{RT}{x_2} - 2\alpha(1-x_2)\right]}{\Delta_f h^0}, \tag{23.25}$$

where $\Delta_f h^0$ is as before the latent heat of fusion of the addition compound, and is positive since the decomposition (fusion) of the complex is endothermic.

We must now consider two cases, depending upon whether the deviations from Raoult's law are positive or negative.

First we consider $\alpha < 0$, corresponding to activity coefficients less than unity and so to negative deviations from Raoult's law (*cf.* chap. XXI, § 3). In this instance, (23.25) shows that when

$$\left(\frac{x_2^l}{x_1^l} - \frac{\nu_2}{\nu_1}\right) < 0,$$

$$\frac{\delta T}{\delta x_2} > \left(\frac{\delta T}{\delta x_2}\right)^{\text{id}}. \tag{23.26}$$

Here, as usual, the superscript id refers to the behaviour of an ideal system. Thus, approaching the indifferent point from the left (lower values of x_2), the curve rises more rapidly than in the case of an ideal system.

Similarly when

$$\left(\frac{x_2^l}{x_1^l} - \frac{\nu_2}{\nu_1}\right) > 0,$$

the freezing point curve descends more rapidly than for an ideal solution.

Hence when the solution exhibits negative deviations from Raoult's law, the maximum at the indifferent point is much sharper than for an ideal solution. The maximum may even become so sharp as to appear in practice more like a discontinuity. This is so for the system iodine + methyl pyridine.*

We now pass to the case where $\alpha > 0$, in which the activity coefficients are greater than unity and deviations from Raoult's law are positive. It is easily shown that here the maximum at the indifferent point becomes flatter than for ideal solutions. If α is positive and sufficiently large, then the solution may have a range of immiscibility (*cf.* chap. XVI, § 9). In this case the phase diagram takes the form shown in fig. 23.10, which is for a system having a lower critical solution temperature.

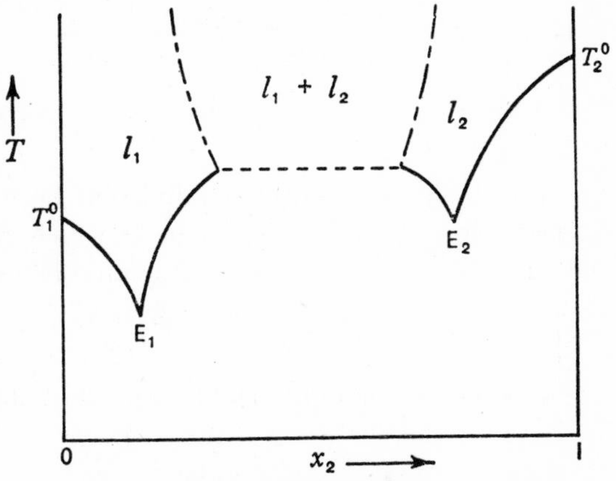

FIG. 23.10. Freezing point diagram for partially miscible liquids with a lower consolute temperature.

An example of this kind of behaviour is found in the formic acid + triethylamine system,† while certain intermetallic compounds such as KZn_{12}, KPb_2 show similar behaviour except that the liquid phase has an upper critical solution temperature.‡

6. Congruent and Incongruent Melting.

Let us now consider, at constant pressure, the solubility curves defined by $\mathbf{A}_A = 0$ and $\mathbf{A}_B = 0$, for equilibrium between the solution and the solid compounds A and B (fig. 23.11). These compounds may be either pure substances or addition compounds.

These two curves intersect at E, and this point divides each curve into two sections, one corresponding to stable equilibrium, the other

* *Cf.* Timmermans [45], p. 259.
† N. I. Joukowsky, *Bull. Soc. Chim. Belg.*, 43, 397 (1934).
‡ *Cf.* Vogel [50].

to metastable equilibrium. The identification of the stable segments follows the same lines as the discussion given in chap. XV, § 7 regarding the triple point.

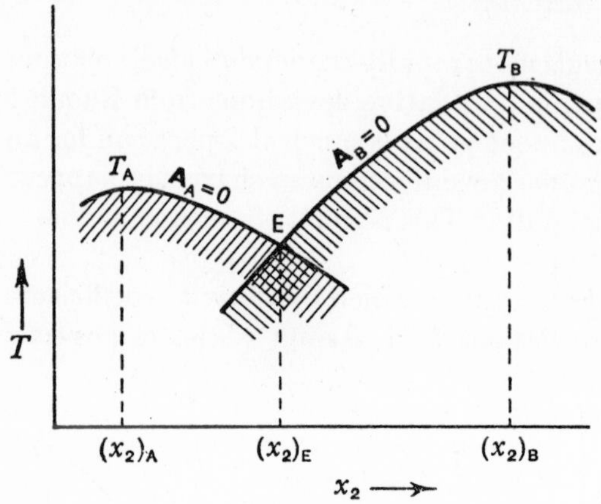

FIG. 23.11.

In effect, for stable equilibrium between A and the solution it is necessary that solid B should not form spontaneously, that is in this region the affinity $\mathbf{A}_B$ of solution of B must be positive. Thus only the branch of the curve $\mathbf{A}_A=0$ for which also $\mathbf{A}_B>0$, will represent stable equilibrium. Similarly only that branch of the curve $\mathbf{A}_B=0$ for which simultaneously $\mathbf{A}_A>0$ will represent stable equilibrium between B and the solution. We must now identify the regions in which $\mathbf{A}_A>0$ and $\mathbf{A}_B>0$.

We have (*cf.* 4.60), at constant composition,

$$\frac{\partial \mathbf{A}_A}{\partial T}=\frac{\mathbf{A}_A+h_{T,p}}{T},$$

so that in the immediate neighbourhood of the line $\mathbf{A}_A=0$

$$\frac{\partial \mathbf{A}_A}{\partial T}=\frac{h_{T,p}}{T}.$$

Furthermore $h_{T,p}$ will be positive (absorption of heat) so that

$$\frac{\partial \mathbf{A}_A}{\partial T}>0. \tag{23.27}$$

Thus $\mathbf{A}_A$ will be negative in the region below the curve $\mathbf{A}_A=0$ in fig. 23.11; similarly for $\mathbf{A}_B$. The regions for which $\mathbf{A}_A<0$ and $\mathbf{A}_B<0$ are shaded in the figure. The portion of the curve $\mathbf{A}_A=0$ which penetrates the region, beyond E, in which $\mathbf{A}_B<0$ thus corresponds to metastable equilibrium, and in the same way the part of $\mathbf{A}_B=0$ to the left of E enters the region where $\mathbf{A}_A<0$, and is hence also the metastable branch.

We must now look at the slopes of the solubility curves in the neighbourhood of E. Equations (23.10)–(23.15) show that if the point E falls *between* the compositions $(x_2)_A$ and $(x_2)_B$ corresponding to the compounds A and B, then the slopes of the two curves are of opposite sign. This is the case depicted in fig. 23.11, and E is then the eutectic point.

On the other hand if

either $(x_2)_E > (x_2)_A$ and $(x_2)_E > (x_2)_B$

or $(x_2)_E < (x_2)_A$ and $(x_2)_E < (x_2)_B$,

that is if E lies outside the range $(x_2)_A (x_2)_B$, then the slopes of the solubility curves at E have the same sign, and we have the situation shown in fig. 23.12; E is then a transition point.

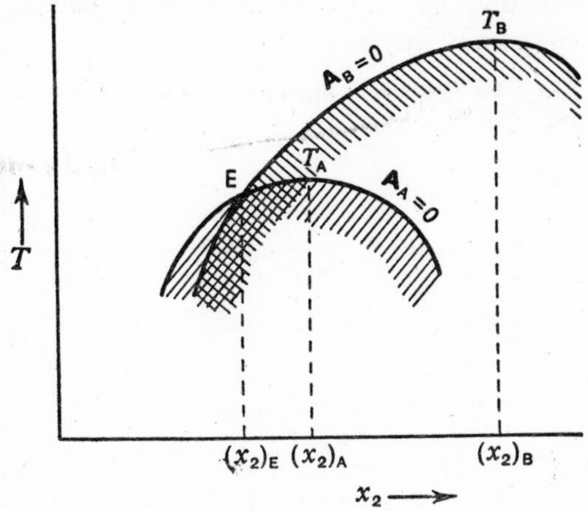

FIG. 23.12.

The fundamental difference between these two cases is that in the first instance the indifferent point T_A occurs in the *stable* branch of the curve $\mathbf{A}_A = 0$, while in the second case the maximum is in the *metastable* branch.

In systems of the first type the addition compound can exist in stable equilibrium with a solution of the same composition as itself. The melting of this compound, to form liquid of the same composition is called *congruent melting.* The examples given earlier in this chapter are all of this type.

The conditions existing in systems of the second type are rather different. In fig. 23.13 the freezing point diagram, including only the stable branches of the curves, is given for a typical system of this kind. The solubility curve of the compound A is reduced to the segment

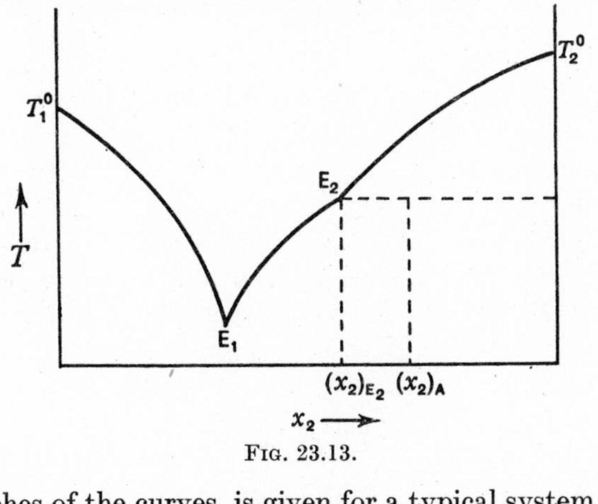

FIG. 23.13.

E_1E_2. If the solid compound A is melted it forms liquid of composition $(x_2)_{E_2}$ together with crystals of component 2. In this case the melting is described as *incongruent*. Systems of this kind are also quite common.*

The case intermediate between congruent and incongruent melting occurs when the point of intersection of the two curves coincides with the indifferent point of one of them. One example of this behaviour is provided by the system gold + antimony which forms an addition compound Au_2Sb.

* *Cf.* for systems of organic compounds Timmermans [45], and for metallic systems Vogel [50].

CHAPTER XXIV

THE THERMODYNAMIC EXCESS FUNCTIONS

1. Thermodynamic Excess Functions.

We have already introduced in § 3 of chap. XX the *thermodynamic functions of mixing* in the case of perfect solutions. These definitions are easily extended to non-ideal solutions. The results obtained provide a useful basis for the classification of non-ideal solutions which will be made in paragraph 5 of this chapter.

Instead of (20.11), we have for the change in free energy resulting from the process of mixing the components 1 and 2 at constant temperature, to form a non-ideal solution :

$$g^M = \mathbf{R}Tx_1 \ln x_1\gamma_1 + \mathbf{R}Tx_2 \ln x_2\gamma_2. \tag{24.1}$$

In this chapter we shall always define the activity coefficients with respect to the symmetrical reference system, (*cf.* chap. XXI, § 3).

The difference between the thermodynamic function of mixing (denoted by superscript M) for an actual system, and the value corresponding to an ideal solution at the same T and p, is called the *thermodynamic excess function* (denoted by superscript E). This quantity represents the excess (positive or negative) of a given thermodynamic property of the solution, over that in the ideal reference solution.

Thus

$$g^E = g^M - g^{M,\text{id}} = \mathbf{R}T(x_1 \ln \gamma_1 + x_2 \ln \gamma_2), \tag{24.2}$$

where g^E is the *excess Gibbs free energy*.

The corresponding excess entropy, enthalpy, volume, energy, heat capacity and compressibility are readily obtained by use of the general thermodynamic formulae.

(*a*) *Excess entropy* (*cf.* 20.17) :

$$s^E = -\frac{\partial g^E}{\partial T}$$

$$s^E = -\mathbf{R}T\left(x_1 \frac{\partial \ln \gamma_1}{\partial T} + x_2 \frac{\partial \ln \gamma_2}{\partial T}\right) - \mathbf{R}(x_1 \ln \gamma_1 + x_2 \ln \gamma_2). \tag{24.3}$$

(*b*) *Excess enthalpy* (*cf.* 20.12) :

$$h^E = -T^2 \frac{\partial \left(\dfrac{g^E}{T}\right)}{\partial T},$$

$$h^E = -\mathbf{R}T^2\left(x_1 \frac{\partial \ln \gamma_1}{\partial T} + x_2 \frac{\partial \ln \gamma_2}{\partial T}\right). \tag{24.4}$$

(c) *Excess volume* (*cf.* 20.14) :

$$v^E = \frac{\partial g^E}{\partial p},$$

$$v^E = RT\left(x_1 \frac{\partial \ln \gamma_1}{\partial p} + x_2 \frac{\partial \ln \gamma_2}{\partial p}\right). \tag{24.5}$$

(d) *Excess energy* (*cf.* 20.16) :

$$u^E = h^E - pv^E,$$

$$u^E = -RT\left\{T\left(x_1 \frac{\partial \ln \gamma_1}{\partial T} + x_2 \frac{\partial \ln \gamma_2}{\partial T}\right) + p\left(x_1 \frac{\partial \ln \gamma_1}{\partial p} + x_2 \frac{\partial \ln \gamma_2}{\partial p}\right)\right\}. \tag{24.6}$$

(e) *Excess heat capacity* (*cf.* 2.17) :

$$c_p^E = \frac{\partial h^E}{\partial T},$$

$$c_p^E = -2RT\left(x_1 \frac{\partial \ln \gamma_1}{\partial T} + x_2 \frac{\partial \ln \gamma_2}{\partial T}\right) - RT^2\left(x_1 \frac{\partial^2 \ln \gamma_1}{\partial T^2} + x_2 \frac{\partial^2 \ln \gamma_2}{\partial T^2}\right). \tag{24.7}$$

(*f*) *Excess compressibility* (*cf.* 12.1) :

$$\kappa^E = -\frac{1}{v}\frac{\partial v^E}{\partial p},$$

$$\kappa^E = -\frac{RT}{v}\left(x_1 \frac{\partial^2 \ln \gamma_1}{\partial p^2} + x_2 \frac{\partial^2 \ln \gamma_2}{\partial p^2}\right). \tag{24.8}$$

It will be seen, by reference to tables 7.2 and 7.1, that quite generally the thermodynamic excess function is the difference between the thermodynamic function of mixing (table 7.2) for the system concerned, and the same function for an ideal system (table 7.1).

The thermodynamic excess functions are also closely related to experimental measurements :

g^E is simply related to the vapour pressure of the solution ;
h^E is the heat of mixing at constant pressure per mole of solution (*cf.* § 2 of this chapter) ;
s^E is defined by*

$$s^E = \frac{h^E - g^E}{T}; \tag{24.9}$$

* One can also envisage a direct determination of s^E based on the Nernst theorem (chap. IX) and on a measurement of specific heats and heats of solution.

v^E is the difference between the mean molar volume of the solution and the sum of the volumes of the pure constituents (sufficient to form 1 mole of solution) before mixing :

$$v^E = v - x_1 v_1^0 - x_2 v_2^0 ; \tag{24.10}$$

u^E is defined by* $h^E - pv^E$;

c_p^E is the difference between the mean molar heat capacity of the solution and the sum of the heat capacities of the pure components, to form one mole of solution, before mixing

$$c_p^E = c_p - x_1 c_{p,1}^0 - x_2 c_{p,2}^0 . \tag{24.11}$$

From a purely thermodynamic standpoint there is nothing to prevent us examining all the properties characteristic of the deviation of a solution from ideality in terms of the activity coefficients. Experimentally, however, the derivatives above those of the second order become more and more difficult to measure precisely. In fact, in the discussion of this chapter we shall only consider g^E, h^E, s^E and v^E ; that is those quantities which can be derived from the activity coefficients and their first differentials with respect to temperature and pressure.

The above excess functions have been defined for one mole of solution. For the whole system we could write

$$G^E = ng^E ; \quad H^E = nh^E ; \quad S^E = ns^E , \quad \text{etc.}$$

It is then easily verified that, taking account of (20.58),

$$\frac{\partial G^E}{\partial T} = -S^E ; \quad \frac{\partial G^E}{\partial n_i} = \boldsymbol{R}T \ln \gamma_i . \tag{24.12}$$

2. Heat of Mixing.

The heat of mixing is defined as the heat absorbed by the system when n_1 moles of component 1 and n_2 moles of component 2 are mixed at constant temperature and pressure.

The principle of conservation of energy (2.15) gives, at constant p,

$$dQ = dH.$$

The heat of mixing is thus equal to the variation, H^M, in the enthalpy which accompanies the mixing ; H^M is, by definition, the *integral heat of mixing*, and is an extensive thermodynamic variable.

* Note that the term pv^E is practically negligible ; thus, for example, for $v^E \simeq 1$ cm.^{3}, $p = 760$ mm. of Hg, so that $pv^E = 10^{-3}$ litre atm. $\simeq 24 \times 10^{-3}$ cal. while h^E is of the order of several calories at least (*cf.* § 4). We shall not distinguish further between h^E and u^E.

The integral heat of mixing *per mole of solution* is equal to the excess enthalpy of mixing defined in the previous paragraph :

$$\frac{H^M}{n} = h^E. \tag{24.13}$$

In effect, we have

$$\begin{aligned} H^M &= H - n_1 h_1^0 - n_2 h_2^0 \\ &= n_1(h_1 - h_1^0) + n_2(h_2 - h_2^0), \end{aligned} \tag{24.13'}$$

where h_1^0 and h_2^0 are the molar enthalpies of the pure substances. Referring to table 7.2 we see that

$$h_i - h_i^0 = h_i^M = -\boldsymbol{R}T^2 \frac{\partial \ln \gamma_i}{\partial T}. \tag{24.14}$$

Equation (24.13′) can therefore be written

$$\frac{H^M}{n} = x_1 h_1^M + x_2 h_2^M = h^E; \tag{24.15}$$

h^E is simply called the heat of mixing. In conformity with the usual convention (*cf.* the definition of dQ in chapter II), h^E is taken as positive when there is an absorption of heat, and negative when there is an evolution of heat on mixing.

We note that by differentiating (24.13) with respect to n_1 and n_2 at constant T and p we have :

$$\frac{\partial H^M}{\partial n_1} = h_1 - h_1^0 = h_1^M; \quad \frac{\partial H^M}{\partial n_2} = h_2 - h_2^0 = h_2^M. \tag{24.16}$$

Thus h_1^M is equal to the heat absorbed (per mole of 1) when a small quantity δn_1 of substance 1 is dissolved in the solution at constant T and p. For this reason it is often called the *heat of solution of component* 1, *differential heat of mixing* or *partial molar heat of mixing.** The partial molar heats may be determined readily from the heat of mixing h^E by the Bakhuis-Rooseboom method described in § 3 of chap. I.

Equation (24.4) shows that the heat of mixing can be calculated from the temperature variation of the activity coefficients. This may be done by measuring the partial vapour pressures of the solution at different temperatures. It is generally preferable, however, to employ a direct calorimetric method, by which h^E is found without having to employ the activity coefficients.

We shall now discuss briefly the dependence of the heat of mixing on the intermolecular forces in solutions.

* For other definitions *cf.* A. Eucken, *Energie und Wärmeeinheit, Handbuch Experimental Physik* VIII, 1 (1929), and van Laar [48], pp. 281–286.

3. Intermolecular Forces in Condensed Phases.

The origin of intermolecular forces in condensed phases is well known.* However, the quantitative theoretical study of such intermolecular forces meets with great difficulties which are dependent on the fact that the distances between the molecules are of only the same order as the dimensions of the molecules themselves. The approximate formulae which are valid when the molecules are greater distances apart (say ten times the molecular diameter) as in a gas under normal conditions, lose all significance in a condensed phase, as we shall show later by an example.†

We consider first the *London dispersion forces* which arise essentially as a result of the perturbation of the electronic orbits in the molecules.‡ If the centres of gravity of two molecules A and B are a distance $r_{A,B}$ apart, then there will be associated with them an attractive potential whose *absolute value* is given by

$$V_{A,B}=\frac{3h}{2}\frac{\nu_A \nu_B}{\nu_A+\nu_B}\alpha_A \alpha_B \cdot \frac{1}{r^6_{A,B}}, \tag{24.17}$$

where h is Planck's constant, α_A and α_B the polarizabilities of the two molecules and $h\nu_A$ and $h\nu_B$ are energies closely related to the ionization potentials of the molecules. If the molecules are identical then the formula reduces to

$$V_{A,A}=\frac{3h}{4}\nu_A \alpha_A^2 \frac{1}{r^6_{A,A}}. \tag{24.17'}$$

Besides this universal cohesion effect, there is also an *induction effect* which results from the deformation of the molecules under the electrostatic forces exerted by neighbouring molecules. This effect is of greatest importance for the interaction between molecules having a large dipole moment and molecules which are easily polarized, for example, between nitro-compounds and aromatic hydrocarbons.§

Finally, the *orientation energy*, resulting from mutual orientation of the molecules by electrostatic effects, must be included. Since the intermolecular distances are so small, it is necessary when considering this energy to take account of the exact location of the electric charges.|| Thus it can be shown spectroscopically¶ that the interaction energy between ethanol and acetone, which arises mainly from the interaction between the carbonyl oxygen of the acetone and the hydroxyl group

* *Cf.* especially Briegleb [2].

† For the formulae applicable to gases, see Fowler and Guggenheim [20], chap. VII.

‡ F. London, *Trans. Faraday Soc.*, 33, 19 (1937) ; *J. Phys. Chem.*, **46**, 305 (1942).

§ *Cf.* Briegleb [2].

|| *Cf.* also E. Bauer and M. Magat, *J. de Phys.*, **9**, 319 (1938) and M. Davies, *Trans. Faraday Soc.*, **26**, 333 (1940).

¶ *Cf.* Prigogine, [38].

of the ethanol, is the same order of magnitude—about 2000 cal./mole—as that between ethanol and dioxane. This is so even though the dipole moment of acetone is quite large, while that of dioxane is zero because of the symmetry of the molecule.*

We may note that in the great majority of cases it is possible to predict which particular atoms of a pair of molecules are most likely to interact strongly.† For example there is strong interaction between acetone and chloroform arising from the negatively charged oxygen of the acetone and the positively charged hydrogen in the chloroform :

$$\begin{array}{c} CH_3\diagdown \\ \diagup \\ CH_3 \end{array} CO\cdots H-C\begin{array}{c}\diagup Cl \\ -Cl. \\ \diagdown Cl \end{array}$$

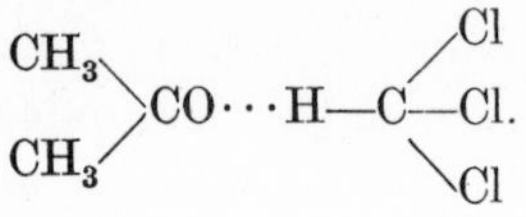

4. Configurational Energy.

To relate heats of mixing to energies of interaction we make use of the *quasicrystalline lattice model* of a liquid. In this the molecules are pictured as occupying points on a lattice whose co-ordination number (or number of nearest neighbours to a given molecule) is z. In the case of liquids z must be regarded as a statistical average.

We shall assume for simplicity that each molecule occupies just one lattice site ; that is to say the molecules in the solution must be of approximately the same size and shape.‡

Let us define a quantity $X_{i,j}$ such that $zX_{i,j}$ gives the number of pairs of nearest neighbour sites such that one site is occupied by an i-molecule and the other by a j-molecule. Each molecule of kind A, forms with its z nearest neighbours, z pairs of sites. Hence the total number of pairs of sites in which an A-molecule occupies at least one site is zN_A, where N_A is the number of molecules of kind A. These pairs will either be A, A or A, B pairs and the total number, counting each A, A pair twice, is

$$zN_A = 2zX_{A,A} + zX_{A,B}, \tag{24.18}$$

whence

$$2X_{A,A} + X_{A,B} = N_A. \tag{24.19}$$

Similarly

$$2X_{B,B} + X_{A,B} = N_B. \tag{24.20}$$

If we take account only of nearest neighbour interactions as contributing to the total energy, and so ignore long-range forces such as

* *Cf.* also, for another example, Hildebrand [28], pp. 82–83.
† *Cf.* A. J. Staverman, *Physica*, **4**, 1141 (1937).
‡ The reasoning which follows can be readily generalized to the case where the molecules have different sizes and shapes. *Cf.* for example, A. R. Miller, *The theory of solutions of high polymers* (Oxford, 1949).

interionic attractions, then the interaction energy of the solution, or the configuration energy, will be of the form

$$W = -zX_{A,A}V_{A,A} - zX_{B,B}V_{B,B} - zX_{A,B}V_{A,B}, \qquad (24.21)$$

where $V_{i,j}$ is the absolute value of the interaction energy between two nearest neighbours i and j.

Taking account of (24.19) and (24.20), this equation can be written

$$W = -N_A\Lambda_A - N_B\Lambda_B + X_{A,B}W_{A,B}, \qquad (24.22)$$

where we have put

$$\Lambda_A = \frac{z}{2}V_{A,A}, \quad \Lambda_B = \frac{z}{2}V_{B,B}; \qquad (24.23)$$

$$W_{A,B} = \frac{z}{2}(V_{A,A} + V_{B,B} - 2V_{A,B}). \qquad (24.24)$$

Λ_A is the absolute value of the potential energy *per molecule* of the pure A liquid; similarly for Λ_B. Furthermore, we may identify Λ_A and Λ_B with the energies of vaporization per molecule of the two pure liquids: $\Delta_v u_A^0/N$ and $\Delta_v u_B^0/N$.

The term $X_{A,B}W_{A,B}$ in (24.22) has a very simple interpretation. It is the change in energy of the system resulting from the mixing of the two pure liquids: as mentioned in paragraph 1 we may identify this with the enthalpy change, *i.e.*

$$H^M = X_{A,B}W_{A,B}. \qquad (24.25)$$

Since $X_{A,B}$ is, by definition, a positive quantity, the sign of ΔH^M is determined by the sign of $W_{A,B}$. If $W_{A,B}$ is positive, the mixing process is accompanied by an absorption of heat, while if it is negative with evolution of heat.

The heat of mixing per mole is thus given by

$$h^E = \frac{H^M}{n} = \mathbf{N}\frac{X_{A,B}}{N_A + N_B}W_{A,B}. \qquad (24.26)$$

We consider first only those intermolecular forces which arise from London dispersion forces. In the model under consideration the distances between all molecules are taken as equal:

$$r_{A,A} = r_{A,B} = r_{B,B} = r. \qquad (24.27)$$

Equations (24.17) and (24.17′) can now be used to obtain

$$W_{A,B} = \frac{z}{2}\frac{3}{2}\frac{h}{r^6}\left[\frac{\nu_A\alpha_A^2}{2} + \frac{\nu_B\alpha_B^2}{2} - 2\frac{\nu_A\nu_B}{\nu_A + \nu_B}\alpha_A\alpha_B\right]. \qquad (24.28)$$

If we note that

$$\frac{\nu_A\nu_B}{(\nu_A + \nu_B)^2} \leqslant \frac{\nu_A\nu_B}{4}, \qquad (24.29)$$

then we conclude that

$$W_{A,B} \geqslant \frac{z}{2}\frac{3}{2}\frac{h}{r^6}\left[\frac{\nu_A\,\alpha_A^2}{2}+\frac{\nu_B\,\alpha_B^2}{2}-\sqrt{\nu_A\,\nu_B\alpha_A^2\,\alpha_B^2}\right],$$

or

$$W_{A,B} \geqslant \frac{z}{2}\,[(V_{A,A})^{1/2}-(V_{B,B})^{1/2}]^2,$$

or

$$W_{A,B} \geqslant [\Lambda_A^{1/2}-\Lambda_B^{1/2}]^2. \tag{24.30}$$

We thus see that if the interactions are caused solely by dispersion forces, then on this model we must always have

$$W_{A,B} \geqslant 0. \tag{24.31}$$

Furthermore, to a first approximation, we may replace the inequality (24.30) by the equality

$$W_{A,B} = [\Lambda_A^{1/2}-\Lambda_B^{1/2}]^2. \tag{24.32}$$

$W_{A,B}$ is thus simply related to the difference between the energies of vaporization of the pure liquids A and B.*

The case in which intermolecular forces arise from dispersion forces only, is exemplified by mixtures of saturated hydrocarbons. So far, only four systems have been studied sufficiently accurately ; they are

n-heptane + *n*-hexadecane,†

n-hexane + *cyclo*hexane,‡

2. 2. 4-trimethylpentane + hexadecane,§

n-octane + tetraethylmethane,§

Figures 24.1 to 24.4 show the results obtained for these systems. The values of g^E have been calculated from vapour pressure data, and those of h^E from calorimetric experiments.

The first three systems have positive heats of mixing in conformity with equation (24.31) ; on the other hand the system tetraethylmethane + *n*-octane constitutes a remarkable exception since here the heat of mixing is negative. That is the isothermal mixing process is accompanied by an evolution of heat. A possible interpretation is the following : we have assumed in deriving (24.30) that the condition

* We stress again that these conclusions are independent of the hypothesis, made to simplify the calculations, that each molecule occupies one site on the lattice. (*Cf.* Miller *loc. cit.*).

† J. N. Brønsted and J. Koefoed, *Kgl. Danske Videnskab Selskab. Mat. Fys. Mdd.*, 22, part 17 (1946). J. H. van der Waals and J. J. Hermans, *Rec. Trav. Chim.*, **68**, 181 (1949).

‡ I. Prigogine and V. Mathot, *J. Chem. Phys.*, **18**, 765 (1950) ; V. Mathot, *Bull. Soc. Chim. Belg.*, **59**, 111 (1950).

§ J. H. van der Waals, *Thesis*, (Groningen, 1950).

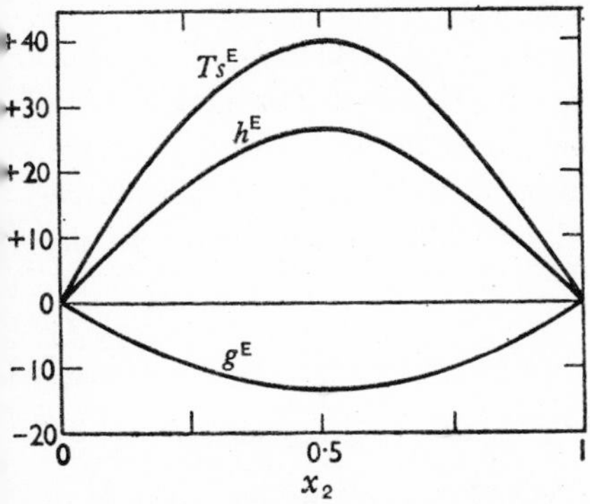

FIG. 24.1. Thermodynamic excess functions
: the system n-heptane (1) + n-hexadecane
at 20 °C.

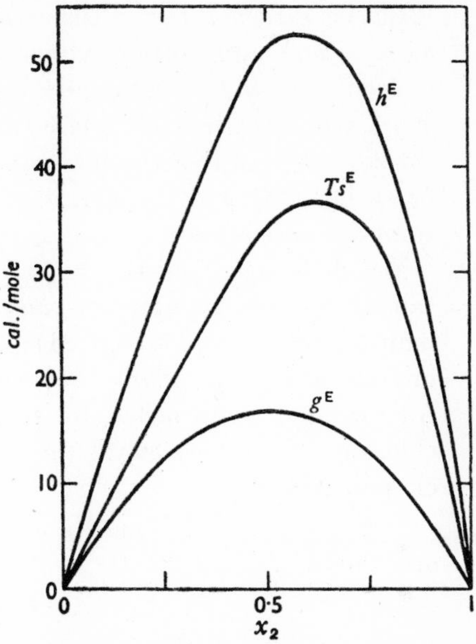

FIG. 24.2. Thermodynamic excess functions for the system n-hexane (1) + cyclohexane (2) at 20 °C.

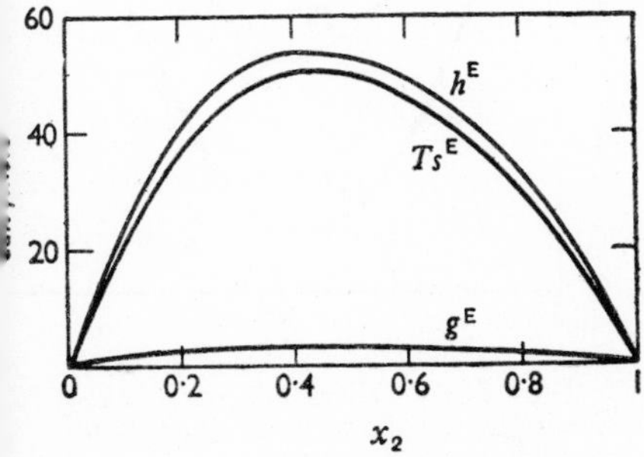

FIG. 24.3. Thermodynamic excess func-
ons for the system 2-2-4-trimethylpentane
) + hexadecane (2) at 24·9 °C.

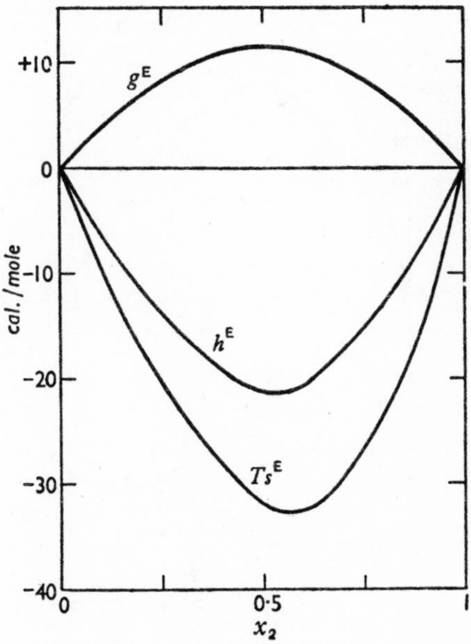

FIG. 24.4. Thermodynamic excess functions for the system n-octane (1) + tetraethylmethane (2) at 50 °C.

(24.27) is satisfied, but in the case of molecules of such different shapes as *n*-octane and tetraethylmethane the surfaces of contact of the molecules may be profoundly altered by the mixing. The value of $W_{A,B}$ will not then be related only to the quantity in brackets in (24.28). We see that the quasicrystalline lattice model employed above must be used with prudence, especially when the molecules are of complicated shapes.

We shall now consider the case where the intermolecular forces are caused by *electrostatic orientation forces* (*e.g. dipole-dipole*). Two limiting cases have to be considered. In the first the electrostatic interactions occur mainly between molecules of the same substance. An example is furnished by solutions of methanol in carbon tetrachloride. If we designate the alcohol by A, then we have (*cf.* also chapter XXV)

$$V_{A,A} \gg V_{B,B} \quad \text{and} \quad V_{A,A} \gg V_{A,B}, \tag{24.33}$$

and therefore from (24.24)

$$W_{A,B} > 0. \tag{24.34}$$

Fig. 24.5 shows the behaviour of this system and we see that h^E is indeed positive.

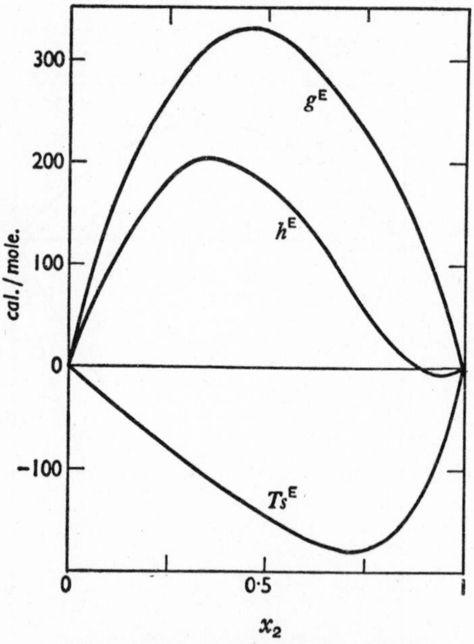

FIG. 24.5. Thermodynamic excess functions for the system carbon tetrachloride (1) + methanol (2) at 35 °C.*

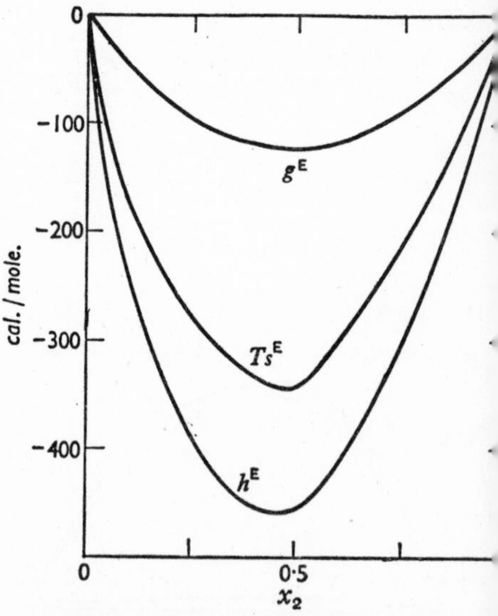

FIG. 24.6. Thermodynamic excess functions for the system chloroform + acetone at 25 °C.†

* G. Scatchard, S. E. Wood and J. M. Mochel, *J. Amer. Chem. Soc.*, 68, 1962 (1946).
† *Cf. Landolt-Börnstein Tables*, p. 1379, Ergb. II. p. 1560.

In the other limiting case the dipolar interaction is mainly between a molecule of A and a molecule of B.

Here

$$V_{A,B} \gg V_{A,A}, \quad V_{A,B} \gg V_{B,B}; \tag{24.35}$$

and

$$W_{A,B} < 0. \tag{24.36}$$

As shown in fig. 24.6 the chloroform + acetone system exhibits this type of behaviour.

5. Classification of Departures from Ideality.

Among imperfect solutions it is useful to distinguish two limiting cases, examples of which will be discussed in the following chapters.

(a) *Regular solutions* for which $|h^E| \gg T|s^E|$.

Hence

$$g^E \gtrsim h^E, \tag{24.37}$$

and the deviations from ideality arise from the heat of mixing.

(b) *Athermal solutions* for which $|h^E| \ll T|s^E|$.

Here

$$g^E \gtrsim -Ts^E, \tag{24.38}$$

and the deviations from ideality have their origin in entropy effects since the heat of mixing is either zero or negligibly small.

We note two further properties of these solutions. First the condition

$$S^E = 0,$$

which characterizes regular solutions means that

$$\left.\begin{aligned} \ln \gamma_1 &\propto \frac{1}{T}, \\ \ln \gamma_2 &\propto \frac{1}{T} \end{aligned}\right\}. \tag{24.39}$$

For, since S^E is zero whatever the values of n_1 and n_2,

$$\frac{\partial S^E}{\partial n_1} = 0; \quad \frac{\partial S^E}{\partial n_2} = 0;$$

and, as a consequence of (24.12),

$$\frac{\partial^2 G^E}{\partial n_1\, \partial T} = 0; \quad \frac{\partial^2 G^E}{\partial n_2\, \partial T} = 0;$$

whence

$$\frac{\partial RT \ln \gamma_1}{\partial T} = 0 \quad \text{and} \quad \frac{\partial RT \ln \gamma_2}{\partial T} = 0,$$

which is equivalent to (24.39). Conversely (24.39) implies that $S^E = 0$, as is easily seen from (24.3). The activity coefficients for regular solutions are thus inversely proportional to the absolute temperature. We see also that the activity coefficient law (16.48) employed to discuss the phenomenon of critical mixing corresponds to a regular solution as defined here.

On the other hand, the condition

$$h^E = 0$$

implies that

$$\ln \gamma_1 \text{ and } \ln \gamma_2 \text{ are both independent of } T. \tag{24.40}$$

For the condition $\partial H^E/\partial n_1 = 0$, means that

$$\frac{\partial^2 (G^E/T)}{\partial T\, \partial n_1} = \frac{\partial}{\partial T}\left(\frac{1}{T}\frac{\partial G^E}{\partial n_1}\right) = \frac{\partial}{\partial T} \mathbf{R} \ln \gamma_1 = 0.$$

Conversely (24.40) means that $h^E = 0$ as is obvious from (24.4). The activity coefficients of athermal solutions are independent of temperature.

6. Excess Thermodynamic Functions in the Region of a Critical Solution Temperature.

It is of interest to examine the behaviour of the excess thermodynamic functions near a critical solution temperature. We start from the equation

$$g = \sum_i x_i \mu_i = \sum_i x_i [\mu_i^0 + \mathbf{R}T \ln x_i] + g^E, \tag{24.41}$$

and use the first equality in (16.28) which must be satisfied at a critical point. For a binary solution we have

$$\left(\frac{\partial^2 g}{\partial x_2^2}\right)_{T,p} = \frac{\mathbf{R}T}{x_1 x_2} + \left(\frac{\partial^2 g^E}{\partial x_2^2}\right)_{T,p} = 0, \tag{24.42}$$

or

$$T\frac{\partial^2 s^E}{\partial x_2^2} - \frac{\partial^2 h^E}{\partial x_2^2} = \frac{\mathbf{R}T}{x_1 x_2} > 0 \tag{24.42$'$}$$

at the consolute temperature.

In the case of an upper consolute temperature for which $\partial^2 h/\partial x_2^2$ (18.84) is negative, this relation can be satisfied if even s^E is zero.

On the other hand for a lower consolute temperature for which $\partial^2 h/\partial x_2^2$ is positive (18.85) we must have

$$T\frac{\partial^2 s^E}{\partial x_2^2} > 0, \tag{24.43}$$

and this must exceed the contribution from h^E sufficiently to satisfy (24.42′). The existence of a lower consolute temperature is thus essentially related to a large deviation of the entropy of mixing from the ideal value.

Let us consider, for example, a case in which h^E and s^E are of the form:

$$\left.\begin{aligned} h^E &= k_h x_1 x_2 \\ Ts^E &= k_s x_1 x_2 \end{aligned}\right\}, \tag{24.44}$$

where k_h and k_s are constants. Then condition (24.42′) gives at the critical point :

$$k_h - k_s = \frac{RT}{2x_1 x_2} > 0. \tag{24.45}$$

If this is an upper critical point, k_h will be positive because of (18.84) and k_s may or may not be equal to zero, although it must always satisfy

$$k_s < k_h. \tag{24.46}$$

Thus in the case considered in § 9 of chap. XVI, we had

$$k_h = \alpha\ ;\ k_s = 0. \tag{24.47}$$

For a lower consolute temperature k_h must be negative, and the absolute values must be such that

$$|\, k_s \,| > |\, k_h \,|, \tag{24.48}$$

and thus k_h may or may not deviate appreciably from zero. The excess functions have the form depicted in fig. 24.7 ; the g^E curve is concave downwards as required by (24.42).

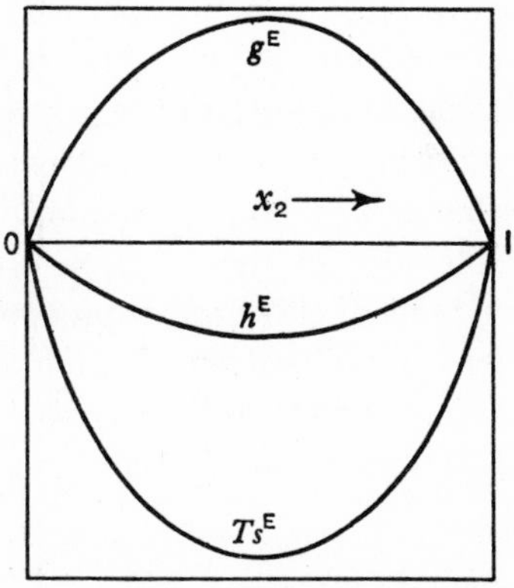

FIG. 24.7. General disposition of the thermodynamic excess functions in the neighbourhood of a lower consolute temperature.

Upper consolute temperatures therefore correspond to phase separation resulting from an energy effect, while lower consolute temperatures result from entropy effects.

CHAPTER XXV

REGULAR SOLUTIONS AND ATHERMAL SOLUTIONS

1. Regular Solutions.

We now return to consider the model, developed in § 4 of the previous chapter, for the evaluation of the configurational energy. We assume that the molecular interactions do not alter the arrangement of the molecules in the solution. The entropy of mixing will then be given by the same equation as for a perfect solution (*cf.* 20.19–20.22). This assumption will only be justified when $W_{A,B}$ is small compared with the thermal energy $\mathbf{k}T$ (about 600 cal./mole at ordinary temperatures). If on the other hand $W_{A,B}$ is, for example, ten times greater than this, as is the case when electrostatic interactions are involved, (*e.g.* in the ethanol + carbon tetrachloride system) then the arrangements of the molecules in the solution will be greatly altered. We shall exclude systems of this kind from consideration at the moment, and return to a closer examination of them later (*cf.* chap. XXVI, § 2).

For regular solutions the enthalpy of mixing is the only cause of departure from ideality, and

$$G^E = H^M = X_{A,B} W_{A,B}. \tag{25.1}$$

It now remains to evaluate $zX_{A,B}$, the number of A, B contacts in the solution. Let us consider two adjacent sites a and b. The probabilities that a is occupied by an A molecule or a B molecule are x_A and x_B, and similarly the probabilities for site b are also x_A and x_B. We deduce then, assuming the differences between the interaction energies do not alter these probabilities, that the probability of an A, B contact is

$$2x_A x_B. \tag{25.2}$$

Now the total number of contacts between nearest neighbours in the solution is $\frac{1}{2}zN$, so that the number of A, B contacts is (*cf.* p. 386)

$$N_{A,B} = zX_{A,B} = \tfrac{1}{2}zN 2x_A x_B = zN x_A x_B. \tag{25.3}$$

Hence equation (25.1) can be written in the more explicit form

$$G^E = N x_A x_B W_{A,B}, \tag{25.4}$$

or, per mole,

$$g^E = h^E = x_A x_B \alpha, \tag{25.5}$$

where

$$\alpha = N W_{A,B}. \tag{25.6}$$

and N is Avogadro's number. Expressed in terms of the numbers of moles n_A and n_B, equation (25.5) can be written

$$G^E = \frac{n_A n_B}{n} \alpha. \tag{25.6'}$$

Making use of (24.12) we see that the activity coefficients will now be given by

$$\left.\begin{aligned} RT \ln \gamma_A &= \alpha (x_B)^2, \\ RT \ln \gamma_B &= \alpha (x_A)^2 \end{aligned}\right\}. \tag{25.7}$$

If the intermolecular forces are essentially dispersion forces then we may, to a first approximation, employ (24.32) in (25.6) to obtain

$$\alpha = [\Lambda_A^{1/2} - \Lambda_B^{1/2}]^2, \tag{25.8}$$

where Λ_A and Λ_B are now the *molar* energies of vaporization.

Equations (25.7) and (25.8) have been generalized by Hildebrand and Scatchard* to include the case where the molecules are of different volumes. Their semi-empirical derivation leads to

$$\left.\begin{aligned} RT \ln \gamma_A &= v_A^0 \left(\frac{v_B^0 n_B}{v_A^0 n_A + v_B^0 n_B}\right)^2 (\delta_A - \delta_B)^2, \\ RT \ln \gamma_B &= v_B^0 \left(\frac{v_A^0 n_A}{v_A^0 n_A + v_B^0 n_B}\right)^2 (\delta_A - \delta_B)^2 \end{aligned}\right\}, \tag{25.9}$$

where

$$\delta_A = \left(\frac{\Lambda_A}{v_A^0}\right)^{1/2}; \quad \delta_B = \left(\frac{\Lambda_B}{v_B^0}\right)^{1/2}; \tag{25.10}$$

and v_A^0 and v_B^0 are the molar volumes of the pure components A and B. The quantities δ_A and δ_B are often called *solubility parameters*.

The main interest of equations (25.9) and (25.10), or more particularly (25.7) and (25.8), is to enable us to calculate the orders of magnitude of the activity coefficients in solutions from a knowledge of the properties of the pure substances. The following table, due to Benesi and Hildebrand,† illustrates clearly the usefulness of these formulae. It refers to saturated solutions of iodine in various solvents at 25 °C. Knowing the composition of the saturated solutions, equations (22.4) or (22.5) enable us to calculate the activity coefficients of iodine in these solutions. If we then apply equation (25.9) to different solvents for which δ_A is known, we can calculate in each case the parameter δ_B for iodine, and compare it with that measured directly, $(\Lambda_B/v_B^0)^{1/2}$. Despite the fact that the activity coefficients vary over the range 1400 to 3·3, the values of

* *Cf.* Hildebrand and Scott, [28′].
† J. H. Hildebrand, *Chem. Rev.* **44**, 42 (1949).

δ_B in the last column are practically constant and very close to the directly determined figure.

TABLE 25.1

Solutions of Iodine in various Solvents at 25 °C

Solvent	*Molar volume*	γ_{I_2} *at saturation*	δ_A (*Solvent*)	δ_B (*Iodine*)
n-C_7F_{16}	227	1 400	5·7	14·2
$SiCl_4$	115·3	51·8	7·6	13·9
CCl_4	97·1	22·5	8·6	14·2
$TiCl_4$	110·5	12·0	9·0	14·1
$CHCl_3$	80·7	11·3	9·3	14·3
CS_2	60·6	4·73	9·9	14·1
$CHBr_3$	87·8	4·19	10·5	14·1
1·2-$C_2H_4Br_2$	86·6	3·30	10·4	14·1
Mean				14·1
I_2	59·0	—	—	13·6

2. Domain of Validity of the Regular Solution Model.

The model employed in the previous paragraph permits us to calculate the approximate activity coefficients, and hence, from (24.2), the excess free energy of a large number of solutions. It is a much cruder approximation when applied to calculate the actual values of

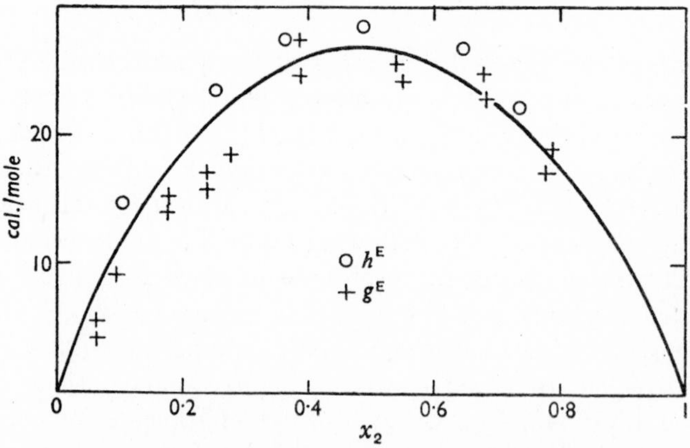

FIG. 25.1. Thermodynamic excess functions for the system benzene (1) + carbon tetrachloride (2).

h^E and of s^E. Figs. 25.1 and 25.2 show the excess thermodynamic functions for the systems benzene + carbon tetrachloride and carbon disulphide + benzene, calculated by Scatchard.* The benzene + carbon tetrachloride system is a regular solution, since the values of g^E and h^E are practically identical. On the other hand in the system carbon disulphide + benzene, h^E is clearly greater than g^E, and this corresponds to $s^E > 0$. This behaviour is frequently observed, and it is instructive to enquire into the interpretation of this excess entropy.

The regular solution model provides no explanation of this excess entropy, nor can it account for a volume change on mixing. To study these problems we need a more detailed model of the liquid state which will enable us to relate these excess quantities to intermolecular forces.

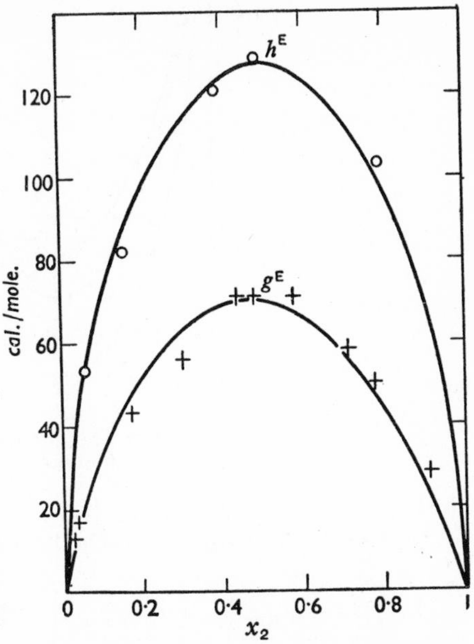

FIG. 25.2. Thermodynamic excess functions for the system carbon disulphide (1) + benzene (2).

3. Intermolecular Forces and Thermodynamic Excess Functions.†

The model of a liquid developed in § 6 of chap. XII can be applied to the present problem. Just as in (12.59) we assume that the law of interaction between a molecule i and a molecule j is of the form

$$\epsilon_{i,j}(r) = -|\epsilon^*_{i,j}|\left\{2\left(\frac{r^*_{i,j}}{r}\right)^6 - \left(\frac{r^*_{i,j}}{r}\right)^{12}\right\}. \tag{25.11}$$

Furthermore we assume that the two kinds of molecule in the solution are spherical and have the same radius, so that

$$r^*_{A,A} = r^*_{A,B} = r^*_{B,B} = r^*. \tag{25.12}$$

This means that the interaction curves for the various types of molecular interaction all have minima at the same value of r, but the depth of the minimum varies from case to case (*cf.* fig. 25.3).

Each molecule will have a free volume $v_f(v)$ given by equation (12.52) taken either with (12.53) and (12.55), or with (12.65).

To calculate the energy of evaporation $\Lambda_A(v)$ or $\Lambda_B(v)$ we proceed in

* G. Scatchard, *Chem. Rev.* 28, 321 (1931).

† For a more detailed account see I. Prigogine and V. Mathot, *J. Chem. Phys.*, 20, 49 (1952).

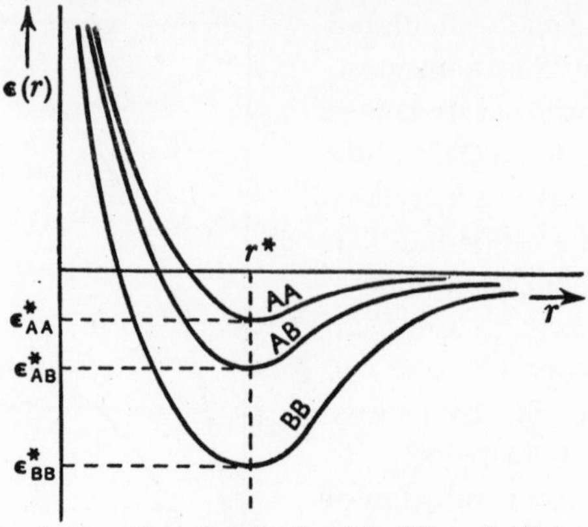

FIG. 25.3. Interaction energies for AA, BB and AB interactions as functions of distance.

the same way as for a pure liquid. If we assume that the molecules are distributed at random in the liquid, then in place of (12.64) we find :

$$\left.\begin{aligned} \Lambda_A(v) &= \frac{N}{2}(x_A \Lambda^*_{A,A} + x_B \Lambda^*_{A,B})\left\{1{\cdot}01\left(\frac{v^*}{v}\right)^4 - 2{\cdot}41\left(\frac{v^*}{v}\right)^2\right\} \\ \Lambda_B(v) &= \frac{N}{2}(x_A \Lambda^*_{A,B} + x_B \Lambda^*_{B,B})\left\{1{\cdot}01\left(\frac{v^*}{v}\right)^4 - 2{\cdot}41\left(\frac{v^*}{v}\right)^2\right\} \end{aligned}\right\}. \qquad (25.13)$$

where we have put :

$$\Lambda^*_{i,j} = z\,|\,\epsilon^*_{i,j}\,|. \qquad (25.14)$$

By employing the notation

$$\left.\begin{aligned} \Lambda^*_A &= x_A \Lambda^*_{A,A} + x_B \Lambda^*_{A,B} \\ \Lambda^*_B &= x_A \Lambda^*_{A,B} + x_B \Lambda^*_{B,B} \\ \Lambda^* &= x_A \Lambda^*_A + x_B \Lambda^*_B \end{aligned}\right\}, \qquad (25.15)$$

we can write down an expression for the free energy of the solution analogous in form to (12.43), in terms of the energies of vaporization and the free volumes. We have only to add the configurational free energy arising from the number of ways of arranging the molecules in the quasicrystalline lattice of the liquid (*cf.* 20.10, 20.10′).

Thus we obtain

$$\begin{aligned} G \simeq F = n_A \boldsymbol{R}T \ln x_A + n_B \boldsymbol{R}T \ln x_B + n_A f^{\ddagger}_A(T) + n_B f^{\ddagger}_B(T) \\ - n\boldsymbol{R}T \ln v_f(v) - n_A \Lambda_A(v) - n_B \Lambda_B(v). \end{aligned} \qquad (25.16)$$

The equation of state can be derived without difficulty from this expression for the free energy (*cf.* 12.40). We find that equation (12.66) remains valid for the solution if we replace Λ^* by the value given in equation (25.15). In the range of existence of the liquid state it can be shown by graphical means that (12.66) is equivalent to the much simpler approximate equation :

$$\left(\frac{v^*}{v}\right)^2 = 1{\cdot}176 - 4{\cdot}183\,\frac{kT}{\Lambda^*}. \tag{25.17}$$

This equation is applicable both to pure liquids and to solutions, provided that in the latter case the appropriate expression is used for Λ^*.

As an example of the use of (25.17) we may now discuss in more detail the excess volume :

$$v^E = v - x_A v_A^0 - x_B v_B^0, \tag{25.18}$$

where v_A^0 and v_B^0 are the molar volumes of the pure liquids at the same temperature and pressure. Writing (25.17) in the form

$$\left(\frac{v}{v^*}\right)^2 = \frac{1}{1{\cdot}176}\cdot\frac{1}{1-\Delta} = \frac{1}{1{\cdot}176}(1+\Delta) \tag{25.19}$$

where we have ignored terms of higher order than the first in Δ, or to the same approximation,

$$\frac{v}{v^*} = \frac{1}{(1{\cdot}176)^{1/2}}\left(1+\frac{\Delta}{2}\right), \tag{25.20}$$

we obtain, for the excess volume

$$\frac{v^E}{v^*} = 1{\cdot}64\left(\frac{kT}{\Lambda^*} - x_A\frac{kT}{\Lambda^*_{A,A}} - x_B\frac{kT}{\Lambda^*_{B,B}}\right). \tag{25.21}$$

We see that the excess volume will be positive or negative depending on the magnitude of $\Lambda^*_{A,B}$ relative to $\Lambda^*_{A,A}$ and $\Lambda^*_{B,B}$. It is convenient to introduce the parameters

$$\delta = \frac{1}{\Lambda^*_{A,A}}(\Lambda^*_{B,B} - \Lambda^*_{A,A});\quad \vartheta = \frac{1}{\Lambda^*_{A,A}}\left(\Lambda^*_{A,B} - \frac{\Lambda^*_{A,A}+\Lambda^*_{B,B}}{2}\right), \tag{25.22}$$

so that (*cf.* 25.15)

$$\Lambda^* = \Lambda^*_{A,A}(1 + x_B\,\delta + 2x_A x_B\vartheta). \tag{25.23}$$

These parameters δ and ϑ are usually numbers small compared with unity ($\sim 10^{-1}$) ; on introducing them into (25.21) we find :

$$\frac{v^E}{v^*} = 1{\cdot}64\,\frac{kT}{\Lambda^*_{A,A}}\left(\frac{1}{1+x_B\delta+2x_A x_B\vartheta} - x_A - \frac{x_B}{1+\delta}\right). \tag{25.24}$$

By expanding the fractions $\{1/(1+x) = 1 - x + x^2 - \ldots\}$ and limiting the series to terms of the second order in δ and ϑ we obtain :

$$\frac{v^E}{v^*} = 1{\cdot}64\,\frac{kT}{\Lambda^*_{A,A}}(-\delta^2 - 2\vartheta + 4x_B\,\delta\,\vartheta + 4x_A x_B\,\vartheta^2)\,x_A x_B. \tag{25.25}$$

The effective values of δ and ϑ depend upon the nature of the intermolecular forces.

In the case of dispersion forces one is probably justified, as a rough approximation, in assuming, (*cf.* 24.32)

$$(\Lambda^*_{A,B})^2 = \Lambda^*_{A,A}\Lambda^*_{B,B}\,; \tag{25.26}$$

whence from (25.22),

$$\vartheta = -\tfrac{1}{2}(1-\sqrt{1+\delta})^2, \tag{25.27}$$

and developing the square root in series, we find neglecting higher order terms,

$$\vartheta = -\frac{\delta^2}{8}. \tag{25.28}$$

Substituting this value in (25.25) :

$$\frac{v^E}{v^*} = -\frac{3}{4}\times 1{\cdot}64\,\frac{kT}{\Lambda^*_{A,A}}\,x_A x_B\,\delta^2 < 0. \tag{25.29}$$

The mixing of two liquids, consisting of molecules of the same size between which only dispersion forces exist, will probably be accompanied by a contraction.

On the other hand there may be specific effects such that, for example, the B, B interactions are much more powerful than A, B or A, A interactions, so that

$$\Lambda^*_{A,A} \simeq \Lambda^*_{A,B} < \Lambda^*_{B,B}. \tag{25.30}$$

In this case

$$\vartheta = -\frac{\delta}{2} \tag{25.31}$$

and

$$\frac{v^E}{v^*} = 1{\cdot}64\,\frac{kT}{\Lambda^*_{A,A}}\,\delta\,[1-\delta(1+x_B+x_B{}^2)]\,x_A x_B. \tag{25.32}$$

In general the second order terms in δ will be small compared with the first order terms so that there will be *an expansion on mixing*. We may expect behaviour of this kind where B is a polar molecule such as an alcohol. A series of systems have been studied recently* which illustrate these predictions, as shown in fig. 25.4. The series of solutions

carbon tetrachloride + tetramethylmethane (I),
carbon tetrachloride + trimethylchloromethane (II),
carbon tetrachloride + dimethyldichloromethane (III),
carbon tetrachloride + methyltrichloromethane (IV),
and carbon tetrachloride + *tert*-butyl alcohol (V),

all consist of approximately spherical molecules of nearly the same size. However in solution I the molecules are non-polar and, as predicted,

* V. Mathot and A. Desmyter, *J. Chem. Phys.*, **21**, 782 (1953).

the volume of mixing is negative. At the other extreme, solution V contains strongly polar molecules and the volume of mixing is positive.

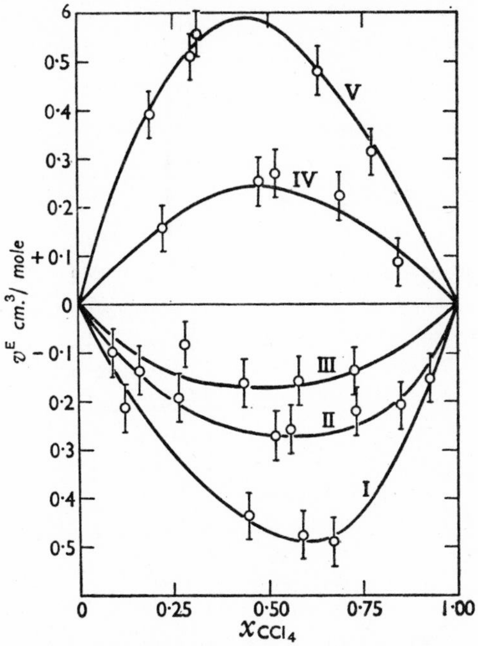

FIG. 25.4. Excess volumes of mixing at 0 °C. for the systems :

I. carbon tetrachloride + tetramethylmethane.
II. carbon tetrachloride + trimethylchloromethane.
III. carbon tetrachloride + dimethyldichloromethane.
IV. carbon tetrachloride + methyltrichloromethane.
V. carbon tetrachloride + *tert*-butyl alcohol (25 °C).

Between these two limiting cases there is a steady gradation of behaviour.

The above method can be applied to a calculation of other excess functions in terms of intermolecular forces. We may note that the excess entropy of mixing is closely related to the excess volume and to the change of the free volume of the solution with composition. We shall not, however, go into any further details here.

4. Athermal Solutions : Influence of the Size of Molecules.

Many solutions are known which show large deviations from Raoult's law, but for which the heat of mixing is practically zero, and in any case is too small to explain the observed deviations from ideality. Among these are solutions of chain molecules having molecular weights very different from the molecular weight of the solvent. Systems of this kind have been studied in a series of interesting researches since

1935 by K. H. Meyer and his collaborators.* They have measured g^E, h^E and Ts^E for the following systems

butyl valerianate (C_9) + benzene,
butyl valerianate + propyl bromide,
dibutyl sebacate (C_{18}) + benzene,
dibutyl sebacate + propyl bromide.

In the rest of this paragraph we shall denote these systems by V.B.; V.P.; S.B.; and S.P. respectively.

All these solutions exhibit essentially the same characteristics, the activity coefficients are less than unity and the heat of mixing, measured calorimetrically or determined from the variation of vapour pressure with temperature, is too small to account for more than a very small part of the negative deviations.

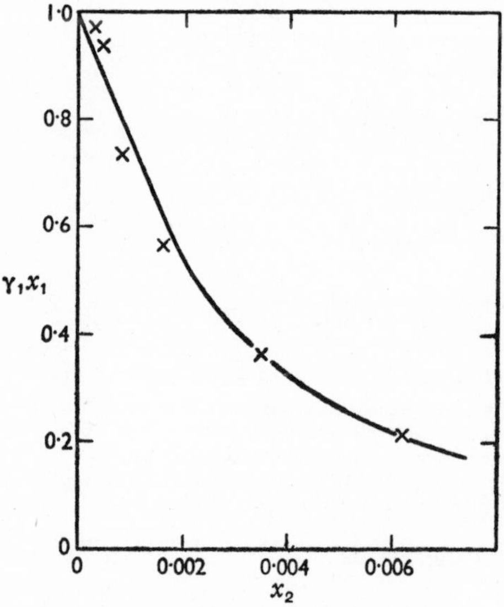

FIG. 25.5. Activity coefficients of toluene in toluene-rubber solutions.

Solutions of macromolecules in a low molecular weight solvent show this phenomenon to a very much greater degree. Fig. 25.5 shows the activity of toluene determined from the vapour pressure as a function of concentration for the toluene-rubber system.† The experimental points correspond to $\gamma_1 \ll 1$, and the fall is even more striking when we note the scale of the abscissa. Furthermore, from measurements of the osmotic pressure of these solutions as a function of temperature the variation of $\ln \gamma$ with T, and hence the heat of solution h_1^M (*cf.* 24.14) of toluene in the mixture can be evaluated. The value found in this way is very small and is quite incapable by itself of accounting for the observed deviations.

Other measurements of the same kind have been made more recently‡ and in all such systems it is found that

$$|h^E| \ll |g^E| \quad \text{and} \quad g^E < 0.$$

* *Cf.* K. H. Meyer and A. van der Wyk, *Helv. Chim. Acta*, 27, 845 (1944).
† K. H. Meyer, E. Wolff and C. H. Boissonnas, *Helv. Chim. Acta*, 23, 430 (1940).
‡ *Cf. e.g.* G. Gee in *Advances in Colloid Science*, vol. II (New York, 1946).

Since $g^E = h^E - Ts^E$, s^E must necessarily be positive and

$$Ts^E \gg h^E.$$

The entropy term overwhelms the heat term and determines the sign and the magnitude of the deviation from ideality. From the molecular point of view, these solutions are characterized essentially by the large difference in size between the two components of the solution, and it is found that the excess entropy increases with the difference between the chain lengths of the components as is shown in fig. 25.6 for the systems V.B., V.P., S.B., and S.P.

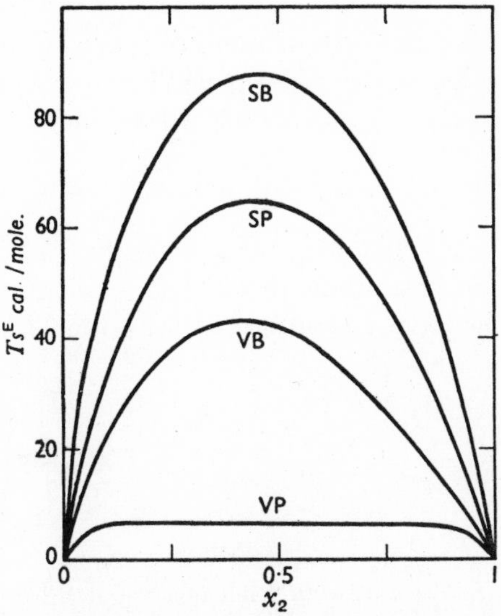

Fig. 25.6. Excess entropy for the systems
V.B.: benzene + butyl valerianate (C_9),
V.P.: propyl bromide + butyl valerianate (C_9),
S.B.: benzene + dibutyl sebacate (C_{18}),
S.P.: propyl bromide + dibutyl sebacate (C_{18}).

Before passing on to the theoretical interpretation of these results we shall first indicate the geometrical parameters to be employed. Once again we shall assume that the solution can be described in terms of a quasi-crystalline lattice (*cf.* chap. XXIV, § 4) having a co-ordination number z, but in the present instance we assume that while one molecule of component A occupies one place in the lattice, B occupies r places. We now designate the number of contacts of B with nearest neighbour molecules by qz.*

The relation between q and r depends upon the geometry of the molecule. For *non-branched chains* there are $(r-2)$ internal segments each of which makes $(z-2)$ contacts with nearest neighbours, and two segments with $(z-1)$ contacts; in all there are $(r-2)(z-2)+2(z-1)$. Thus

$$qz = r(z-2)+2. \tag{25.33}$$

For *branched chains*, there is one less contact with nearest neighbours at each branching point, but one extra contact at the end of each branched chain; hence qz is still given by (25.33).

* E. A. Guggenheim, *Proc. Roy. Soc.*, **A183**, 203 (1944); *Mixtures*, (Oxford, 1952); A. R. Miller, *Proc. Camb. Phil. Soc.*, **43**, 422 (1947), V. Mathot, *J. Chim. Phys.*, **47**, 384 (1950).

For *cyclic chains*, there are no terminal segments so that

$$qz = r(z-2). \tag{25.34}$$

In all three cases, when r is sufficiently large q is proportional to r, since

$$\lim_{r\to\infty} \frac{q}{r} = 1 - \frac{2}{z}. \tag{25.35}$$

In the case of more *compact* (non-chain) molecules such as discs or spheres, the ratio q/r will be less. For *spheres*, when $r \to \infty$, the number of nearest neighbours will become negligible in comparison with r:

$$\lim_{r\to\infty} \frac{q}{r} = 0. \tag{25.36}$$

The following diagrams illustrate the formulae (25.33) and (25.34) for a two-dimensional lattice with $z=6$. For a linear trimer molecule we have, in conformity with (25.33)

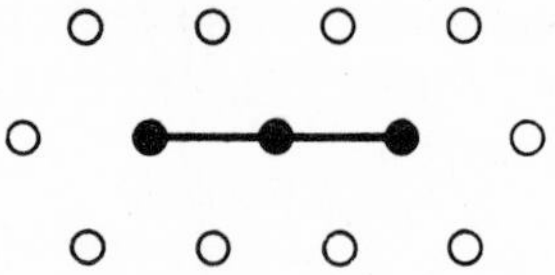

$qz = 14$ contacts with nearest neighbours ; hence

$$q = 14/6 = 7/3.$$

It is necessary, incidentally, to avoid confusion between the number of neighbours to the molecule and the number of nearest neighbour *contacts*.

On the other hand for a triangular trimer

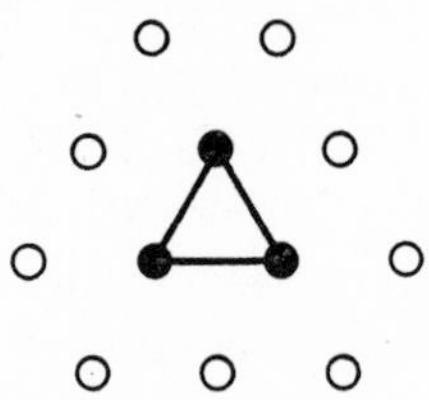

$$qz = 12 \quad \text{and} \quad q = 12/6 = 2.$$

The departures from the laws of perfect solutions depend essentially on the values of the parameters r and q.

The theoretical problem consists of the evaluation of the number of configurations, that is of the extension of equation (20.19) to the case where the two components have different dimensions or shapes. We shall concern ourselves first of all with chain molecules, which may be branched or not, but we exclude ring molecules and compact molecules.

Statistical methods lead, in the case of athermal solutions, or where the heat of mixing is sufficiently small, to the following approximate expression for the excess entropy.*

$$\frac{S^E}{k}=\tfrac{1}{2}z(N_A+qN_B)\ln(N_A+qN_B)-(N_A+N_B)\ln(N_A+N_B)$$
$$-(N_A+rN_B)(\tfrac{1}{2}z-1)\ln(N_A+rN_B). \quad (25.37)$$

To a rather crude approximation we may take $r \gtrsim q$, which corresponds to the physically rather unreal assumption that $z\to\infty$, and simplify this equation to

$$\frac{S^E}{k}=(N_A+rN_B)\ln(N_A+rN_B)-(N_A+N_B)\ln(N_A+N_B). \quad (25.38)$$

We see immediately from this equation that the excess entropy is *positive*, which corresponds to the statistical result that the number of configurations is here much greater than that corresponding to a perfect solution, given by (20.19).

Starting from (25.37) we can calculate the activity coefficients, since (24.12) gives for athermal solutions

$$\boldsymbol{R}T\ln\gamma_i=\frac{\partial G^E}{\partial n_i}=-T\frac{\partial S^E}{\partial n_i}, \quad (25.39)$$

whence, using (25.33) also, we obtain †

$$\left.\begin{aligned}\gamma_A&=\frac{(N_A+N_B)(N_A+rN_B)^{\frac{1}{2}z-1}}{(N_A+qN_B)^{\frac{1}{2}z}},\\ \gamma_B&=\frac{(N_A+N_B)(N_A+rN_B)^{(\frac{1}{2}z-1)r}}{(N_A+qN_B)^{\frac{1}{2}zq}}\end{aligned}\right\}. \quad (25.40)$$

These equations simplify, if we make z tend to infinity, to

$$\gamma_A=\frac{N_A+N_B}{N_A+rN_B};\quad \gamma_B=\frac{N_A+N_B}{N_A+rN_B}. \quad (25.41)$$

We see that the activity coefficients are both less than unity. Starting from (25.40) and (21.34) the partial vapour pressure of A and B can be calculated easily. The results are given in fig. 25.7; which shows the way in which the negative deviations from Raoult's law depend upon the differences in molecular size.

* *Cf.* A. R. Miller, *The theory of solutions of high polymers,* (Oxford, 1949).
† *Cf.* Miller, *loc. cit.*, p. 66.

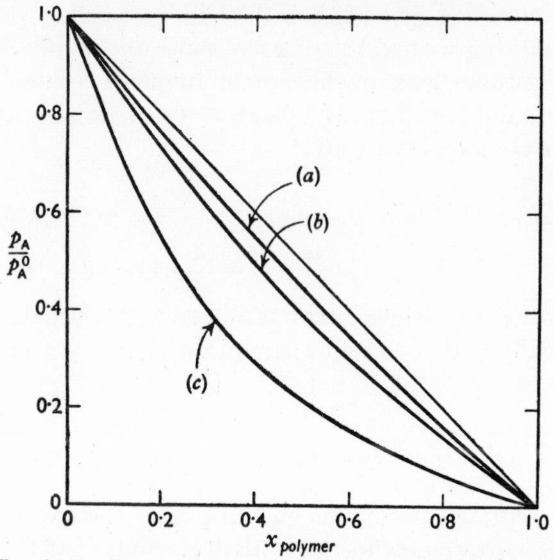

FIG. 25.7. Vapour pressures predicted by equation (25.37). (*a*) $r=2$, (*b*) $r=3$, (*c*) $r=10$.

Fig. 25.8 shows the vapour pressure of benzene in the system benzene + rubber, as a function of the volume fraction defined by

$$\varphi = \frac{N_A}{N_A + rN_B}. \tag{25.42}$$

The calculated curve is in satisfactory agreement with the experimental points.

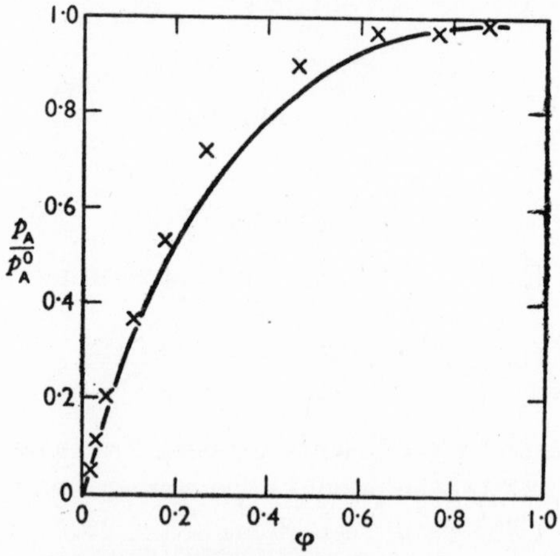

FIG. 25.8. Vapour pressure of benzene in the system rubber + benzene.*
φ = volume fraction of benzene,
× experimental points,
— calculated from equation (25.37).

* G. Gee and L. R. G. Treloar, *Trans. Faraday Soc.*, 38, 147 (1942).

5. Effect of the Shape of Molecules.

In the previous paragraph we limited ourselves to the case of chain molecules where the relation between q and r is given by equation (25.33). For more compact molecules such as discs or spheres, the value of q, for a given value of r, will be less than that given by this equation.

Although the general statistical theory has not yet been developed for these cases, it can be shown that the reduction in q has the effect of diminishing the magnitude of the excess entropy.* The deviations from ideality will be less, but will still be negative. This effect has been observed for macromolecules, where for substances of the same molecular weight, the deviations for chain molecules are much greater than for spherical molecules.†

We also notice that if a chain returns on itself or touches itself at various points, the value of q is also reduced on this account. The formulae developed in the previous paragraph are not valid for long chains unless we ignore their flexibility.‡

Finally for two components which are of approximately the same size, but are of different shapes, then

$$r_A = r_B, \quad \textit{but} \quad q_A \neq q_B, \tag{25.43}$$

and the configurational entropy only deviates a little from the ideal value.§

6. Excess Entropy in Hydrocarbon Solutions.

Equation (25.37) enables us to interpret the existence of a positive excess entropy of mixing in the solutions mentioned in paragraph 3. Similarly, for solutions of n-heptane + n-hexadecane (*cf.* chap. XXIV, § 4) or benzene + diphenyl‖ the order of magnitude of the excess entropy is in agreement with (25.37).

In the system n-octane + tetraethylmethane the behaviour is quite different (fig. 24.4). Here $r_A \simeq r_B$, and the configurational entropy in this case is close to the ideal value. However, the observed excess entropy is of the same magnitude as that for the benzene-diphenyl system, but is *negative*, whereas the configurational excess entropy is always positive. The interpretation of the excess entropy in systems

* V. Mathot, *Thesis*, (Brussels, 1949); E. A. Guggenheim and M. L. McGlashan, *Proc. Roy. Soc.*, **A203**, 435 (1950)

† V. Schultz, *Z. Naturforsch.*, 2a, **27**, 348, 411 (1947); M. Huggins, *J. Chim. Phys.*, **44**, 9 (1947); B. Zimm, *J. Chem. Phys.*, **14**, 164 (1946).

‡ A. J. Staverman, *Rec. Trav. Chim.*, **69**, 163 (1950).

§ V. Mathot, *Bull. Soc. Chim. Belg.*, **59**, 111 (1950).

‖ H. Tompa, *J. Chem. Phys.*, **16**, 292 (1948); J. H. Baxendale and B. V. Enüstün, *Phil. Trans. Roy. Soc.*, **243**, 182 (1951); D. H. Everett and M. F. Penney, *Proc. Roy. Soc.* **A212**, 164 (1952.)

of this kind must therefore be sought elsewhere. It is probably related to the fact that, because of the very different symmetries of the two molecules, the rotational and vibrational motion is profoundly altered by mixing (*cf.* § 2). As a result there is a change in the entropy of rotation, and possibly of vibration, which manifests itself as the excess entropy. Systems such as benzene + diphenyl on the one hand, and n-octane + tetraethylmethane on the other, probably represent two limiting types between which there is a series of intermediate cases.

CHAPTER XXVI

ASSOCIATED SOLUTIONS

1. Definition of an Associated Solution.

In the last chapter we examined systems for which the heat of mixing was either negligible (athermal solutions), or of the same magnitude as the thermal energy (regular solutions). In the present chapter we discuss the large class of solutions for which the heat of mixing attains very much larger values.

Let us consider, as a first example, a solution containing acetic acid. When two acetic acid molecules are close to one another, there will always be a certain interaction energy between them. This energy is particularly high when the hydrogen of each hydroxyl group (with a net positive charge) is immediately opposite an oxygen atom (an electronegative atom), that is to say in the relative configuration :

$$CH_3 . C \underset{\diagdown O \cdots H—O}{\overset{\diagup O—H \cdots O}{}} C . CH_3.$$

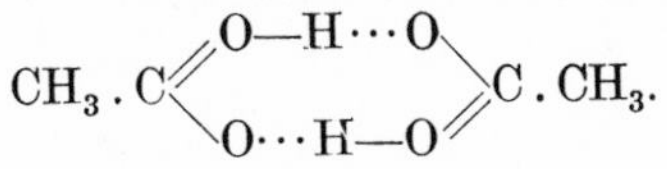

The interaction energy is very much greater than the thermal energy— some 8,000 cal./mole compared with a thermal energy of some 600 cal./mole so that this configuration will be relatively stable.

When this stable configuration has been formed, each of the acid molecules is restricted in its rotational degrees of freedom, and moreover it is found spectroscopically that some of the internal vibrational motions are modified.* The interaction between these molecules has therefore changed the rotational and vibrational states of each. In general, we can classify the molecules in a solution into two groups :

(a) those whose rotations and vibrations are not altered by the presence of neighbouring molecules ; we say that these are *free molecules*, or *monomolecules*.

(b) those whose state of rotation or vibration has been altered by neighbouring molecules ; these molecules are described as associated, and form *association complexes*.

In view of this definition of *association complexes*, we see immediately that we shall only expect to encounter these complexes in solutions

---

* *Cf.* R. M. Badger and S. H. Bauer, *J. Chem. Phys.*, **5**, 605 (1937).

containing molecules which have considerable electric charges near the surface of the molecule, such as in molecules containing the groups NH_2, OH, ... ; we call solutions of molecules of this kind *associated solutions*.

2. Thermodynamic Properties of Associated Solutions.

Let us consider an associated solution of A and B, and suppose that there exist in this solution complexes A_i formed from i monomolecules A (i may be 1, 2, 3 ...); complexes B_i, and finally complexes $A_i B_j$ resulting from the association of i molecules of A with j molecules of B. If the total number of moles of A and B in the solution are n_A and n_B, and if the number of moles of the various complexes actually present are n_{A_i}, n_{B_i}, $n_{A_i B_j}$, then

$$\left.\begin{aligned} n_A &= \sum_i i n_{A_i} + \sum_i \sum_j i n_{A_i B_j}, \\ n_B &= \sum_i i n_{B_i} + \sum_i \sum_j j n_{A_i B_j} \end{aligned}\right\}. \tag{26.1}$$

In the particular case where *only A* is associated (26.1) reduces to

$$n_A = \sum_i i n_{A_i}; \tag{26.2}$$

while if neither A nor B associates with itself, but an addition complex AB is formed, then

$$n_A = n_{A_1} + n_{AB}; \quad n_B = n_{B_1} + n_{AB}. \tag{26.3}$$

We now designate the chemical potentials of the complexes in solution by μ_{A_i}, μ_{B_i}, $\mu_{A_i B_j}$, and the macroscopic chemical potentials of components A and B by μ_A, μ_B, and proceed to find the relationship between these chemical potentials. The complexes will be in equilibrium among themselves, and with the monomers A_1 and B_1. The possible reactions among these species may be represented by

$$A_i = iA_1; \quad B_i = iB_1; \quad A_iB_j = iA_1 + jB_1;$$

and at equilibrium we must have

$$\mu_{A_i} = i\mu_{A_1}; \quad \mu_{B_i} = i\mu_{B_1}; \quad \mu_{A_i B_j} = i\mu_{A_1} + j\mu_{B_1}. \tag{26.4}$$

Let us now evaluate the total differential of G (6.19), at constant T and p, in the associated system which we regard as a mixture of the various complexes. Making use of (26.1) and (26.4) we have

$$\begin{aligned} \delta G &= \sum_i \mu_{A_i} \delta n_{A_i} + \sum_i \mu_{B_i} \delta n_{B_i} + \sum_i \sum_j \mu_{A_i B_j} \delta n_{A_i B_j} \\ &= \mu_{A_1} \sum_i i \, \delta n_{A_i} + \mu_{B_1} \sum_i i \, \delta n_{B_i} + \mu_{A_1} \sum_i \sum_j i \, \delta n_{A_i B_j} + \mu_{B_1} \sum_i \sum_j j \, \delta n_{A_i B_j} \\ &= \mu_{A_1} \delta n_A + \mu_{B_1} \delta n_B. \end{aligned} \tag{26.5}$$

On the other hand for any binary system at constant T, p

$$\delta G = \mu_A \, \delta n_A + \mu_B \, \delta n_B. \tag{26.6}$$

These two equations must be identical for all values of δn_A and δn_B, so it is necessary that:

$$\mu_A = \mu_{A_1}; \quad \mu_B = \mu_{B_1}. \tag{26.7}$$

The macroscopic chemical potentials μ_A and μ_B are therefore equal to the chemical potentials of the monomer molecules. This result is quite independent of any assumptions as to the mode of association. It is exact both for associated solutions and associated gases (such as acetic acid vapour), and depends only on the assumption that the complexes are in thermodynamic equilibrium with one another.

It is observed experimentally that associated solutions exhibit large deviations from ideal behaviour, and it seems reasonable to attribute at least the major part of these deviations to interactions leading to the formation of associated complexes.

If we regard the solution as formed from monomer molecules and complexes, all interactions between molecular species which are great enough to lead to association are excluded by definition. For if one molecule of an i-complex exerts a sufficiently high interaction on a j-complex that the vibrational and rotational states of the molecules are altered, then, by definition, an $(i+j)$ complex has been formed. It follows therefore that the monomer-complex system must be approximately ideal since the particles present exert only normal intermolecular forces on one another.

If we neglect for the moment deviations from ideality arising from the different sizes and shapes of complexes and monomers (*cf.* § 4) we arrive at the picture of an *ideal associated solution*. This is, by definition, a solution which, regarded as a mixture of monomer molecules and complexes, is perfect, that is ideal at all concentrations. In a solution of this kind the chemical potentials of the monomer molecules are given by

$$\left.\begin{aligned} \mu_{A_1} &= \mu_{A_1}^{\ominus}(T, p) + \boldsymbol{R}T \ln x_{A_1}, \\ \mu_{B_1} &= \mu_{B_1}^{\ominus}(T, p) + \boldsymbol{R}T \ln x_{B_1} \end{aligned}\right\}, \tag{26.8}$$

where x_{A_1} and x_{B_1} are the *effective* mole fractions of the monomers of A and B. That is to say

$$\left.\begin{aligned} x_{A_1} &= \frac{n_{A_1}}{\sum_i n_{A_i} + \sum_i n_{B_i} + \sum_i \sum_j n_{A_i B_j}}, \\ x_{B_1} &= \frac{n_{B_1}}{\sum_i n_{A_i} + \sum_i n_{B_i} + \sum_i \sum_j n_{A_i B_j}} \end{aligned}\right\}. \tag{26.9}$$

We deduce therefore from (26.7) that, (*cf.* 7.63)

$$\left.\begin{aligned} \mu_A^{\ominus} + RT \ln x_A \gamma_A &= \mu_{A_1}^{\ominus} + RT \ln x_{A_1}, \\ \mu_B^{\ominus} + RT \ln x_B \gamma_B &= \mu_{B_1}^{\ominus} + RT \ln x_{B_1} \end{aligned}\right\}, \tag{26.10}$$

whence

$$\gamma_A = \frac{x_{A_1}}{x_A} \exp\left\{\frac{\mu_{A_1}^{\ominus} - \mu_A^{\ominus}}{RT}\right\}; \quad \gamma_B = \frac{x_{B_1}}{x_B} \exp\left\{\frac{\mu_{B^1}^{\ominus} - \mu_B^{\ominus}}{RT}\right\}. \tag{26.11}$$

When $x_A \to 1$, the effective mole fraction of monomer molecules tends to a certain limit $x_{A_1}^0$, the mole fraction of monomers in the pure liquid, which depends only upon the pressure and temperature, while in the symmetrical reference system, γ_A tends to unity. Hence

$$x_{A_1}^0 = \exp\left\{-\left(\frac{\mu_{A_1}^{\ominus} - \mu_A^{\ominus}}{RT}\right)\right\},$$

and (26.11) can be written

$$\gamma_A = \frac{1}{x_{A_1}^0} \cdot \frac{x_{A_1}}{x_A}. \tag{26.12}$$

Similarly

$$\gamma_B = \frac{1}{x_{B_1}^0} \cdot \frac{x_{B_1}}{x_B}. \tag{26.12'}$$

When only the molecules of one component, say A, are associated (*e.g.* in the system ethanol + carbon tetrachloride), it is more convenient to employ as system of reference a very dilute solution of A in B. As $x_A \to 0$, $x_{A_1}/x_A \to 1$ and A is present as monomers only. It follows that in this reference system $\mu_{A_1}^{\ominus} = \mu_A^{\ominus}$ and hence from (26.11) that

$$\gamma_A^* = \frac{x_{A_1}}{x_A} = x_{A_1}^0 \gamma_A. \tag{26.13}$$

On the other hand when $x_B \to 1$, $\gamma_B^* \to 1$ and $x_{B_1} \to 1$ so that

$$\gamma_B^* = \frac{x_{B_1}}{x_B} = \gamma_B. \tag{26.13'}$$

The mole fraction of monomer B_1 is here

$$x_{B_1} = \frac{n_B}{\sum_i n_{A_i} + n_B},$$

so that the activity coefficient of B will be, by virtue of (26.13'),

$$\gamma_B^* = \frac{n_A + n_B}{\sum n_{A_i} + n_B}. \tag{26.13''}$$

We now return to the parameters which determine γ_A and γ_B relative to the symmetrical system of reference. Substituting (26.9) in (26.12) we obtain

$$\gamma_A = \frac{1}{x^0_{A_1}} \frac{n_{A_1}}{n_A} \frac{n_A + n_B}{\sum_i n_{A_i} + \sum_i n_{B_i} + \sum_i \sum_j n_{A_i B_j}}$$

$$= \frac{1}{x^0_{A_1}} \beta_A \chi_{AB}. \tag{26.14}$$

and similarly

$$\gamma_B = \frac{1}{x^0_{B_1}} \beta_B \chi_{AB}, \tag{26.15}$$

where β_A and β_B are the fractions of molecules A and B respectively which exist as monomers :

$$\beta_A = \frac{n_{A_1}}{n_A}; \quad \beta_B = \frac{n_{B_1}}{n_B}, \tag{26.16}$$

and χ_{AB} may be regarded as *the average number of particles per complex*. It is the total number of molecules of A and B, divided by the total number of complexes :

$$\chi_{AB} = \frac{n_A + n_B}{\sum_i n_{A_i} + \sum_i n_{B_i} + \sum_i \sum_j n_{A_i B_j}}. \tag{26.17}$$

Thus the values of the activity coefficients in an associated solution are determined by the parameters β_A, β_B and χ_{AB}, and are independent of the complexity of the mode of association provided only that the *mixture of complexes* may be regarded as an ideal solution.

Consider first the particular case in which only A is associated. In place of (26.17) we introduce the average degree of association of A molecules defined by

$$\chi_A = \frac{\sum_i i n_{A_i}}{\sum_i n_{A_i}} = \frac{n_A}{\sum_i n_{A_i}}, \tag{26.18}$$

which is simply related to χ_{AB} by

$$\chi_{AB} = \frac{n_A + n_B}{\dfrac{n_A}{\chi_A} + n_B} = \frac{1}{\dfrac{x_A}{\chi_A} + x_B}. \tag{26.19}$$

Equations (26.14) and (26.15) now become

$$\gamma_A = \frac{1}{x^0_{A_1}} \beta_A \frac{1}{\dfrac{x_A}{\chi_A} + x_B}; \quad \gamma_B = \frac{1}{\dfrac{x_A}{\chi_A} + x_B}. \tag{26.20}$$

From this we see that

$$\gamma_B > 1$$

so that systems of this kind exhibit *positive* deviations from Raoult's law.

As noted above, for systems of this kind it is more convenient to use the asymmetrical system of reference of a very dilute solution of A in B. Then, using (26.20), equations (26.13) and (26.13′) lead to

$$\gamma_A^* = \beta_A \frac{1}{\dfrac{x_A}{\chi_A} + x_B}\,; \quad \gamma_B^* = \frac{1}{\dfrac{x_A}{\chi_A} + x_B}, \tag{26.21}$$

and to the remarkable result that

$$\frac{\gamma_A^*}{\gamma_B^*} = \beta_A. \tag{26.22}$$

Thus in any solution of this type the ratio of the activity coefficients of A and B, in terms of the asymmetrical reference system, is equal to the fraction of A molecules in the monomeric state.

For systems where the only type of association is between different molecules (*e.g.* chloroform + ethyl ether), $x_{A_1}^0 = x_{B_1}^0 = 1$, and we have from (26.14) and (26.15)

$$\gamma_A = \beta_A \chi_{AB}\,; \quad \gamma_B = \beta_B \chi_{AB}. \tag{26.23}$$

We note that if the mutual association is very marked, β_A and β_B may tend to zero while χ_{AB} remains non-zero. Thus, for example, if the association leads to a single complex A_3B, n_{A_1} and n_{B_1} can be simultaneously nearly zero, while χ_{AB} will have a value of four. It follows therefore that γ_A and γ_B tend to zero as the association becomes stronger. In this case therefore, the deviations from Raoult's law are *negative*.

3. Activity Coefficients and Spectroscopic Properties of Associated Solutions.

The results established in the preceding paragraph may be verified by comparing the thermodynamic properties and the spectroscopic properties of associated solutions. Let us consider, for example, a solution of ethanol in carbon tetrachloride. The valency vibration of the OH group gives rise to two distinct infra-red absorption bands depending upon whether the OH group is in a monomer or in an associated complex. The fraction of molecules of alcohol which remain in the monomeric state can therefore be determined from measurements of the intensity of the OH vibration band.* It follows therefore that we can test equation (26.22) by comparing the values of β_A determined spectroscopically with the ratio γ_A^*/γ_B^* found by the usual thermodynamic methods.† Experimental data are available to test this equation for the systems methanol + carbon tetrachloride (fig. 26.1) ethanol + carbon tetrachloride, *tert*-butanol + carbon tetrachloride, *tert*-butanol + carbon disulphide, *tert*-butanol + cyclohexane, benzyl alcohol + carbon tetrachloride.‡

Fig. 26.1 shows that equation (26.22) is obeyed quite accurately and that the deviations from ideality can be almost entirely accounted for

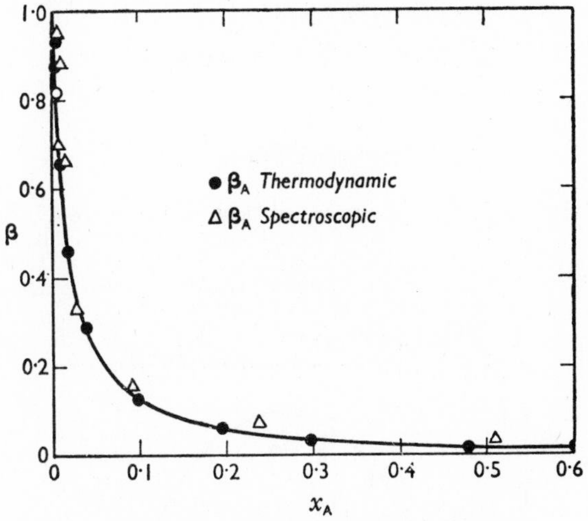

FIG. 26.1. Test of equation (26.22) for the system methanol (A) + carbon tetrachloride (B).
● thermodynamic§
Δ spectroscopic‖

by complex formation. Careful examination of the available data shows, however, that in solutions very concentrated in alcohol (except for the system ethanol + carbon tetrachloride) β tends to become larger than γ_A^*/γ_B^*. It is interesting to examine the importance of this deviation on the excess free energy g^E (24.2). This excess energy can

* J. Errera and H. Sack, *Trans. Faraday Soc.*, 34, 728 (1938); J. Errera, H. Sack and R. Gaspart, *J. Chem, Phys*, 8, 63 (1940); I. Prigogine, *Mem. Ac. Roy. Belg.* (*Cl. Sc.*), 20, part 2 (1943); R. Mecke and J. Kreuger, *Zeit. physik. Chem.*, B, 49, 313 (1941); R. Mecke and H. Kempter, *Naturwiss.*, 27, 583 (1939); E. G. Hoffmann, *Zeit. physik. Chem.*, B, 53, 179 (1943).

† R. Mecke, *Z. Electrochem.*, 52, 107 (1948); I. Prigogine, V. Mathot and A. Desmyter, *Bull. Soc. Chim. Belg.*, 58, 547 (1949).

‡ I. Prigogine, V. Mathot and A. Desmyter, *loc. cit.*; I. Prigogine and A. Desmyter, *Trans. Faraday Soc.*, 47, 1137 (1951).

§ Niini, *Ann. Acad. Sci. Fenn.*, A55, 8 (1940).

‖ A. Hoffmann, *loc. cit.*

be divided into two parts, one arising from the presence of complexes and the other corresponding to all other residual causes,

$$g^E = g^E_{\text{assn}} + g^E_{\text{res}}. \tag{26.24}$$

We may now introduce activity coefficients γ''_A and γ''_B corresponding to g^E_{res},

$$g^E_{\text{res}} = x_A \mathbf{R}T \ln \gamma''_A + x_B \mathbf{R}T \ln \gamma''_B. \tag{26.25}$$

The logarithms of γ''_A and γ''_B can be expressed as series in the mole fractions as in (21.50) and for the present purpose we retain terms up to the third power in mole fractions. We have then

$$\left.\begin{aligned} \ln \gamma''_A &= \alpha_2 x_B^2 + \alpha_3 x_B^3 \\ \ln \gamma''_B &= (\alpha_2 + \tfrac{3}{2}\alpha_3) x_A^2 - \alpha_3 x_A^3 \end{aligned}\right\}, \tag{26.26}$$

and therefore

$$g^E_{\text{res}} = \mathbf{R}T x_A x_B \left[\alpha_2 + \frac{\alpha_3}{2}(1 + x_B)\right]. \tag{26.27}$$

The parameters α_2 and α_3 can be obtained as follows. We have the formula

$$\frac{\gamma_A}{\gamma_B} = \left(\frac{\gamma'_A}{\gamma'_B}\right)\left(\frac{\gamma''_A}{\gamma''_B}\right) = \beta \frac{\gamma''_A}{\gamma''_B}.$$

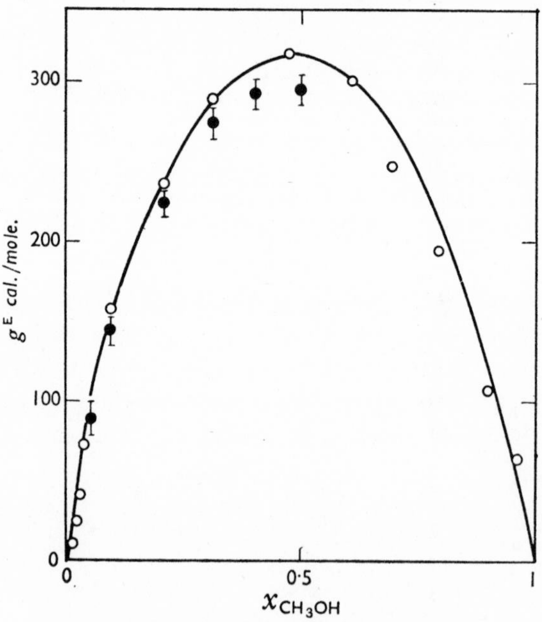

FIG. 26.2. Excess free energy in the system methanol + carbon tetrachloride.

○ g^E ● g^E_{assn}

Choosing now a very dilute solution of A in B as standard reference state,* and employing (26.26), we obtain

$$\ln \frac{\gamma_A^*}{\gamma_B^*} = \ln \beta - (2\alpha_2 + 3\alpha_3) x_A + \tfrac{3}{2} \alpha_2 x_A^2. \tag{26.28}$$

If the experimental values of γ_A^*/γ_B^* and β are known, α_2 and α_3 can be evaluated. Substitution of these in (26.27) gives g^E_{res}. In fig. 26.2 g^E and g^E_{assn} are shown for the system methanol + carbon tetrachloride at 20 °C. The major part of g^E thus arises from association, and the residual contribution is probably to be attributed to effects arising from dispersion forces analogous to those which determine the properties of regular solutions.

4. Domain of Validity of the Ideal Associated Solution Model.

The model of an ideal associated solution developed in the preceding paragraphs constitutes a limiting case to which various corrections should be made. We see first that the equations (26.14) and (26.15) for the activity coefficients lead to the following value of the excess free energy

$$\begin{aligned} g^E &= x_A RT \ln \frac{\beta_A \chi_{AB}}{x^0_{A_1}} + x_B RT \ln \frac{\beta_B \chi_{AB}}{x^0_{B_1}} \\ &= x_A RT \ln \frac{\beta_A}{x^0_{A_1}} + x_B RT \ln \frac{\beta_B}{x^0_{B_1}} + RT \ln \chi_{AB}, \end{aligned} \tag{26.29}$$

and from this we find the heat of mixing to be, (*cf.* 24.4),

$$h^E = -x_A RT^2 \frac{\partial \ln \dfrac{\beta_A}{x^0_{A_1}}}{\partial T} - x_B RT^2 \frac{\partial \ln \dfrac{\beta_B}{x^0_{B_1}}}{\partial T} - RT^2 \frac{\partial \ln \chi_{AB}}{\partial T}. \tag{26.30}$$

This heat of mixing, calculated on the basis of the model of ideal associated solutions, must be interpreted as a *heat of reaction* resulting from the formation or dissociation of complexes. Besides this contribution we must also expect to find in the heat of mixing a contribution from less intense intermolecular forces, of the type mentioned at the end of the previous paragraph, which do not result in complex formation. In the simplest case these interactions contribute a term to h^E and g^E of the form

$$x_A x_B \alpha. \tag{26.31}$$

* If the reference system is a very dilute solution of A in B the first equation of (26.26) becomes

$$\ln \gamma_A^{\prime\prime *} = \alpha_2 x_B^2 + \alpha_3 x_B^3 - \alpha_2 - \alpha_3.$$

It follows that (26.29) must be replaced by*

$$g^E = x_A RT \ln \frac{\beta_A}{x^0_{A_1}} + x_B RT \ln \frac{\beta_B}{x^0_{B_1}} + RT \ln \chi_{AB} + x_A x_B \alpha, \tag{26.32}$$

and the activity coefficients become (*cf.* 24.12 and 25.7)

$$\left.\begin{aligned} RT \ln \gamma_A &= RT \ln \frac{\beta_A \chi_{AB}}{x^0_{A_1}} + \alpha x_B^2, \\ RT \ln \gamma_B &= RT \ln \frac{\beta_B \chi_{AB}}{x^0_{B_1}} + \alpha x_A^2 \end{aligned}\right\}. \tag{26.33}$$

We must also consider the correction to the entropy of mixing arising from the difference in size of the complexes. This can be evaluated approximately in the case where only component A is associated and where the complexes are in the form of chains. It can be shown, using methods analogous to those used in deriving (25.40), that (26.21) must be replaced by †

$$\begin{aligned} \ln \gamma_A^* &= \ln \beta_A + x_A \left(1 - \frac{1}{\chi_A}\right), \\ \ln \gamma_B^* &= x_A \left(1 - \frac{1}{\chi_A}\right), \end{aligned} \tag{26.34}$$

where the asymmetrical system of reference is used. We note that this correction does not affect the validity of (26.22), but that each activity coefficient is given by a slightly different equation in terms of β_A and χ_A.

To examine this effect in more detail, we put

$$\theta \equiv 1 - \frac{1}{\chi_A}, \tag{26.35}$$

and expand $\ln \gamma_B^*$ in powers of θ. Depending upon whether we take (26.21) or (26.34) for $\ln \gamma_B^*$ we obtain

$$\ln \gamma_B^* = x_A \theta + \tfrac{1}{2} x_A^2 \theta^2 + \ldots \tag{26.36}$$

or

$$\ln \gamma_B^* = x_A \theta. \tag{26.37}$$

The discrepancy between the two expressions only enters with the term of second order in θ. In a dilute solution of A in B, the difference in size of the complexes compared with the monomer play only a negligible role since χ_A will be close to unity. However, if the association is considerable ($\chi_A \to \infty$) the effect is much greater :

$$\lim_{\chi_A \to \infty} \gamma_B^* = \frac{1}{1 - x_A}, \tag{26.38}$$

* *Cf.* O. Rodlich and A. T. Kister, *J. Chem. Phys.*, **15**, 849 (1947).
† I. Prigogine, *et al*, *loc. cit.*

according to the simple model (26.21), while

$$\lim_{x_A \to \infty} \gamma_B^* = e^{x_A}, \qquad (26.39)$$

when we take account of the entropy correction.

We see from these equations that when x_A tends to unity $\gamma_B^* \to \infty$ on the basis of equation (26.38), but tends to the finite limit $e = 2{\cdot}7 \ldots$ when calculated from (26.39). In other words, the model of an ideal associated solution applied to this kind of system leads to positive deviations which may become infinite, but if we assume the complexes which are formed to be chains and if we take into account the difference between the size of complex and solvent, then the deviations from ideality cannot be greater than the limiting value e.

This result can be interpreted quite easily. If we neglect the entropy correction, the association of one component of a solution leads to *positive* deviations from Raoult's law. On the other hand, the existence of long chains, if it is the only factor involved, leads to negative deviations from Raoult's law (*cf.* chap. XXV, § 4). The combination of these two factors leads to deviations which, although still positive, are very much smaller than those predicted on the basis of the association effect alone.

By taking the complexes as chains we have obtained the maximum value of the entropy effect (*cf.* chap. XXV, § 4). If the complexes are

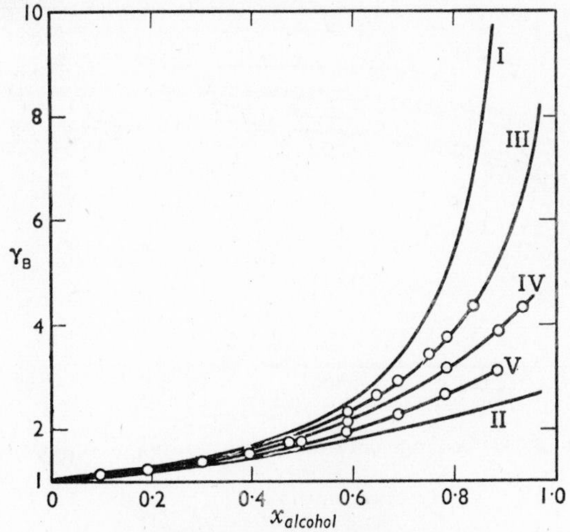

FIG. 26.3. Activity coefficients of carbon tetrachloride in the systems
$CCl_4 + C_2H_5OH$ (curve III),
$CCl_4 + CH_3OH$ (curve IV),
$CCl_4 + C_6H_5OH$ (curve V).
The limiting laws (26.38) and (26.39) are shown by curves I and II respectively.

rings or more compact molecules, the results will be intermediate between those given by (26.21) and (26.34).

Fig. 26.3 shows that for the systems methanol + carbon tetrachloride, ethanol + carbon tetrachloride and benzyl alcohol + carbon tetrachloride, the activity coefficients of carbon tetrachloride become greater than the limiting value given by (26.39). This shows that in concentrated solutions the complexes cannot be regarded as simple chains, but must to some extent be in the form of closed rings, or, more likely, two- and three-dimensional aggregates.

5. Modes of Association.

In this paragraph we shall consider systems in which only one of the components is associated, and shall employ equations (26.21). These formulae contain two parameters β_A and χ_A. As we have seen β_A can be determined spectroscopically, while χ_A is generally deduced from determinations of γ_B by means of cryoscopic measurements (*cf.* 22.8).

The two activity coefficients are related by equation (21.45); substituting (26.21) into this equation we obtain:

$$x_A \frac{\partial \ln \beta_A}{\partial x_A} = \frac{\partial \ln \left(\dfrac{x_A}{\chi_A} + x_B\right)}{\partial x_A}. \tag{26.40}$$

Now, if for example β_A is determined from spectroscopic data as a

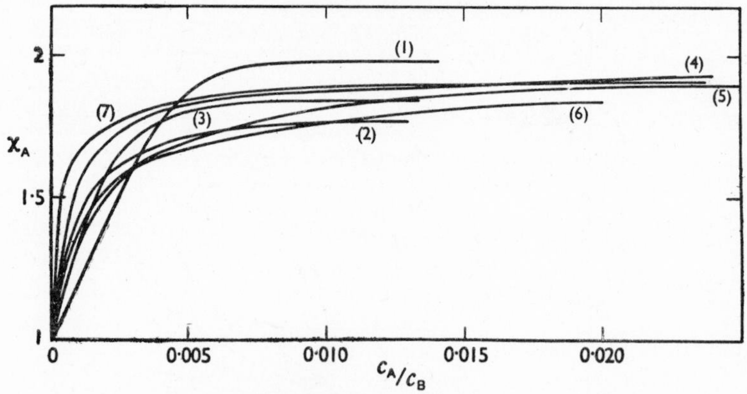

FIG. 26.4. Average degree of association χ_A of various acids in benzene.*

(1) *trans*-cinnamic acid,
(2) phenylpropionic acid,
(3) phenylacetic acid,
(4) cyclohexyl carboxylic acid,
(5) benzoic acid,
(6) *o*-toluic acid,
(7) *m*-toluic acid.

* J. Pirotte, *Mémoire de licence*, University of Brussels (1947–48).

function of x_A, this equation enables us to evaluate χ_A. Remembering that $\chi_A \to 1$ for $x_A \to 0$, the integrated form of (26.40) may be written,

$$\ln\left(\frac{x_A}{\chi_A}+x_B\right)=\int_0^{x_A} x_A \frac{\partial \ln \beta_A}{\partial x_A}\,dx_A.$$

In very dilute solutions ($x_A \ll 1$) the logarithm can be expanded to give

$$\ln\left(\frac{x_A}{\chi_A}+x_B\right)\simeq x_A\left(\frac{1}{\chi_A}-1\right),$$

so that

$$\frac{1}{\chi_A}-1=\frac{1}{x_A}\int_0^{x_A} x_A \frac{\partial \ln \beta_A}{\partial x_A}\,dx_A. \qquad (26.41)$$

Figs. 26.4 and 26.5 give the value of χ_A for solutions of acids, alcohols and phenol in various solvents. In the case of the acids, χ_A was determined from cryoscopic measurements, while for the alcohols and phenol from spectroscopic data. There is a striking difference between the behaviour of the acids compared with the alcohols and phenol. For acids χ_A rises rapidly to a saturation value of about two. On the other hand, for alcohols and phenol, χ_A continues to rise steadily and reaches values much greater than two, and furthermore the curves are strongly dependent on both the solvent and temperature.

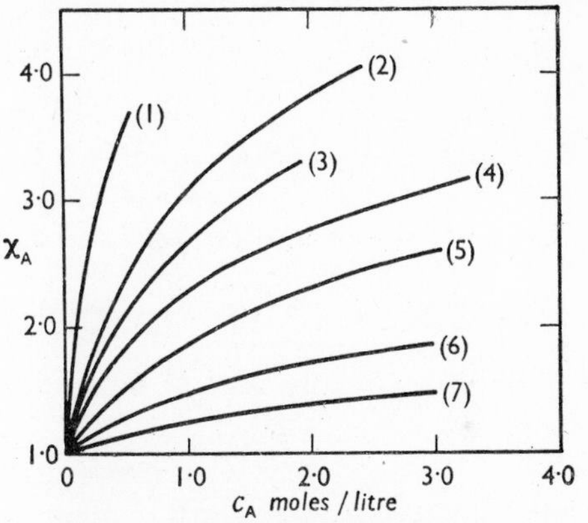

FIG. 26.5. Average degree of association χ_A of various alcohols and of phenols.*

(1) phenol in carbon tetrachloride at −20 °C.,
(2) methanol in carbon tetrachloride at 20 °C.,
(3) ethanol in carbon tetrachloride at 20 °C.,
(4) phenol in carbon tetrachloride at 20 °C.,
(5) chlorophenol in carbon tetrachloride at 20 °C.,
(6) phenol in chlorobenzene at 20 °C.,
(7) phenol in benzene at 20 °C.

These two modes of association may be described approximately by assuming that in the first case there is only one kind of complex, generally bimolecular, while in the second there are a great variety of complexes the distribution of which depends on the concentration and temperature.

In view of these general conclusions we now consider the two separate cases depending upon whether the association leads to one kind of complex molecule, or to chain-like complexes of varying sizes.

* R. Mecke, *Z. Electrochem*, 52, 269 (1948).

*Formation of a single kind of Association Complex.**

Let us suppose that only one kind of complex molecule is formed and that this contains λ molecules of A. Then we have only to consider one equilibrium

$$\lambda A = A_\lambda,$$

for which

$$\mu_{A_\lambda} = \lambda \mu_A. \tag{26.42}$$

We recall that we are assuming the solution of complex molecules in the monomer to be ideal. Then in a solution sufficiently dilute that we can put the mole fractions proportional to concentrations (*cf.* 20.47 and 20.70), we write the mass action equation for the system as

$$c_{A_\lambda} = K_{c,\lambda} c^\lambda_{A_1}. \tag{26.43}$$

From this, employing the definition of χ_A (26.18) we have

$$\left.\begin{aligned} c_A &= \sum_i i c_{A_i} = c_{A_1} + \lambda K_{c,\lambda} c^\lambda_{A_1}, \\ \sum_i c_{A_i} &= \frac{c_A}{\chi_A} = c_{A_1} + K_{c,\lambda} c^\lambda_{A_1} \end{aligned}\right\}. \tag{26.44}$$

Subtracting the second of these equations from the first we have

$$c_A - c_A/\chi_A = (\lambda - 1) K_{c,\lambda} c^\lambda_{A_1}, \tag{26.45}$$

while multiplying the second by λ and subtracting from the first gives

$$c_A - \lambda c_A/\chi_A = -(\lambda - 1) c_{A_1}. \tag{26.46}$$

This latter equation can be solved for c_{A_1} and the value substituted in (26.45) to give†

$$\frac{1 - \dfrac{1}{\chi_A}}{\left(\dfrac{\lambda}{\chi_A} - 1\right)^\lambda c_A^{\lambda-1}} = \frac{K_{c,\lambda}}{(\lambda - 1)^{\lambda-1}}, \tag{26.47}$$

which for the simple case of double molecule formation reduces to

$$\frac{1 - \dfrac{1}{\chi_A}}{\left(\dfrac{2}{\chi_A} - 1\right)^2 c_A} = K_{c,2}. \tag{26.48}$$

* *Cf.* J. Kreuzer, *Z. physik. Chem.*, **B53**, 213 (1943); K. L. Wolf, *Z. physik. Chem.*, 61, 191 (1949).

† *Cf.* J. Kreuzer, *loc. cit.*

TABLE 26.1

Test of equations (26.48) and (26.64) for solutions of phenylacetic acid (A) in nitrobenzene (B)

c_A(g/100 g *nitrobenzene*)	ΔT_f	χ_A	$K_{c,2}$ (26.48)	K_c (26.64)
1·126	0·363	1·58	4·5	0·81
3·629	1·069	1·73	4·6	0·46
4·289	1·242	1·75	4·8	0·31
5·426	1·557	1·78	5·2	0·26
8·288	2·323	1·78	3·4	0·17
10·52	2·913	1·80	3·1	0·14
13·41	3·655	1·82	3·4	0·11

TABLE 26.2

Test of equations (26.48) and (26.64) for solutions of benzyl alcohol (A) in nitrobenzene (B)

c_A (g/100 g *nitrobenzene*)	ΔT_f	χ_A	$K_{c,2}$ (26.48)	K_c (26.64)
1·577	0·930	1·085	0·067	0·058
2·694	1·502	1·14	0·078	0·057
4·120	2·152	1·23	0·102	0·070
5·762	2·794	1·30	0·14	0·068
7·396	3·352	1·35	0·15	0·064
9·028	3·852	1·46	0·26	0·074
11·36	4·468	1·53	0·34	0·074

In table 26.1 are given data for the association of phenylacetic acid (A) in nitrobenzene (B) for which χ_A was determined from the cryoscopic data of Brown and Bury.* The values of $K_{c,2}$ derived from (26.48) are reasonably constant. This behaviour is however rather uncommon and the more usual behaviour is illustrated in table 26.2 where $K_{c,2}$ for benzyl alcohol in nitrobenzene shows a rapid trend with c_A. A similar lack of constancy is exhibited in the data for propionic acid in nitrobenzene and *trans*-cinnamic acid in benzene. In these instances it seems probable that several different types of complex are in equilibrium with one another.

Chain Association.

We now consider association complexes which may contain a variable number of monomer molecules. The equilibrium constant for the reaction

$$A_1 + A_i = A_{i+1}$$

* F. S. Brown and C. R. Bury, *J. Phys. Chem.*, 30, 694 (1926); *cf.* W. F. K. Wynne-Jones and G. S. Rushbrooke, *Trans. Faraday Soc.*, 40, 345 (1944).

is

$$\frac{c_{A_{i+1}}}{c_{A_1}\, c_{A_i}} = K_{c,\,i}. \tag{26.49}$$

In the very simplest case we might suppose this equilibrium constant to be almost independent of i so that*

$$K_{c,1} \simeq K_{c,\,2} \simeq \ldots \simeq K_c. \tag{26.50}$$

Then

$$c_{A_{i+1}} = c_{A_1} c_{A_i} K_c. \tag{26.51}$$

Starting from the association into double molecules and applying this equation successively we obtain

$$c_{A_i} = c_{A_1}^i K_c^{\,i-1}. \tag{26.52}$$

The total concentration of A molecules is

$$c_A = \sum_i i\, c_{A_i} = \sum_i i\, c_{A_1}^i K_c^{\,i-1}. \tag{26.53}$$

Putting

$$y = c_{A_1} K_c, \tag{26.54}$$

we see that

$$\frac{c_A}{c_{A_1}} = \sum_i i\, y^{i-1} = \frac{d}{dy} \sum_i y^i. \tag{26.55}$$

We notice that, from (26.49), y must be a dimensionless quantity and we assume that it is always less than unity. We can now apply the well-known property of a geometric progression :

$$\sum_{i=1}^{\infty} y^i = \frac{y}{1-y}, \quad y < 1, \tag{26.56}$$

which substituted in (26.55) gives

$$\frac{c_A}{c_{A_1}} = \sum_i i\, y^{i-1} = \frac{1}{(1-y)^2}, \tag{26.57}$$

or

$$\frac{c_A}{c_{A_1}} = \frac{1}{(1 - c_{A_1} K_c)^2}. \tag{26.58}$$

The equilibrium constant K_c is therefore

$$K_c = \frac{1}{c_{A_1}} \left(1 - \sqrt{\frac{c_{A_1}}{c_A}}\right). \tag{26.59}$$

* E. W. Lassettre, *J. Amer. Chem. Soc.*, **59**, 1383 (1937) ; *Chem. Rev.* **20**, 259 (1937) ; K. H. Meyer, *Helv. Chim. Acta*, **20**, 1321 (1947) ; H. Kempter and R. Mecke, *Naturwiss*, **27**, 583 (1939).

This equation enables one to make a calculation of the monomer concentration c_{A_1} in terms of c_A and K_c. The validity of this calculation depends upon the correctness of the assumption made in (26.50).

Equation (26.59) may be tested if the extent of association can be determined spectroscopically. If (26.59) holds, the graph of c_{A_1} against $\sqrt{c_{A_1}/c_A}$ should be linear. Fig. 26.6 shows this test applied to the data

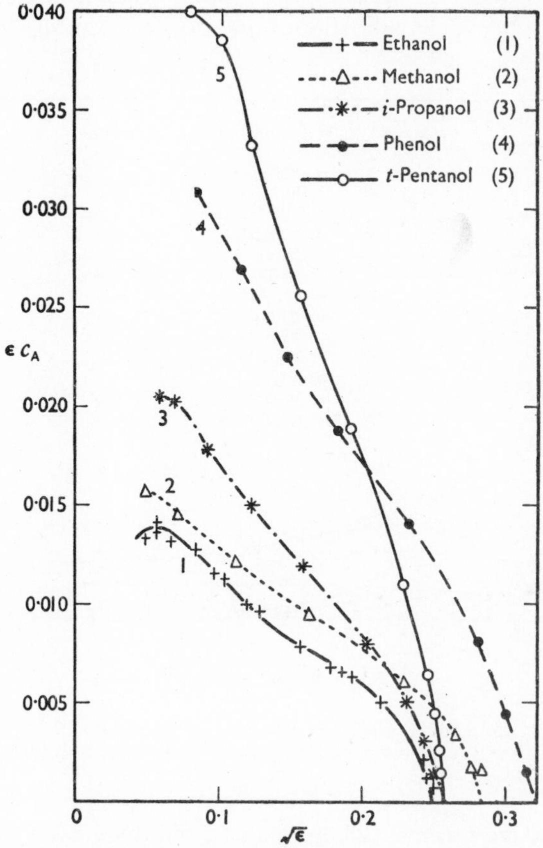

FIG. 26.6. Association of alcohols and phenol in carbon tetrachloride solutions.*

for the degree of association of various alcohols and of phenol in carbon tetrachloride solutions.* The optical density (ϵ) of the solution for the second harmonic of the OH band of the monomer is multiplied by the total alcohol concentration: this gives the residual concentration of monomer in the solution and is plotted as ordinate. The abscissa is

* Hoffmann, *loc. cit.*

the square root of the optical density which is proportional to $\sqrt{c_{A_1}/c_A}$. The predicted linearity is only observed over limited ranges of concentration; this shows clearly that the assumption in (26.50) is only a first approximation.

If we accept equation (26.59) appreciating its limitations, we may estimate the concentration of the various complexes by employing (26.52). This has been done for the system ethanol + cyclohexane at a series of concentrations and the results are shown in fig. 26.7.

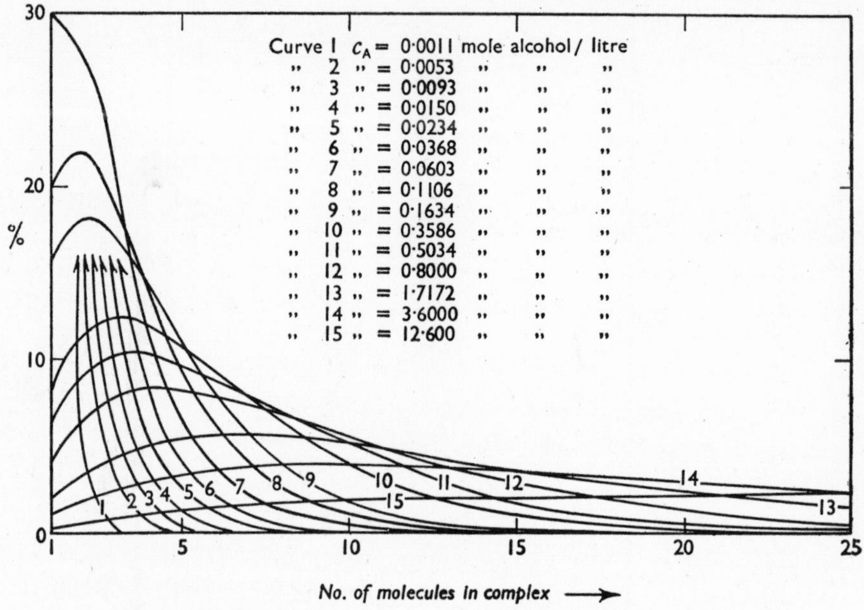

FIG. 26.7. Complex formation in ethanol + cyclohexane at 6 °C. Each curve gives the distribution of complexes of various sizes for a given total concentration of alcohol.

An alternative form of (26.59) may be obtained by writing it in the form

$$\frac{\beta_A c_A}{1-\sqrt{\beta_A}} = \frac{1}{K_c} \tag{26.60}$$

where β_A is defined in (26.16).

Another test of this treatment is to employ freezing point data in the following way. We have on the one hand (26.58)

$$c_A = \frac{c_{A_1}}{(1-c_{A_1}K_c)^2} \tag{26.61}$$

while from (26.52), using (26.56),

$$\Sigma c_{A_i} = \Sigma K_c^{i-1} c_{A_1}^i = \frac{c_{A_1}}{1 - c_{A_1} K_c}. \qquad (26.62)$$

Hence, from 26.58

$$\chi_A = \frac{c_A}{\Sigma c_{A_i}} = \frac{1}{1 - c_{A_1} K_c} \qquad (26.63)$$

or

$$c_{A_1} = \left(1 - \frac{1}{\chi}\right) \frac{1}{K_c}.$$

On substituting this in (26.61) we obtain

$$\frac{\chi_A(\chi_A - 1)}{c_A} = K_c. \qquad (26.64)$$

Hence by evaluating χ_A from cryoscopic measurements the constancy of K_c in this formula can be tested. For the system phenylacetic acid + nitrobenzene the data in table 26.1 show that K_c is not constant, but that the data are in closer agreement with the assumption of dimer association. However, the figures in table 26.2 show that the equations for dimerisation are not consistent with the behaviour of benzyl alcohol in nitrobenzene, but that in this case K_c is practically constant. This indicates that benzyl alcohol associates in nitrobenzene to form a series of association complexes.

6. Activity Coefficients and Thermodynamic Excess Functions.*

We shall now show how the activity coefficients and thermodynamic excess functions can be evaluated explicitly in a particularly simple case, namely that in which the only complexes formed are the double molecules AB. A solution which appears to correspond to this case is the mixture acetone + chloroform.

From the law of mass action we have

$$\frac{n_{A_1} n_{B_1}}{n_{AB}(n_{A_1} + n_{B_1} + n_{AB})} = K \qquad (26.65)$$

whence making use of (26.3) and the fact that $n_{AB} \to 0$ when $K \to \infty$,

$$\left.\begin{aligned} n_{AB} &= \tfrac{1}{2}\left[n_A + n_B - \left(n_A^2 + n_B^2 - 2n_A n_B \frac{1-K}{1+K}\right)^{1/2}\right] \\ n_{A_1} &= \tfrac{1}{2}\left[n_A - n_B + \left(n_A^2 + n_B^2 - 2n_A n_B \frac{1-K}{1+K}\right)^{1/2}\right] \\ n_{B_1} &= \tfrac{1}{2}\left[n_B - n_A + \left(n_A^2 + n_B^2 - 2n_A n_B \frac{1-K}{1+K}\right)^{1/2}\right] \end{aligned}\right\}. \qquad (26.66)$$

* L. Sarolea, *Trans. Faraday Soc.*, 49, 8 (1953).

Substituting these equations in (26.12), and setting both $x^0_{A_1}$ and $x^0_{B_1}$ equal to unity,

$$\left.\begin{aligned} \gamma_A &= \frac{x_A - x_B + \left(x_A^2 + x_B^2 - 2x_A x_B \dfrac{1-K}{1+K}\right)^{1/2}}{x_A\left[1+\left(x_A^2 + x_B^2 - 2x_A x_B \dfrac{1-K}{1+K}\right)^{1/2}\right]} \\ \gamma_B &= \frac{x_B - x_A + \left(x_A^2 + x_B^2 - 2x_A x_B \dfrac{1-K}{1+K}\right)^{1/2}}{x_B\left[1+\left(x_A^2 + x_B^2 - 2x_A x_B \dfrac{1-K}{1+K}\right)^{1/2}\right]} \end{aligned}\right\} . \qquad (26.67)$$

The excess functions then follow directly (*cf.* 24.2–24.4),

$$g^E = x_A RT \ln \gamma_A + x_B RT \ln \gamma_B, \qquad (26.68)$$

$$s^E = -x_A R \ln \gamma_A - x_B R \ln \gamma_B - \frac{2x_A x_B h_{T,p}}{T(1+K)\left[1+\left(x_A^2 + x_B^2 - 2x_A x_B \dfrac{1-K}{1+K}\right)^{1/2}\right]}, \qquad (26.69)$$

$$h^E = -\frac{2x_A x_B h_{T,p}}{(1+K)\left[1+\left(x_A^2 + x_B^2 - 2x_A x_B \dfrac{1-K}{1+K}\right)^{1/2}\right]}. \qquad (26.70)$$

In these equations $h_{T,p} = (\partial H/\partial \xi)_{T,p}$ is the heat of reaction corresponding to the equilibrium governed by the constant K (*cf.* 7.37).

In fig. 26.8 equation (26.68) is compared with the experimental data for the system acetone + chloroform.* The full line is calculated

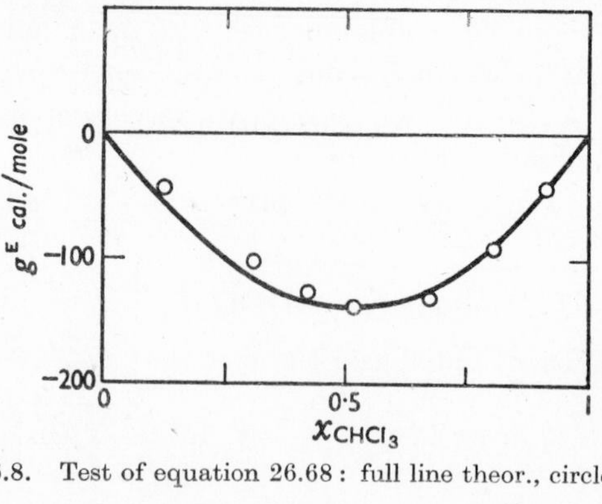

FIG. 26.8. Test of equation 26.68: full line theor., circles exptl.

from (26.68) taking $K = 0{\cdot}77$, while the circles are calculated values from Zawidski's experimental data. In the same way we can compare (26.70) with the data for the heat of mixing obtained by Hirobi.†

* J. v. Zawidski, *Zeit. physik. Chem.*, 35, 129 (1900).
† H. Hirobi, *J. Fac. Sci. Tokyo*, 1, 155 (1925).

Here again we find good agreement on putting the heat of dissociation of the complex equal to -2700 cal./mole.

It is interesting to discuss in more detail the entropy change accompanying the dissociation of the complex. We have in general (7.54, 7.80)

$$RT \ln K = -\left(\frac{\partial H^{\text{id}}}{\partial \xi}\right)_{T,p} + T\left(\frac{\partial S^{\text{id}}}{\partial \xi}\right)_{T,p} \tag{26.71}$$

where, since we are assuming the complexes to form an ideal solution in the monomers, $(\partial H^{\text{id}}/\partial \xi)_{T,p} = (\partial H/\partial \xi)_{T,p}$. Let us suppose that each monomer A or B can be oriented in η ways with respect to the neighbouring molecules, while on the other hand the complex AB corresponds to only one way of orienting an A and a B molecule. The dissociation of AB will then increase the number of orientations by a factor of η^2, and this will correspond to an entropy change

$$\left(\frac{\partial S^{\text{id}}}{\partial \xi}\right)_{T,p} = 2R \ln \eta. \tag{26.72}$$

Taking the values of K and $\partial H/\partial \xi$ found above, we find for acetone + chloroform

$$\eta = 8.$$

This value is of the same order of magnitude as the number of nearest neighbours, and gives a reasonable interpretation of the entropy change. It seems therefore worthwhile attempting a more detailed discussion of the excess entropy of an associated solution.

7. Excess Entropy in Associated Solutions.*

First we rewrite equation (26.69) in the form

$$\frac{s^E}{R} = \frac{1}{x_A + x_B}\left[-2n_{AB} \ln \eta + \ln \frac{(n_{A_1} + n_{B_1} + n_{AB})!}{n_{A_1}!\, n_{B_1}!\, n_{AB}!} - \ln \frac{(n_A + n_B)!}{n_A!\, n_B!}\right]. \tag{26.73}$$

This is obtained by employing (26.66) and (26.67), which on substitution in (26.69) give

$$\frac{s^E}{R} = x_A \ln x_A - x_A \ln \frac{n_{A_1}}{n_{A_1} + n_{B_1} + n_{AB}} + x_B \ln x_B - x_B \ln \frac{n_{B_1}}{n_{A_1} + n_{B_1} + n_{AB}}$$
$$- \frac{2x_A x_B h_{T,p}}{RT(1+K)\left[1 + \left(x_A^2 + x_B^2 - 2x_A x_B \frac{1-K}{1+K}\right)^{1/2}\right]}. \tag{26.74}$$

By employing Stirling's approximation $x! = (x/\mathrm{e})^x$, remembering that

* Sarolea, *loc. cit.*

$n_A = n_{A_1} + n_{AB}$, $n_B = n_{B_1} + n_{AB}$ and using (26.65), (26.71) and (26.72) the preceding equation can be written.

$$\frac{s^E}{\mathbf{R}} = \frac{1}{n_A+n_B}\left\{-2n_{AB}\ln\eta + \ln\frac{(n_{A_1}+n_{B_1}+n_{AB})!}{n_{A_1}!\,n_{B_1}!\,n_{AB}!} - \ln\frac{(n_A+n_B)!}{n_A!\,n_B!}\right\}$$

$$-\frac{h_{T,p}}{2RT}\left[\frac{4n_An_B-(1+K)\left\{n_A+n_B+\left(n_A^2+n_B^2-2n_An_B\frac{1-K}{1+K}\right)^{1/2}\right\}\times\left\{n_A+n_B-\left(n_A^2+n_B^2-2n_An_B\frac{1-K}{1+K}\right)^{1/2}\right\}}{(1-K)\left\{n_A+n_B+\left(n_A^2+n_B^2-2n_An_B\frac{1-K}{1+K}\right)^{1/2}\right\}}\right]. \tag{26.75}$$

It can be easily shown that the coefficient of $h_{T,p}$ is zero so that (26.75) reduces to (26.73).

Equation (26.73) has a very simple interpretation. The excess entropy is made up first of a term related to the loss of orientations by the monomolecules on association to form the complex ; this term is always negative. The two other terms represent the differences between the configurational entropy of the solution and that of a perfect solution (*cf.* 20.19). It is readily shown, using Stirling's formula, that the contribution of these two terms to the entropy is (i) positive if $n_{AB} < n_{A_1} + n_{B_1}$, (ii) zero if $n_{AB} = n_{A_1} + n_{B_1}$ and (iii) negative if $n_{AB} > n_{A_1} + n_{B_1}$. The configurational contribution to the excess entropy thus arises from two effects. First a reduction in the number of independent units in the system which makes a negative contribution and is the major effect in the case of very strong association (case iii), and secondly the introduction of a third molecular species which makes a positive contribution and is the controlling factor when the association is feeble (case i).

If we apply (26.73) to the system acetone + chloroform discussed above we find that the term $-2n_{AB}\ln\eta$ always determines the sign of s^E. The excess entropy in this case is then associated mainly with the loss in the number of orientations of the monomolecules. Another similar case is that of methanol + carbon tetrachloride (*cf.* fig. 24.5). On the other hand we must notice that for the systems acetone + ethanol and acetone + isopropyl alcohol the excess entropy is *positive*.*

We may now consider the solutions of a number of non-electrolytes in water. Here we have to consider water as a particularly complex example of an associated liquid. Data are available for the following systems :

* A. R. Gordon and W. G. Hines, *J. Can. Res.*, 24, 246 (1946) ; *Landolt-Börnstein Tabellen, Erg.* II, p. 1560.

water + methanol,* water + ethanol,† water + n-propanol,† water + acetone.‡

As an example of the kind of behaviour observed we show in fig. 26.9 the excess functions g^E, h^E and Ts^E for the system water + ethanol.

One remarkable feature shown in this figure is that not only is the excess entropy negative, but also

$$T \mid s^E \mid > \mid h^E \mid , \quad (26.76)$$

so that it is the value of the excess entropy which determines the sign of the deviations from ideality. We have here a mixture which at 25 °C is formed with the evolution of heat, and yet exhibits positive deviations from Raoult's law. All the systems listed above exhibit a similar behaviour.

It seems then, that just as in the case of polymer solutions, the excess entropy plays an essential part, but in the case of aqueous solutions, in contrast to polymer solutions where $s^E > 0$ and $g^E < 0$, we have $s^E < 0$ and $g^E > 0$. The particular structural characteristics of water are clearly responsible for the magnitude of the excess entropy.

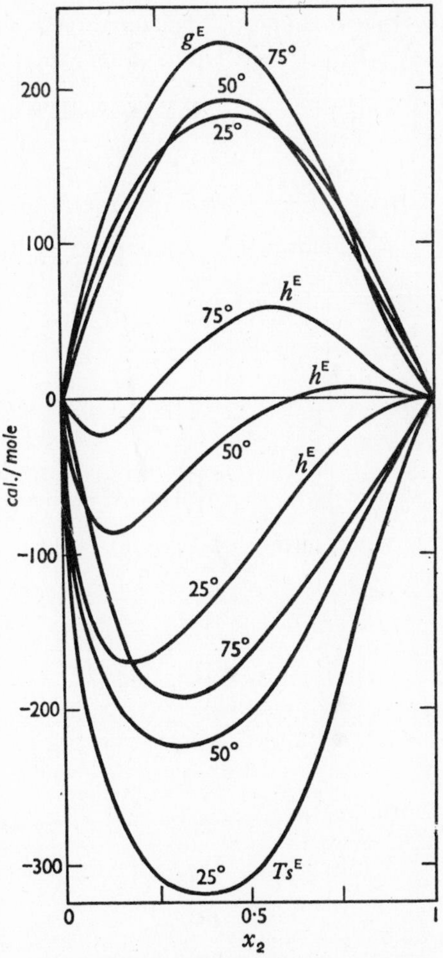

FIG. 26.9. Thermodynamic excess functions for the system water (1) + ethanol (2) at 25 °C., 50 °C. and 75 °C.

It is also interesting to observe that the general disposition of the excess functions in fig. 26.9 recalls that in the region of a lower critical solution temperature, (*cf.* fig. 24.7). In fact we have already mentioned that associated systems often exhibit lower consolute temperatures.

* *Landolt-Börnstein Tabellen*, 5th Ed., p. 1565; M. Ewert, *Thesis*, Bruxelles, 1935; *Bull. Soc. Chim. Belg.*, **45**, 493 (1936); *Int. Crit. Tables*, **3**, 299.

† E. Bose, *Zeit. physik. Chem.*, **58**, 585 (1907); Ewert, *loc. cit.*; *Int. Crit. Tables*, **3**, 290.

‡ *Int. Crit. Tables*, **3**, 290; **5**, 157.

8. Association and Phase Separation.*

We have already examined in § 9 of chapter XVI the formation of two phases from a regular solution, and we now consider the influence of association upon this phenomenon.

It is most convenient to begin from equation (26.33) for the activity coefficients, and to limit ourselves to association of one component only (A). In this case we have (*cf.* 26.20)

$$RT \ln \gamma_B = RT \ln \frac{1}{\dfrac{x_A}{\chi_A} + x_B} + \alpha x_A^2. \tag{26.77}$$

At a critical solution temperature we must have (*cf.* 16.15)

$$\frac{\partial \ln x_B \gamma_B}{\partial x_B} = \frac{1}{x_B} - \frac{1 - 1/\chi_A + x_A\, \partial(1/\chi_A)/\partial x_B}{x_A/\chi_A + x_B} - \frac{2\alpha}{RT} x_A,$$
$$= 0, \tag{26.78}$$

and also

$$\frac{\partial^2 \ln x_B \gamma_B}{\partial x_B^2} = -\frac{1}{x_B^2} - \frac{x_A\{\partial^2(1/\chi_A)/\partial x_B^2\} - 2\partial(1/\chi_A)/\partial x_B}{x_A/\chi_A + x_B}$$
$$+ \left[\frac{1 - 1/\chi_A + x_A \partial(1/\chi_A)/\partial x_B}{x_A/\chi_A + x_B}\right]^2 + \frac{2\alpha}{RT}$$
$$= 0. \tag{26.79}$$

These equations may also be written in the form :

$$\frac{\chi_A - 1 + x_A \chi_A\, \partial(1/\chi_A)/\partial x_B}{x_A + \chi_A x_B} - \frac{1}{x_B} + \frac{2\alpha}{RT} x_A = 0, \tag{26.80}$$

$$\frac{\chi_A\,[x_A\{\partial^2(1/\chi_A)/\partial x_B^2\} - 2\partial(1/\chi_A)/\partial x_B]}{x_A + \chi_A x_B} + \frac{1}{x_B^2} - \left(\frac{1}{x_B} - \frac{2\alpha}{RT} x_A\right)^2 - \frac{2\alpha}{RT} = 0. \tag{26.81}$$

We can easily verify that if we consider a non-associated solution, that is if

$$\chi_A = 1, \quad \frac{\partial \chi_A}{\partial x_B} = 0, \quad \frac{\partial^2 \chi_A}{\partial x_B^2} = 0, \tag{26.82}$$

these equations reduce to those for regular solutions.

It is interesting now to see in the limiting case, where

$$\alpha/RT = 0, \tag{26.83}$$

whether association alone can give rise to phase separation.

Equations (26.80) and (26.81) give under these circumstances

$$\frac{\partial(1/\chi_A)}{\partial x_B} = \frac{1}{\chi_A x_A x_B}; \quad \frac{\partial^2(1/\chi_A)}{\partial x_B^2} = \frac{2}{x_B} \frac{\partial(1/\chi_A)}{\partial x_B}; \tag{26.84}$$

* I. Prigogine, 3rd National Congress of Science, Brussels, June 1950.

or

$$\frac{\partial \chi_A}{\partial x_B} = -\frac{\chi_A}{x_A x_B} < 0\,; \quad \frac{\partial^2 \chi_A}{\partial x_B^2} = \frac{2\chi_A}{x_A x_B^2} > 0. \tag{26.85}$$

We see, therefore, that for association alone to give rise to phase separation, χ_A must decrease with x_B and the curvature must be positive (concave upwards). Thus on plotting χ_A as a function of $x_A = 1 - x_B$ we should obtain a curve of the general form shown in fig. 26.10.

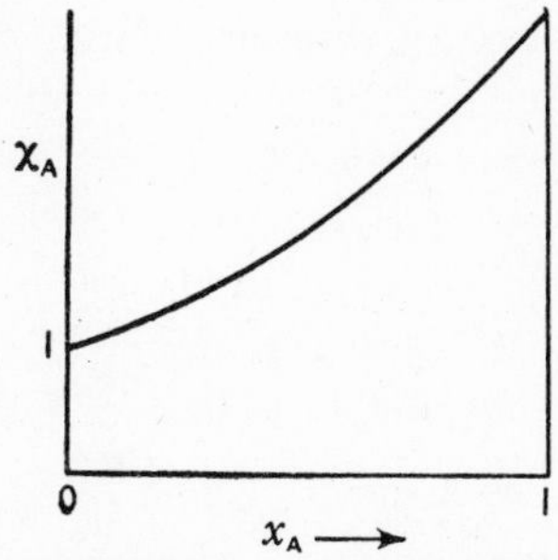

FIG. 26.10. Average degree of association χ_A satisfying conditions (26.85).

If we now look at the experimental curves for χ_A (*cf.* figs. 26.4 and 26.5) we see that, contrary to the above requirements

$$\frac{\partial^2 \chi_A}{\partial x_B^2} < 0. \tag{26.86}$$

We conclude that the type of association normally observed is not sufficient by itself to produce phase separation. For this to happen we should need a mode of association leading to very large complexes. However, the role of association is important, and as we shall see below, leads to a reduction in the value of α needed to cause separation into two phases.

Critical phenomena usually occur in moderately concentrated solutions ($x_A > 0{\cdot}2$), and in this region χ_A does not usually vary very rapidly with mole fraction (*cf.* figs. 26.4 and 26.5). We may then, for the purpose of an approximate calculation,* put

$$\frac{\partial \chi_A}{\partial x_B} \simeq 0, \quad \frac{\partial^2 \chi_A}{\partial x_B^2} \simeq 0. \tag{26.87}$$

Equations (26.80) and (26.81) now simplify to

$$1 - \frac{2\alpha}{RT} x_A x_B (x_A + \chi_A x_B) = 0, \tag{26.88}$$

$$1 - 3x_A + \frac{2\alpha}{RT} x_A^2 x_B \qquad = 0. \tag{26.89}$$

α/RT may be eliminated from these equations to give the following quadratic equation for x_A:

$$3x_A^2(\chi_A - 1) - 2x_A(2\chi_A - 1) + \chi_A = 0, \tag{26.90}$$

or

$$x_A = \frac{(2\chi_A - 1) - \sqrt{\chi_A^2 - \chi_A + 1}}{3(\chi_A - 1)}. \tag{26.91}$$

The sign of the square root has been chosen such that when χ_A tends to 1, the critical point tends to $x_A = 0{\cdot}5$.

* The calculation may also be made without this approximation but as the final results lead to the same conclusions, the more elaborate calculation is not given here.

We see then that *the concentrations at the critical point are determined solely by* χ_A. The value of α/RT needed to produce phase separation at this concentration is now obtained by substituting the critical value of x_A back into (26.88) or (26.89).

Table 26.3 gives a set of values of x_A at the critical point for various values of α/RT and χ_A. We see that the values of α/RT needed to cause separation of two phases decreases as the extent of association increases, and at the same time the concentration at the critical point moves to lower values of x_A. If the energies of interaction which contribute to α are relatively small, then χ_A must be fairly large before phase separation will occur. On the other hand, if a strongly associated solution of the type under discussion does not show phase separation, then α must be very small.

TABLE 26.3

Effect of Association on Phase Separation

χ_A	$\frac{\alpha}{RT_c}$	$(x_A)_c$
1	2	0·50
2	1·3	0·42
5	0·61	0·37
10	0·32	0·35
∞	0	0·33

9. Association in Ternary Systems.*

We shall only give detailed consideration to the simplest case where we have a dilute solution of A and S in a solvent B and where the only complexes formed are between A and S.

The only equilibrium we have to consider will be

$$\frac{c_{AS}}{c_{A_1}c_{S_1}} = K_c, \tag{26.92}$$

where c_{AS}, c_{A_1}, c_{S_1} refer to the concentrations of complexes AS and monomeric molecules of A and S, respectively. These concentrations must, of course, satisfy

$$\left.\begin{aligned} c_{AS}+c_{A_1} &= c_A \\ c_{AS}+c_{S_1} &= c_S \end{aligned}\right\}, \tag{26.93}$$

so that (26.92) can be written

$$c_{A_1} = \frac{c_A}{1+K_c(c_S-c_{AS})}. \tag{26.94}$$

* I. Prigogine, *J. Chim. Phys.*, **45**, 19 (1948).

We shall now test this equation by reference to several systems containing ethyl alcohol (A), carbon tetrachloride (B) and a third component (S) which is capable of forming complexes with the alcohol.

If we consider solutions very dilute in alcohol and containing an excess of the active solute S then the alcohol will be present either as monomer or as AS complexes. Furthermore since c_{AS} cannot be greater than c_A, it can be neglected in comparison with c_S so that (26.94) can be written approximately

$$c_{A_1} = \frac{c_A}{1+K_c c_S}. \tag{26.95}$$

For a series of solutions with c_S constant, a graph of c_{A_1} against c_A should be linear through the origin with a slope $1/(1+K_c c_S)$.

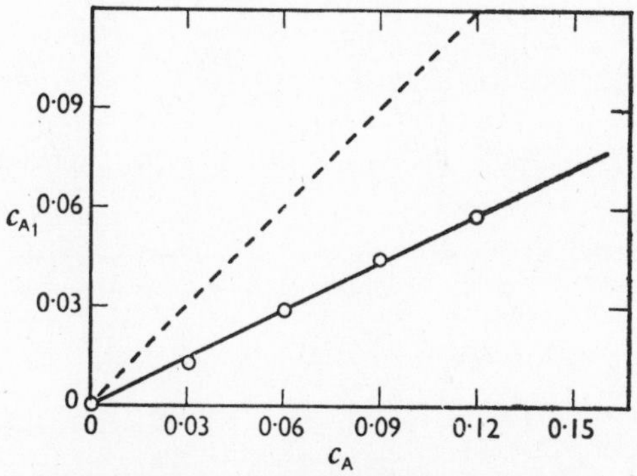

FIG. 26.11. Concentration of monomolecules of alcohol in the system ethanol + carbon tetrachloride + acetone (concentrations in volume per cent.); dotted line corresponds to no association.

This prediction has been confirmed by a spectroscopic examination of systems of this kind. Figs. 26.11 and 26.12 show the results for

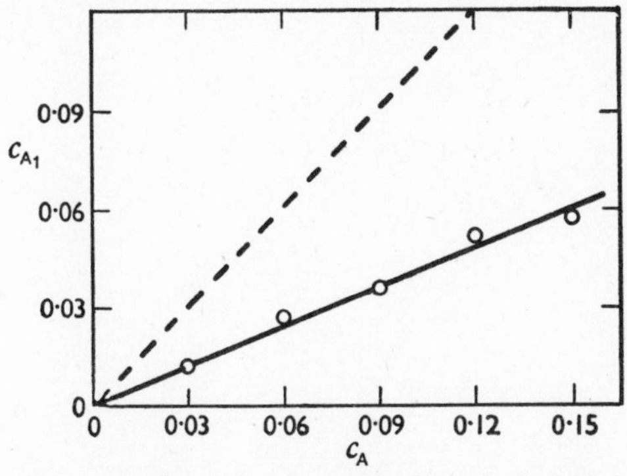

FIG. 26.12. Concentration of monomolecules of alcohol in the system ethanol + carbon tetrachloride + ethyl acetate (concentrations in volume per cent.); dotted line corresponds to no association.

acetone and ethyl acetate as active component, while in table 26.4 are given the values of K_c for a series of active components. One can also calculate the behaviour of solutions more concentrated in alcohol, but we shall not go into the details of this.*

TABLE 26.4

Association constants K_c for alcohols with active solutes in carbon tetrachloride solution

System	K_c *mole/litre*
Ethanol + benzaldehyde - -	1·76
,, + pyridine - - -	2·70
,, + piperidine - -	4·60
,, + acetone - - -	2·9
,, + dipropyl ether -	1·2
,, + ethyl acetate - -	2

* I. Prigogine, *Bull. Soc. Chim. Belg.*, 50, 153 (1941).

CHAPTER XXVII

ELECTROLYTE SOLUTIONS

1. Condition of Electroneutrality.

We pass on in this chapter to a brief study of solutions which contain charged molecular species, but which are nevertheless electrically neutral as a whole. If we designate the charge on an ion by z_i, taking the charge on a proton as the unit of positive charge, then for the solution to be electrically neutral

$$\sum_i z_i n_i = 0. \tag{27.1}$$

For example, for an aqueous solution of sodium chloride

$$n_{\mathrm{Na}^+} - n_{\mathrm{Cl}'} + n_{\mathrm{H}^+} - n_{\mathrm{OH}'} = 0. \tag{27.2}$$

Equation (27.1) thus gives us a new relation between the numbers of moles of different components present in the system.

2. Chemical Potential of an Ion.

Let us consider a phase which can be neutral or charged electrically but which is not under the influence of any external electric charges. Then we can write the total free energy of the system in the form, *cf.* (6.1),

$$F^{\text{tot}} = F^{\text{tot}}(T, V, n_1, \dots n_c). \tag{27.3}$$

We call this free energy the *total* free energy since we suppose it to include the macroscopic electrostatic free energy F^{el} due to the electrical charge carried by the phase. We then call the quantity

$$F = F^{\text{tot}} - F^{\text{el}}, \tag{27.4}$$

the *ordinary free energy.**

In the interior of a phase which is uniformly ionized the electric field is zero, since any excess charges will be confined to the boundary surface of the phase, or more exactly to a superficial layer. At any point in the phase where the field is zero,† the chemical potential of the ion i is defined by

$$\mu_i = \left(\frac{\partial F}{\partial n_i}\right)_{T,V}. \tag{27.5}$$

* We shall return to a more detailed discussion of this point in Vol. III of this work.

† For a more general definition in regions where the field is not zero, *cf.* I. Prigogine, P. Mazur and R. Defay, *J. Chim. Phys.*, 50, 146 (1953).

If the phase under consideration is neutral then of course F^{tot} is the same as F. In this chapter we shall study only electroneutral systems, which remain electroneutral during the course of any transformations considered, and which do not exchange electrical energy with their surroundings. The function F will then possess all the properties which we have established for the case of non-ionic systems.

The condition of electroneutrality (27.1), which prevents us considering all the $n_1 \dots n_c$ as independent variables, also limits the possibility of knowing the values of all the partial derivatives (27.5). In fact, if we limit ourselves to neutral solutions, then we can never know the chemical potential of each ion, but only certain combinations of chemical potentials. An example will make clear the nature of this limitation. Suppose we consider the process of solution of a crystal of NaCl (phase 1) in water (phase 2). In solution, NaCl is dissociated into ions Na^+ and Cl^- so that we can describe the phenomenon of dissolution in terms of the reaction co-ordinates ξ_{Na^+} and $\xi_{Cl'}$ which correspond to the passage of sodium and chloride ions respectively into the solution. If we suppose that initially there are no ions in solution, then we have simply

$$\xi_{Na^+} = n_{Na^+}\,; \quad \xi_{Cl'} = n_{Cl'}, \tag{27.6}$$

where n_{Na^+} and $n_{Cl'}$ are the numbers of ions in solution. We assume that the dissolution of a crystal of NaCl occurs with the two phases at the same electrical potential and is not accompanied by the transport of a nett charge from one phase to the other. The numbers of negative and positive charges which go into solution are then equal and

$$\xi_{Na^+} = \xi_{Cl'} = \xi, \tag{27.7}$$

the common value of these reaction co-ordinates.

The uncompensated heat for this reaction is, from (3.31) and (6.73)

$$\begin{aligned} dQ' &= \mathbf{A}_{Na^+}\, d\xi_{Na^+} + \mathbf{A}_{Cl'}\, d\xi_{Cl'}, \\ &= (\mu'_{Na^+} - \mu''_{Na^+})\, d\xi_{Na^+} + (\mu'_{Cl'} - \mu''_{Cl'})\, d\xi_{Cl'}. \end{aligned} \tag{27.8}$$

Because of (27.7) this becomes

$$dQ' = (\mu'_{Na^+} + \mu'_{Cl'} - \mu''_{Na^+} - \mu''_{Cl'})\, d\xi \geqslant 0. \tag{27.9}$$

It is, therefore, not necessary for both of the affinities $\mathbf{A}_{Na^+}$ and $\mathbf{A}_{Cl'}$ to be separately zero when equilibrium is established; all that we can deduce from (27.9) is that their sum $(\mathbf{A}_{Na^+} + \mathbf{A}_{Cl'})$ is zero, that is

$$\mu'_{Na^+} + \mu'_{Cl'} = \mu''_{Na^+} + \mu''_{Cl'}. \tag{27.10}$$

We see that the chemical potentials of the individual ions do not appear separately either in the equation for the uncompensated heat, or in the conditions for equilibrium.

3. Balance of Charges in a Chemical Reaction.

In electroneutral systems, electric charges can be transferred from one ion to another, as for example in the chemical reaction

$$Fe^{3+} + Ce^{3+} = Fe^{2+} + Ce^{4+} ; \tag{27.11}$$

but ions cannot be discharged by an electrode reaction since these processes involve transfer of charge to or from the phase. We shall consider only chemical reactions which satisfy both the mass balance expressed by the stoichiometric equation :

$$\sum_i \nu_i M_i = 0, \tag{27.12}$$

and the electrical charge balance :

$$\sum_i \nu_i z_i = 0. \tag{27.13}$$

It is often convenient to discuss chemical reactions in terms of the two or more electrochemical reactions into which they can be divided. For example the chemical reaction (27.11) can be regarded as the sum of the two electrochemical reactions

$$Fe^{3+} + e = Fe^{2+}, \tag{27.14}$$

$$Ce^{3+} - e = Ce^{4+},$$

where e represents an electron.

4. Mean Chemical Potentials and Mean Ionic Activity Coefficients.

For a weak electrolyte such as acetic acid the condition of equilibrium for the ionization reaction is

$$\mu_{HAc} = \mu_{H^+} + \mu_{Ac'}. \tag{27.15}$$

We have seen in § 2 that if we consider only electroneutral systems, the chemical potentials of the two ions cannot be measured separately. For this reason it is convenient to define the *mean chemical potential* of the two ions by the relation

$$\mu_{\pm} = \tfrac{1}{2}(\mu_{Ac'} + \mu_{H^+}), \tag{27.16}$$

so that (27.15) may be written

$$\mu_{HAc} = 2\mu_{\pm}. \tag{27.17}$$

In the general case of an electrolyte which dissociates into ν_+ cations each with a charge z_+, and ν_- anions of charge z_-, we have, from (27.13),

$$z_+\nu_+ + z_-\nu_- = 0, \tag{27.18}$$

and so we can define a mean chemical potential by the relation

$$\mu_{\pm} = \frac{\nu_+ \mu_+ + \nu_- \mu_-}{\nu_+ + \nu_-}. \tag{27.19}$$

Corresponding to each chemical potential there is an activity coefficient defined in terms of equation (20.4). By convention, the activity coefficients of electrolytes are always expressed in terms of the ideal dilute solution as standard reference state, *cf.* chap. XXI, § 3. Thus in the case of an aqueous NaCl solution we may write

$$\left.\begin{aligned} \mu_{Na^+} &= \mu^{\ominus}_{Na^+}(T, p) + \boldsymbol{R}T \ln x_{Na^+} \gamma^*_{Na^+}, \\ \mu_{Cl'} &= \mu^{\ominus}_{Cl'}(T, p) + \boldsymbol{R}T \ln x_{Cl'} \gamma^*_{Cl'} \end{aligned}\right\}. \tag{27.20}$$

The activity coefficients, just like the chemical potentials, can only occur in certain combinations, and never alone in equilibrium equations. Thus the mean chemical potential of the Na^+ and Cl^- ions is

$$\mu_{\pm} = \tfrac{1}{2}(\mu_{Na^+} + \mu_{Cl'}) = \tfrac{1}{2}(\mu^{\ominus}_{Na^+} + \mu^{\ominus}_{Cl'}) + \tfrac{1}{2}\boldsymbol{R}T \ln x_{Na^+} x_{Cl'} \gamma^*_{Na^+} \gamma^*_{Cl'}, \tag{27.21}$$

which can be written

$$\mu_{\pm} = \mu^{\ominus}_{\pm} + \boldsymbol{R}T \ln x^{1/2}_{Na^+} x^{1/2}_{Cl'} \gamma^*_{\pm}, \tag{27.22}$$

where we have put

$$\gamma^{*2}_{\pm} = \gamma^*_{Na^+} \gamma^*_{Cl'}. \tag{27.23}$$

In general, corresponding to the mean chemical potential (27.19) there corresponds a mean ionic activity coefficient given by

$$\ln \gamma^*_{\pm} = \frac{\nu_+ \ln \gamma^*_+ + \nu_- \ln \gamma^*_-}{\nu_+ + \nu_-}, \tag{27.24}$$

or

$$\gamma^{*(\nu_+ + \nu_-)}_{\pm} = \gamma^{*\nu_+}_{+} \gamma^{*\nu_-}_{-}. \tag{27.25}$$

If we have in the same solution several electrolytes with common ions, the mean ionic activity coefficients corresponding to the various possible pairs of ions are not independent.* Thus in an aqueous solution containing the ions Na^+, K^+, Cl^-, NO_3^- we have

$$\gamma^{*2}_{Na^+, NO_3'} = \gamma^*_{Na^+} \gamma^*_{NO_3'}; \quad \gamma^{*2}_{Na^+, Cl'} = \gamma^*_{Na^+} \gamma^*_{Cl'};$$

$$\gamma^{*2}_{K^+, NO_3'} = \gamma^*_{K^+} \gamma^*_{NO_3'}; \quad \gamma^{*2}_{K^+, Cl'} = \gamma^*_{K^+} \gamma^*_{Cl'};$$

whence

$$\frac{\gamma^*_{Na^+, NO_3'}}{\gamma^*_{K^+, NO_3'}} = \frac{\gamma^*_{Na^+, Cl'}}{\gamma^*_{K^+, Cl'}}. \tag{27.26}$$

We shall now consider several examples to illustrate how the thermodynamic equations established in the previous chapters can be applied without difficulty to electrolytes, provided we take account of the consequences of the electroneutrality condition.

* Guggenheim, [26'], p. 303.

5. Law of Mass Action.

The application of the law of mass action is straightforward. For example in the case of the oxidation-reduction equilibrium

$$2Fe^{3+} + Sn^{2+} \rightleftharpoons 2Fe^{2+} + Sn^{4+}$$

the equilibrium constant may be written, using (20.70), as

$$K_c = \frac{c^2_{Fe^{2+}}\, c_{Sn^{4+}}}{c^2_{Fe^{3+}}\, c_{Sn^{2+}}} \frac{\gamma^{*2}_{Fe^{2+}}\, \gamma^{*}_{Sn^{2+}}}{\gamma^{*2}_{Fe^{3+}}\, \gamma^{*}_{Sn^{4+}}}. \tag{27.27}$$

The activity coefficient factor may be written in terms of the mean ionic activity coefficients to give

$$\frac{\gamma^{*2}_{Fe^{2+}}\, \gamma^{*}_{Sn^{4+}}}{\gamma^{*2}_{Fe^{3+}}\, \gamma^{*}_{Sn^{2+}}} = \frac{(\gamma^{*}_{Fe^{2+}}\, \gamma^{*2}_{Cl'})^2 (\gamma^{*}_{Sn^{4+}}\, \gamma^{*4}_{Cl'})}{(\gamma^{*}_{Fe^{3+}}\, \gamma^{*3}_{Cl'})^2 (\gamma^{*}_{Sn^{2+}}\, \gamma^{*2}_{Cl'})} = \frac{\gamma^{*6}_{Fe^{2+},Cl'}\, \gamma^{*5}_{Sn^{4+},Cl'}}{\gamma^{*8}_{Fe^{3+},Cl'}\, \gamma^{*3}_{Sn^{2+},Cl'}}.$$

As another example we may consider the ionization of a weak 1-1 : electrolyte :

$$AB \rightleftharpoons A^+ + B^-$$

The degree of dissociation of an electrolyte, which we may denote ϵ,* is the ratio of the number of molecules dissociated to the total number of molecules whether dissociated or not. If c^0 is the total concentration of AB, we then have

$$c_{AB} = (1-\epsilon)c^0\,;\quad c_+ = \epsilon c^0\,;\quad c_- = \epsilon c^0.$$

The law of mass action gives

$$K_c = \frac{\gamma^*_- c_-\, \gamma^*_+ c_+}{\gamma^*_{AB}\, c_{AB}} = \frac{\gamma^*_-\gamma^*_+}{\gamma^*_{AB}} \frac{\epsilon^2 c^0}{1-\epsilon}$$

$$= \frac{\gamma^{*2}_{\pm}}{\gamma^*_{AB}} \frac{\epsilon^2 c^0}{1-\epsilon}. \tag{27.28}$$

If the solution is sufficiently dilute $\gamma^*_{\pm} \to 1$ and $\gamma^*_{AB} \to 1$, and we have the *Ostwald dilution law* :

$$K_c = \frac{\epsilon^2 c^0}{1-\epsilon}. \tag{27.29}$$

If $c^0 \to 0$, then $\epsilon \to 1$ and the dissociation is complete.

6. Vapour Pressure of Electrolyte Solutions.

For the equilibrium between an electrolyte in the vapour phase, and the ions which it forms in solution we have

$$\mu^g_M = \nu_+\mu_+ + \nu_-\mu_-, \tag{27.30}$$

where μ^g_M is the chemical potential of M in the vapour phase (10.34). From the second of the equations (21.25) we have therefore :

$$p_M = k(x_+\gamma^*_+)^{\nu_+}(x_-\gamma^*_-)^{\nu_-} = k x_+^{\nu_+} x_-^{\nu_-} \gamma^{*(\nu_+ + \nu_-)}_{\pm} \tag{27.31}$$

* *Cf.* Chap, I, p. 12.

For dilute solutions this equation takes on one of the two forms :

$$p_M = k_c c_+^{\nu_+} c_-^{\nu_-} \gamma_\pm^{*(\nu_+ + \nu_-)}, \tag{27.31'}$$

$$p_M = k_m \mathrm{m}_+^{\nu_+} \mathrm{m}_-^{\nu_-} \gamma_\pm^{*(\nu_+ + \nu_-)}. \tag{27.31''}$$

The ideal vapour pressure of the electrolyte is

$$p_M^{\mathrm{id}} = k_m \mathrm{m}_+^{\nu_+} \mathrm{m}_-^{\nu_-}, \tag{27.32}$$

so that

$$\gamma_\pm^{*(\nu_+ + \nu_-)} = \frac{p_M}{p_M^{\mathrm{id}}}. \tag{27.33}$$

It is thus possible in principle to determine the mean activity coefficient of the electrolyte by dividing the actual vapour pressure of the electrolyte over the solution by that over an ideal solution which is obtained by finding k_m by extrapolation to very dilute solutions (*cf.* 21.27). In fact the methods outlined in the two following paragraphs are more precise and more easily applied.

7. Solubility.

Excluding the formation of mixed crystals, the equilibrium between a crystalline substance i, and the ions which are formed from it in solution is governed by the equation :

$$\mu_i^s(T, p) = \nu_+ \mu_+ + \nu_- \mu_-, \tag{27.34}$$

where μ_i^s is the chemical potential of the solid and depends only upon T and p. For a saturated solution we have therefore

$$x_+^{\nu_+} x_-^{\nu_-} \gamma_\pm^{*(\nu_+ + \nu_-)} = K_x(T, p), \tag{27.35}$$

which in a very dilute solution can be written

$$c_+^{\nu_+} c_-^{\nu_-} \gamma_\pm^{*(\nu_+ + \nu_-)} = K_c(T, p). \tag{27.35'}$$

The equilibrium constant K_c, which is the limiting value to which $c_+^{\nu_+} c_-^{\nu_-}$ tends in very dilute solution, is called the *solubility product*.

For example we may consider the solubility of silver chloride in aqueous nitric acid solutions at 25 °C and at atmospheric pressure. We assume that AgCl dissociates practically completely in solution, in accordance with the reaction

$$AgCl \rightarrow Ag^+ + Cl^-. \tag{27.36}$$

Since silver chloride solutions are very dilute we may define the solubility as the stoichiometric concentration of silver chloride in the solution in equilibrium with pure crystals. The solubility defined in this way is denoted by S. Then

$$c_{Ag^+}c_{Cl'}\gamma_{\pm}^{*2} = S^2\gamma_{\pm}^{*2} = K_c(T, p). \tag{27.37}$$

In discussing the relation between the activity coefficients of electrolytes and the concentration of the solution, use is made of the *ionic strength*, defined by

$$I = \tfrac{1}{2}\sum_i z_i^2 c_i. \tag{27.38}$$

In a nitric acid solution of concentration c, saturated with silver chloride, the ionic strength is simply

$$I = c + S \tag{27.39}$$

since the concentration of hydroxyl ions is quite negligible.

It is found experimentally that the solubility is related in a simple way to the ionic strength: at sufficiently low ionic strengths the logarithm of the solubility of silver chloride varies linearly with the square root of I as illustrated by the experimental data in fig. 27.1.* The straight line has the equation

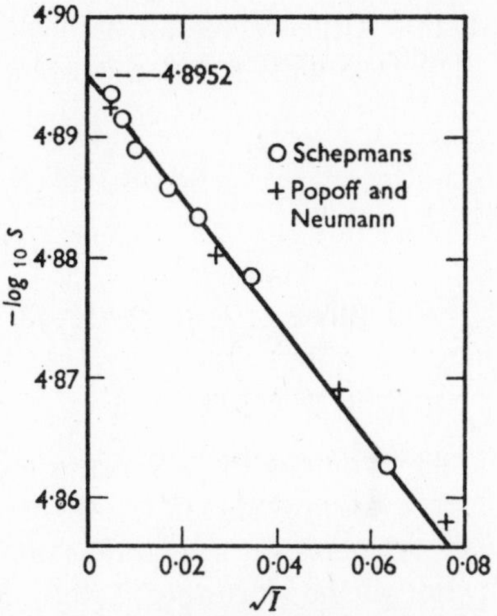

FIG. 27.1. Solubility of silver chloride in the presence of nitric acid.

$$-\log_{10} S = 4{\cdot}8952 - 0{\cdot}512\sqrt{I}. \tag{27.40}$$

On comparison with (27.37), which may be written

$$-\log_{10} S = -\tfrac{1}{2}\log_{10} K_c + \log_{10}\gamma_{\pm}^{*}, \tag{27.41}$$

we see that

$$\log_{10}\gamma_{\pm}^{*} = -0{\cdot}512\sqrt{I}, \tag{27.42}$$

$$\log_{10} K_c = -9{\cdot}7904, \tag{27.43}$$

$$K_c = 1{\cdot}621 \times 10^{-10}. \tag{27.44}$$

Solubility measurements provide one important method of determining activity coefficients. The theoretical interpretation of these results will be considered later (§ 10).

8. Osmotic Coefficient.

The osmotic pressure (20.86), the lowering of freezing point (22.9), and the elevation of boiling point (21.59) are all proportional to the logarithm of the activity of the solvent (*cf.* 20.9), given by

$$\ln a_1 = \ln x_1\gamma_1 = \phi \ln x_1 \tag{27.45}$$

where ϕ is the osmotic coefficient.

* A. Pinkus and R. Schepmans, *Bull. Soc. Chim. Belg.*, **47**, 337 (1938).

Suppose we have a solution obtained by mixing n_1 moles of solvent and n_2 moles of an electrolyte. Then if n_u is the number of moles of 2 undissociated we have

$$n_u = n_2(1-\epsilon)\ ;\ \ n_+ = \nu_+ \epsilon n_2\ ;\ \ n_- = \nu_- \epsilon n_2, \tag{27.46}$$

where ϵ is the degree of dissociation.

The true mole fraction of solvent is then

$$x_1 = \frac{n_1}{n_1 + n_u + n_+ + n_-} = \frac{n_1}{n_1 + n_2(1 - \epsilon + \nu\epsilon)}, \tag{27.47}$$

where

$$\nu = \nu_+ + \nu_- \tag{27.48}$$

is the number of ions produced by each molecule of electrolyte. (It should be noted that ν as used in this chapter differs from that defined in equation (2.25) as $\nu = \sum_i \nu_i$).

To evaluate ϕ from freezing point measurements it is thus necessary to have a knowledge of ϵ. If this is not known then we can do no more than calculate an apparent osmotic coefficient ϕ_a, which is calculated as though the substance 2 were not dissociated ($\epsilon = 0$) ; or a coefficient ϕ_d by assuming complete dissociation ($\epsilon = 1$). These are related by the equations

$$\phi \ln x_1 = \phi_a \ln x_{1,a} = \phi_d \ln x_{1,d}, \tag{27.49}$$

where

$$x_{1,a} = \frac{n_1}{n_1 + n_2}\ ;\ \ x_{1,d} = \frac{n_1}{n_1 + \nu n_2}. \tag{27.50}$$

In very dilute solutions, the lowering of freezing point θ is given by (*cf.* 22.10–22.12),

$$\theta = \phi\theta_c(\mathrm{m}_u + \mathrm{m}_+ + \mathrm{m}_-) = \phi\theta_c \mathrm{m}_2(1 - \epsilon + \nu\epsilon) \tag{27.51}$$

where θ_c is the cryoscopic constant of the solvent and m_2 the stoichiometric molality of the solution. To the same degree of approximation also :

$$\theta = \phi_a \theta_c \mathrm{m}_2 = \phi_d \theta_c \nu \mathrm{m}_2. \tag{27.52}$$

In the same way the osmotic pressure can be written in three forms :

$$\left.\begin{aligned} \pi &= \phi\ RT(c_u + c_+ + c_-) = \phi RT c_2(1 - \epsilon + \nu\epsilon) \\ \pi &= \phi_a RT c_2 \\ \pi &= \phi_d RT \nu c_2 \end{aligned}\right\}. \tag{27.53}$$

For dilute solutions then we have

$$\phi_a = \nu\phi_d = \phi(1 - \epsilon + \nu\epsilon). \tag{27.54}$$

For example at 0 °C, in an aqueous solution of acetic acid of molality 0·002138, the three osmotic coefficients have the values*

$$\phi = 1{\cdot}000\,; \quad \phi_a = 1{\cdot}084\,; \quad \phi_d = 0{\cdot}5421.$$

In this case ϕ is given approximately by ϕ_a since ϵ is very small (under these conditions $\epsilon = 0{\cdot}084$). On the other hand for solutions of strong electrolytes ϕ approximates to ϕ_d.

9. Cryoscopic Determination of Mean Ionic Activity Coefficient.

By eliminating ϵ between equations (27.46) we have

$$n_2 = n_u + \frac{n_+ + n_-}{\nu}. \tag{27.55}$$

Now at constant T and p, the Gibbs-Duhem equation (6.39) may be written

$$n_1\,\delta\mu_1 + n_u\,\delta\mu_u + n_+\,\delta\mu_+ + n_-\,\delta\mu_- = 0, \tag{27.56}$$

where component 1 is the solvent.
But

$$\frac{n_+}{\nu_+} = \frac{n_-}{\nu_-} = \frac{n_+ + n_-}{\nu}, \tag{27.57}$$

so that substituting for n_+ and n_- in (27.56) and using the definition of mean chemical potential (27.19) we have

$$n_1\,\delta\mu_1 + n_u\,\delta\mu_u + (n_+ + n_-)\,\delta\mu_\pm = 0. \tag{27.58}$$

For a *strong electrolyte* $n_u = 0$, and this equation reduces to

$$n_1\,\delta\mu_1 + \nu n_2\,\delta\mu_\pm = 0. \tag{27.59}$$

While for a *weak electrolyte* the condition of equilibrium of the dissociation reaction gives

$$\mu_u = \nu_+\mu_+ + \nu_-\mu_- = \nu\mu_\pm, \tag{27.60}$$

so that (27.58) can be written in either of the two following forms

$$n_1\,\delta\mu_1 + n_2\,\delta\mu_u = 0, \tag{27.61}$$

$$n_1\,\delta\mu_1 + \nu n_2\,\delta\mu_\pm = 0, \tag{27.62}$$

the second of which is identical with (27.59).

Let us examine the case of a dilute solution of a strong 1 : 1 electrolyte. Then $\mathrm{m}_+ = \mathrm{m}_- = \mathrm{m}_2$ and, (*cf.* 27.22),

$$\mu_\pm = \mu_\pm^{\mathrm{m}}(T, p) + \boldsymbol{R}T \ln \mathrm{m}_2\gamma_\pm^*. \tag{27.63}$$

* P. Van Rysselberghe, *J. Phys. Chem.*, 39, 415 (1935).

The chemical potential of the solvent may be written in the form

$$\mu_1 = \mu_1^0 + RT\phi \ln x_1 = \mu_1^0 - RT\phi\, \Sigma x_s = \mu_1^0 - \frac{RTM_1\phi}{1000}(\mathrm{m}_+ + \mathrm{m}_-)$$

$$= \mu_1^0 - \frac{2RTM_1}{1000}\phi \mathrm{m}_2. \tag{27.64}$$

Now (27.59) gives

$$\delta\mu_\pm = -\frac{n_1}{\nu n_2}\delta\mu_1 = -\frac{1000}{\nu \mathrm{m}_2 M_1}\delta\mu_1. \tag{27.65}$$

At constant T and p (27.63), (27.64) and (27.65) lead to*

$$\delta \ln \gamma_\pm^* = -\frac{\delta[\mathrm{m}_2(1-\phi)]}{\mathrm{m}_2}. \tag{27.66}$$

Since the very dilute solution is taken as standard state $\gamma_\pm^* \to 1$ as $\mathrm{m}_2 \to 0$, so that this equation can be integrated to give

$$\ln \gamma_\pm^* = -\int_0^{\mathrm{m}_2} \frac{d[\mathrm{m}_2(1-\phi)]}{\mathrm{m}_2}. \tag{27.67}$$

If we know, from cryoscopic measurements, ϕ as a function of m_2 we can calculate $\gamma_\pm^*$; in this case ϕ is identical with ϕ_d. We must observe however, that the integration from $\mathrm{m}_2 = 0$ gives quite different results depending on the analytical form we assume to extrapolate the experimental curve $\phi(\mathrm{m}_2)$ to infinite dilution. The limiting law of Debye and Hückel, which we shall discuss in the next paragraph, provides a theoretical basis for this extrapolation.†

The case of a weak electrolyte can be treated in a similar manner. We have already seen that (27.62) is the same as (27.59) so that equation (27.65) is also valid for a weak electrolyte. Now

$$\mu_1 = \mu_1^0 + RT\phi_d \ln x_{1,d} = \mu_1^0 - RT\phi_d \frac{M_1}{1000}\nu \mathrm{m}_2, \tag{27.68}$$

$$\mu_\pm = \mu_\pm^{\mathrm{m}} + RT \ln \mathrm{m}_\pm \gamma_\pm^*, \tag{27.69}$$

where

$$\mathrm{m}_\pm^\nu = \mathrm{m}_+^{\nu_+}\mathrm{m}_-^{\nu_-} = \nu_+^{\nu_+}\nu_-^{\nu_-}\epsilon^\nu \mathrm{m}_2^\nu. \tag{27.70}$$

Employing equation (27.65) we thus obtain

$$\delta \ln \mathrm{m}_\pm \gamma_\pm^* = \frac{\delta(\phi_d \mathrm{m}_2)}{\mathrm{m}_2}, \tag{27.71}$$

which combined with (27.70) gives

$$\delta \ln \gamma_\pm^* = -\delta \ln \epsilon - \frac{\delta[\mathrm{m}_2(1-\phi_d)]}{\mathrm{m}_2}. \tag{27.72}$$

* *Cf.* Lewis and Randall [32], p. 343; Harned and Owen [27], equn. (1–9–11).
† *Cf.* Harned and Owen, *loc. cit.*, p. 289; Van Rysselberghe, *loc. cit.*

In an infinitely dilute solution $\gamma_{\pm}^{*} \to 1$ and $\epsilon \to 1$ so that, on integration:

$$\ln \gamma_{\pm}^{*} = \ln \frac{1}{\epsilon} - \int_0^{m_2} \frac{d\,[m_2(1-\phi_d)]}{m_2}. \tag{27.73}$$

Yet another method of evaluating $\gamma_{\pm}^{*}$ has been suggested by Van Rysselberghe,* which, provided we assume the validity of the Debye-Hückel law, does not require a knowledge of ϵ. He has also† given a clear discussion of the relationship between the three ways of discussing electrolyte solutions, ignoring the dissociation (as in ϕ_a above), knowing the actual degree of ionization (as in ϕ) or assuming complete dissociation (as in ϕ_d). He has also derived the relationship between the three activity coefficients defined in these three ways.

10. Limiting Law for Strong Electrolytes.

We have already indicated (chap. XXI, § 5) that the activity coefficients in a strong electrolyte solution exhibit characteristics quite different from those of non-electrolytes. In a sufficiently dilute non-electrolyte solution (*cf.* 21.42),

$$1 - \phi \propto c_2, \tag{27.74}$$

while for a strong electrolyte it is found experimentally that

$$1 - \phi \propto c_2^{1/2}. \tag{27.75}$$

As we have already seen, the derivative of $(1-\phi)$ at the origin is finite in the case of a non-electrolyte, but infinite for an electrolyte. This behaviour of strong electrolytes is related to the long range electrostatic forces between the ions in the solution.‡ The statistical theory, in the form developed by Debye and Hückel, leads to the following expression for the activity coefficient of an ion with a charge z_i, in a very dilute solution in which the ionic strength is I (*cf.* 27.38):

$$\log_{10}\gamma_i^{*} = -z_i^2 \frac{\sqrt{2\pi}}{2{\cdot}3026} \frac{e^2 N^2}{(\epsilon RT)^{3/2}} \sqrt{I}, \tag{27.76}$$

where N is the Avogadro number, e the electronic charge, ϵ the dielectric constant of the solvent, and R the gas constant; the ionic strength is in units of moles/cm.³. If I is expressed in moles/litre, we must multiply by $10^{3/2}$; then for aqueous solutions at 25 °C, we find

$$\log_{10}\gamma_i^{*} = -0{\cdot}507\, z_i^2 \sqrt{I}. \tag{27.77}$$

* *Loc. cit.*

† P. Van Rysselberghe, *Bull. Ac. Roy. Belg.* (*Cl. Sc.*), 20, 234 (1934); *J. Phys. Chem.*, 39, 415 (1935).

‡ S. R. Milner, *Phil. Mag.*, 23, 551 (1912); P. Debye and E. Hückel, *Phys. Zeit.*, 24, 185 (1924); *cf.* Falkenhagen [18]; Harned and Owen [27]; Fowler and Guggenheim, [20], chap. IX.

This equation is in excellent agreement with that deduced from experimental results, for example that given in § 7 (27.42).

From (27.76) we can easily derive the mean ionic activity coefficient, and from (27.66) the osmotic coefficient in a very dilute solution.

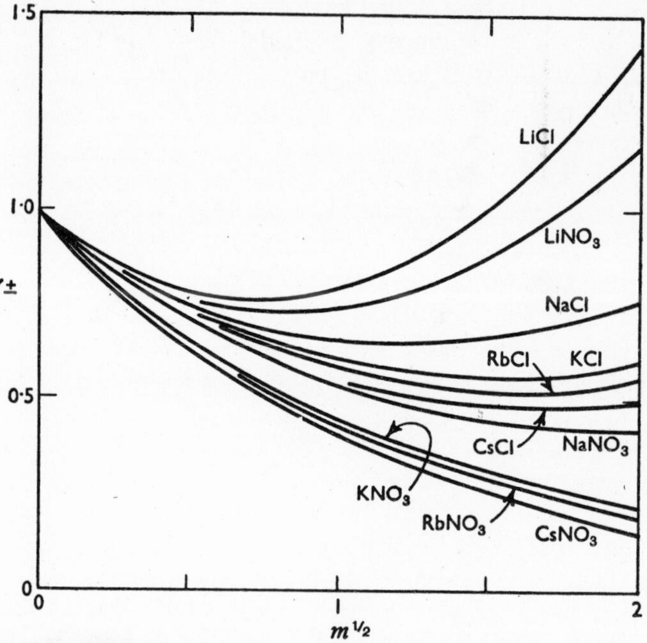

FIG. 27.2. Mean ionic activity coefficients of some strong electrolytes.

The mean activity coefficients of a number of strong 1 : 1 electrolytes are shown in fig. 27.2. It is seen that these curves tend towards the same limiting line in very dilute solutions.

11. Concentrated Solutions.

The theory of concentrated electrolyte solutions is still in an undeveloped form. Various corrections have been suggested to make the Debye-Hückel law valid for more concentrated solutions,* but these are either empirical or at best on an uncertain theoretical basis and we shall not develop them further.

At higher concentrations it is no longer legitimate to consider the solution as a simple continuous medium, but it is necessary to take account of the molecular structure, and more particularly the change of this structure with increasing concentration of ions. It is found for example that in the case of the alkali metal chlorides the deviations from the Debye-Hückel limiting law diminishes in the series Li, Na, K,

* *Cf.* Harned and Owen, [27].

Rb, and Cs. The heats of hydration of these ions vary in the same order.* Thus it seems that the deviations from the limiting law are related to the intensity of the interaction energy between the dissolved ions and the solvent. A similar conclusion is suggested by Stewart's † observation that the variation of the partial molar volume of ions with concentration is closely linked with the change of the structure of water in the same solutions, as revealed by X-ray studies. Unfortunately there are no satisfactory quantitative theories to account for these complex phenomena.

* *Cf*. J. D. Bernal and R. H. Fowler, *J. Chem. Phys.*, **1**, 515 (1933); J. Beck, *Phys. Zeit.*, **40**, 474 (1939); D. D. Eley, *Trans. Faraday. Soc.*, **40**, 184 (1944).

† G. W. Stewart, *J. Chem. Phys.*, **7**, 869 (1939).

CHAPTER XXVIII

AZEOTROPY

1. Conditions for an Azeotropic Transformation.

An azeotropic transformation is said to occur when, in a closed system, the mass of one of the phases increases at the expense of the others, without changing the composition of any of these phases.

In this paragraph we shall investigate the conditions under which a transformation of this kind can occur, restricting ourselves for the moment to a two-phase system in which there are no chemical reactions other than the passage of components from one phase to another.

From the definition of an azeotropic transformation we must have

$$\frac{dx_i'}{dt}=0, \quad \frac{dx_i''}{dt}=0, \quad (i=1, 2 \ldots c), \tag{28.1}$$

or more explicitly (*cf.* 1.3) :

$$\frac{dn_i'}{dt}-x_i'\frac{dn'}{dt}=0\,; \quad \frac{dn_i''}{dt}-x_i''\frac{dn''}{dt}=0. \tag{28.2}$$

Furthermore if the system is closed

$$\frac{dn_i'}{dt}=-\frac{dn_i''}{dt}; \quad \frac{dn'}{dt}=-\frac{dn''}{dt}. \tag{28.3}$$

The conditions (28.2) therefore mean that, on the one hand,

$$x_i'=x_i'', \quad (i=1, 2 \ldots c), \tag{28.4}$$

and on the other :

$$\frac{1}{x_1'}\frac{dn_1'}{dt}=\frac{1}{x_2'}\frac{dn'}{dt}=\ldots=\frac{dn'}{dt}. \tag{28.5}$$

These conditions for an azeotropic change fall into two groups.* The first, (28.4), expresses the fact that both phases must have the same composition in terms of mole fractions : the system is one of *uniform composition*. The second group, (28.5), show that the rate of transfer of each component is proportional to its mole fraction in the system.

It is easily verified that the necessary conditions (28.4) and (28.5), if

* Th. De Donder, *Affinité* III, [8], p. 27 ; *Bull. Ac. Roy. Belg.* (*Cl. Sc.*), **18**, 888 (1932) ; G. Schouls, *Bull. Ac. Roy. Belg.* (*Cl. Sc.*), **17**, 47 (1931) ; **18**, 1160 (1932) ; *Bull. Soc. Chim. Belg.*, **49**, 214 (1940) ; for the general case of any number of phases and reactions, *cf.* R. Defay, *Bull. Ac. Roy. Belg.* (*Cl. Sc.*), **39**, 465 (1943).

they are satisfied at all instants, are also sufficient to ensure that the mole fraction of each phase remains constant throughout the transformation ; it is indeed self-evident from a general consideration of the above conditions.

We shall therefore limit ourselves for the rest of this chapter to a consideration of systems of uniform composition. The relationship between these and the occurrence of azeotropic transformations is so close that we shall call such systems *azeotropic states.* The study of the conditions relating to the rates of transfer will be deferred until the last volume of this work, when it will be shown that these conditions correspond to the minimum rate of entropy production.

Azeotropic transformations in systems in which chemical reactions may take place in addition to transfers from one phase to another, or which have more than two phases, are not necessarily associated with states of uniform composition but with the more general class of *indifferent states.* A study of systems of uniform composition is a natural introduction to the more general question of indifferent states.

We shall not repeat here any discussion of the properties already established for states of uniform composition. It will be recalled that a state of uniform composition corresponds to an extreme value (maximum, minimum, or inflexion with a horizontal tangent) of the equilibrium pressure at constant temperature, or of the equilibrium temperature at constant pressure (Gibbs-Konovalow theorems, chap. XVIII, §§ 6 and 9).

2. Heat of Azeotropic Vaporization.

Consider an *equilibrium azeotropic transformation*, that is to say an equilibrium transformation as defined in § 1 of chapter XIX but during which, in addition, the composition remains constant. We now proceed to show that a transformation of this kind must take place at constant temperature and pressure.

In an equilibrium transformation, the affinities of transfer must all remain zero ; thus

$$\left.\begin{aligned} \boldsymbol{A}_1 &= \mu_1'(T, p, x_2^0 \dots x_c^0) - \mu_1''(T, p, x_2^0 \dots x_c^0) = 0 \\ \boldsymbol{A}_2 &= \mu_2'(T, p, x_2^0 \dots x_c^0) - \mu_2''(T, p, x_2^0 \dots x_c^0) = 0 \end{aligned}\right\}, \qquad (28.6)$$

where the index 0 means that x_i remains at a constant value, and is the same in both phases. We thus have two equations and only two variables, T and p ; hence in general there is only one value of T and p corresponding to each set of given values of $x_1^0, \dots x_c^0$. It follows then that *the temperature and pressure must remain constant in the course of the transformation considered.*

Furthermore, the quantity of heat received by the system during the transformation, which is given in general by (2.13)

$$dQ = C_{p,\xi}\, dT + h_{T,\xi}\, dp + \sum_i (h_{T,p})_i\, d\xi_i, \tag{28.7}$$

reduces to the simple form :

$$dQ = \sum_i \Delta_{\prime}^{\prime\prime} h_i\, d\xi_i. \tag{28.8}$$

In this equation $\Delta_{\prime}^{\prime\prime} h_i$ is the heat content change accompanying the transfer of component i from the first to the second phase, and ξ_i is the extent of this transfer. Since the composition remains constant

$$d\xi_i = dn_i^{\prime\prime} = x_i\, dn^{\prime\prime}.$$

Where one phase is a vapour, (28.8) may be written

$$\frac{dQ}{dn^g} = \sum_i x_i\, \Delta_e h_i. \tag{28.9}$$

This gives the heat received by the system per mole of mixture evaporated azeotropically at constant T and p. It is called the latent heat of azeotropic vaporization, which we shall denote by $\Delta_a h$:

$$\Delta_a h = \sum_i x_i\, \Delta_e h_i. \tag{28.10}$$

Since the system is of uniform composition, this can be written in terms of the molar enthalpies of the two phases (*cf.* 2.36 and 1.25)

$$\sum_i x_i\, \Delta_e h_i = \sum_i x_i (h_i^g - h_i^l) = h^g - h^l, \tag{28.11}$$

so that we have

$$\frac{dQ}{dn^g} = \Delta_a h = h^g - h^l. \tag{28.12}$$

In the same way we can find the change in the volume of the system, per mole of mixture evaporated azeotropically :

$$\frac{dV}{dn^g} = \sum_i x_i\, \Delta_e v_i = v^g - v^l, \tag{28.13}$$

while for the entropy change

$$\frac{dS}{dn^g} = \sum_i x_i\, \Delta_e s_i = s^g - s^l. \tag{28.14}$$

Finally we observe, that because of equation (19.1) which applies to all equilibrium changes :

$$\frac{dQ}{dn^g} = T\, \frac{dS}{dn^g} \tag{28.15}$$

or

$$h^g - h^l = T\,(s^g - s^l). \tag{28.16}$$

These formulae are closely analogous to those for the evaporation of a pure substance; this is because in both cases the transformation takes place at constant temperature, pressure and composition.

3. Activity Coefficients in States of Uniform Composition.*

We shall still confine our attention to binary, two-phase systems for which, if the composition of the system is uniform, equations (18.28) and (18.29) reduce to:

$$\left.\begin{aligned}\ln\frac{\gamma_1''}{\gamma_1'} &= \int_{T_1^0}^{T}\frac{\Delta_{\prime}^{\prime\prime}h_1^0}{RT^2}\,dT - \frac{1}{RT}\int_{p_1^0}^{p}\Delta_{\prime}^{\prime\prime}v_1^0\,dp,\\ \ln\frac{\gamma_2''}{\gamma_2'} &= \int_{T_1^0}^{T}\frac{\Delta_{\prime}^{\prime\prime}h_2^0}{RT^2}\,dT - \frac{1}{RT}\int_{p_2^0}^{p}\Delta_{\prime}^{\prime\prime}v_2^0\,dp\end{aligned}\right\}. \tag{28.17}$$

First we consider a fixed pressure p^0. Then, assuming the heats of transfer to be independent of temperature in the range considered, we have

$$\ln\frac{\gamma_1''}{\gamma_1'} = -\frac{\Delta_{\prime}^{\prime\prime}h_1^0}{R}\left(\frac{1}{T}-\frac{1}{T_1^0}\right);\quad \ln\frac{\gamma_2''}{\gamma_2^1} = -\frac{\Delta_{\prime}^{\prime\prime}h_2^0}{R}\left(\frac{1}{T}-\frac{1}{T_2^0}\right). \tag{28.18}$$

In these equations T is the azeotropic temperature; T_1^0 and T_2^0 are the temperatures at which the two pure substances exist in equilibrium in the two phases at the given pressure.

If the system consists of a liquid phase and a vapour phase, then we may, to a first approximation, assume the vapour to be an ideal gas mixture for which γ_1'' and γ_2'' are equal to unity; furthermore T_1^0 and T_2^0 are then the boiling points of the two pure substances at the pressure concerned.

As an example let us consider a mixture of ethanol and carbon tetrachloride which forms an azeotropic mixture.† At a pressure of one atm. the azeotropic temperature is 65·08 °C.

For this system we have for alcohol:

$$T_1^0 = 351\ °\mathrm{K};\quad \Delta_e h_1^0 = 9{,}970\ \text{cal./mole};$$

and for carbon tetrachloride:

$$T_2^0 = 350\ °\mathrm{K};\quad \Delta_e h_2^0 = 6{,}800\ \text{cal./mole}.$$

Hence

$$\ln\gamma_1^l = \frac{9{,}970}{2}\left(\frac{1}{338}-\frac{1}{351}\right) \simeq 0{\cdot}50$$

$$\ln\gamma_2^l = \frac{6{,}800}{2}\left(\frac{1}{338}-\frac{1}{350}\right) \simeq 0{\cdot}35,$$

* I. Prigogine, *J. Phys. Rad.*, **5**, 185 (1944).
† Lecat, [31], p. 195.

whence

$$\gamma_1^l \simeq 1{\cdot}65 \quad \text{and} \quad \gamma_2^l \simeq 1{\cdot}42.$$

If the temperature, rather than the pressure, is fixed we have, again taking the vapour phase as an ideal gas mixture (*cf.* 18.24)

$$\Delta_e v_1^0 \simeq \Delta_e v_2^0 \simeq RT/p \tag{28.19}$$

so that

$$\gamma_1' = p/p_1^0\,; \quad \gamma_2' = p/p_2^0. \tag{28.20}$$

The system *n*-hexane + ethyl iodide* at 60 °C forms an azeotrope with a vapour pressure of 640 mm. For the pure components

$$p_1^0 = 575 \text{ mm. (hexane)}\,; \quad p_2^0 = 510 \text{ mm. (ethyl iodide)}$$

so that

$$\gamma_1^l \simeq 1{\cdot}11\,; \quad \gamma_2^l \simeq 1{\cdot}25.$$

Similarly for the ethanol + carbon tetrachloride system considered above, at 65·08 °C,

$$p_1^0 = 448{\cdot}8 \text{ mm.},$$

$$p_2^0 = 530{\cdot}9 \text{ mm.},$$

while $p = 760$ mm.

Hence

$$\gamma_1^l \simeq 1{\cdot}69\,; \quad \gamma_2^l \simeq 1{\cdot}43,$$

in agreement with the values obtained above.

The activity coefficients in azeotropic states are therefore easily evaluated. If, for a system possessing an azeotrope, an empirical formula is used to represent the activity coefficients (*e.g.* § 5, of chap. XXI), then two of the parameters can be calculated from a knowledge of the position of the azeotropic point.†

4. Regular Solutions and States of Uniform Composition.

We have shown above that the activity coefficients of the components of an azeotropic mixture may be calculated from a knowledge of the properties of the pure components, and the temperature and pressure of the azeotropic state. In this paragraph we shall investigate the prediction of states of uniform composition from a knowledge of the behaviour of the activity coefficients as functions of temperature and pressure.

We have already seen that the activity coefficients of non-electrolyte solutions may be written as a series expansion in the mole fractions (chap. XXI, § 5). We shall limit ourselves to the simple equations (21.52), although an analogous calculation can be made for any activity coefficient law.

* Timmermans, [45], p. 180.

† *Cf.* H. C. Carlson and A. P. Colburn, *Ind. Eng. Chem.*, 34, 581 (1942).

For a solution in the presence of vapour, we have, at a given temperature :

$$\ln \gamma_1^l = \alpha_2 x_2^2 ; \quad \ln \gamma_2^l = \alpha_2 x_1^2 ; \tag{28.21}$$

whence, because of (28.20), in a state of uniform composition

$$\ln p/p_1^0 = \alpha_2 x_2^2 ; \quad \ln p/p_2^0 = \alpha_2 x_1^2 . \tag{28.22}$$

Hence if α_2 is known we can immediately calculate the pressure and composition of the azeotrope at the temperature considered. If α_2 is not known, then the validity of (28.22) can be tested by dividing one equation by the other to eliminate α_2 to give

$$\frac{x_2^2}{(1-x_2)^2} = \frac{\ln p/p_1^0}{\ln p/p_2^0} . \tag{28.23}$$

Solving for x_2 we find

$$x_2 = \left\{ 1 + \sqrt{\frac{\ln p/p_2^0}{\ln p/p_1^0}} \right\}^{-1} . \tag{28.24}$$

We must take the positive value of the square root since x_2 must of course be less than unity. This equation is due to Kireev.* Thus for the system n-hexane + ethyl iodide for which the data are given above, we calculate for the azeotropic mixture at 60 °C, a mole fraction of ethyl iodide of 0·41 ; the observed value is 0·39. This discrepancy is to be attributed partly to the assumption that in the solutions considered the activity coefficients are given by (28.21) and partly to neglect of vapour imperfection.

Now consider the system at constant pressure. To employ equations (28.18) to calculate the azeotropic temperature T, we must know the effect of temperature on the coefficient α_2. As a first approximation we may use equation (21.52′) in which α_2 is assumed to be inversely proportional to T ; that is we assume the solutions are regular.

Equations (28.18) then give, neglecting vapour imperfection,

$$\left.\begin{aligned} \frac{\alpha}{RT} x_2^2 &= \frac{\Delta_e h_1^0}{R}\left(\frac{1}{T} - \frac{1}{T_1^0}\right), \\ \frac{\alpha}{RT} x_1^2 &= \frac{\Delta_e h_2^0}{R}\left(\frac{1}{T} - \frac{1}{T_2^0}\right) \end{aligned}\right\} . \tag{28.25}$$

Eliminating α between these two equations we have

$$\frac{x_2^2}{(1-x_2)^2} = \frac{\Delta_e h_1^0}{T_1^0} \frac{T_2^0}{\Delta_e h_2^0} \frac{T_1^0 - T}{T_2^0 - T} . \tag{28.26}$$

We see that $\Delta_e h^0/T$ is the entropy of evaporation of the pure liquid

* V. A. Kireev, *Acta Physicochem. U.R.S.S.*, **14**, 371 (1941), *cf.* E. F. G. Herington, *J. Chem. Soc.*, **1947**, 597.

at its b.p., so that for a pair of liquids having the same Trouton constant we have approximately

$$\frac{x_2}{1-x_2}=\sqrt{\frac{T_1^0-T}{T_2^0-T}}. \tag{28.27}$$

Alternatively, if the ratio of Trouton constants is c^2,

$$\frac{x_2}{1-x_2}=c\sqrt{\frac{T_1^0-T}{T_2^0-T}}. \tag{28.27'}$$

These equations may be tested using two sets of data due to Lecat. In the first place we have the data for nine azeotropic systems formed by acetone with a series of organic compounds all of which are "normal" liquids in that their Trouton constants are roughly equal.* The data are shown plotted in terms of (28.27) in fig. 28.1; the theoretical equation is reasonably well satisfied except for the acetone + methyl acetate system. Equation (28.27′) must be regarded as of a semi-empirical nature as liquids with widely different Trouton constants can hardly be expected to form regular solutions. It is interesting to see, however, whether this equation can be applied to the extensive series of azeotropes formed by ethanol with organic halogen compounds.†

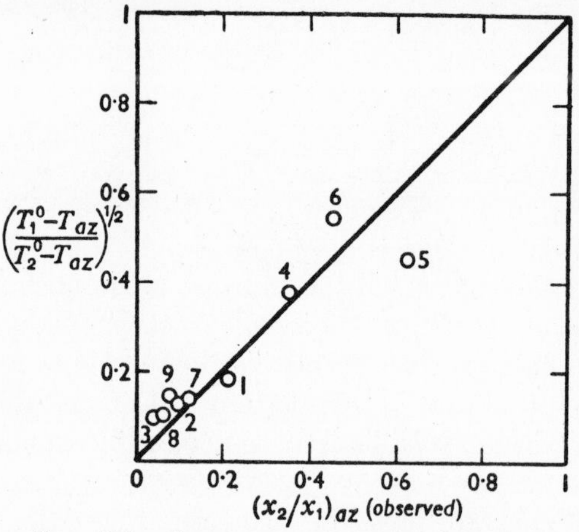

FIG. 28.1. Azeotropes of systems containing acetone. Component 1 is in each case that whose boiling point is nearer to the azeotropic temperature.

Acetone + *iso*butylchloride		1
	ethyl iodide	2
	butyl bromide	3
	propyl mercaptan	4
	methyl acetate	5
	diallyl	6
	n-hexane	7
	cyclohexane	8
	ethyl propyl ether	9

The data for these, at 1 atm. pressure, are given in table 28.1; the quantities δ and Δ also given in the table will be discussed later (§ 9).

The Trouton constant of ethanol is about 28 cal./deg. mole, while most of the other substances have normal values. We have therefore taken $c^2=1{\cdot}4$; the results are shown in fig. 28.2, where the points are numbered according to the serial numbers in table 28.1. To simplify the

* M. Lecat, *L'Azeotropisme*, 1st part (Bruxelles, 1918).
† Lecat, [31], p. 195.

representation, the indices 1 and 2 for each pair of liquids have been chosen so that x_2/x_1 is less than unity ; c^2 has been taken as 1·4 or 1/1·4 as the case may be.

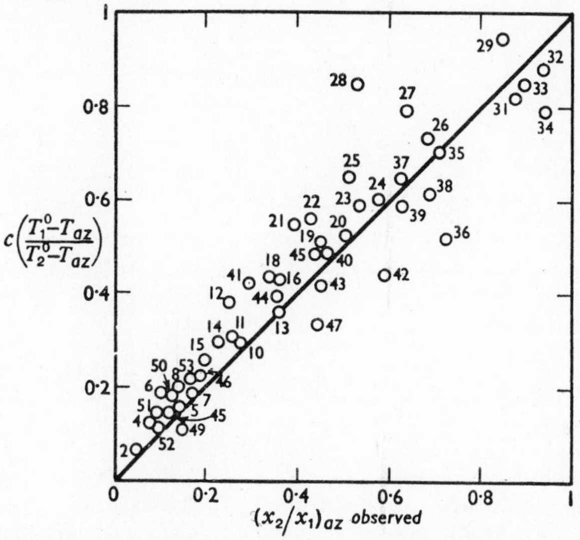

FIG. 28.2. Test of equation (28.27′) for azeotropes of ethanol + a halogen compound.

The general agreement with equation (28.27′) is remarkably good ; for mixtures of formic acid with organic halogen compounds the agreement is however much less satisfactory.*

5. States of Uniform Composition in Mixed Crystals.

Considerations essentially similar to those above apply also to states of uniform composition in a continuous series of mixed crystals. Equation (21.52′) can be applied not only to a liquid solution but also to mixed crystals, so that instead of (28.25), we have at all points of uniform composition :

$$\left.\begin{aligned} \frac{\alpha^s - \alpha^l}{RT}\, x_2^2 &= \frac{\Delta_f h_1^0}{R}\left(\frac{1}{T} - \frac{1}{T_1^0}\right) \\ \frac{\alpha^s - \alpha^l}{RT}\, x_1^2 &= \frac{\Delta_f h_2^0}{R}\left(\frac{1}{T} - \frac{1}{T_2^0}\right) \end{aligned}\right\}, \qquad (28.28)$$

where $\Delta_f h_1^0$ and $\Delta_f h_2^0$ are the heats of fusion of components 1 and 2. On division we obtain an equation similar to (28.26) except that heats of fusion appear in place of heats of evaporation. Furthermore, if the entropies of fusion are equal, we obtain (28.27).

* I. Prigogine, *loc. cit.*

TABLE 28.1

Azeotropes formed between ethanol (*B.P.* 78.3 °C) *and various halogen compounds*

No.	*Halogen Compound* (H)	*B. P.* (760 mm.) ; °C		*Δ*	δ	*Com-position*
		H	*Azeo-trope*			$(w_H)_{az}$
1	*cis*-1-chloropropene - -	32·8	32·1	45·5	0·7	—
2	*iso*-propyl chloride - -	34·8	34·5	43·5	0·3	0·03
3	*trans*-1-chloropropene -	37·4	36·7	40·9	0·7	—
4	ethyl bromide - - -	38·4	37·6	39·9	0·8	0·03
5	methyl iodide - - -	42·5	41·2	35·8	1·3	0·032
6	allyl chloride - - -	45·3	43·5	33·0	1·8	0·05
7	propyl chloride - -	46·65	45·0	31·65	1·65	0·06
8	*trans*-dichloroacetylene -	48·35	46·5	29·95	1·85	0·06
9	2-bromopropene - -	48·35	46·2	29·95	2·15	—
10	ethylidine chloride - -	57·35	54·6	20·95	2·65	0·115
11	*cis*-1-bromopropene - -	57·8	54·6	20·5	3·2	0·09
12	2-chlorobutene-1 - -	58·5	53·8	19·8	4·7	0·115
13	*iso*-propyl bromide - -	59·35	55·0	18·95	4·15	0·12
14	*cis*-dichloroacetylene -	60·25	57·7	18·5	2·55	0·098
15	chloroform - - -	61·2	59·35	17·1	1·85	0·07
16	*trans*-2-chlorobutene-2 -	62·6	57·0	15·7	5·6	0·154
17	*trans*-1-bromopropene -	63·25	58·7	15·05	4·55	—
18	*cis*-1-chlorobutene-1 -	63·5	58·0	14·8	5·5	0·148
19	*cis*-2-chlorobutene-2 -	66·8	60·2	11·5	6·6	0·184
20	*trans*-1-chlorobutene-1 -	68·1	61·4	10·2	6·7	0·202
21	*iso*-butyl chloride - -	68·9	61·45	9·45	7·4	0·163
22	chlorohydroxyacetone -	70·5	64·0	7·8	6·5	0·15
23	allyl bromide - - -	70·5	62·8	7·8	7·7	0·17
24	propyl bromide - -	71·0	62·75	7·3	8·25	0·175
25	ethyl iodide - - -	72·3	63·0	6·0	9·3	0·13
26	*trans*-chloro-bromo-ethylene - - -	75·3	66·3	3·0	9·0	0·18
27	carbon tetrachloride -	76·75	65·08	1·65	11·7	0·158
28	butyl chloride - - -	78·5	66·0	0·2	12·3	0·21
29	2-bromobutene-1 - -	81·0	67·5	2·7	10·8	0·222
30	ethylene chloride - -	83·5	70·5	5·2	7·8	—
31	*cis*-chloro-bromo-ethylene	84·6	72·4	6·3	5·9	0·267
32	*trans*-2-bromobutene-2 -	85·55	69·1	7·25	9·1	0·267
33	*cis*-1-bromobutene-1 -	86·15	69·7	7·85	8·6	0·276
34	trichloroethylene - -	86·95	70·9	8·65	7·4	0·27
35	*iso*-propyl iodide - -	89·45	71·7	11·15	6·6	0·275
36	dichloro-bromo-methane -	90·1	75·5	11·8	2·8	0·28
37	*iso*-butyl bromide - -	91·4	72·45	13·1	5·85	0·35
38	*cis*-2-bromobutene-2 -	93·9	72·3	15·6	6·0	0·336
39	*trans*-1-bromobutene-1 -	94·7	72·9	16·4	5·4	0·357

TABLE 28.1 (*contd.*)

No.	Halogen Compound (H)	B. P. (760 mm.); °C H	B. P. (760 mm.); °C Azeotrope	Δ	δ	Composition $(w_H)_{az}$
40	1, 2-dichloropropane-	96·25	74·7	17·95	3·6	0·473
41	dibromomethane	97·0	75·5	18·7	2·8	0·45
42	*iso*-amyl chloride	99·8	74·8	21·5	3·5	0·42
43	butyl bromide	100·3	75·0	22·0	3·3	0·43
44	allyl iodide	102·0	75·2	23·7	3·1	0·43
45	propyl iodide	102·4	75·4	24·1	2·9	0·44
46	*as*-dichloro-bromo-ethylene	107·5	77·25	29·2	1·25	0·605
47	*trans*-dibromo-acetylene	108	75·7	29·7	2·6	0·36
48	*cis*-dibromo-acetylene	112	77·8	33·7	0·5	0·675
49	1, 1, 2-trichloro-ethane	113·65	77·8	35·35	0·5	0·70
50	*sym-cis*-dichloro-bromo-ethylene	113·8	77·4	35·5	0·9	0·691
51	*iso*-amyl bromide	120·3	77·7	42·0	0·6	0·76
52	*iso*-butyl iodide	121·0	77·65	42·7	0·65	0·73
53	tetrachloroethylene	121·2	76·65	42·9	1·65	$\simeq$0·63

The applicability of (28.27) is illustrated by fig. 28.3 which refers to a series of binary alloys. Again the indices 1 and 2 have been chosen so that x_2/x_1 is less than unity. The systems Mn+Co; Fe+V; Ni+Pd agree well with the formula, while Au+Cu, Ni+V and Cu+Mn are in poor agreement presumably because one of the phases (probably the solid) cannot be regarded as a regular solution.

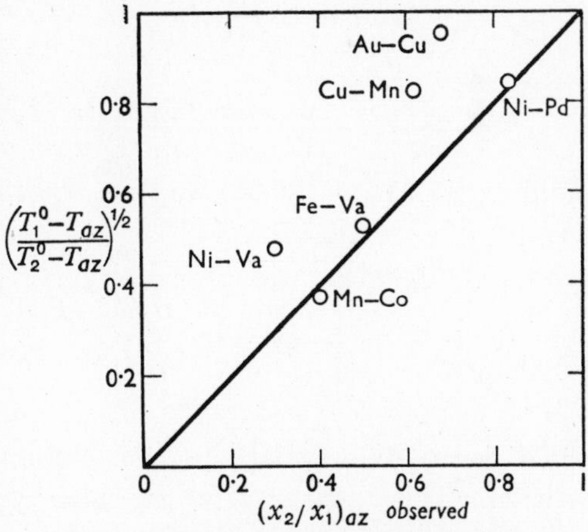

FIG. 28.3. Test of equation (28.27) in the case of mixed crystals.

From the position of the state of uniform composition, we can calculate $\alpha^s - \alpha^l$ using (28.28). Thus for Co+Mn we find a value of 1070 cal./mole. This is very large and indicates that the departure from ideality, measured by the magnitude of α, is very much greater in the solid state than in liquids.

6. The Line of Uniform Composition.

We are now in a position to study the series of states of uniform composition which are obtained when T, p and x_2 all vary simultaneously. These three variables are always related by the two equatoins (28.17); it follows therefore that only one of them can be varied independently, so that the states of uniform composition fall on a line called the *azeotropic line*. The differential relations which this line must satisfy are examined below.*

We recall that an equilibrium displacement of a two-phase binary system must satisfy equations (18.44); however, at all points along the line of uniform composition

$$x_2' = x_2'' = x_2 \quad \text{and} \quad \delta x_2' = -\delta x_2'' = \delta x_2 \tag{28.29}$$

so that equations (18.44) reduce to

$$\Delta_\prime'' v_1\, \delta p - \frac{\Delta_\prime'' h_1}{T}\, \delta T - x_2 \left[\frac{\partial^2 g''}{\partial x_2''^2} - \frac{\partial^2 g'}{\partial x_2'^2}\right] \delta x_2 = 0,$$

$$\Delta_\prime'' v_2\, \delta p - \frac{\Delta_\prime'' h_2}{T}\, \delta T + (1 - x_2) \left[\frac{\partial^2 g''}{\partial x_2''^2} - \frac{\partial^2 g'}{\partial x_2'^2}\right] \delta x_2 = 0. \tag{28.30}$$

These two equations can now be solved for $\delta p / \delta x_2$ and $\delta T / \delta x_2$ to give:

$$\frac{\delta p}{\delta x_2} = - \frac{x_1 \Delta_\prime'' h_1 + x_2 \Delta_\prime'' h_2}{\Delta_\prime'' v_2 \Delta_\prime'' h_1 - \Delta_\prime'' v_1 \Delta_\prime'' h_2} \left[\frac{\partial^2 g''}{\partial x_2''^2} - \frac{\partial^2 g'}{\partial x_2'^2}\right], \tag{28.31}$$

$$\frac{1}{T} \frac{\delta T}{\delta x_2} = - \frac{x_1 \Delta_\prime'' v_1 + x_2 \Delta_\prime'' v_2}{\Delta_\prime'' v_2 \Delta_\prime'' h_1 - \Delta_\prime'' v_1 \Delta_\prime'' h_2} \left[\frac{\partial^2 g''}{\partial x_2''^2} - \frac{\partial^2 g'}{\partial x_2'^2}\right]. \tag{28.32}$$

Dividing (28.31) by (28.32) we then obtain

$$\boxed{\frac{\delta p}{\delta T} = \frac{x_1 \Delta_\prime'' h_1 + x_2 \Delta_\prime'' h_2}{T \{x_1 \Delta_\prime'' v_1 + x_2 \Delta_\prime'' v_2\}}}, \tag{28.33}$$

which is the differential equation defining the line of uniform composition. This equation is of the same type as the Clausius-Clapeyron equation which determines the line of co-existence of two phases of the same pure substance. This equation can indeed be simplified further, and put in a form even more akin to the Clausius-Clapeyron equation.

* W. Mund, *Bull. Soc. Chim. Belg.*, **38**, 322 (1929); G. Schouls [41]; *Bull. Ac. Roy. Belg. (Cl. Sc.)*, **16**, 628 ,1412 (1930); **17**, 47 (1931).

For from (28.9), (28.13) and (28.16) we can write the last equation in the equivalent forms :

$$\frac{\delta p}{\delta T}=\frac{1}{T}\frac{dQ/dn''}{dV/dn''}, \tag{28.34}$$

$$\frac{\delta p}{\delta T}=\frac{\Delta_a h}{T\Delta_a v}, \tag{28.35}$$

$$\frac{\delta p}{\delta T}=\frac{s''-s'}{v''-v'}. \tag{28.36}$$

If we make the usual assumption that the vapour phase is perfect and the volume of the condensed phase is negligible we find

$$\frac{\partial \ln p}{\partial T}=\frac{\Delta_a h}{RT^2}. \tag{28.37}$$

As an example of the application of this equation, fig. 28.4 shows $\ln p$ plotted against $1/T$ for three typical systems. The slopes of the

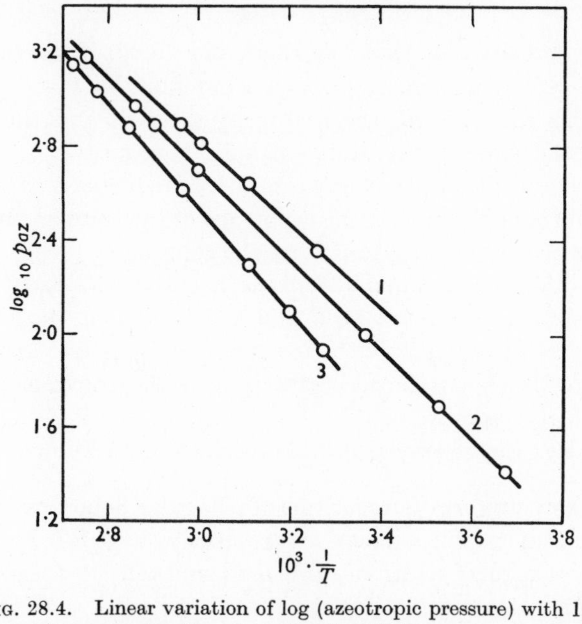

FIG. 28.4. Linear variation of log (azeotropic pressure) with $1/T$.
1. ethanol + carbon tetrachloride. 2. ethanol + ethyl acetate. 3. ethanol + water.

three lines so obtained give the heats of azeotropic evaporation ; we find for example* for water + ethanol $\Delta_a h \simeq 10{,}000$ cal./mole, while for ethanol + ethyl acetate $\Delta_a h \simeq 8700$ cal./mole.†

* I. Prigogine, *Bull. Soc. Chim. Belg.*, 52, 95 (1943) ; for the experimental data see *e.g.* R. W. Merriman, *J. Chem. Soc.*, 103, 1790, 1801 (1913) ; W. Mund and G. Heim, *Bull. Soc. Chim. Belg.*, 41, 349 (1932).

† The careful experimental measurements of Mund and Heim (*loc. cit.*) show that the heat of azeotropic evaporation of this system varies from 8809 to 8290 cal./mole in the temperature range 20°–90 °C.

We notice that the value of $\Delta_a h$ for the alcohol+water system is close to the latent heat of evaporation of ethanol, while that for the second system lies between that for the two pure liquids.

The differential equation (28.32) has a very interesting consequence which we shall now examine. Making the same approximations again, (*cf.* 28.19), (28.32) can be rewritten

$$\frac{1}{T}\frac{\delta T}{\delta x_2}=\frac{1}{\Delta_e h_2-\Delta_e h_1}\left[\frac{\partial^2 g''}{\partial x_2''^2}-\frac{\partial^2 g'}{\partial x_2'^2}\right], \tag{28.38}$$

whence

$$\frac{\delta x_2}{\delta T}=\frac{\Delta_e h_2-\Delta_e h_1}{T\left[\dfrac{\partial^2 g''}{\partial x_2''^2}-\dfrac{\partial^2 g'}{\partial x_2'^2}\right]}. \tag{28.39}$$

The sign of the denominator of this expression is determined by

$$\frac{\partial^2 g''}{\partial x_2''^2}-\frac{\partial^2 g'}{\partial x_2'^2}. \tag{28.40}$$

We have already seen that (*cf.* 18.68 and 18.69) if this expression is positive the azeotrope corresponds to a minimum in T, or a maximum in p. In this case we call the azeotropy *positive*, and the derivative $\delta x_2/\delta T$ has the same sign as $\Delta_e h_2-\Delta_e h_1$.

In other words, if the azeotropy is positive, an increase in temperature increases the mole fraction in the azeotrope of the component which has the greater heat of evaporation from the solution.

On the other hand when (28.40) is negative the azeotropic state corresponds to a maximum in T and a minimum in p; this state is called *negative azeotropy*. If the azeotropy is negative, an increase in temperature decreases the mole fraction of the component with the higher heat of evaporation.

These rules, due to Wrewsky,* are verified in all known cases.

7. The Line of Uniform Composition for Regular Solutions.

Starting from (28.22), we may first replace α_2 by $\alpha/\boldsymbol{R}T$, corresponding to the case of regular solutions, and then subtract the second equation from the first. On rearranging the terms we have

$$x_2=\frac{1}{2}+\frac{\boldsymbol{R}T}{2\alpha}\ln\frac{p_2^0}{p_1^0}. \tag{28.41}$$

The logarithm of the vapour pressure of a pure substance is very nearly a linear function of $1/T$ so that the composition of the azeotrope given by (28·41) will be a linear function of T.† This conclusion is confirmed

* M. Wrewsky, *Zeit. physik. Chem.*, **83**, 551 (1913); *cf.* also H. Masing, *Zeit. physik. Chem.* **81**, 223 (1911).

† E. A. Coulson and E. F. G. Herington, *J. Chem. Soc.*, **1947**, 597; *cf.* O. Redlich and P. W. Schutz, *J. Amer. Chem. Soc.*, **66**, 1007 (1944).

by a large number of experimental results, among which may be mentioned those for the systems benzene + cyclohexane, ethyl acetate + carbon tetrachloride, ethanol + chloroform.

If we know α and the vapour pressure curves of the two liquids we can calculate the azeotropic composition at a given temperature. In particular, if the vapour pressures of the two liquids are equal, then the azeotrope, if it exists, will have a mole fraction of 0·5 of each component.

Equation (28.41) also enables us to deduce another general rule. For on differentiation with respect to temperature, we obtain:

$$\frac{\delta x_2}{\delta T} = \frac{R}{2\alpha} \ln \frac{p_2^0}{p_1^0} + \frac{RT}{2\alpha} \left(\frac{1}{p_2^0} \frac{dp_2^0}{dT} - \frac{1}{p_1^0} \frac{dp_1^0}{dT} \right). \tag{28.42}$$

If the two components have vapour pressures which are closely similar, this may be written approximately :

$$\frac{\delta x_2}{\delta T} = \frac{RT}{2\alpha p^0} \left(\frac{dp_2^0}{dT} - \frac{dp_1^0}{dT} \right), \tag{28.43}$$

where

$$p_1^0 \sim p_2^0 \sim p^0. \tag{28.44}$$

If we consider the case where $\alpha > 0$, then the system will have a positive azeotrope (*cf.* 28.22), so that from (28.43) we deduce that *if two components, whose vapour pressures are approximately equal, form a positive azeotrope, then a rise in temperature increases the mole fraction in the azeotrope of that component whose saturation vapour pressure when pure increases the more rapidly with temperature.**

A similar inverse rule is obtained if α is negative and we are dealing with a negative azeotrope. Essentially similar rules, but making no reference to the relative magnitude of the vapour pressures of the two substances, were discovered empirically by Roozeboom.†

We must stress that these rules cannot be generalized even if the solutions are accurately regular. For it is necessary also to ensure that the vapour pressures of the pure liquids are close enough together to make the sign of (28.43) dependent only on the relative magnitudes of dp_2^0/dT and dp_1^0/dT. There are indeed a number of exceptions to Roozeboom's empirical rule, for example in water + ethanol and propanol + *iso*amyl iodide.‡ In these two cases the vapour pressures of the two components differ by too much for the rule to be applicable.

* This rule is very similar to the general law of Wrewsky, as would be expected from the Clausius-Clapeyron equation. The difference between the two rules is that Wrewsky's is based on a knowledge of the latent heats of evaporation of the components *from the azeotropic solution*, while the present rule is expressed in terms of more readily available quantities, the latent heats of evaporation of the pure liquids.

† Bakhuis Roozeboom, *Die heterogenen Gleichgewichte*, II, 1, (Leipzig, 1904), p. 66.

‡ *Cf.* Lecat, [31], p. 185.

The azeotropic pressure of a regular solution can be expressed as a function of temperature by substituting the value of x_2 given by (28.41) into (28.22), and then taking one half of the sum of the two equations (28.22):

$$\ln p = \tfrac{1}{2} \ln p_1^0 p_2^0 + \frac{\alpha}{4RT} + \frac{RT}{4\alpha} [\ln p_2^0/p_1^0]^2. \tag{28.45}$$

If the vapour pressures of the two components are similar, we have approximately

$$\ln p = \tfrac{1}{2} \ln p_1^0 p_2^0 + \frac{\alpha}{4RT}, \tag{28.46}$$

which, as before, is a linear function of $1/T$.

8. Conditions for Existence of an Azeotrope.

For an azeotrope to exist in a liquid + vapour system it is sufficient that the equations (28.20)

$$\gamma_1^l(T, p, x_2) = \frac{p}{p_1^0}; \quad \gamma_2^l(T, p, x_2) = \frac{p}{p_2^0}; \tag{28.47}$$

have a real solution. In the state of uniform composition the activity coefficient of each component must therefore be inversely proportional to the vapour pressure of the pure substance.

For a system to exhibit azeotropy it is thus necessary for it to depart sufficiently from ideality that the ratio of the activity coefficients can, for certain values of p and x_2, reach the value p_2^0/p_1^0. Thus if the activity coefficients of a particular system always lie between 1 and 2, while the ratio of vapour pressures of the pure substances is 3, then the system cannot form an azeotrope.

The conditions for an azeotrope may, for some systems, be satisfied for all values of T, while for others only in a certain temperature range. Following Lecat, we may call the first case *absolute azeotropy*, and the second *limited azeotropy*.*

It is clear that if $p_1^0 = p_2^0$, then the smallest deviation from ideality will be sufficient to introduce a maximum or minimum into the total vapour pressure curve. Hence if the vapour pressure curves of two pure liquids intersect at a temperature T_a, then a mixture of them will exhibit azeotropy at this temperature, and in its vicinity. The point of intersection of the vapour pressure curves is often called the *Bancroft point*.† In the absence of a Bancroft point there is no general criterion for predicting whether two liquids will form an azeotrope.

For regular solutions, however, the condition for azeotropy can be

* M. Lecat, *Ann. Soc. Scient. Brux.*, **49B**, 274 (1929).

† W. D. Bancroft, *The Phase Rule*, (New York, 1897), p. 119.

expressed quite simply. Since the mole fraction of the azeotrope must lie between 0 and 1, only those systems for which the solution of equation (28.41) lies between these limits can show azeotropy : *i.e.*

$$0 \leqslant \tfrac{1}{2} + \frac{RT}{2\alpha} \ln p_2^0/p_1^0 \leqslant 1. \tag{28.49}$$

The necessary and sufficient condition that a regular solution shall have an azeotrope at a temperature T is therefore

$$-1 \leqslant \frac{RT}{\alpha} \ln p_2^0/p_1^0 \leqslant 1, \tag{28.50}$$

or taking absolute values,

$$\frac{|\alpha|}{RT} \geqslant |\ln p_2^0/p_1^0|. \tag{28.51}$$

9. Lecat's Δ-δ Rule.

We define Δ as the absolute difference between the boiling points of the two components, and δ as the absolute difference between the boiling point of the azeotrope and that of the more volatile component, for positive azeotropes, and the less volatile for negative azeotropes. The quantity δ is called the *azeotropic deviation*, (figs. 28.5 (*a*) and (*b*)).

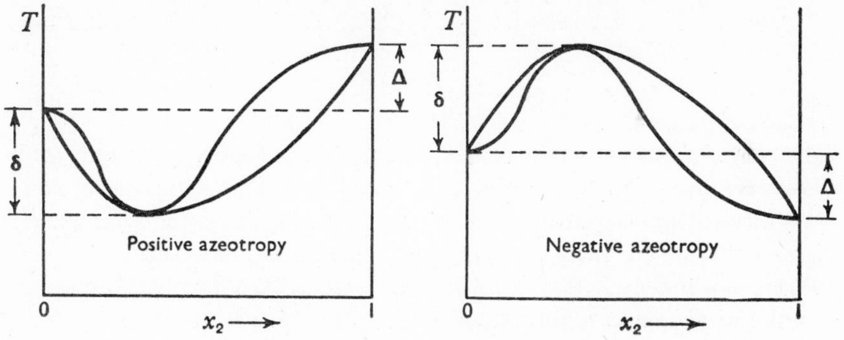

(*a*) (*b*)

FIGS. 28.5 (*a*) and (*b*). The azeotropic deviation δ in the case of positive and negative azeotropy.

Lecat has investigated empirically the relationships between Δ and δ for a series of systems with one common component, and the second components all of the same general chemical character. For such series of systems, at constant pressure, Lecat found* that the graph of δ against Δ was normally a smooth curve :

$$\delta = c_0 + c_1 \Delta + c_2 \Delta^2 + \dots, \tag{28.52}$$

* Lecat [31], p. 191.

but that for most cases c_3 ... could be neglected to give

$$\delta = c_0 + c_1 \Delta + c_2 \Delta^2. \tag{28.53}$$

The existence of an approximate relation of this kind is indeed to be expected for a series of regular solutions. For if we eliminate x_2 between the two equations (28.25) we find

$$\left(\frac{\Delta_e h_2^0}{T_2^0} - \frac{\Delta_e h_1^0}{T_1^0}\right)^2 T^2 + 2\left[\left(\frac{\Delta_e h_1^0}{T_1^0} + \frac{\Delta_e h_2^0}{T_2^0}\right)\alpha + (\Delta_e h_1^0 - \Delta_e h_2^0)\left(\frac{\Delta_e h_2^0}{T_2^0} - \frac{\Delta_e h_1^0}{T_1^0}\right)\right] T$$
$$+ [\alpha^2 - 2\alpha(\Delta_e h_1^0 + \Delta_e h_2^0) + (\Delta_e h_1^0 - \Delta_e h_2^0)^2] = 0. \tag{28.54}$$

This may be simplified if we assume the entropies of evaporation from the solution to obey Trouton's rule, and put

$$\Delta_e h_1^0 / T_1^0 \simeq \Delta_e h_2^0 / T_2^0 \simeq 20 \text{ cal./deg. mole.}$$

We obtain

$$\alpha^2 - 40\alpha(T_1^0 + T_2^0 - 2T) + 400(T_1^0 - T_2^0)^2 = 0. \tag{28.55}$$

Let us suppose that the azeotropy is positive ($\alpha > 0$) and choose the indices so that $T_1^0 < T_2^0$. Then

$$\left.\begin{aligned} T_1^0 &= T + \delta, \\ T_2^0 &= T_1^0 + \Delta = T + \delta + \Delta \end{aligned}\right\}. \tag{28.56}$$

Hence substituting into (28.55):

$$\alpha^2 - 40\alpha(2\delta + \Delta) + 400\Delta^2 = 0 \tag{28.57}$$

or

$$\delta = \frac{\alpha}{80} - \frac{\Delta}{2} + \frac{5\Delta^2}{\alpha}. \tag{28.58}$$

This then predicts a relation between δ and Δ provided that tne systems are chosen so that α is roughly constant. This will be approximately true if one component A is the same in all systems and the others B_1, B_2 ... are substances of similar chemical constitution.

As an example we may consider the azeotropes formed between ethanol and halogen organic compounds; the data have already been given in table 28.1. We may obtain approximate values for α in these systems by solving (28.55) when T_1^0, T_2^0 and T are known. These values are given in table 28.2 under the same serial numbers as in table 28.1. The values of α lie in the range 830–1260 cal./mole, with a mean value of 950. Putting this value into (28.58) we obtain

$$\delta = 12 - \frac{\Delta}{2} + \frac{\Delta^2}{190}. \tag{28.59}$$

The data are plotted in fig. 26.8, in which the full curve corresponds to equation (28.59). The general agreement with Lecat's empirical rule is satisfactory, despite the fact that α is not exactly constant, and,

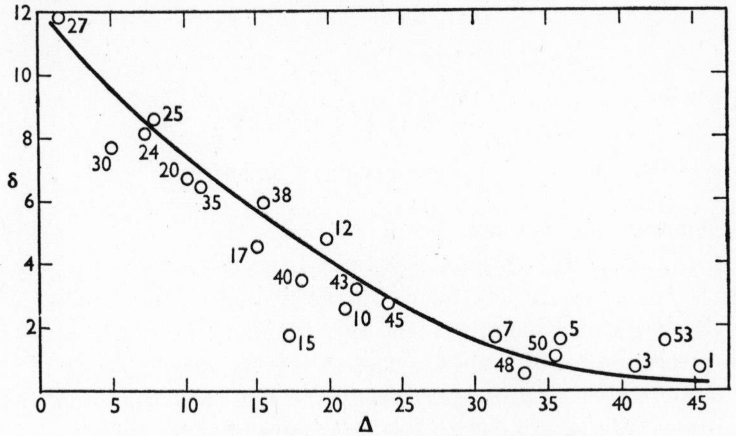

FIG. 28.6. Test of equation (28.59) for solutions of halogen compounds in ethanol.

more important, despite the fact that these alcohol solutions are not examples of regular solutions. The above discussion can, therefore, only be regarded as providing a qualitative understanding of the significance of the $\delta - \Delta$ relation.

TABLE 28.2

No.	Δ	δ	α (*calc*)
1	45·5	0·7	1160
3	40·9	0·7	1060
5	35·8	1·4	1060
7	31·65	1·65	950
10	20·95	2·65	834
12	19·8	4·7	1000
15	17·1	1·85	660
17	15·05	4·55	860
20	10·2	6·7	880
24	7·3	8·25	930
27	1·65	11·7	1000
30	5·2	7·8	820
33	7·85	8·6	980
35	11·15	6·6	920
38	15·6	6·0	1008
40	17·95	3·6	850
43	22·0	3·3	940
45	24·1	2·9	950
48	33·7	0·5	860
50	35·5	0·9	980
53	42·9	1·65	1260

Mean α : 950 cal/mole

CHAPTER XXIX

INDIFFERENT STATES

1. Object of this Chapter.

In the preceding chapter we studied the properties of states of uniform composition in two-phase binary systems. As was demonstrated by the work of Duhem, Saurel and Jouguet, these states of uniform composition are but a special case of a much larger family of thermodynamic states : *indifferent states*. We shall end this book therefore, with a chapter dealing with the properties of such states.

2. Independent Reactions : Jouguet's Criterion.

We recall first the definition of independent reactions introduced in chapter I, § 6. If we have a system containing c constituents, which can undergo r' reactions other than transfers of molecules from one phase to another, then we have (*cf.* 1.62) for each reaction a stoichiometric equation :

$$\sum_i \nu_{i,\rho} M_i = 0, \quad (i=1 \dots c\,;\ \rho=1 \dots r'). \tag{29.1}$$

The reactions 1 ... r' are said to be independent if none of the stoichiometric equations can be derived by linear combination of any of the others.

This definition can be expressed in an alternative form by noting that the equations (29.1) can be considered as r' homogeneous equations in the variables $M_1 \dots M_c$. The condition that these equations are linearly independent is that, from the table of coefficients (called a *matrix*)

$$\begin{bmatrix} \nu_{1,1} & \cdots\cdots & \nu_{c,1} \\ \vdots & & \vdots \\ \nu_{1,r'} & \cdots\cdots & \nu_{c,r'} \end{bmatrix}, \tag{29.2}$$

it is possible to form at least one determinant of order r' different from zero.* This is Jouguet's criterion† which enables one to see quickly

* See : A. C. Aitkin, *Determinants and Matrices*, (Edinburgh, 1939), p. 64, or W. L. Ferrar, *Algebra* (Oxford, 1941), p. 94.

† E. Jouguet, [30], p. 67 ; R. Defay, [12], equation 12.

in a complex case whether the reactions under consideration are distinct or not.*

An alternative form of this criterion may be obtained by multiplying the first column of (29.2) by M_1, the second by M_2, etc :

$$\begin{bmatrix} \nu_{1,1}M_1 & \cdots\cdots & \nu_{c,1}M_c \\ \vdots & & \vdots \\ \nu_{1,r'}M_1 & \cdots\cdots & \nu_{c,r'}M_c \end{bmatrix}. \tag{29.3}$$

All the determinants formed from this new matrix will be zero or not in the same way as the corresponding determinant derived from (29.2). We can say therefore that the r' reactions are distinct if one can form from (29.3) at least one determinant of order r' which is not zero.

We note that we must always have

$$\boxed{r' < c} \tag{29.4}$$

for if not then

(*a*) if $r' > c$, it is impossible to form any determinant of order r', and

(*b*) if $r' = c$, then there is only one determinant of order r' and this must be zero for by summing the columns we obtain a row of zeros because of equation (29.1).

We may now calculate the number of independent reactions, including transfers from one phase to another.

If each component is soluble in all phases, the number of transport reactions is $c(\phi - 1)$ (*cf*. chap. XIII, § 1) so that the total number of independent reactions is :

$$r = r' + c(\phi - 1). \tag{29.5}$$

On the other hand if there are j conditions of insolubility, which we shall express in terms of the weight fraction w_i (*cf*. 13.8), there are j equations of the form :

$$w_i^\alpha = 0. \tag{29.5'}$$

The number of transport reactions is now

$$r'' = c(\phi - 1) - j \tag{29.6}$$

so that

$$r = r' + c(\phi - 1) - j. \tag{29.7}$$

In each of these equations r' is determined by Jouguet's criterion.

* In a recent paper, S. R. Brinkley, *J. Chem. Phys.*, **14**, 563, 686 (1946) has proposed another criterion for determining the number of independent components $c' = c - r'$ starting from the stoichiometric coefficients of the elements in each compound. For a criticism of this method *cf*. I. Prigogine and R. Defay, *J. Chem. Phys.*, **15**, 614 (1947). For a discussion of the relation between Brinkley's criterion and that of Jouguet *cf*. A. Penecloux, *C. R.* **228**, 1729 (1949).

3. Variance.

Whether the system is in equilibrium or not we shall always use the term variance to mean the value given by the phase rule :

$$w = 2 + (c - r') - \phi. \tag{29.8}$$

4. Definition of Indifferent States.

Let us consider a closed system whose state (*cf.* chap. XIII, § 7) is determined completely by T, p, the weight fractions of each component in the various phases, and the mass of each phase, *i.e.*, by the variables :

$$T, p, w_1^1 \dots w_c^\phi, m^1, \dots m^\phi. \tag{29.9}$$

Suppose there is a second state of the same system

$$T', p', w_1^{1'} \dots w_c^{\phi'}, m^{1'}, \dots m^{\phi'}. \tag{29.10}$$

Then since both states can be formed in the same closed system, the variables in (29.10) must be related to those in (29.9) by the conditions (*cf.* 13.13) :

$$\sum_\alpha m_i^{\alpha'} = \sum_\alpha m_i^\alpha + \sum_{\rho=1}^{r'} \nu_{i,\rho} M_i \xi_\rho \tag{29.11}$$

where the extents of change ξ_ρ are all taken as zero in the initial state. These equations simply represent the conditions of conservation of mass in the system.

We now enquire whether there exist, in the set of states (29.10) accessible to the closed system (*i.e.* compatible with the conservation of mass), states which differ from the initial state (29.9) in the mass of *at least one* of the phases, but in which all the weight fractions remain the same.

$$w_i^{\alpha'} = w_i^\alpha \text{ for all } i, \alpha. \tag{29.12}$$

For such a state to exist it is necessary that the equations (29.12) shall be compatible with the so-called conditions of enclosure (29.11). As we shall prove, this is not possible unless the variables in (29.9) have values satisfying certain conditions. If these conditions are satisfied the state defined by (29.9) is called an *indifferent state.*

We now proceed to find the conditions that (29.11) and (29.12) are compatible.

We note that

$$m_i^\alpha = w_i^\alpha m^\alpha, \tag{29.13}$$

and take account of (29.12) ; then (29.11) may be written

$$\sum_\alpha w_i^\alpha (m^{\alpha'} - m^\alpha) = \sum_{\rho=1}^{r'} \nu_{i,\rho} M_i \xi_\rho. \tag{29.14}$$

If we now put

$$m^{\alpha'} - m^\alpha = \Delta m^\alpha, \tag{29.15}$$

and develop the set of equations (29.14) we have

$$\left.\begin{array}{l} w_1^1 \Delta m^1 + w_1^2 \Delta m^2 + \dots + w_1^\phi \Delta m^\phi - \nu_{1,1} M_1 \xi_1 - \dots \nu_{1,r'} M_1 \xi_{r'} = 0 \\ \vdots \\ w_c^1 \Delta m^1 + w_c^2 \Delta m^2 + \dots + w_c^\phi \Delta m^\phi - \nu_{c,1} M_c \xi_1 - \dots \nu_{c,r'} M_c \xi_{r'} = 0 \end{array}\right\} \quad (29.16)$$

These may be regarded as a set of c equations among the $\phi + r'$ unknowns $\Delta m^1 \dots \Delta m^\phi, \xi_1 \dots \xi_{r'}$.

To say that (29.9) is an indifferent state is in effect to say that we can find a solution to this set of equations giving $\Delta m^1 \dots \Delta m^\phi, \xi_1 \dots \xi_{r'}$, such that *at least one* of the Δm terms is non-zero.

We notice to begin with that we cannot have a solution in which some of the ξ_ρ are different from zero while *all* the Δm^α are zero, for the existence of such a solution would imply that the equations

$$\left.\begin{array}{l} \nu_{1,1} M_1 \xi_1 + \dots \nu_{1,r'} M_1 \xi_{r'} = 0 \\ \vdots \\ \nu_{c,1} M_c \xi_1 + \dots \nu_{c,r'} M_c \xi_{r'} = 0 \end{array}\right\} \quad (29.17)$$

have non-zero solutions for $\xi_1 \dots \xi_{r'}$. But this is impossible if the reactions are independent, since then at least one of the determinants of order r' formed from the coefficients of these equations is non-zero. The conditions of indifference of the system are simply the conditions of compatibility (with non-zero solutions) of the set of homogeneous equations (29.16).

For a more detailed discussion it is best to subdivide the cases according to the variance of the system: we shall consider first systems for which the variance is one or zero, and then the case of polyvariant systems.

5. Indifferent States in Monovariant or Invariant Systems.

In this case $w < 2$ and so, from (29.8), $c < \phi + r'$. In the set of equations (29.16) we have therefore fewer equations than unknowns. The equations must therefore always admit of certain non-zero solutions, for we can give arbitrary non-zero values to either one or two of the Δm^α, and still solve the equations.

Hence *monovariant and invariant systems are always indifferent.*

Examples :

(*a*) *Decomposition of calcium carbonate :*

$$CaCO_3(s) \rightleftharpoons CaO(s) + CO_2(g). \quad (29.18)$$

In this case we have $c = 3$, $\phi = 3$, $r' = 1$ whence $w = 1$. If a molecule of $CaCO_3$ decomposes, then it increases the amounts of CaO and CO_2 without altering the mole fraction in any of the phases. It is quite clear that this simple system is always indifferent in all its states whether they be equilibrium states or not.

(*b*) *Eutectic point of a four-phase system :*

Consider equilibrium between

NaCl + ice + aqueous solution of NaCl + water vapour.

We have $c=2$, $\phi=4$, $r'=0$ so that $w=0$. This invariant system is clearly indifferent for water vapour may condense to ice without altering the mole fraction in any phase ; furthermore the solution can deposit crystals of ice and of NaCl simultaneously in such a way as not to alter the mole fractions.

6. Indifferent States in Polyvariant Systems.

Here we have $w \geqslant 2$ and so $c \geqslant \phi + r'$. If the equations (29.16) are to be compatible, that is if the system is indifferent, it is necessary and sufficient that *all* the determinants of order $\phi + r'$, formed from the coefficients of the unknowns in the equations (29.16) :*

$$\begin{bmatrix} w_1^1 \dots\dots w_1^\phi & \nu_{1,1}M_1 \dots\dots \nu_{1,r'}M_1 \\ \vdots \qquad \vdots & \vdots \qquad\qquad \vdots \\ w_c^1 \dots\dots w_c^\phi & \nu_{c,1}M_c \dots\dots \nu_{c,r'}M_c \end{bmatrix}, \tag{29.19}$$

shall be zero.

These are the general conditions of indifference.†

We now enquire as to the number of distinct conditions which are implied by (29.19). In a system of n equations among n unknowns there is only one condition of compatibility (for non-zero solutions). Each additional equation brings with it a supplementary condition of compatibility.‡ In the set of equations (29.16) we have c homogeneous equations with $(\phi + r')$ unknowns. There must then be $1 + c - (\phi + r')$ conditions of compatibility ; from the phase rule this must be equal to $w - 1$.

There are therefore $w - 1$ conditions of indifference.

Two corollaries follow from the above discussion. The first is that if the set of homogeneous equations has one non-zero solution, then it has an infinity of such solutions. All closed systems which are in an indifferent state, characterized by the weight fractions $w_1^1 \dots w_c^\phi$,

* In this matrix the signs of the coefficients of $\nu_{i,\rho}M_i$ have been reversed. This will only alter the sign of the determinants derived from this matrix, and will not affect their absolute value which is all that interests us here.

† R. Defay, [12], equation 25. Previously Duhem, Saurel and Jouguet had given the conditions of indifference in the form of determinants involving the " concentrations of independent components ", which are themselves complicated functions of the actual concentrations of *all* the components (*cf.* Jouguet, [30], p. 81).

‡ *Cf.* Aitkin, *loc. cit.*, p. 71 ; Ferrar, *loc. cit.*, p. 99.

may thus exist in an infinity of states, identical in the composition of the phases, but differing in the masses of the phases.

Secondly, we notice that the conditions of indifference are completely independent of the temperature and pressure. Therefore if a system is indifferent in a state T, p, $w_1^1 \dots w_c^\phi$, then it is also indifferent in any other state, T', p', $w_1^1 \dots w_c^\phi$, in which the weight fractions are the same. It is true of course that if one of these states is an equilibrium state, then, in general, the other is not.

7. Examples of Polyvariant Indifferent Systems.

Let us consider first systems in which the only reactions are transfers across phase boundaries, *i.e.* $r' = 0$.

(*a*) *Two-phase binary systems.*

In this case $c = 2$, $\phi = 2$, $r' = 0$ whence $w = 2$. There will therefore be just one condition of indifference. The matrix (29.19) is simply

$$\begin{bmatrix} w_1^1 & w_1^2 \\ w_2^1 & w_2^2 \end{bmatrix},$$

so that the condition of indifference is that the determinant of order 2 shall be zero :

$$\begin{vmatrix} w_1^1 & w_1^2 \\ w_2^1 & w_2^2 \end{vmatrix} = \begin{vmatrix} w_1^1 & w_1^2 \\ 1 - w_1^1 & 1 - w_1^2 \end{vmatrix} = 0 ;$$

whence

$$w_1^1 = w_1^2. \tag{29.20}$$

Hence for this system to be indifferent, it is necessary and sufficient that the two phases shall have the same composition. We thus find, as a special case of indifferent states, the states of uniform composition discussed in the preceding chapter.

(*b*) *Three-phase ternary systems.*

Here $c = 3$, $\phi = 3$, $r' = 0$; whence $w = 2$. From (29.19) we find that the only condition of indifference is that

$$\begin{vmatrix} w_1^1 & w_1^2 & w_1^3 \\ w_2^1 & w_2^2 & w_2^3 \\ w_3^1 & w_3^2 & w_3^3 \end{vmatrix} = 0. \tag{29.21}$$

It can then be shown quite easily that, if this condition is satisfied, then the mass of phase 3, for example, can be increased at the expense of phases 1 and 2 without changing the composition of any of the phases.

The condition (29.21) has a simple geometrical interpretation. It

that, in the triangular diagram fig. 29.1, the three points representing the three phases shall lie on a straight line.

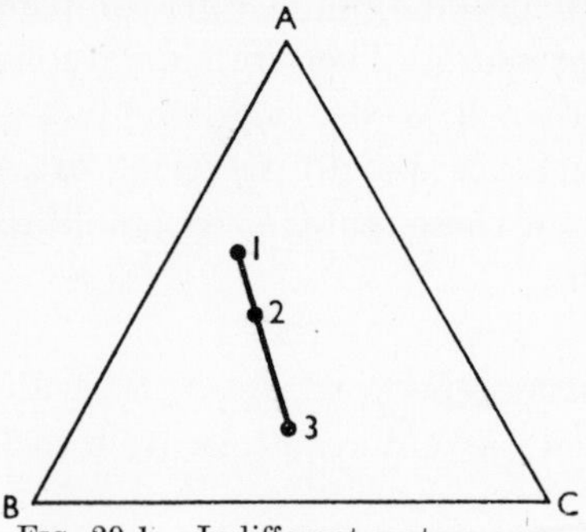

FIG. 29.1. Indifferent system composed of three phases 1, 2 and 3.

In the following two examples we shall consider systems in which chemical reaction can take place.

(*a*) *Divariant system with one chemical reaction.*

As an example we may consider the system in which

$$NH_3(g) + HCl(g) \rightleftharpoons NH_4Cl(s).$$

There are three components, two phases and one chemical reaction, so that $w = 2$.

Then (29.19) leads to just one determinant; and the condition for indifference is

$$\begin{vmatrix} w^g_{NH_3} & 0 & -M_{NH_3} \\ w^g_{HCl} & 0 & -M_{HCl} \\ w^g_{NH_4Cl} & 1 & +M_{NH_4Cl} \end{vmatrix} = 0. \tag{29.22}$$

Here in the solid phase $w^s_{NH_3} = 0$ and $w^s_{HCl} = 0$ while $w^s_{NH_4Cl} = 1$. This gives immediately

$$\frac{w^g_{NH_3}}{w^g_{HCl}} = \frac{M_{NH_3}}{M_{HCl}}. \tag{29.23}$$

The system will therefore be indifferent if the weight fractions of ammonia and hydrogen chloride in the gas phase are in the same ratio as their molecular weights. The condition, in this simple case, is obvious, since under these conditions a molecule of solid ammonium chloride can decompose, or be formed without altering the composition of the gas phase.

(*b*) *Addition compounds.*

In the case of a solution in the presence of a solid phase consisting of crystals of an addition compound (*cf.* chap. XXIII, §§ 2 and 3) it can be easily verified that the system is in an indifferent state if the composition of the solution is the same as that of the crystals.

8. Polyphase Systems with Two Phases of Uniform Composition.

We now proceed to prove that *any* polyphase system containing two phases of the same composition is in an indifferent state.

If α and β are the two phases with the same composition, then by hypothesis,

$$w^\alpha_i = w^\beta_i, \quad i = 1, \dots c. \tag{29.24}$$

The matrix (29.19) has two identical columns and thus all determinants of order $(\phi+r')$ formed from this matrix must be zero; hence the system is in an indifferent state.

The inverse of this theorem is clearly not true, for in § 5 we have already seen examples of indifferent systems in which no pair of phases has the same composition. In two-phase non-reacting systems all indifferent states are states of uniform composition, for in the case of only two phases (29.19) reduces to

$$\begin{bmatrix} w_1^1 & w_1^2 \\ \vdots & \vdots \\ w_c^1 & w_c^2 \end{bmatrix}$$

from which we deduce, as the conditions of indifference,

$$\frac{w_1^1}{w_1^2} = \frac{w_2^1}{w_2^2} = \dots = \frac{w_c^1}{w_c^2} = \frac{\sum_i w_i^1}{\sum_i w_i^2} = 1. \tag{29.25}$$

We see that the concept of indifferent states is much more general than that of states of uniform composition. All states of uniform composition of two or more phases are indifferent, but by no means all indifferent states involve phases of the same composition. The properties discussed in the previous chapter in connection with states of uniform composition are nearly all a consequence of the fact that these states are indifferent states, and we shall find most of these properties exhibited in the more general case.

9. Polyphase Systems having a pair of Indifferent Phases.

In this paragraph we establish the theorem that:

if in a polyphase system two of the phases are indifferent with respect to one another, then the whole system is an indifferent system.

Two phases are said to be indifferent with respect to one another if a system limited to these two phases is indifferent.

In the complete system containing ϕ phases, let us suppose that phases 1 and 2 are indifferent with respect to one another. Suppose that the number of chemical reactions occurring in these two phases, apart from transfers from one phase to the other, is b. This is the number of reactions which can occur in a system limited to two portions of these phases in contact. If these phases are indifferent, then from (29.19) the composition of the phases must be such that all determinants of order $(b+2)$ formed from the lines of the matrix (here abbreviated to the first line)

$$[w_1^1 \; w_1^2 \quad \nu_{1,1}M_1 \dots \nu_{1,b}M_1] \tag{29.26}$$

must be zero. On the other hand, for the complete system, the matrix (29.19) can be represented by:

$$[w_1^1 \; w_1^2 \;\; \nu_{1,1}M_1 \ldots \nu_{1,b}M_1 \;\; w_1^3 \ldots w_1^\phi \;\; \nu_{1,(b+1)}M_1 \ldots \nu_{1,r'}M_1]. \quad (29.27)$$

We see immediately that all determinants of order $(\phi+r')$ formed from the lines of this table must be zero, since any such determinant can be developed in terms of a series of minors formed from the elements of the first $(b+2)$ columns. All these minors are zero because of (29.26) hence all the determinants are zero and the whole system is indifferent.

We may note that if phases 1 and 2 form, when alone, a system with a variance of one or less, then they must always be indifferent, and there is no further condition of indifference. The above theorem remains valid however, for in order to construct determinants of order $(b+2)$ from (29.27) we must include one or more lines consisting only of zeros; and any such determinant must be zero.

10. Saurel's Theorem: the Indifferent Line.

If we express the state of a system in terms of intensive variables, then the representative points of a system in equilibrium form a continuum in w dimensions. The equilibrium indifferent states, or static indifferent states, will also be represented in this continuum but they must satisfy in addition, the further $(w-1)$ conditions of indifference (29.19). These $(w-1)$ relations among the w variables leave only one independent variable: the *static* indifferent states of the system hence fall on a line, called *the indifferent line*.

This important theorem, which is valid whatever the number of components, phases or reactions, was discovered by Saurel.* The existence of this line had previously been pointed out for bivariant systems by both Gibbs† and Duhem;‡ the remarkable result of Saurel's theorem is that this continuum remains a line whatever the variance of the system.

We note that in a non-reacting two-phase system, the indifferent line is simply the line of uniform composition.

As an example to demonstrate the application of Saurel's theorem let us reconsider the reaction;

$$NH_3(g) + HCl(g) = NH_4Cl(s). \quad (29.28)$$

We shall assume that the ammonium chloride molecule exists only in the solid state, and is completely dissociated in the vapour. As we

* P. Saurel, *J. Phys. Chem.*, **5**, 21 (1901). *Cf.* also Jouguet, [30], p. 83.
† Gibbs, [23], p. 99.
‡ Duhem, [15], IV, p. 298.

saw above, this system is indifferent when the gas phase is an equimolecular mixture of NH_3 and HCl; that is when

$$x_{NH_3} = x_{HCl} = 0{\cdot}5. \tag{29.29}$$

Now the condition of equilibrium in the system is

$$\gamma_{NH_3} x_{NH_3} \gamma_{HCl} x_{HCl} = K(T, p), \tag{29.30}$$

where the activity coefficients are functions of T, p and x_{NH_3}. Therefore, along the indifferent line

$$\gamma_{NH_3}(T, p, x = 0{\cdot}5)\, \gamma_{HCl}(T, p, x = 0{\cdot}5) = 4K(T, p), \tag{29.31}$$

which gives T as a function of p.

If the gas phase is ideal, then

$$1 = 4K(T, p) \tag{29.32}$$

and the indifferent line still has a real existence. This fact illustrates an important difference between indifferent states and states of uniform composition. In chapter XXVIII we found that states of uniform composition could exist only if the system departed sufficiently from ideality. Here we see that the indifferent line can exist whether or not the system is ideal.

We may now proceed to calculate the equation of the indifferent line assuming the gas phase to be ideal.

We have, from (7.36) and (7.37),

$$\ln K(T, p) = \ln K(T_0, p_0) + \int_{T_0}^{T} \frac{(\partial H^{id}/\partial \xi)_{T,p}}{\mathbf{R}T^2}\, dT - \frac{1}{\mathbf{R}T} \int_{p_0}^{p} (\partial V^{id}/\partial \xi)\, dp. \tag{29.33}$$

As a first approximation we may assume $(\partial H^{id}/\partial \xi)_{T,p}$ to be independent of temperature in the range T_0 to T, and we may also neglect the partial molar volume of the condensed phase compared with that of the vapour phase. We then have

$$(\partial V/\partial \xi)_{T,p} \simeq -v_{HCl} - v_{NH_3} \simeq -2\mathbf{R}T/p, \tag{29.34}$$

and (29.33) becomes approximately

$$\ln K(T, p) = \ln K_0 - \frac{(\partial H^{id}/\partial \xi)_{T,p}}{\mathbf{R}} \left(\frac{1}{T} - \frac{1}{T_0}\right) + 2 \ln \frac{p}{p_0}. \tag{29.35}$$

According to (29.32) this must equal ln 0·25, so that

$$-\frac{(\partial H^{id}/\partial \xi)_{T,p}}{\mathbf{R}} \left(\frac{1}{T} - \frac{1}{T_0}\right) + 2 \ln \frac{p}{p_0} = -\ln 4K_0, \tag{29.36}$$

whence

$$\ln p = \frac{(\partial H^{id}/\partial \xi)_{T,p}}{2\mathbf{R}T} + \textit{constant}. \tag{29.37}$$

The indifferent line is thus given approximately by a simple equation analogous to the integrated form of the Clausius-Clapeyron equation.

11. Static Indifferent States and Duhem's Theorem.

We found in chapter XIII that the equilibrium state of a *closed system*, corresponding to given initial conditions, is completely determined by *two* variables (Duhem's theorem). For polyvariant systems ($w \geqslant 2$) it is sufficient, in general, to give the temperature and pressure in order to determine completely the state of the system (chap. XIII, 7); that is to determine all the variables T, p, $w_1^1 \ldots w_c^\phi$, $m^1 \ldots m^\phi$.

It will be recalled that the calculation of the values of $w_1^1 \ldots w_c^\phi$; $m^1 \ldots m^\phi$, as functions of T and p, was carried out by using equations (13.17), the equilibrium conditions (13.18) and (13.19) and the conditions of enclosure (13.13). However, in certain exceptional circumstances these equations have a solution $w_1^1 \ldots w_c^\phi$; $m^1 \ldots m^\phi$ in which the weight fractions satisfy (29.19), the conditions for indifference. This solution is then no longer unique as these values of the weight fractions render (13.13) indeterminate. The coefficients of equations (13.13) form the same matrix as (29.19). When the determinants formed from the lines of this matrix are zero, then the system of equations (13.13) has an infinity of solutions for $m^1 \ldots m^\phi$, $\xi_1 \ldots \xi_{r'}$.

We see therefore, that if a system is in an indifferent state, the variables T and p are no longer sufficient to determine its state completely.

The name *indifferent state* seems to have had its origin in the fact that certain equilibrium states, even though completely defined by the temperature, pressure and composition of each phase, are " indifferent " to the mass of the phases present. Monovariant and invariant systems, which we have already seen to be indifferent, exhibit in all their equilibrium states this " indifference to the masses of the phases ". For example, in the very simplest case of a monovariant system, a pure liquid in the presence of its vapour, we find just these properties. For at constant temperature, and hence at constant pressure, a closed system containing a pure substance can have an infinite range of equilibrium states which depend simply on the volume in which the system is confined. These equilibrium states differ only in the amounts of the two phases.

Quite generally, if we fix the temperature of a monovariant closed system, the equilibrium conditions fix the pressure and composition of the phases, but the masses of the separate phases are not determined, since in the system of equations of enclosure (13.13) the number of equations (c) is less than ($\phi + r'$) the total number of unknowns $m^1 \ldots m^\phi$, $\xi_1 \ldots \xi_{r'}$.

12. Generalization of the Gibbs-Konovalow Theorems.

We met these theorems in studying the properties of states of uniform composition (chap. XVIII, § 6) ; we shall now examine them in a more general form as a property of all static indifferent states in a polyvariant system.

These theorems, in which we consider the effect either of an isothermal or isobaric displacement were demonstrated by Gibbs and Konovalow for bivariant systems and generalized by Saurel. They can only be applied to systems having a variance of at least two ; systems of smaller variance are not susceptible to such displacements.

First Theorem :

If in any isothermal equilibrium displacement the system passes through an indifferent state, then the pressure passes through an extreme value.

Conversely :

If, among the pressures which maintain the system in equilibrium at a constant temperature, there exists an extreme value of p, then the state corresponding to this extreme value is an indifferent state.

In dealing with polyvariant systems it must be remembered that the pressure cannot be regarded as exhibiting an extreme value at a given point unless it represents an extreme value with respect to all possible isothermal equilibrium displacements through that point. For example the surface shown in fig. 29.2 exhibits an extreme value at M, but not at M_1, M_2, M_3. These points are respectively the indifferent points in the binary systems A+B, B+C and C+A. The pressure is an extremum with respect to isothermal equilibrium displacements involving only the appropriate binary system, but not with respect to all possible isothermal equilibrium changes. For example, M_1 is not an extremum relative to a displacement towards M.

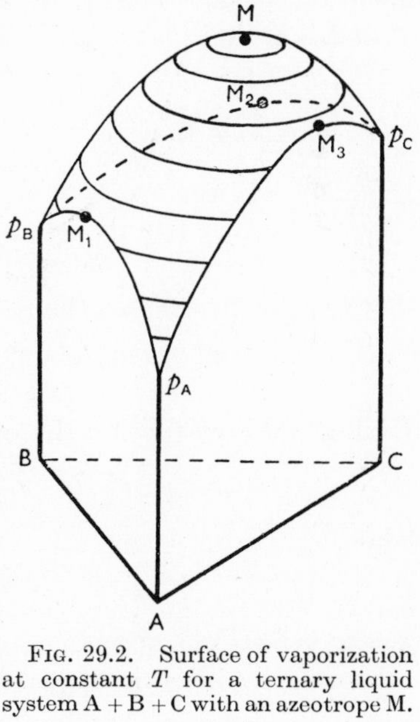

FIG. 29.2. Surface of vaporization at constant T for a ternary liquid system A + B + C with an azeotrope M.

Even though the state M_1 is the limit to which the ternary system tends when the amount of C tends to zero, the Gibbs-Konovalow theorem, in the form stated above, does not apply to limiting cases of this kind. Thus this theorem deals in this example with the indifferent states of the ternary system and does not include the indifferent states of the binary systems which the components can form when taken two-by-two.

Before proving this theorem, we now state the second theorem which relates to isobaric displacements.

Second Theorem :

If in any isobaric equilibrium displacement the system passes through an indifferent state then the temperature passes through an extreme value.

Conversely :

If, among the temperatures which maintain the system in equilibrium at a given fixed pressure, there is an extreme temperature, then the state corresponding to this temperature is indifferent.

Let us consider to fix our ideas the case of a three-phase four-component system in which one chemical reaction (other than transfers between phases) can occur. The extension to the more general case is immediate.*

The system considered here is divariant :

$$w = 2 + (4-1) - 3 = 2. \tag{29.38}$$

Instead of employing the *molar* chemical potentials it is more convenient in this case to employ the *specific* chemical potential defined by

$$\underline{\mu}_i^\alpha = \left(\frac{\partial G^\alpha}{\partial m_i^\alpha}\right)_{T,p}. \tag{29.39}$$

These are related since

$$m_i^\alpha = n_i^\alpha M_i, \tag{29.40}$$

so that

$$\mu_i^\alpha = \underline{\mu}_i^\alpha M_i. \tag{29.41}$$

For each of the phases the Gibbs-Duhem equation can be written

$$S^\alpha\, \delta T - V^\alpha\, \delta p + \sum_i m_i^\alpha\, \delta \underline{\mu}_i^\alpha = 0. \tag{29.42}$$

Dividing this equation by the mass m^α of the phase we have

$$\underline{s}^\alpha\, \delta T - \underline{v}^\alpha\, \delta p + \sum_i w_i^\alpha\, \delta \underline{\mu}_i^\alpha = 0, \tag{29.43}$$

where

$$\underline{s}^\alpha \equiv S^\alpha / m^\alpha;\quad \underline{v}^\alpha \equiv V^\alpha / m^\alpha, \tag{29.44}$$

are respectively the specific entropy and specific volume of the phase.

Along an equilibrium displacement we have

$$\underline{\mu}_i^1 = \underline{\mu}_i^2 = \underline{\mu}_i^3 \, (i = 1, \ldots 4) \tag{29.45}$$

* *Cf.* Defay, [12].

and hence

$$\delta\underline{\mu}_i^1 = \delta\underline{\mu}_i^2 = \delta\underline{\mu}_i^3 = \delta\underline{\mu}_i. \tag{29.46}$$

Suppose that the reaction taking place in the system has the stoichiometric equation

$$\sum_i \nu_i M_i = 0, \tag{29.47}$$

then its affinity will be

$$\mathbf{A} = -\sum_i \nu_i M_i \underline{\mu}_i. \tag{29.48}$$

Along the path of an equilibrium change, $\mathbf{A} = 0$, and hence

$$\sum_i \nu_i M_i \underline{\mu}_i = 0. \tag{29.49}$$

We shall examine first the case of isothermal equilibrium displacements. The three Gibbs-Duhem equations and (29.49) must be satisfied simultaneously at constant temperature ($\delta T = 0$)

$$\left.\begin{aligned} -\underline{v}^1\,\delta p + w_1^1\,\delta\underline{\mu}_1 + w_2^1\,\delta\underline{\mu}_2 + w_3^1\,\delta\underline{\mu}_3 + w_4^1\,\delta\underline{\mu}_4 &= 0 \\ -\underline{v}^2\,\delta p + w_1^2\,\delta\underline{\mu}_1 + w_2^2\,\delta\underline{\mu}_2 + w_3^2\,\delta\underline{\mu}_3 + w_4^2\,\delta\underline{\mu}_4 &= 0 \\ -\underline{v}^3\,\delta p + w_1^3\,\delta\underline{\mu}_1 + w_2^3\,\delta\underline{\mu}_2 + w_3^3\,\delta\underline{\mu}_3 + w_4^3\,\delta\underline{\mu}_4 &= 0 \\ \nu_1 M_1\,\delta\underline{\mu}_1 + \nu_2 M_2\,\delta\underline{\mu}_2 + \nu_3 M_3\,\delta\underline{\mu}_3 + \nu_4 M_4\,\delta\underline{\mu}_4 &= 0 \end{aligned}\right\}. \tag{29.50}$$

Let us consider a state of the system defined by particular values of the variables T, p, $w_1^1 \dots w_4^3$, and calculate the variation in pressure δp, along an isothermal equilibrium displacement starting from this point. This displacement must satisfy (29.50). The four equations between the five variables δp, $\delta\underline{\mu}_1$, $\delta\underline{\mu}_2$, $\delta\underline{\mu}_3$, $\delta\underline{\mu}_4$ mean that only one of these variables say $\delta\underline{\mu}_4$, can be assigned an arbitrary value. This is in accordance with the fact that the system is divariant, and we have already put $\delta T = 0$ arbitrarily; we can therefore only vary one other intensive quantity independently.

Thus if we give $\delta\underline{\mu}_4$ an arbitrary non-zero value, we can calculate the other four variations by solving the four equations :

$$\left.\begin{aligned} -\underline{v}^1\,\delta p + w_1^1\,\delta\underline{\mu}_1 + w_2^1\,\delta\underline{\mu}_2 + w_3^1\,\delta\underline{\mu}_3 &= -w_4^1\,\delta\underline{\mu}_4, \\ -\underline{v}^2\,\delta p + w_1^2\,\delta\underline{\mu}_1 + w_2^2\,\delta\underline{\mu}_2 + w_3^2\,\delta\underline{\mu}_3 &= -w_4^2\,\delta\underline{\mu}_4, \\ -\underline{v}^3\,\delta p + w_1^3\,\delta\underline{\mu}_1 + w_2^3\,\delta\underline{\mu}_2 + w_3^3\,\delta\underline{\mu}_3 &= -w_4^3\,\delta\underline{\mu}_4, \\ \nu_1 M_1\,\delta\underline{\mu}_1 + \nu_2 M_2\,\delta\underline{\mu}_2 + \nu_3 M_3\,\delta\underline{\mu}_3 &= -\nu_4 M_4\,\delta\underline{\mu}_4 \end{aligned}\right\}. \tag{29.51}$$

The solution for δp is

$$\begin{vmatrix} -\underline{v}^1 & w_1^1 & w_2^1 & w_3^1 \\ -\underline{v}^2 & w_1^2 & w_2^2 & w_3^2 \\ -\underline{v}^3 & w_1^3 & w_2^3 & w_3^3 \\ 0 & \nu_1 M_1 & \nu_2 M_2 & \nu_3 M_3 \end{vmatrix} \delta p = \begin{vmatrix} -\ w_4^1 & u_1^1 & w_2^1 & w_3^1 \\ -\ w_4^2 & w_1^2 & w_2^2 & w_3^2 \\ -\ w_4^3 & w_1^3 & w_2^3 & w_3^3 \\ -\nu_4 M_4 & \nu_1 M_1 & \nu_2 M_2 & \nu_3 M_3 \end{vmatrix} \delta \underline{\mu}_4. \tag{29.52}$$

If the initial state is one in which the pressure exhibits an extreme value in an isothermal displacement, then $\delta p = 0$ and (29.52) shows that since $\delta \mu_4$ is chosen to be non-zero,

$$\begin{vmatrix} w_4^1 & w_1^1 & w_2^1 & w_3^1 \\ w_4^2 & w_1^2 & w_2^2 & w_3^2 \\ w_4^3 & w_1^3 & w_2^3 & w_3^3 \\ \nu_4 M_4 & \nu_1 M_1 & \nu_2 M_2 & \nu_3 M_3 \end{vmatrix} = 0. \tag{29.53}$$

Reference to (29.19) shows immediately that this equality, when the columns and lines of the determinant are interchanged is precisely the condition that the system is indifferent. This proves that if a given state is one in which the pressure passes through an extreme value at constant temperature, then the state is indifferent.

Conversely, if the state is indifferent, then (29.53) is satisfied and, from (29.52), $\delta p = 0$; that is p passes through an extreme value.

The above argument depends on the assumption that the determinant on the left hand side of (29.52) is not zero.

If, in the rare case,

$$\begin{vmatrix} -\underline{v}^1 & w_1^1 & w_2^1 & w_3^1 \\ -\underline{v}^2 & w_1^2 & w_2^2 & w_3^2 \\ -\underline{v}^3 & w_1^3 & w_2^3 & w_3^3 \\ 0 & \nu_1 M_1 & \nu_2 M_2 & \nu_3 M_3 \end{vmatrix} = 0, \tag{29.54}$$

at the same time as (29.53) is satisfied, then we have the *doubtful case*. Since the system is divariant, the two conditions (29.53) and (29.54) between the two intensive variables chosen to determine the equilibrium states, fix the values of these variables. The doubtful case is thus represented by a point on the line of indifference.

Isobaric equilibrium displacements can be examined in an exactly similar manner, and we can thus prove the second theorem enunciated above.

These two theorems are general and include as particular cases the theorems established in chap. XVIII, § 6 and in chap. XXIII. They do not however apply to monovariant or invariant systems. Thus the eutectic point, which is certainly an indifferent point, does not represent, mathematically, an extreme value of T or p; for it is the point of intersection of two curves each of which refers to a two-phase system (*e.g.* solution + ice or solution + salt) under constant pressure. Only at the eutectic do three phases (solution + salt + ice) coexist. A monovariant three-phase system does not have an isobaric curve.

We now consider two further examples.

Example 1 : *Ternary system with three liquid phases.*

Let us consider a three component system which, in a certain range of composition, forms three liquid layers. At a given temperature and

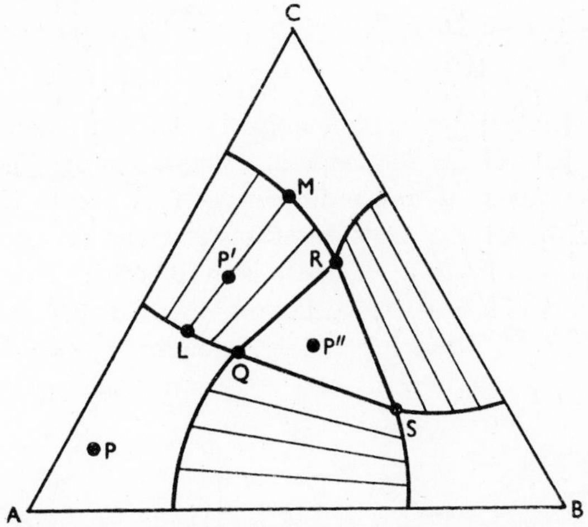

FIG. 29.3. Phase diagram at constant T and p for ternary system forming three liquid phases.

pressure the phase diagram will be of the form shown in fig. 29.3.

A system whose overall composition is represented by a point P forms one phase; a system such as P' separates into two phases L and M, while a system P'' gives rise to three phases Q, R and S. The lines such as LM are the *binodals* joining the phases which coexist in equilibrium.

Now let us consider a system which exhibits *two* regions like QRS. The portion of the phase diagram (at constant T and p) in the neighbourhood of these regions pqr and uvw will be like fig. 29.4. Now consider what happens when the temperature is changed at constant pressure. Suppose for example that as the temperature rises, the

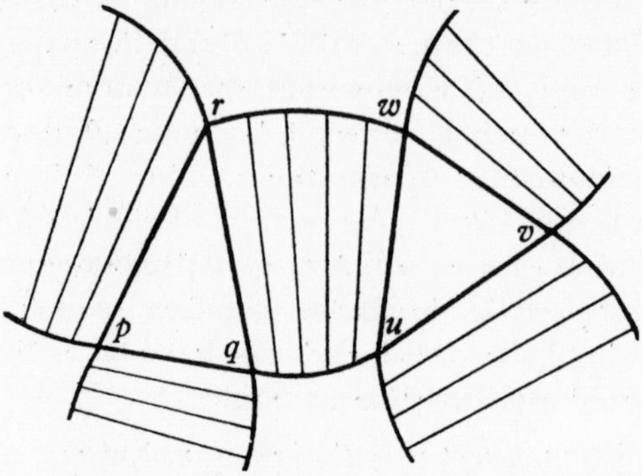

FIG. 29.4. Phase diagram at constant T and p for ternary system with two immiscibility triangles.

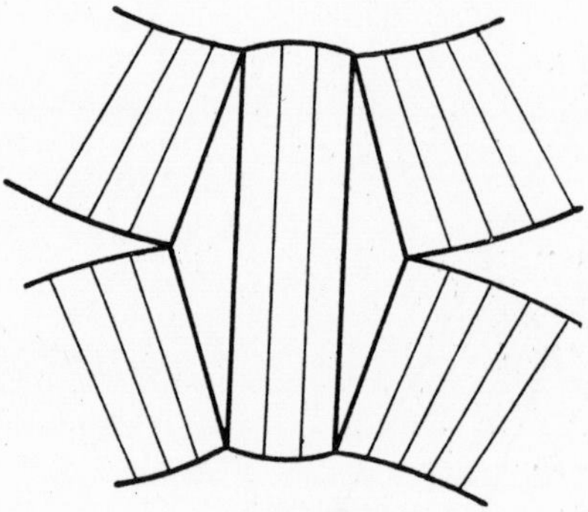

FIG. 29.5.

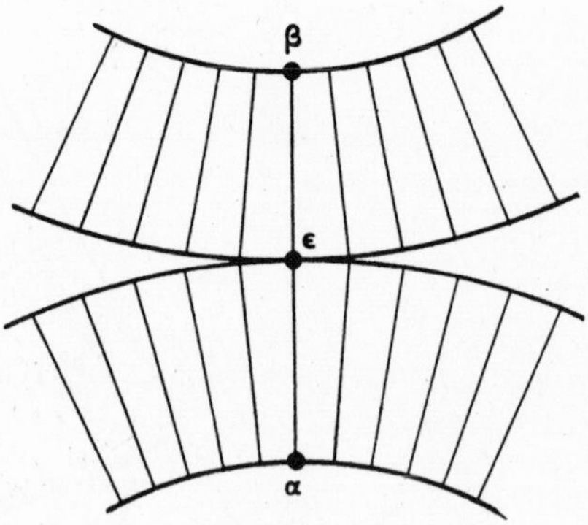

FIG. 29.6.

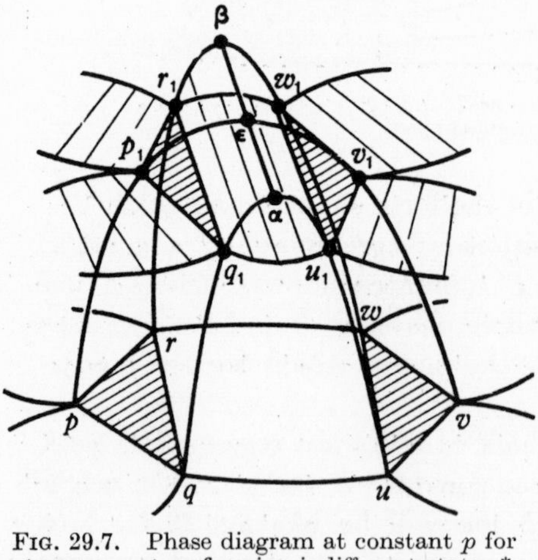

FIG. 29.7. Phase diagram at constant p for ternary system forming indifferent states.*

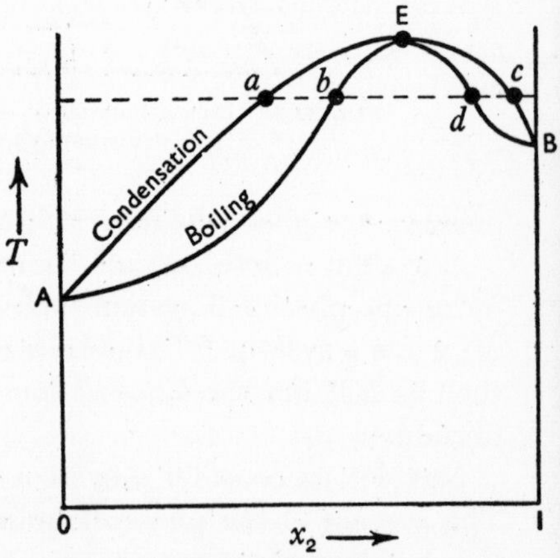

FIG. 29.8. Phase diagram at constant p for binary system forming an azeotrope.

* *Cf.* Vogel [50], p. 352.

triangles *pqr* and *uvw* contract (*cf.* fig. 29.5), and that at a certain temperature we reach the conditions shown schematically in fig. 29.6.

At the temperature corresponding to fig. 29.6, we have three phases α, ϵ, β on a straight line. The system must therefore be in an indifferent state (*cf.* fig. 29.1), and hence because of the Gibbs-Konovalow theorem the temperature of coexistence must pass through an extremum. If we suppose this to be a maximum, then the system will be represented by a diagram of the kind shown in fig. 29.7, which represents conditions of constant p, and in which temperature is plotted vertically.

This example also shows how indifferent states are a generalization of states of uniform composition. Thus we may compare fig. 29.7 with the phase diagram (fig. 29.8) of vaporization of a binary liquid with an azeotrope.

The lines of coexistence $AaEcB$ and $AbEdB$ correspond to the curves $pp_1\epsilon v_1 v$, $rr_1\beta w_1 w$, $qq_1\alpha u_1 u$; and the point of uniform composition E corresponds to the indifferent system $\alpha\epsilon\beta$.

Example 2 : The $HCl+NH_3+NH_4Cl$ *system.*

Assuming the system to be ideal we have

$$x(1-x)=K(T, p), \tag{29.55}$$

where x is the mole fraction of HCl. We may make use of the approximate equation (29.37) for $\ln K$, to obtain

$$\ln x(1-x)=\ln K_0+\frac{(\partial H^{\text{id}}/\partial \xi)_{T,p}}{\mathbf{R}}\left(\frac{1}{T_0}-\frac{1}{T}\right)+2\ln\frac{p}{p_0}. \tag{29.56}$$

We notice that $x(1-x)$, and hence also $\ln x(1-x)$, passes through a maximum value when $x=0{\cdot}5$ corresponding to the presence of an indifferent state (*cf.* 29.29).

First of all, let us consider T fixed at the value T_0, then we have

$$\ln x(1-x)=2\ln\frac{p}{p_0}+\ln K_0, \tag{29.57}$$

whence

$$\ln p=\tfrac{1}{2}\ln x(1-x)+\textit{constant}. \tag{29.58}$$

We see therefore that, in accordance with the Gibbs-Konovalow theorem, when $\ln x(1-x)$ passes through the maximum value in the indifferent state, so also does p.

Finally, considering a constant pressure p_0, we find

$$\ln x(1-x)=\ln K_0+\frac{(\partial H^{\text{id}}/\partial \xi)_{T,p}}{\mathbf{R}}\left(\frac{1}{T_0}-\frac{1}{T}\right), \tag{29.59}$$

whence

$$\frac{1}{T}=\frac{-\boldsymbol{R}}{(\partial H^{\mathrm{id}}/\partial\xi)_{T,p}}\ \ln x(1-x)+\mathit{constant}. \tag{29.60}$$

Thus T passes through a minimum value in the indifferent state.

13. Variation of p as a function of T in Monovariant Systems.

Consider a monovariant system, consisting of ϕ phases, c constituents and in which r' chemical reactions can occur. Then since the variance is one, we must have

$$c+1=\phi+r'. \tag{29.61}$$

We may write down a Gibbs-Duhem equation for each phase (*cf.* 29.43), and a stoichiometric equation (29.49) for each reaction.

At equilibrium, therefore,

$$\left.\begin{array}{l}
-\underline{v}^{1}\ \delta p+w_1^1\,\delta\underline{\mu}_1+\ldots\ldots\ldots+w_c^1\,\delta\underline{\mu}_c\quad=-\ \underline{s}^1\,\delta T\\
\qquad\vdots\qquad\qquad\qquad\qquad\qquad\vdots\qquad\qquad\qquad\vdots\\
-\underline{v}^{\phi}\ \delta p+w_1^{\phi}\,\delta\underline{\mu}_1+\ldots\ldots\ldots+w_c^{\phi}\,\delta\underline{\mu}_c\quad=-\ \underline{s}^{\phi}\,\delta T\\
\qquad\nu_{1,1}M_1\,\delta\underline{\mu}_1+\ldots\quad\ldots.+\nu_{c,1}M_c\,\delta\underline{\mu}_c=0\\
\qquad\qquad\vdots\qquad\qquad\qquad\qquad\vdots\\
\qquad\nu_{1,r'}M_1\,\delta\underline{\mu}_1+\ldots\ldots\ldots+\nu_{c,r'}M_c\,\delta\underline{\mu}_c=0
\end{array}\right\}. \tag{29.62}$$

If δT is given, then these equations enable the other $(c+1)$ unknowns δp, $\delta\underline{\mu}_1$ .... $\delta\underline{\mu}_c$ to be found. In particular, on solving for δp we find

$$\frac{\delta p}{\delta T}=\frac{\begin{vmatrix}
\underline{s}^1 & w_1^1\ldots\ldots\ldots w_c^1\\
\vdots & \vdots\qquad\qquad\vdots\\
\underline{s}^{\phi} & w_1^{\phi}\ldots\ldots\ldots w_c^{\phi}\\
0 & \nu_{1,1}M_1\ldots\ldots\ldots\nu_{c,1}M_c\\
\vdots & \vdots\qquad\qquad\vdots\\
0 & \nu_{1,r'}M_1\ldots\ldots\ldots\nu_{c,r'}M_c
\end{vmatrix}}{\begin{vmatrix}
\underline{v}^1 & w_1^1\ldots\ldots\ldots w_c^1\\
\vdots & \vdots\qquad\qquad\vdots\\
\underline{v}^{\phi} & w_1^{\phi}\ldots\ldots\ldots w_c^{\phi}\\
0 & \nu_{1,1}M_1\ldots\ldots\ldots\nu_{c,1}M_c\\
\vdots & \vdots\qquad\qquad\vdots\\
0 & \nu_{1,r'}M_1\ldots\ldots\ldots\nu_{c,r'}M_c
\end{vmatrix}}. \tag{29.63}$$

Example : Crystallization of Calcium Chloride Hexahydrate.

This system has three components (1) H_2O, (2) $CaCl_2$ and (3) $CaCl_2 . 6H_2O$; three phases vapour (g), solution (l), solid (s) ; and one chemical reaction can occur :

$$6H_2O + CaCl_2 = CaCl_2 . 6H_2O,$$

which can be written

$$6M_1 + M_2 = M_3. \tag{29.64}$$

Hence the system is monovariant. The solid phase consists only of $CaCl_2 . 6H_2O$, so that $w_1^s = 0$, $w_2^s = 0$ and $w_3^s = 1$. In addition we shall assume that the hydrate is completely dissociated in solution so that $w_3^l = 0$, $w_1^l + w_2^l = 1$. Finally the vapour phase contains only water, so that $w_1^g = 1$, $w_2^g = 0$, $w_3^g = 0$.

Equation (29.63) now becomes

$$\frac{\delta p}{\delta T} = \frac{\begin{vmatrix} \underline{s}^g & 1 & 0 & 0 \\ \underline{s}^l & w_1^l & w_2^l & 0 \\ \underline{s}^s & 0 & 0 & 1 \\ 0 & -6M_1 & -M_2 & +M_3 \end{vmatrix}}{\begin{vmatrix} \underline{v}^g & 1 & 0 & 0 \\ \underline{v}^l & w_1^l & w_2^l & 0 \\ \underline{v}^s & 0 & 0 & 1 \\ 0 & -6M_1 & -M_2 & +M_3 \end{vmatrix}}. \tag{29.65}$$

Remembering that $w_1^l = 1 - w_2^l$ and $-6M_1 = M_2 - M_3$ these determinants reduce to

$$\frac{\delta p}{\delta T} = \frac{(\underline{s}^g - \underline{s}^l) M_2 - w_2^l M_3 (\underline{s}^g - \underline{s}^s)}{(\underline{v}^g - \underline{v}^l) M_2 - w_2^l M_3 (\underline{v}^g - \underline{v}^s)}, \tag{29.66}$$

and finally, since

$$\frac{M_2}{M_3} = \frac{111}{219} = 0{\cdot}506, \tag{29.67}$$

$$\frac{\delta p}{\delta T} = \frac{0{\cdot}506 (\underline{s}^g - \underline{s}^l) - w_2^l (\underline{s}^g - \underline{s}^s)}{0{\cdot}506 (\underline{v}^g - \underline{v}^l) - w_2^l (\underline{v}^g - \underline{v}^s)}. \tag{29.68}$$

The entropies which appear in this equation are not very accurately known and we shall limit ourselves to a general consideration of the nature of the curve defined by (29.68). One thing is certain, namely that the entropy difference $(\underline{s}^g - \underline{s}^l)$ between vapour and liquid is very much greater than $(\underline{s}^l - \underline{s}^s)$ between liquid and solid. If we replace $\underline{s}^g - \underline{s}^s$ by

$$(\underline{s}^g - \underline{s}^l) + (\underline{s}^l - \underline{s}^s), \tag{29.69}$$

and make a similar substitution for the volumes, we find*

$$\frac{\delta p}{\delta T} = \frac{(\underline{s}^g - \underline{s}^l) - \dfrac{w_2^l}{0{\cdot}506 - w_2^l}(\underline{s}^l - \underline{s}^s)}{(\underline{v}^g - \underline{v}^l) - \dfrac{w_2^l}{0{\cdot}506 - w_2^l}(\underline{v}^l - \underline{v}^s)}. \tag{29.70}$$

When the solution is dilute in calcium chloride, as it is at low temperatures, the second term in the numerator is negligible in comparison with $(\underline{s}^g - \underline{s}^l)$, which is very close to the entropy of vaporization of pure water. The same reasoning may be applied to the terms in the

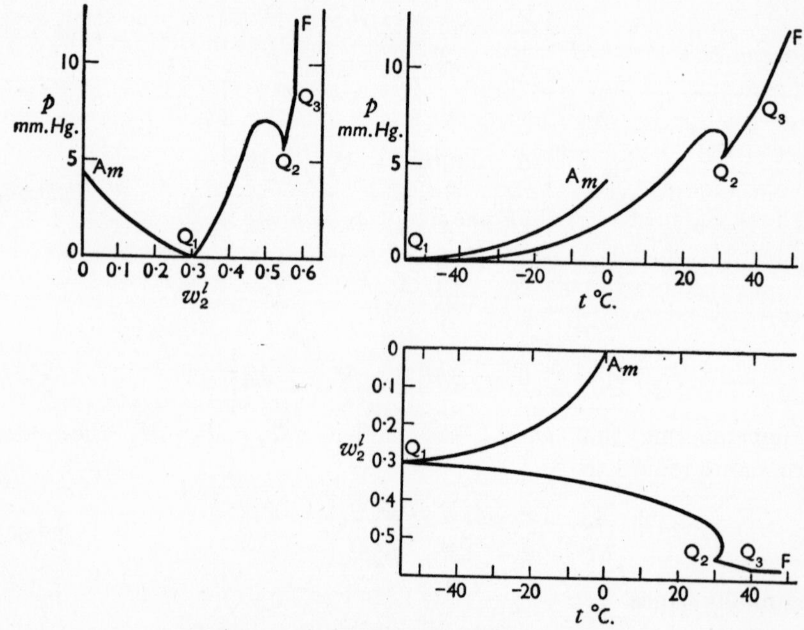

FIG. 29.9. The system $H_2O + CaCl_2$ + hydrate.

Projections on the planes (p, w_2^l), (T, p) and (T, w_2^l) of the line of monovariance in the (T, p, w_2^l) space. The various sections of the curves correspond to the following equilibria:

A_mQ_1 : ice + solution + vapour,
Q_1Q_2 : $CaCl_2 . 6H_2O$ + solution + vapour,
Q_2Q_3 : $CaCl_2 . 4H_2O$ + solution + vapour,
Q_3F : $CaCl_2 . 2H_2O$ + solution + vapour.

* G. W. Morey in *A Commentary on the Scientific Writings of J. Willard Gibbs*, vol. I, (New Haven, 1936), p. 256.

denominator. Hence initially the graph of T as a function of p is very close to that for pure water.

In fig. 29.9 the phase diagrams for the H_2O–$CaCl_2$ system are shown, the branch Q_1Q_2 corresponds to the system we are examining at the moment.

As the temperature rises, w_2^l increases and the influence of the second term in both numerator and denominator becomes more important; $\delta p/\delta T$ at first increases (although remaining smaller than the value for pure water) and then decreases and passes through zero when

$$\frac{w_2^l}{0{\cdot}506 - w_2^l} = \frac{\underline{s}^g - \underline{s}^l}{\underline{s}^l - \underline{s}^s}. \tag{29.71}$$

This occurs at $w_2^l = 0{\cdot}485$, and at this point the entropy of vaporization is about 23 times the entropy of solution (*cf.* fig. 29.9).*

If the temperature is increased further w_2^l still increases and $\delta p/\delta T$ becomes negative. A little later on, however, the denominator becomes zero and the curve $p(T)$ has a vertical tangent and at this point the temperature reaches a maximum value. Past this point the curve turns yet further and T and p decrease together; $\delta p/\delta T$ is once again positive since both numerator and denominator of (29.70) are negative. On this branch of the curve we find the point at which the ratio of $CaCl_2$ to H_2O becomes the same in the solution as in the crystal; that is when $w_2^l = 0{\cdot}506$. This point can be called the " melting point of the hydrate " under its own vapour pressure.

Writing (29.70) in the form

$$\frac{\delta p}{\delta T} = \frac{(0{\cdot}506 - w_2^l)(\underline{s}^g - \underline{s}^l) - w_2^l(\underline{s}^l - \underline{s}^s)}{(0{\cdot}506 - w_2^l)(\underline{v}^g - \underline{v}^l) - w_2^l(\underline{v}^l - \underline{v}^s)}, \tag{29.72}$$

we see that this point is given by

$$\frac{\delta p}{\delta T} = \frac{\underline{s}^l - \underline{s}^s}{\underline{v}^l - \underline{v}^s}. \tag{29.73}$$

The melting of the hydrate in this case is accompanied by an increase in volume and an increase in entropy, so that $\delta p/\delta T$ is positive, which is in accordance with the position of this point on the p/T curve. In the case of $CaCl_2 . 6H_2O$, the melting point of the hydrate is so close to the maximum in T that it is difficult to distinguish between them in practice; this distinction is clear in other cases.

Finally, following the melting point of the hydrate, the curve continues backwards to Q_2 at which point four phases co-exist:

$$CaCl_2 . 6H_2O + CaCl_2 + \text{solution} + \text{vapour}.$$

* H. W. Bakhuis Roozeboom, *Zeit. physik. Chem.*, **4**, 31 (1889).

14. Variation of p with T along the Indifferent Line.

Consider again a system of ϕ phases, c components in which r' chemical reactions can occur, but we shall not limit ourselves, as in the previous paragraph, to a monovariant system.

We may now write down a set of equations like (29.62) in which $\phi + r'$ terms appear on the left hand side, and the rest on the right. To simplify the notation we write $\psi = \phi + r' - 1$:

$$\left.\begin{array}{rcl} -\underline{v}^1\,\delta p + \sum\limits_{i=1}^{i=\psi} w_i^1\,\delta\underline{\mu}_i & = & -\sum\limits_{i=\psi+1}^{i=c} w_i^1\,\delta\underline{\mu}_i - \underline{s}^1\,\delta T \\ \vdots & & \vdots \\ -\underline{v}^\phi\,\delta p + \sum\limits_{i=1}^{i=\psi} u_i^\phi\,\delta\mu_i & = & -\sum\limits_{i=\psi+1}^{i=c} w_i^\phi\,\delta\underline{\mu}_i - s^\phi\,\delta T \\ \sum\limits_{i=1}^{i=\psi} \nu_{i,1} M_i\,\delta\underline{\mu}_i & = & -\sum\limits_{i=\psi+1}^{i=c} \nu_{i,1} M_i\,\delta\underline{\mu}_i \\ \vdots & & \vdots \\ \sum\limits_{i=1}^{i=\psi} \nu_{i,r'} M_i\,\delta\underline{\mu}_i & = & -\sum\limits_{i=\psi+1}^{i=c} \nu_{i,r'} M_i\,\delta\underline{\mu}_i \end{array}\right\}. \qquad (29.74)$$

These equations can be regarded as $\phi + r'$ equations between the $\phi + r'$ unknowns $\delta p, \delta\underline{\mu}_1 \ldots \delta\underline{\mu}_\psi$; the solutions for δp can be summarized in the form:

$$\begin{aligned} |-\underline{v}^1\, w_1^1 \ldots w_\psi^1|\,\delta p &= -\Big|\sum_{i=\psi+1}^{i=c} w_i^1\,\delta\underline{\mu}_i + \underline{s}^1\,\delta T \quad w_1^1 \ldots w_\psi^1\Big| \\ &= -\Sigma\,\delta\underline{\mu}_i\,|w_i^1\, w_1^1 \ldots w_\psi^1| - \delta T\,|\underline{s}^1\, w_1^1 \ldots w_\psi^1|. \end{aligned} \qquad (29.75)$$

But all the determinants of the form $|w_i^1\, w_1^1 \ldots w_\psi^1|$, that is to say

$$\begin{vmatrix} w_i^1 & w_1^1 & \cdots\cdots & w_\psi^1 \\ \vdots & \vdots & & \vdots \\ w_i^\phi & w_1^\phi & \cdots\cdots & w_\psi^\phi \\ \nu_{i,1} M_i & \nu_{1,1} M_1 & \cdots\cdots & \nu_{\psi,1} M_\psi \\ \vdots & \vdots & & \vdots \\ \nu_{i,r'} M_i & \nu_{1,r'} M_1 & \cdots\cdots & \nu_{\psi,r'} M_\psi \end{vmatrix}, \qquad (29.76)$$

are zero along the indifferent line, for these determinants are all derived from the matrix (29.19).

Along the line of indifference, equation (29.75) thus gives

$$\frac{\delta p}{\delta T}=\frac{\begin{vmatrix} \underline{s}^1 & w_1^1 & \cdots\cdots & w_\psi^1 \\ \vdots & \vdots & & \vdots \\ \underline{s}^\phi & w_1^\phi & \cdots\cdots & w_\psi^\phi \\ 0 & \nu_{1,1}M_1 & \cdots\cdots & \nu_{\psi,1}M_\psi \\ \vdots & \vdots & & \vdots \\ 0 & \nu_{1,r'}M_1 & \cdots\cdots & \nu_{\psi,r'}M_\psi \end{vmatrix}}{\begin{vmatrix} \underline{v}^1 & w_1^1 & \cdots\cdots & w_\psi^1 \\ \vdots & \vdots & & \vdots \\ \underline{v}^\phi & w_1^\phi & \cdots\cdots & w_\psi^\phi \\ 0 & \nu_{1,1}M_1 & \cdots\cdots & \nu_{\psi,1}M_\psi \\ \vdots & \vdots & & \vdots \\ 0 & \nu_{1,r'}M_1 & \cdots\cdots & \nu_{\psi,r'}M_\psi \end{vmatrix}} \qquad (29.77)^*$$

with

$$\psi=\phi+r'-1.$$

Comparison of (29.77) with (29.63) shows immediately the close similarity between the indifferent line of a polyvariant system, and the equilibrium line of a monovariant system. This similarity is perhaps less surprising when we remember that all equilibrium states of a monovariant system are indifferent states. Thus (29.63) can be regarded as a particular case of (29.77), for in this case, since $w=1$,

$$\psi=\phi+r'-1=c. \qquad (29.78)$$

Note: In the case of a two-phase system of c non-reacting components, (29.77) reduces to

$$\frac{\delta p}{\delta T}=\frac{\begin{vmatrix} \underline{s}^1 & w_1^1 \\ \underline{s}^2 & w_1^2 \end{vmatrix}}{\begin{vmatrix} \underline{v}^1 & w_1^1 \\ \underline{v}^2 & w_1^2 \end{vmatrix}}\,. \qquad (29.79)$$

Since in a system of this kind the indifferent line is the line of uniform composition, $w_1^1=w_1^2$, and

$$\frac{\delta p}{\delta T}=\frac{\underline{s}^1-\underline{s}^2}{\underline{v}^1-\underline{v}^2}\,. \qquad (29.80)$$

* Gibbs gave for the indifferent line of a divariant system an expression for $\delta p/\delta T$ (see [23] equation (129)), as a function of the *independent components*. This equation was generalized by Saurel, *loc. cit.*, for polyvariant systems ; see also Jouguet [30], pp. 140 and 141. The above expression involving the weight fractions and stoichiometric coefficients of the chemical reactions is due to Defay, [12] equation (45).

We thus obtain equation (28.36) once more except that the entropy and volume are expressed per unit mass. Similarly, we may put (29.77) into a form analogous to (28.35) in terms of a latent heat of azeotropic transformation.*

Example : Once again we may consider the ammonia + hydrogen chloride system. We have three components and two phases with one chemical reaction.

$$\begin{array}{lll} \text{Components:} & 1 \quad\; 2 \quad\; 3; & \\ \text{Reaction:} & NH_3 + HCl = NH_4Cl, & \\ \qquad\text{or} & M_1 + M_2 = M_3, & (29.81) \end{array}$$

$$\begin{array}{lllll} \text{with weight fractions in the gas phase} & (1) & w_1^1 + w_2^1 + w_3^1 = 1, & & (29.82) \\ \text{and in the solid phase} & (2) & 0 \quad\; 0 \quad\; w_3^2 = 1. & & \end{array}$$

On applying equation (29.77) to this system we find

$$\frac{\delta p}{\delta T} = \frac{\begin{vmatrix} \underline{s}^1 & w_1^1 & w_2^1 \\ \underline{s}^2 & 0 & 0 \\ 0 & -M_1 & -M_2 \end{vmatrix}}{\begin{vmatrix} \underline{v}^1 & w_1^1 & w_2^1 \\ \underline{v}^2 & 0 & 0 \\ 0 & -M_1 & -M_2 \end{vmatrix}}. \tag{29.83}$$

But the ψ components which appear in (29.77) are any components taken from the c components of the system. Thus (29.83) can equally well be written :

$$\frac{\delta p}{\delta T} = \frac{\begin{vmatrix} \underline{s}^1 & w_1^1 & w_3^1 \\ \underline{s}^2 & 0 & 1 \\ 0 & -M_1 & M_3 \end{vmatrix}}{\begin{vmatrix} \underline{v}^1 & w_1^1 & w_3^1 \\ \underline{v}^2 & 0 & 1 \\ 0 & -M_1 & M_3 \end{vmatrix}}. \tag{29.84}$$

We shall make use of (29.84) rather than (29.83) since on expanding (29.83) and taking account of the conditions of indifference we obtain an indeterminate value of the form 0/0. On the other hand (29.84) gives for the numerator

$$\underline{s}^1 M_1 - \underline{s}^2 (w_1^1 M_3 + w_3^1 M_1),$$

* For this see Defay [12], equation (71). For a divariant system see Gibbs [23], p. 99; for polyvariant systems see Saurel, *loc. cit.*, and Jouguet [30], § 52.

or making use of (29.81) and (29.82):

$$\underline{s}^1 M_1 - \underline{s}^2[w_1^1(M_1 + M_2) + M_1(1 - w_1^1 - w_2^1)]$$
$$= \underline{s}^1 M_1 - \underline{s}^2[M_1 + w_1^1 M_2 - w_2^1 M_1].$$

If we now make use of the condition of indifference (29.23) this reduces to

$$(\underline{s}^1 - \underline{s}^2) M_1. \tag{29.85}$$

The denominator reduces in a similar fashion to give

$$\frac{\delta p}{\delta T} = \frac{\underline{s}^1 - \underline{s}^2}{\underline{v}^1 - \underline{v}^2}. \tag{29.86}$$

In this case it is easy to show that (29.84) or its equivalent (29.86) can be put in the form of a Clausius-Clapeyron equation. For in the indifferent state considered, the system can undergo an equilibrium transformation* without any effect on the composition of the phases. We can show, just as in § 2 of chapter XXVIII that this change takes place at constant T and p. The intensive variables $\underline{s}^1$, $\underline{s}^2$, $\underline{v}^1$, $\underline{v}^2$ are thus constant during the transformation, so that on differentiating

$$S = \underline{s}^1 m^1 + \underline{s}^2 m^2, \tag{29.87}$$

remembering that $dm^1 = -dm^2$, we have

$$\frac{dS}{dm^2} = \underline{s}^2 - \underline{s}^1. \tag{29.88}$$

The heat received by the system in this equilibrium transformation is (*cf.* 28.15)

$$\frac{dQ}{dm^2} = T\frac{dS}{dm^2} = T(\underline{s}^2 - \underline{s}^1). \tag{29.89}$$

In the same way the change of volume is

$$\frac{dV}{dm^2} = \underline{v}^2 - \underline{v}^1. \tag{29.90}$$

Putting these expressions into (29.86) then gives

$$\frac{\delta p}{\delta T} = \frac{\dfrac{1}{T}\dfrac{dQ}{dm^2}}{\dfrac{dV}{dm^2}}, \tag{29.91}$$

which is an equation of the Clausius-Clapeyron type. This equation can easily be put into a form related to the approximate equation

* *Cf.* chap. XIX, § 1.

(29.37). For if we assume that the ammonium chloride exists only in the solid state, and if the heat of the reaction

$$NH_3(g) + HCl(g) = NH_4Cl(s)$$

is written as $(\partial H/\partial \xi)_{T,p}$, while $dm^2 = M_3\, d\xi$, we have

$$\frac{\delta p}{\delta T} = \frac{(\partial H/\partial \xi)_{T,p}}{T(\partial V/\partial \xi)_{T,p}}, \tag{29.92}$$

or making the approximation (29.34)

$$\frac{\delta \ln p}{\delta T} = -\frac{(\partial H/\partial \xi)_{T,p}}{2RT^2}. \tag{29.93}$$

15. Sub-systems of a Monovariant System.

To examine more deeply the relations between monovariant and indifferent systems we shall now introduce the idea of a *sub-system.**

Let us consider a monovariant system having ϕ phases. If, from this system, we remove one or more of these phases we are left with a system of ϕ_s phases ($\phi_s < \phi$) which constitutes what we shall call a sub-system of the monovariant system being considered. The monovariant system itself we shall call the *parent system.*

In general, suppression of certain phases involves also the suppression of certain components which are absent from the phases left behind, and of certain reactions which can no longer take place. We shall denote the number of components in the sub-system by c_s and the number of chemical reactions which can occur by r_s'. We must of course always have

$$\phi_s < \phi\; ; \quad c_s \leqslant c\; ; \quad r_s' \leqslant r'. \tag{29.94}$$

In the following discussion we shall number the phases remaining in the sub-system 1 to ϕ_s, and those which have been removed $\phi_s + 1$ to ϕ ; similarly we shall suppose that components 1 to c_s are retained and also reactions 1 to r_s'. Furthermore we shall denote by i all components which are suppressed as a result of removal of the phases $\phi_s + 1$ to ϕ. Component i is thus absent from the phases $1 \ldots \phi_s$, and does not participate in any of the reactions $1 \ldots r_s'$. Hence we have

$$\left.\begin{aligned} w_i^1 &= \ldots = w_i^{\phi_s} = 0, \\ \nu_{i,1} &= \ldots = \nu_{i,r_s'} = 0 \end{aligned}\right\}. \tag{29.95}$$

The sub-system must of course be made up of phases which are in the same physico-chemical state as in the parent system. The variables

* *Cf.* R. Defay and I. Prigogine, *Bull. Ac. Roy. Belg.*, (*Cl. Sc.*), **29**, 525 (1943).

$T, p, w_1^1 \ldots w_{c_s}^{\phi_s}$ have the same values in both systems. If the parent system is in equilibrium, so is the sub-system.

Since the sub-system has fewer phases than the monovariant parent system, it is very often polyvariant. However, there are cases where the sub-system itself is also monovariant. This occurs when the loss of phases and of chemical reactions is exactly compensated for by the reduction in the number of components.

16. Indifferent Sub-System.

It may happen that in the state considered, the sub-system is indifferent. Then all the determinants of order $(\phi_s + r_s')$ formed with the lines of the following indifference matrix (29.96) are zero (*cf.* 29.19):

$$\begin{bmatrix} w_1^1 & \cdots & w_1^{\phi_s} & \nu_{1,1}M_1 & \cdots & \nu_{1,r_s'}M_1 \\ \vdots & & \vdots & \vdots & & \vdots \\ w_{c_s}^1 & \cdots & w_{c_s}^{\phi_s} & \nu_{c_s,1}M_{c_s} & \cdots & \nu_{c_s,r_s'}M_{c_s} \end{bmatrix}. \tag{29.96}$$

This indifferent state must lie on the indifferent line of the sub-system considered.

If $\delta_s p$ is the increase in pressure which accompanies an increase in temperature δT in the sub-system along the indifferent line, then we have at the point considered (*cf.* 29.77)

$$\frac{\delta_s p}{\delta T} = \frac{\begin{vmatrix} \underline{s}^1 & w_1^1 & \cdots & w_{\psi_s}^1 \\ \vdots & \vdots & & \vdots \\ \underline{s}^{\phi_s} & w_1^{\phi_s} & \cdots & w_{\psi_s}^{\phi_s} \\ 0 & \nu_{1,1}M_1 & \cdots & \nu_{\psi_s,1}M_{\psi_s} \\ \vdots & \vdots & & \vdots \\ 0 & \nu_{1,r_s'}M_1 & \cdots & \nu_{\psi_s,r_s'}M_{\psi_s} \end{vmatrix}}{\begin{vmatrix} \underline{v}^1 & w_1^1 & \cdots & w_{\psi_s}^1 \\ \vdots & \vdots & & \vdots \\ \underline{v}^{\phi_s} & w_1^{\phi_s} & \cdots & w_{\psi_s}^{\phi_s} \\ 0 & \nu_{1,1}M_1 & \cdots & \nu_{\psi_s,1}M_{\psi_s} \\ \vdots & \vdots & & \vdots \\ 0 & \nu_{1,r_s'}M_1 & \cdots & \nu_{\psi_s,r_s'}M_{\psi_s} \end{vmatrix}} \tag{29.97}$$

where we have introduced the abbreviation

$$\psi_s = \phi_s + r_s' - 1. \tag{29.98}$$

17. Monovariant System with an Indifferent Sub-system.

*When, in moving along the monovariant line, a monovariant system of ϕ phases passes through a point at which ϕ_s of these phases form an indifferent sub-system, then the projection on the (T, p) plane of the monovariant line, is at this point tangential to the projection of the indifferent line of the sub-system.**

To prove this theorem it is sufficient to establish that at the point under consideration

$$\boxed{\frac{\delta p}{\delta T}=\frac{\delta_s p}{\delta T}} \tag{29.99}$$

where $\delta p/\delta T$ is given by (29.63) and $\delta_s p/\delta T$ by (29.97).

Consider first the determinant formed from the first (ϕ_s+r_s') lines of (29.96). Since, by definition, $(\psi_s+1)=(\phi_s+r_s')$, we have

$$\begin{vmatrix} w_1^1 & \cdots\cdots & w_1^{\phi_s} & \nu_{1,1}M_1 & \cdots\cdots & \nu_{1,r_s'}M_1 \\ \vdots & & \vdots & \vdots & & \vdots \\ w_{\psi_s+1}^1 & \cdots\cdots & w_{\psi_s+1}^{\phi_s} & \nu_{(\psi_s+1),1}M_{\psi_s+1} & \cdots\cdots & \nu_{(\psi_s+1),r_s'}M_{\psi_s+1} \end{vmatrix}=0. \tag{29.100}$$

If we denote by $D_{\psi_s+1}^{\alpha}$ the minor (including its sign) relative to $w_{\psi_s+1}^{\alpha}$, and by $D_{(\psi_s+1),\rho}$ the minor (including its sign) relative to $\nu_{(\psi_s+1),\rho}M_{\psi_s+1}$ in the determinant (29.100), then the development of this determinant in terms of the elements in the last line will be

$$\sum_{\alpha=1}^{\alpha=\phi_s} w_{\psi_s+1}^{\alpha}D_{\psi_s+1}^{\alpha} + \sum_{\rho=1}^{\rho=r_s'} \nu_{(\psi_s+1),\rho}M_{\psi_s+1}D_{(\psi_s+1),\rho}=0. \tag{29.101}$$

The other determinants defining the indifferent state can be formed by replacing the last line of (29.100), by one of the other lines of (29.96) which have not been used; that is to say the line relating to a component between (ψ_s+1) and c_s. The development of such a determinant will make use of the same set of minors as in (29.101), and we have in general

$$\sum_{\alpha=1}^{\alpha=\phi_s} w_i^{\alpha}D_{\psi_s+1}^{\alpha} + \sum_{\rho=1}^{\rho=r_s'} \nu_{i,\rho}M_iD_{(\psi_s+1),\rho}=0 \tag{29.102}$$

where $i=(\psi_s+2), \ldots c_s$.

But because of (29.101) this equation is also valid for $i=\psi_s+1$. Furthermore it is evident that it is also valid for $i=1 \ldots \phi_s$, for then

* R. Defay and I. Prigogine, *loc. cit.*

it represents the development of a determinant which has two lines identical, and is zero because of that fact.

Finally, (29.102) is also valid for $i=(c_s+1)\ldots c$, because of the equations (29.95); it is therefore valid for all values of i from 1 to c inclusive.

It is now easy to transform equation (29.63) for $\delta p/\delta T$ into the form (29.97). Consider the numerator of (29.63) and in this determinant multiply

the first line by $D^1_{\psi_s+1}$,

the second line by $D^2_{\psi_s+1}$,

....

the ϕ_s-th line by $D^{\phi_s}_{\psi_s+1}$;

the first line of νM by $D_{(\psi_s+1),1}$,

....

the r'_s-th line of νM by $D_{(\psi_s+1),r'_s}$;

and add these lines. Then because of (29.102) the determinant becomes

$$\frac{1}{D^1_{\psi_s+1}}\begin{vmatrix} \sum\limits_{\alpha=1}^{\alpha=\phi_s} \underline{s}^{\alpha} D^{\alpha}_{\psi_s+1} & 0 & \cdots & 0 \\ \underline{s}^2 & w^2_1 & \cdots & w^2_c \\ \vdots & \vdots & & \vdots \\ \underline{s}^{\phi} & w^{\phi}_1 & \cdots & w^{\phi}_c \\ 0 & \nu_{1,1}M_1 & \cdots & \nu_{c,1}M_c \\ \vdots & \vdots & & \vdots \\ 0 & \nu_{1,r'}M_1 & \cdots & \nu_{c,r'}M_c \end{vmatrix}$$

$$= \frac{\sum\limits_{\alpha=1}^{\alpha=\phi_s} \underline{s}^{\alpha} D^{\alpha}_{\psi_s+1}}{D^1_{\psi_s+1}} \begin{vmatrix} w^2_1 & \cdots & w^2_c \\ \vdots & & \vdots \\ w^{\phi}_1 & \cdots & w^{\phi}_c \\ \nu_{1,1}M_1 & \cdots & \nu_{c,1}M_c \\ \vdots & & \vdots \\ \nu_{1,r'}M_1 & \cdots & \nu_{c,r'}M_c \end{vmatrix} \qquad (29.103)$$

By carrying out the same process on the denominator of (29.63), and simplifying by cancelling common factors we obtain finally

$$\frac{\delta p}{\delta T} = \frac{\sum\limits_{\alpha=1}^{\alpha=\phi_s} \underline{s}^{\alpha} D^{\alpha}_{\psi_s+1}}{\sum\limits_{\alpha=1}^{\alpha=\phi_s} \underline{v}^{\alpha} D^{\alpha}_{\psi_s+1}},$$

which, written in full, is

$$\frac{\delta p}{\delta T}=\frac{\begin{vmatrix} w_1^1 \; \cdots\cdots \; w_1^{\phi_s} & \nu_{1,1}M_1 & \cdots\cdots & \nu_{\;,r_s'}M_1 \\ \vdots \qquad\qquad \vdots & \vdots & & \vdots \\ w_{\psi_s}^1 \; \cdots\cdots \; w_{\psi_s}^{\phi_s} & \nu_{\psi_s,1}M_{\psi_s} & \cdots\cdots & \nu_{\psi_s,r_s'}M_{\psi_s} \\ \underline{s}^1 \; \cdots\cdots \; \underline{s}^{\phi_s} & 0 & \cdots\cdots & 0 \end{vmatrix}}{\begin{vmatrix} w_1^1 \; \cdots\cdots \; w_1^{\phi_s} & \nu_{1,1}M_1 & \cdots\cdots & \nu_{1,r_s'}M_1 \\ \vdots \qquad\qquad \vdots & \vdots & & \vdots \\ w_{\psi_s}^1 \; \cdots\cdots \; w_{\psi_s}^{\phi_s} & \nu_{\psi_s,1}M_{\psi_s} & \cdots\cdots & \nu_{\psi_s,r_s'}M_{\psi_s} \\ \underline{v}^1 \; \cdots\cdots \; \underline{v}^{\phi_s} & 0 & \cdots\cdots & 0 \end{vmatrix}} . \tag{29.104}$$

But writing the determinants in (29.104) lines for columns we see that they are none other than the determinants in (29.97) so that we have

$$\frac{\delta p}{\delta T}=\frac{\delta_s p}{\delta T}, \tag{29.105}$$

which proves the theorem.

18. An Example.

Let us consider the five-component, four-phase monovariant system :

vapour phase : H_2O,

liquid phase : $H_2O+SiO_2+K_2O \,.\, SiO_2$,

solid phase 1 : $K_2O \,.\, 2SiO_2$,

solid phase 2 : $K_2O \,.\, SiO_2 \,.\, \frac{1}{2}H_2O$.

Two chemical reactions can take place in the system, namely

$$K_2O \,.\, SiO_2+SiO_2=K_2O \,.\, 2SiO_2,$$
$$2K_2O \,.\, SiO_2+H_2O=2K_2O \,.\, SiO_2 \,.\, \tfrac{1}{2}H_2O.$$

Hence $$w=2+(5-2)-4=1.$$

Morey* has shown that on the monovariant line of this system (or more correctly on the metastable extension of this line), there is a point where the sub-system liquid + solid 1 + solid 2 is indifferent. This is a kind of eutectic where the liquid can, without altering its composition precipitate both crystals of $K_2O \,.\, 2SiO_2$ and $K_2O \,.\, SiO_2 \,.\, \frac{1}{2}H_2O$. The line of indifference of this sub-system, and the monovariant line of the parent system are, at this point, tangential when projected on the (T, p) plane.

* G. W. Morey, *loc. cit.*, (p. 488) ; pp. 233–293.

19. Morey and Schreinemakers' Theorem of Coincidence.*

Consider ϕ_s phases which form an indifferent sub-system. The monovariant curves of all the parent systems containing these ϕ_s phases in the same state, when projected on the (T, p) plane, have a common tangent at the point corresponding to this state.

This follows immediately since all the projections of monovariant lines must, because of the theorem proved in § 17, be tangents at the same point to the same lines of indifference, corresponding to the common sub-system.

20. Particular Case where the Sub-system is itself Monovariant.†

If the sub-system also is monovariant, then it is indifferent in all its states and the indifferent line of the sub-system is also its equilibrium line. It then follows from the theorem of § 17 that the projection of the monovariant line of the parent system on the (T, p) plane is coincident with the projection of the monovariant line of the sub-system.

The Morey-Schreinemakers' theorem when applied to this case may be written : The monovariant curves of all monovariant systems which have a monovariant sub-system in common, are coincident when projected on the (T, p) plane.

21. An Example.

An example of this behaviour is found in the five component, four phase system :

vapour : H_2O,
liquid : $H_2O + SiO_2 + K_2O \,.\, SiO_2$,
solid 1 : $K_2O \,.\, 2SiO_2$,
solid 2 : $K_2O \,.\, 2SiO_2 \,.\, H_2O$,

in which two reactions can occur :

$$K_2O \,.\, SiO_2 + SiO_2 = K_2O \,.\, 2SiO_2,$$
$$K_2O \,.\, 2SiO_2 + H_2O = K_2O \,.\, 2SiO_2 \,.\, H_2O.$$

We have

$$w = 2 + (5 - 2) - 4 = 1.$$

If we remove the liquid phase we have the sub-system vapour + solid 1 + solid 2 which now has only three components, and in which only the second of the reactions can occur. The projection of the monovariant line of this sub-system on the (T, p) plane is coincident with the projection of the monovariant line of the parent system.‡

* G. W. Morey, *loc. cit.*, p. 274 ; F. A. H. Schreinemakers, *Proc. Acad. Sci. Amsterdam*, **19**, 514–27 (1926).
† R. Defay and I. Prigogine, *loc. cit.*
‡ Morey, *loc. cit.*, pp. 276, 277.

22. Similarity between Indifferent States and Monovariant Systems.

We have already seen that all the states of a monovariant system are indifferent states. On the other hand, if a polyvariant system is in an indifferent state, then its properties are in many ways analogous to those of monovariant systems.

In a closed monovariant system, at each temperature there is a corresponding equilibrium state in which p and the composition of the phases w_i^α are determined, but in which the masses of each phase are arbitrary because in the set of equations (29.16) there are fewer equations than unknowns ($c < \phi + r'$ since $w = 1$).

In the same way, for an indifferent state of a closed polyvariant system, the temperature is sufficient to determine p and the composition of the phases, but not the masses of the individual phases. Furthermore, as we have seen, the law governing the variations δp and δT along an indifferent line, are of just the same form as the law which relates δp and δT along the equilibrium states of a monovariant system. However, a profound difference is apparent between monovariant systems, and indifferent states of a polyvariant system when we consider the possibility of a closed system moving along the line of indifference. A closed monovariant system can clearly traverse its indifferent line, for this is simply its equilibrium line ; on the other hand, for a polyvariant closed system the ability to move along the indifferent line is exceptional as we shall now proceed to show.

23. Jouguet's Theorem on the Accessibility of the Indifferent line of a closed Polyvariant System.*

Let us consider a closed system characterized by the given initial masses of its components $m_1^0, \dots m_c^0$. Its state at any instant will be determined by the values of the variables

$$T, p, w_1^1, \dots w_c^\phi, m^1 \dots m^\phi. \tag{29.106}$$

We shall now denote by

r' the number of independent chemical reactions,

r'' the number of transfer reactions between phases,

j the number of insolubility conditions of the type (29.5′).

Jouguet has considered two types of system,

Type 1 : those for which $r' + r'' = 1$,

Type 2 : those for which $r' + r'' > 1$.

There is no need to consider systems for which $r' + r'' = 0$ for such systems cannot undergo any mass transfers at all.

* Jouguet, [30], § 16.

Before stating Jouguet's theorems, we shall examine the physical meaning of the above subdivision. For this we notice that the conditions which determine the values of the variables (29.106) at equilibrium in an indifferent state can be classified into three groups :

A. Relations involving only the weight fractions.

1. The ϕ equations $\sum_i w_i^\alpha = 1$.

2. The j conditions of insolubility (29.5′).

3. The $w - 1 = 1 + c - r' - \phi$ conditions of indifference resulting from the matrix (29.19).

Taking account of (29.6), we see that the total number of relations of type A is

$$1 + c\phi - (r' + r''). \qquad (29.107)$$

B. Relations involving T, p and composition.

1. The r' conditions of equilibrium for the chemical reactions.

2. The r'' conditions of equilibrium for the transfer reactions.

There are then $(r' + r'')$ relations of type B.

C. Relations involving the composition and masses of the phases.

These are the c conditions of enclosure (13.13), namely

$$\sum_\alpha w_i^\alpha m^\alpha - \sum_{\rho=1}^{\rho=r'} \nu_{i,\rho} M_i \xi_\rho = m_i^0, \quad (i = 1 \dots c). \qquad (29.108)$$

These equations introduce the auxiliary variables $\xi_1 \dots \xi_{r'}$ which must be eliminated.

This classification of the equations giving the conditions that a closed system shall be in an indifferent state, enables us to see the significance of the two categories of system distinguished above.

We see that in systems of the first category where $r' + r'' = 1$, the number of equations of type A is $c\phi$. In this case these $c\phi$ equations are sufficient to establish the values of the $c\phi$ weight fractions $w_1^1 \dots w_c^\phi$. The composition of the system characterized by these weight fractions is thus independent of T and p. This is the same for all indifferent states of the system.

We see, therefore, that for all systems in the first category, T and p may vary along the indifferent line, but the composition of the system remains constant.

On the other hand, for systems of the second kind, the equations A are not by themselves sufficient to determine all the mole fractions. To determine these mole fractions and the pressure p it is necessary to employ equations A and B simultaneously. These number $(1 + c\phi)$ and enable us to evaluate the $(1 + c\phi)$ unknowns p, $w_1^1, \dots w_c^\phi$ as functions of T. In general therefore the composition of the system varies with temperature.

In systems of the second type, the composition varies in general from point to point along the indifferent line.

Jouguet has investigated whether, if we are given a closed system in any equilibrium state, it is possible by means of an equilibrium change to reach an indifferent state. He has proved the following theorems.

Systems of the first type : $r'+r''=1$:

(i) in general the system will be unable to reach an indifferent state, but

(ii) if the system can, as a special case, reach an indifferent state, then it can move along the whole of the indifferent line.

We shall give an example of this in a simple case.

Example : Indifferent point of a salt hydrate in equilibrium with solution of the salt.

Fig. 29.10 gives data obtained by Bakhuis Roozeboom for the solubilities and freezing points of aqueous solutions of ferric chloride.

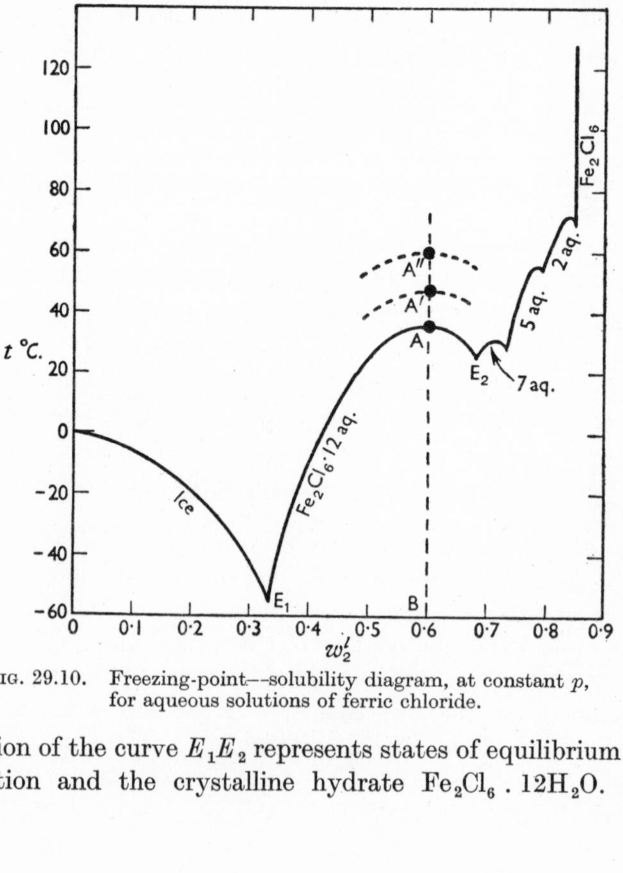

FIG. 29.10. Freezing-point—solubility diagram, at constant p, for aqueous solutions of ferric chloride.

The portion of the curve E_1E_2 represents states of equilibrium between the solution and the crystalline hydrate $Fe_2Cl_6 \cdot 12H_2O$. In this region the system consists of two phases (solution and crystal) and one reaction can take place :

$$\left.\begin{array}{c} Fe_2Cl_6 \,.\, 12H_2O\,(s) = Fe_2Cl_6\,(aq) + 12H_2O, \\ \text{which we may represent by} \\ M_1 = M_2 + 12M_3. \end{array}\right\} . \quad (29.109)$$

We assume that the addition compound dissociates completely in solution, that is to say it exists in the solid state only. We then have

$$c = 3,\ r' = 1,\ r'' = 0,\ r' + r'' = 1$$

so that

$$w = 2 + (3 - 1) - 2 = 2.$$

The system is therefore bivariant, and of the first category. The curve E_1E_2 passes through a maximum value of the temperature at A ; hence by the converse of the second Gibbs-Konovalow theorem the point A is an indifferent point. We may now set the determinant derived from (29.19) (of which there is only one in this case because the system is only bivariant) equal to zero :

$$\begin{vmatrix} 0 & 1 & -M_1 \\ w_2^1 & 0 & M_2 \\ w_3^1 & 0 & 12M_3 \end{vmatrix} = 0, \quad (29.110)$$

where phase 1 is the solution and phase 2 the solid. This reduces to

$$\frac{w_2^1}{w_3^1} = \frac{M_2}{12M_3}, \quad (29.111)$$

which shows that at A the weight composition of the solution is the same as that of the crystal. And furthermore, this condition, which ensures that the state is indifferent, is independent of T and p. Thus if we draw the phase diagram at another pressure we obtain another isobaric curve (dotted) with a maximum at A' which lies on the same ordinate AB. Corresponding to the isobaric phase diagrams at a series of pressures p, p', p'' ... we have an indifferent line which is the vertical line $BAA'A''$....

Remembering that

$$w_2^1 + w_3^1 = 1, \quad (29.112)$$

equation (29.111) gives, with (29.109),

$$w_2^1 = \frac{M_2}{M_1};\quad w_3^1 = \frac{2M_3}{M_1}. \quad (29.113)$$

It is seen immediately that if we make up a closed system from the initial masses m_1^0, m_2^0 and m_3^0, this system cannot, in general, attain any of the indifferent states $A, A', A'' \ldots$.

For the equations of enclosure (29.108) may be written in this case

$$\left.\begin{aligned} 0+m^2-M_1\xi &= m_1^0, \\ w_2^1 m^1+0-M_2\xi &= m_2^0, \\ w_3^1 m^1+0-12M_3\xi &= m_3^0 \end{aligned}\right\}. \tag{29.114}$$

These equations enable us to calculate m^1, m^2 and ξ when the system has attained a final state the composition of which is given by the weight fractions w_i^α. But if this composition is that corresponding to an indifferent state then the weight fractions must also satisfy (29.110).

Hence the determinant formed from the coefficients of equations (29.114) is zero and these equations have in general no solution if the initial masses m_1^0, m_2^0 and m_3^0 are chosen arbitrarily. This shows that a closed system, made up from arbitrary initial masses of the three components, cannot in general attain an indifferent state. However, if the initial masses are chosen so that

$$\begin{vmatrix} m_1^0 & 1 & M_1 \\ m_2^0 & 0 & -M_2 \\ m_3^0 & 0 & -12M_3 \end{vmatrix} = 0, \tag{29.115}$$

then the set of equations (29.114) is no longer incapable of solution, and the system thus constituted can attain an indifferent state. The condition (29.115) gives immediately

$$\frac{m_2^0}{m_3^0} = \frac{M_2}{12M_3} = \frac{325}{216}. \tag{29.116}$$

Only systems made up in this way can reach the indifferent state, and all systems which can attain one indifferent state can reach them all as they all correspond to the same composition.

We can thus demonstrate these two propositions of Jouguet in this simple case.

We notice that the mass m_1^0 of the hydrate does not appear in the condition (29.116), so that this mass may be chosen quite arbitrarily.

*General Proof.**

The above demonstration can be generalized immediately to all bivariant systems since for such systems the number of conditions of enclosure (29.108) is always, as in the above example, $(\phi + r')$; and this

* Jouguet, [30]; Defay, [12].

is the same as the number of unknowns $m^1 \dots m^\phi$, $\xi_1 \dots \xi_{r'}$. These conditions can always be expressed in a form similar to (29.115) if these equations are to be compatible with an indifferent state.

This condition of compatibility is in general a relation between $m_1^0 \dots m_c^0$, and these masses cannot be chosen at random.

If the variance is greater than two, the number of equations of enclosure (c) is greater than $\phi + r'$ and, for each additional equation, there will have to be an additional equation of compatibility. In all there will therefore be

$$1 + c - (\phi + r')$$

conditions of compatibility. These will be relations between the $m_1^0 \dots m_c^0$ and the composition of the indifferent state. The existence of these relations means that the initial amounts $m_1^0 \dots m_c^0$ cannot be chosen completely at random if we wish the system to be such that it can reach an indifferent state. Finally, if as a result of a suitable choice of initial composition, the system is able to reach an indifferent state, then it can reach all possible indifferent states, for in systems of the type under consideration, all the indifferent states have the same composition.

Systems of the second type : $r' + r'' > 1$.

Case 1 : $w = 2$. All closed divariant systems of the second category can in general* attain an indifferent state if one exists.

Case 2 : $w > 2$. A polyvariant closed system of the second category cannot in general achieve an indifferent state ; although it may reach an indifferent point if the initial masses instead of being taken at random, are chosen correctly.

In both cases, unless the equations exhibit a singularity, a closed system of the second kind cannot move along the indifferent line.

We shall first prove this theorem for a very simple bivariant system, namely a binary solution in the presence of vapour. The only reactions which play any part in this system are the transfers of components 1 and 2 from one phase to the other.

The condition of indifference is (*cf.* 29.20) :

$$\begin{vmatrix} w_1^l & w_1^g \\ w_2^l & w_2^g \end{vmatrix} = 0, \qquad (29.117)$$

or

$$w_1^l = w_1^g. \qquad (29.118)$$

* Within certain limits of compositions (*e.g.* if the composition along the indifferent line varies between certain limiting values only) and in the absence of singularities in the equations (*e.g.* if the ratios of certain weight fractions remain constant along the indifferent line as in the example (c) of § 7).

Since $r' = 0$ the conditions of enclosure (29.108) are,

$$w_1^l m^l + w_1^g m^g = m_1^0,$$
$$w_2^l m^l + w_2^g m^g = m_2^0. \tag{29.119}$$

These equations are not in general compatible with (29.117) unless

$$\begin{vmatrix} w_1^g & m_1^0 \\ w_2^g & m_2^0 \end{vmatrix} = 0, \tag{29.120}$$

or

$$\frac{m_1^0}{m_2^0} = \frac{w_1^g}{w_2^g} = \frac{w_1^g}{1 - w_1^g}. \tag{29.121}$$

In this case the composition corresponding to the indifferent state which is here the azeotropic composition, depends upon the temperature. Thus if certain values of m_1^0 and m_2^0 are given, it is in general possible to find a temperature such that the azeotropic composition satisfies (29.121). A closed system of this kind, chosen at random, can in general reach an indifferent state if one exists, but it cannot move along the indifferent line, for the other values of the composition along the line cannot be reached from the initial state.

*General Proof**

For the c conditions of enclosure (29.108) to be compatible in an indifferent state, it is necessary and sufficient that the initial masses $m_1^0 \dots m_c^0$ shall satisfy the $1 + c - (\phi + r')$ conditions of compatibility which we have enumerated in studying systems in the first category. These conditions of compatibility are between the initial masses and the composition of the phases in the indifferent state, which, as we have seen, are completely determined, as a function of T, by the relations A and B.

We have therefore $1 + c - (\phi + r')$ relations between $m_1^0 \dots m_c^0$ and T. If we eliminate T we are left with $c - (\phi + r')$ equations between the variables $m_1^0 \dots m_c^0$.

Case 1 : $w = 2$, whence $c = \phi + r'$. In this case therefore $m_1^0 \dots m_c^0$ can be chosen quite arbitrarily. Hence all closed bivariant systems of the second category can, in general, reach an indifferent state if it exists.

Case 2 : $w > 2$, whence $c > \phi + r'$. The masses $m_1^0 \dots m_c^0$ are now related by $c - (\phi + r')$ equations, and hence they cannot all be chosen arbitrarily. If they are chosen arbitrarily, then the system cannot, in general, reach an indifferent state.

In both these cases, ($w \geqslant 2$), once the masses have been chosen, T

* Jouguet [30] ; Defay [12].

can be determined from the $1+c-(\phi+r')$ conditions of compatibility, which as we have already seen are equations relating $m_1^0 \dots m_c^0$ and T. This value of T determines the particular indifferent state in which the system can exist. A closed system of the second category cannot therefore, in general, move along the indifferent line.

24. Existence of the Non-equilibrium Indifferent States.

It can be shown that if we do not confine ourselves to equilibrium states, the necessary condition that a given closed system can exist in an indifferent state is that*

$$r'+r'' \geqslant w. \tag{29.122}$$

For of the relations A, B and C enumerated in the previous paragraph, the equations B only are conditions of equilibrium. If we do not limit ourselves to equilibrium states, then these equations need not be satisfied. On the other hand equations A and C must be satisfied by all systems in an indifferent state, whether or not in equilibrium.

As we have seen in the previous paragraph, if the conditions of enclosure (29.108) are to have a solution in $m^1 \dots m^\phi$, $\xi_1 \dots \xi_{r'}$ when the w_i^α refer to the composition of an indifferent state, then $1+c-(\phi+r')$ conditions of compatibility must be satisfied. These conditions consist of a set of equations between $m_1^0 \dots m_c^0$ and the w_i^α.

Let us suppose that we are given the initial masses at random, and let us enquire whether the closed system thus constituted can exist in an indifferent state, whether static or not. This clearly cannot be possible unless there exists an indifferent state in which the weight fractions satisfy the $1+c-(\phi+r')$ conditions of compatibility. However, the composition variables must also satisfy the $1+c\phi-(r'+r'')$ equations A. In all we have therefore

$$2+(c-r')-\phi+c\phi-(r'+r'')=w+c\phi-(r'+r''), \tag{29.123}$$

equations to be satisfied. Since there are $c\phi$ composition variables, these equations cannot be satisfied in general unless

$$c\phi \geqslant w+c\phi-(r'+r''),$$

that is to say

$$r'+r'' \geqslant w, \tag{29.124}$$

which is the required condition.

We note that algebraically this condition is generally both necessary and sufficient. If, however, the algebraic solution gives negative values for one or more of the w_i^α, then the solution is not physically significant. Thus the condition (29.124) is always a necessary condition, but is not always sufficient.

* *Cf* Defay [12].

Example : Consider a two-phase system of three non-reacting components. We have $r'=0$, $r''=3$, so that $r'+r''=3$; it will therefore be trivariant $w=3$.

If the system is closed and contains the arbitrary masses $m_1^0 \dots m_c^0$, then since $r'+r''=w$, it is possible for the system to exist in an indifferent state. Let us verify the existence of this state and calculate the composition of the phases.

The indifference matrix (29.19) may be written

$$\begin{bmatrix} w_1^1 & w_1^2 \\ w_2^1 & w_2^2 \\ w_3^1 & w_3^2 \end{bmatrix}, \tag{29.125}$$

and gives for the conditions of indifference

$$w_1^1=w_1^2 ; \quad w_2^1=w_2^2 ; \quad w_3^1=w_3^2. \tag{29.126}$$

The conditions of enclosure (29.108) are

$$\begin{aligned} w_1^1\ m^1+w_1^2\ m^2&=m_1^0, \\ w_2^1\ m^1+w_2^2\ m^2&=m_2^0, \\ w_3^1\ m^1+w_3^2\ m^2&=m_3^0. \end{aligned} \tag{29.127}$$

These equations will only be compatible with (29.126) if

$$\begin{vmatrix} w_1^1 & m_1^0 \\ w_2^1 & m_2^0 \end{vmatrix}=0 \quad \text{and} \quad \begin{vmatrix} w_1^1 & m_1^0 \\ w_3^1 & m_3^0 \end{vmatrix}=0, \tag{29.128}$$

whence

$$\frac{w_1^1}{m_1^0}=\frac{w_2^1}{m_2^0}=\frac{w_3^1}{m_3^0}=\frac{1}{m^0} \tag{29.129}$$

where

$$m^0=m_1^0+m_2^0+m_3^0. \tag{29.130}$$

The composition of the indifferent state is obtained by solving between (29.129) and (29.126) :

$$\begin{aligned} w_1^2&=w_1^1=m_1^0/m^0, \\ w_2^2&=w_2^1=m_2^0/m^0, \\ w_3^2&=w_3^1=m_3^0/m^0. \end{aligned} \tag{29.131}$$

Here the case is so simple that we could have foreseen this result by inspection, but the interest of the calculation is that it demonstrates the method which can be applied to much more complicated cases.

We note that there is no difficulty in practice in obtaining a system having the composition (29.131). For we could make up separately a liquid phase and vapour phase each having the desired composition, and then place them in contact at the same temperature and pressure. *The system made up in this way will not, in general, be in equilibrium*, even though we attempt to adjust T and p to attain equilibrium. For, in effect, we have only two variables T and p, but we have *three* conditions of equilibrium

$$\underline{\mu}_1^1 = \underline{\mu}_1^2\,; \quad \underline{\mu}_2^1 = \underline{\mu}_2^2\,; \quad \underline{\mu}_3^1 = \underline{\mu}_3^2.$$

It is therefore, in general, impossible to find T and p to satisfy all three conditions.

However, we can find the appropriate values of T and p such that the system initially in the above state will undergo an azeotropic transformation in time. This is possible because, at any time t, we have to satisfy the two conditions (28.5) referring to the rates of transfer :

$$\frac{\dfrac{dm_1^1}{dt}}{w_1^1} = \frac{\dfrac{dm_2^1}{dt}}{w_2^1} = \frac{\dfrac{dm_3^1}{dt}}{w_3^1}\,. \tag{29.132}$$

We see, for example, that the theorem (29.122) enables us to determine, whether we can expect to find an indifferent state compatible with the arbitrary masses $m_1^0 \ldots m_c^0$ which constitute the closed system. If this state exists then a further analysis concerned with the rates of transfer enables us to decide whether or not an azeotropic transformation is realisable starting from this state.*

* *Cf.* the study of rates of azeotropic distillation of G. Schouls, *Bull. Soc. Chim. Belg.*, **49**, 214 (1940). The problem considered by Mlle. Schouls is somewhat different from that studied here in that the masses $m_1^0 \ldots m_c^0$ were not given *a priori*.

APPENDIX

SINCE the typescript of this book was completed early in 1952 there have been further important advances in several of the fields with which it deals. This is particularly true of the problems of intermolecular forces in gases, phase changes and the thermodynamics of solutions. The two latter have been the subject of recent conferences and the reports of their proceedings * contain important papers on topics discussed in the present volume.

It would have been impossible to incorporate this recent work in the main text, and inconvenient to have inserted substantial footnotes. This appendix therefore draws attention to some of the more important recent contributions which may be followed up by the reader, together with some additional commentary on certain sections of the text.

CHAPTER I

§ 4, p. 10

In this book we have preferred to call ξ *the extent of reaction* or *reaction co-ordinate*, rather than employ the literal translation *degree of advancement of the reaction*. Very recently a proposal has been made† to call ξ, in French, simply *l'avancement* and it has been suggested that the corresponding word might be employed in English.

Furthermore, we have called a change involving the increase of ξ by unity *one equivalent of reaction*. This is not entirely satisfactory since it is neither necessary nor always customary to write the stoichiometric equation for a reaction so that one chemical equivalent of each reactant and product is involved, but once the stoichiometric equation has been written down in order to define what is meant by ξ, the unit of reaction is also defined. The French phrase *la réaction a marché une fois* does not admit of direct translation. An alternative suggestion † has been made that when ξ increases by unity the reaction should be said to have *advanced by one de donder*.

So far no firm recommendations have been made on these points, but

* *Changements de Phases :* Societé de Chimie Physique (Paris, 1952), referred to below as *Changements de Phases ; Discussions of the Faraday Society No.* 15 : *The Equilibrium properties of solutions of non-electrolytes* (London, 1953), referred to below as *Faraday Soc. Discussions*, 15.

† By the Comité International de Thermodynamique et de Cinetique Electrochimique.

attention is drawn to them now so that readers may not be confused if these suggestions are adopted and appear in the literature.

CHAPTER II

§ 5, p. 28

The equations for the heat capacities of gases as a function of temperature given in table 2.2, are mostly based on direct experimental measurements. Similar equations can be derived when the fundamental vibration frequencies of the gas molecules have been determined spectroscopically (*cf.* chap. X, § 3, p. 119). Crawford and Parr * have recently published tables which enable one to write down an equation of the form

$$c_p^0 = a + bT + cT^2$$

when these frequencies are known.

CHAPTER VII

§ 7, p. 104

Other examples of the application of thermodynamics to the calculation of equilibria in technically important reactions are discussed by Rossini.†

CHAPTER XI

A standard work of reference on intermolecular forces is due to appear very shortly.‡ The different methods of approach to the study of intermolecular forces between like and unlike molecules are carefully discussed in this book. These methods include studies of both thermodynamic properties (e.g. virial coefficients) and also of non-equilibrium measurements (e.g. thermal conductivity, diffusion and thermal diffusion).

The results of virial coefficient measurements are also discussed by E. A. Guggenheim.‖ For an interesting recent discussion of the data concerning intermolecular forces between unlike molecules see A. Michels and A. J. M. Boerboom.¶ The relationship between virial coefficients and intermolecular forces has also been discussed in some detail by Guggenheim, and by J. S. Rowlinson.**

* B. L. Crawford and R. G. Parr, *J.Chem.Phys.* **16**, 233 (1948)

† *Chemical Thermodynamics*, (New York, London, 1950), chap. 34.

‡ *The Properties of Gases*, J. O. Hirschfelder, C. F. Curtiss, R. B. Bird, E. L. Spotz, (New York, Wiley).

‖ *Mixtures* (Oxford, 1952), chap. VIII.

¶ *Bull. Soc. Chim.* 62, 119 (1953).

** *Faraday Soc. Discussions*, 15, 108 (1953).

An important result especially in connexion with the theory of solutions is that if the intermolecular potentials are represented by formulae of the form (25.11), the experimental data for *non-polar* mixtures are in good agreement with the rules

$$r^*_{A,B} = \tfrac{1}{2}(r^*_{A,A} + r^*_{B,B}), \qquad (1)$$

$$\epsilon^*_{A,B} = (\epsilon^*_{A,A}\, \epsilon^*_{B,B})^{\frac{1}{2}}. \qquad (2)$$

Formula (1) would be exact for a hard sphere model, and formula (2) is related to the theory of London forces (*cf.* chap. XXIV, §§ 3 and 4).

CHAPTER XII

§ 6, p. 168, *et seq.*

The present state of development of the cell model for pure liquids is summarized in an excellent review article by J. de Boer.* The main defect of the cell model is that the calculated entropy is much too small. Some recent improvements overcome this difficulty, at least partially, by taking account of " holes ",† and of multiple occupation of cells.‡

The statistical foundation of the cell model has been studied by J. Kirkwood.|| Some further improvements have been recently introduced by J. E. Mayer and G. Careri.¶

CHAPTER XIII

§ 2, p. 177 (*cf.* also chap. XIV)

It is still uncertain whether or not the solid-liquid equilibrium line terminates at a critical point. Münster ** has recently given theoretical reasons for believing that all first-order transitions possess a critical point, but this conclusion is contrary to that reached by Domb,†† whose theory predicts the absence of a solid-fluid critical point. The experimental work of Simon and his co-workers ‡‡ on the melting line of helium shows no evidence for a critical point up to a pressure of 9,000 atm. and a temperature of 56° K. Alder and Jura |||| have, however, made calculations which suggest that a solid-fluid critical point should

* *Proc. Roy. Soc.* A, **215**, 3 (1952).

† S. Ono, *Mem. Fac. Engng. Kyushu*, **10**, 196 (1947) ; H. M. Peck and T. L. Hill *J. Chem. Phys.*, **18**, 1252 (1950) ; J. S. Rowlinson and C. F. Curtiss, *J. Chem. Phys.*, **19** 1519 (1951).

‡ J. A. Pople, *Phil. Mag.*, **42**, 459 (1951) ; P. Janssens and I. Prigogine, *Physica*, **16**, 895 (1951).

|| *J. Chem. Phys.*, **18**, 380 (1950).

¶ *J. Chem. Phys.*, **20**, 1001, 1117 (1952).

** A. Münster, *Z. Electrochem.*, **55**, 593 (1951).

†† C. Domb, *Phil. Mag.*, **42**, 1316 (1951).

‡‡ F. Simon, *Changements de Phases*, p. 329.

|||| B. J. Alder and G. Jura, *J. Chem. Phys.*, **20** ,1491 (1952).

be observed but at much higher pressures than those which have so far been studied. For helium they predict a critical point at 29,000 atm. and 90° K. Even higher pressures are predicted for Ne and A.

CHAPTER XIV

§ 5, p. 200

A review of thermodynamic and other studies of the process of melting has been given recently by Ubbelohde.*

CHAPTER XVI

§ 1, p. 229 (*cf.* chap. XVIII, footnote, p. 284)

The discussion of the critical point given here follows the classical treatment of van der Waals. Several years ago Mayer and his co-workers † gave theoretical reasons for believing that this simple treatment was inadequate. They suggested that, in effect, the critical state does not correspond to a single point in the p-V-T diagram, but rather that the co-existence curve (dotted in fig. 16.1) has a horizontal top. It was believed at first that this prediction was borne out by experiment, but recent careful measurements, in particular those of Schneider and his colleagues ‡ indicate that in the absence of a vertical gravitational field the co-existence curve would have a definite maximum corresponding to a unique set of critical conditions. This problem, and the related one of critical solution phenomena in binary mixtures (*cf.* § 5), has been discussed in detail recently.||

No agreement was reached and it appears that the existence of an anomalous critical region remains subject to question from the point of view of both theory and experiment.

§ 3, p. 233

An excellent review of the statistical theory of condensation has recently been given by J. de Boer.¶

CHAPTER XVIII

§ 9, p. 284

For further discussion regarding the footnote,† see above under chap. XVI.

* A. R. Ubbelohde, *Quart. Rev. Chem. Soc.*, **4**, 356 (1950).

† J. E. Mayer and co-workers, *J. Chem. Phys.*, **5**, 67, 74 (1937); **6**, 87, 101 (1938); *cf.* Mayer and Mayer [34], chap. 13.

‡ *cf. e.g.* M. A. Weinberger and W. G. Schneider, *Canad. J. Chem.*, **30**, 422 (1952).

|| *Changements de Phases*, pp. 33–92.

¶ *Changements de Phases*, p. 8.

§ 10, p. 288

For a more recent discussion of phenomena related to the effect of pressure on critical solution phenomena see the contribution of Timmermans and Lewin.*

CHAPTER XIX

§ 3, p. 295

A recent extensive discussion of the thermodynamic and kinetic properties of glasses has been published recently by Davies and Jones.†

§ 4, p. 296

In two recent papers ‡ the equations developed in this paragraph, and extensions of them, have been applied to the phenomena associated with the vitreous state.

§ 6, p. 299

The discussion of co-operative phenomena given here is based on the simple Bragg-Williams model. The modern theories of order-disorder changes have undergone rapid development recently. The situation in 1938 is admirably reviewed by Nix and Shockley ; || more recent summaries of both theoretical and experimental developments will be found in papers by Lipson ¶ and Wannier.** See also Guggenheim,†† Rushbrooke, ‡‡ and footnote p. 305.

CHAPTER XXI

§§ 6, 7 and 8, pp. 341–347

An increasing amount of attention has been given recently to the problem of manipulating the Duhem-Margules equation in the most convenient way for any particular application.

Recent papers deal mainly with the problems of testing the thermodynamic consistency of experimental vapour pressure data, and of calculating partial pressures and activity co-efficients of both components from measured total pressures.

The former aspect is dealt with by Herington and his co-workers ||||

* J. Timmermans and J. Lewin, *Faraday Soc. Discussions*, **15**, 195 (1953) ; J. Timmermans, *ibid*, 278.

† R. O. Davies and G. O. Jones, *Adv. in Physics*, **2**, 370 (1953).

‡ R. O. Davies, *Changements de Phases*, p. 425 ; R. O. Davies and G. O. Jones, *Proc. Roy. Soc., A*, **217**, 26 (1953).

|| See ref. on p. 300.

¶ H. Lipson, *Progress in Metal Physics*, **2**, 1 (London, 1950).

** G. H. Wannier, *Rev. Mod. Phys.*, **17**, 50 (1945).

†† E. A. Guggenheim, *Mixtures* (Oxford, 1952), chap. VII.

‡‡ G. S. Rushbrooke, *Changement de Phases*, p. 177.

|||| E. F. G. Herington, *Nature*, **160**, 610 (1947) ; E. A. Coulson and E. F. G. Herington, *Trans. Faraday Soc.*, **44**, 629 (1948) ; E. F. G. Herington, *J. Appl. Chem.*, **2**, 19 (1952) ; *Research*, **3**, 41 (1950) ; *J. Appl. Chem.*, **2**, 11 (1952) ; *J. Inst. Petroleum*, **37**, 457 (1951).

in a series of papers which supplement those quoted in this chapter. The problem has also been discussed briefly by Schultze.*

The calculation of partial pressures from total pressure curves is the subject of papers by Stein and Voetter,† Kohler,‡ Nowotny and Orlicek,|| and by Barker.¶

In addition the mathematical properties of the Duhem-Margules equation are dealt with by Kamke.**

§ 10, p. 354

The depression of the condensation point (dew point) of water vapour by the addition of the vapour of an organic liquid immiscible with water may be applied to the determination of the molecular weight of the organic substance by using equation (18.23) in an approximate form.††

CHAPTER XXII

§ 1, p. 358

Hildebrand ‡‡ has recently shown empirically, that the solubilities of non-electrolytes in solutions from which chemical interactions are absent, yield nearly straight lines when plotted as logarithm of mole fraction against log T, except near the m.p. of the solute.

CHAPTER XXIII

§§ 4 and 5

This discussion of addition compounds covers only those compounds which are completely dissociated on melting, and the change in shape of the freezing point curve near a maximum is attributed to deviations of the liquid phase from ideality (§ 5). In many instances there is good evidence that addition compounds exist also in the liquid phase ; when this occurs the curvature of the freezing point curve near the maximum is related to the equilibrium constant for the dissociation of the addition compound in the liquid.|||| One example of this behaviour which has

* W. Schultze, *Z. physik. Chem.*, **198**, 314 (1951).
† M. v. Stein and H. Voetter, *Z. physik. Chem.*, **201**, 97 (1952).
‡ F. Kohler, *Monatsh.*, **82**, 913 (1951).
|| H. Nowotny and A. F. Orlicek, *Monatsh*, **81**, 791 (1950).
¶ J. A. Barker, *Aust. J. Chem.*, **6**, 207 (1953).
** D. Kamke, *Z. physik. Chem.*, **199**, 35 (1952).
†† C. Tourneaux, C. Devin and L. Revequet, *C. R.*, **233**, 520 (1951).
‡‡ J. H. Hildebrand, *J. Chem. Phys.*, **20**, 190 (1952).
|||| J. J. van Laar, *Z. physik. Chem.*, **66**, 197 (1909) ; an elementary treatment is given by S. T. Bowden, *The Phase Rule and Phase Reactions* (London, 1945), pp. 157, 162 ; *cf.* Hildebrand and Scott, [28′], p. 296.

been studied in detail recently is the $N_2O_5 + H_2O$ system in which the equilibria

$$N_2O_5 + H_2O \rightleftharpoons 2\,HNO_3(l) \rightleftharpoons 2\,HNO_3(s)$$

are set up.*

CHAPTER XXIV

§ 4, p. 386

Interesting work on the excess heat capacity of a number of binary systems, including several discussed in this paragraph, has been reported by Staveley and his co-workers.†

§ 6, p. 392

The thermodynamic arguments of this paragraph have been elaborated by Copp and Everett,‡ and the qualitative conclusions are confirmed by recent work on aqueous amine solutions.||

The molecular conditions for the occurrence of a lower critical point have also been investigated in several recent papers.¶

It appears that a lower critical point is not to be observed with mixtures of spherical molecules with isotropic force fields. The phenomenon seems to be related mainly to modification of the rotational degrees of freedom of the molecules.

CHAPTER XXV

§ 3, p. 397

In the model employed in this paragraph, the interaction curves differ only in the depth of the minimum, while the equilibrium distances or effective molecular radii are the same for both components.** The extension of the theory to molecules of different size, where $r^*_{A,A}$, $r^*_{B,B}$ and $r^*_{A,B}$ are different, has been made recently.†† Solutions in which one kind of molecule can be regarded as an r-mer of the other have also been considered.‡‡ The effect of non-random mixing has been shown to be relatively unimportant, especially for non-polar molecules.||||

* R. J. Gillespie, E. D. Hughes and C. K. Ingold, *J. Chem. Soc.*, **1950**, 2552; K. W. Dunning and W. J. Dunning, *J. Chem. Soc.*, **1952**, 2993.

† L. A. K. Staveley, K. R. Hart and W. I. Tupman, *Faraday Soc. Discussions*, **15**, 130 (1953).

‡ J. L. Copp and D. H. Everett, *Faraday Soc. Discussions*, **15**, 174, 272 (1953); *cf.* E. A. Guggenheim, *ibid*, 271.

|| F. Kohler, *Monatsh.*, **82**, 913 (1951); A. Bellemans, *J. Chem. Phys.*, **21**, 368 (1953); J. L. Copp and D. H. Everett, *loc. cit.*

¶ G. S. Rushbrooke, *Changements de Phases*, p. 177; I. Prigogine, *ibid.*, p. 95; A. Bellemans, *loc. cit*; J. S. Rowlinson, *Proc. Roy. Soc.*, A, **214**, 192 (1951); J. A. Barker and W. Fock, *Faraday Soc. Discussions*, **15**, 188 (1953).

** *cf.* also J. A. Pople, *Trans. Faraday Soc.*, **49**, 591 (1953).

†† I. Prigogine and A. Bellemans, *Faraday Soc. Discussions*, **15**, 80 (1953).

‡‡ I. Prigogine, N. Trappeniers and V. Mathot, *ibid.*, 93.

|||| I. Prigogine and G. Garikian, *Physica*, **16**, 239 (1950); J. Kirkwood and Z. Salsburg, *J. Chem. Phys.*, **20**, 1538 (1953).

An alternative and interesting approach to this problem has been made by Longuet-Higgins,* who assumes no model for the liquid state. This *conformal solution theory* is, however, restricted to first order terms in δ and ϑ (*cf.* 25.22). It seems certain however that in many real solutions the higher order terms are important and that the deviations from ideality may even begin with second order terms. Thus the theory of conformal solutions cannot account for a contraction on mixing of two liquids consisting of molecules of the same size. Equation (25.29) shows that this effect depends on the second order term in δ. Brown and Longuet-Higgins † have shown that the higher order terms cannot be introduced into the theory without employing a model for the liquid state. The interesting point which is illustrated both by the conformal theory and the cell model is the way in which the excess entropy depends upon the change of structure of the solution with changes in composition.

CHAPTER XXVI

§ 7, p. 429

Another approach to the problem of solutions with strongly anisotropic molecular force fields has been developed by Tompa ‡ and by Barker.||

The effect of rotational degrees of freedom on the cell model has also been studied by Pople.¶

§ 8, p. 432

The arguments of this paragraph leading to the conclusion that an ideal associated solution cannot split into two phases are based on rather special features of the model. A more general argument was given by Washburn ** and attention has been drawn to it by Haase.††

The chemical potentials of all species present are of the form (*cf.* 7.1):

$$\mu_i = \mu_i^\ominus (T, p) + RT \ln x_i$$

where $\mu_i^\ominus$ is independent of the composition. If two liquid phases exist in equilibrium, then

$$\mu_i' = \mu_i'', \quad (\text{all } i).$$

But since $\mu_i^\ominus$ will be the same in both phases

$$x_i' = x_i'', \quad (\text{all } i).$$

* H. C. Longuet-Higgins, *Proc. Roy. Soc.*, A, **205**, 247 (1951).
† W. B. Brown and H. C. Longuet-Higgins, *Proc. Roy. Soc.*, A, **209**, 416 (1951).
‡ H. Tompa, *J. Chem. Phys.*, **21**, 250 (1953).
|| J. A. Barker, *J. Chem. Phys.*, **19**, 1430 (1951); **20**, 794, 1526 (1952).
¶ J. A. Pople, *Faraday Soc. Discussions*, **15**, 35 (1953).
** E. W. Washburn, *Trans. Amer. Electrochem. Soc.*, **22**, 330 (1912).
†† R. Haase, *Faraday Soc. Discussions*, **15**, 271 (1953).

The phases are therefore identical and the solution cannot have a critical solution point.

The influence of association on phase separation as expressed by table 26.3 has been verified quite recently by Huet, Philippot and Bono * for the system ethanol + carbon disulphide. This system has an upper consolute temperature at

$$T_c = 250° \text{ K}.$$

By simultaneous spectroscopic and thermodynamic study it has been possible to show that at this temperature

$$\chi = 8 \pm 1 \quad \text{(where } \chi \text{ is the mean degree of association).}$$

The calculated values of $\frac{\alpha}{RT_c}$ and $(x_A)_c$ are (*cf.* table 26.3)

$$\frac{\alpha}{RT_c} = 0{\cdot}5\,; \quad (x_A)_c = 0{\cdot}36\,;$$

while the observed values are :

$$\frac{\alpha}{RT_c} = 0{\cdot}5\,; \quad (x_A)_c = 0{\cdot}28.$$

The association thus decreases in a marked way the value of α necessary to cause phase separation.

* *Bull. Soc. Chim. Belg.*, **62**, 436 (1953).

BIBLIOGRAPHY

(1) Adam, N. K., *The Physics and Chemistry of Surfaces*, 3rd Edition (Oxford, 1941).

(2) Briegleb, G., *Zwischenmoleculäre Kräfte* (Stuttgart, 1937).

(3) Chapman, S., and Cowling, T. G., *Mathematical Theory of Non-uniform Gases* (Cambridge, 1939).

(4) Darmois, E., *L'état liquide de la matière* (Paris, 1943).

(5) De Donder, Th., *Leçons de Thermodynamique et de Chimie physique* (new edition by F. H. van den Dungen and G. van Lerberghe) (Paris, 1920).

(6) De Donder, Th., *L'Affinité*, 1st Edition (Paris, 1927).

(7) De Donder, Th., *L'Affinité*, 2nd Part (Paris, 1931).

(8) De Donder, Th., *L'Affinité*, 3rd Part (Paris, 1934).

(9) De Donder, Th., *L'Affinité*, (new edition by P. van Rysselberghe) (Paris, 1936).

(9′) De Donder, Th., and Van Rysselberghe, P., *The Thermodynamic Theory of Affinity* (Stanford, 1936).

(10) De Donder, Th., *Théorie mathématique de l'electricité* (Paris, 1925).

(11) Defay, R., *Etude thermodynamique de la tension superficielle* (Paris, 1934).

(12) Defay, R., *Azéotropisme—Equations nouvelles des états indifférents*, *Bull. Ac. Roy. Belg.* (*Cl. Si.*) [5], **17**, 940, 1066 (1931) ; reproduced as supplement to [7].

(13) Defay, R., *Des divers manières de definir l'adsorption*, *Mém. Ac. Roy. Belg.* (*Cl. Sc.*), *Mémoires en*-8°, vol. **20**, no. 6 (1946).

(14) Dehlinger, U., *Chemische Physik der Metalle und Legierungen* (Leipzig, 1939).

(15) Duhem, P., *Traité élémentaire de Mécanique Chimique*, 4 vols. (Paris, 1899).

(16) Duhem, P., *Traité d'Energétique*, 2 vols. (Paris, 1911).

(17) Eucken, A., *Grundriss der Physikalischen Chemie*, 4th Edition (Leipzig, 1934).

(18) Falkenhagen, H., *Electrolytes*, trans. R. P. Bell (Oxford, 1934).

(19) Fowler, R. H., *Statistical Mechanics*, 2nd Edition (Cambridge, 1936).

(20) Fowler, R. H., and Guggenheim, E. A., *Statistical Thermodynamics* (Cambridge, 1939).

(21) Frenkel, J., *The Kinetic Theory of Liquids* (Oxford, 1946).

(22) Freundlich, H., *Kapillarchemie* (Leipzig, 1923).

(23) Gibbs, J. W., *Collected Works*, 2 vols. (New York, 1928).

(24) Glasstone, S., *Theoretical Chemistry* (New York, 1944).

(25) Glasstone, S., Laidler, K. J., and Eyring, H., *Theory of Rate Processes* (New York, 1941).

(26) Guggenheim, E. A., *Modern Thermodynamics by the Methods of J. W. Gibbs* (London, 1933).

(26′) Guggenheim, E. A., *Thermodynamics* (Amsterdam, 1949).

(27) Harned, H. S., and Owen, B. B., *The Physical Chemistry of Electrolyte Solutions*, 2nd Edition (New York, 1950).

(28) Hildebrand, J. H., *Solubility of Non-electrolytes*, 2nd Edition (New York, 1936).

(28′) Hildebrand, J. H., and Scott, R. L., *Solubility of Non-electrolytes* (New York, 1949).

(29) Hückel, E., *Adsorption und Kapillarkondensation* (Leipzig, 1928).

(30) Jouguet, E., *Notes de Mécanique Chimique*, Journ. Ecole Polytech. (Paris), 2nd series, 21, 61 (1921).

(31) Lecat, M., *Azéotropisme et Distillation* (in *Traité de Chimique Organique*, ed. V. Grignard, vol. I) (Paris, 1935).

(32) Lewis, G. N., and Randall, M., *Thermodynamics* (New York, 1923).

(33) Marcelin, A., *Solutions superficielle* (Paris, 1931).

(34) Mayer, J. E., and Mayer, M. G., *Statistical Mechanics* (New York, 1940).

(35) Parks, G. S., and Huffman, H. M., *The Free Energies of some Organic Compounds* (New York, 1932).

(36) Planck, M., *Thermodynamik*, 9th Edition (Berlin and Leipzig, 1930); English translation, 3rd Edition (London, 1927).

(37) Prigogine, I., *Thermodynamique des phénomènes irreversibles*, (Liège, 1947).

(38) Prigogine, I., *Contribution à l'étude . . . de la liaison d'hydrogène et la structure des solutions*, *Mém. Ac. Roy. Belg.* (*Cl. Sc.*), Mémoires en-8°, **20**, part 2 (1943).

(39) Rey, M., *Equilibres chimique et Métallurgie* (Liège, 1939).

(40) Rideal, E. K., *An Introduction to Surface Chemistry* (Cambridge, 1930).

(41) Schouls, G., *Etude de l'azéotropisme dynamique*, *Bull. Ac. Roy. Belg.* (*Cl. Sc.*), **16**, 628 (1930); 1412 (1931); **17**, 47 (1931); **18**, 1160 (1932). Reprinted as supplement to [7].

(42) Schottky, W., Ulich, H., and Wagner, C., *Thermodynamik* (Berlin, 1929).

(43) Slater, J. C., *Introduction to Chemical Physics* (New York, 1939).

(44) Schumacher, H. J., *Chemische Gasreactionen* (Dresden and Leipzig, 1938).

(45) Timmermans, J., *Les Solutions concentrées* (Paris, 1936).

(46) Ulich, H., *Chemische Thermodynamik* (Dresden and Leipzig, 1938).

(47) van der Waals, J. D., and Kohnstamm, P., *Lehrbuch der Thermodynamik*, 2 vols. (Leipzig and Amsterdam, 1908).

(48) van Laar, J. J., *Thermodynamik einheitlicher Stoffe und binärer Gemische* (*Groningen*, 1936).

(49) van Lerberghe, G., *Calcul des Affinités Physico-Chimiques* (Paris, 1931).

(50) Vogel, D., *Die Heterogenen Gleichgewichte*; in Masing, *Handbuch der Metallphysik*, vol. II (Leipzig, 1937).

INDEX OF AUTHORS

INDEX OF SUBJECTS

References to chapter and section headings are given in bold type